Elementary Differential Equations

EARL D. RAINVILLE

Late Professor of Mathematics

The University of Michigan

PHILLIP E. BEDIENT

Professor of Mathematics

Franklin and Marshall College

Elementary
Differential
Equations FOURTH EDITION

The Macmillan Company,   Collier-Macmillan Limited, London

Third Printing, 1970

Earlier editions copyright 1949 and 1952, © 1958, and © copyright 1964 by The Macmillan Company.

A portion of this material appears under the title *A Short Course in Differential Equations*, © copyright 1964 and 1969 by The Macmillan Company.

Some material in this book is from *The Laplace Transform: An Introduction*, © copyright 1963 by Earl D. Rainville.

Library of Congress catalog card number: 69-10274

The Macmillan Company,
Collier-Macmillan Canada, Ltd., Toronto, Ontario

Printed in the United States of America

Preface to
the Fourth Edition

It is the belief of the present author that the success of the previous editions of this book has been largely due to Professor Rainville's ability to write in a style which was readily accessible to the serious student. The present edition attempts to maintain that accessibility while making some changes in content and emphasis. In particular, the chapter on existence theorems has been expanded to include a proof of an existence and uniqueness theorem. The chapter on numerical methods has been rewritten and includes several additional topics.

As in earlier editions, I have attempted to exhibit both the techniques for obtaining solutions and the basic ideas and theories behind these techniques. A number of exercises of a more theoretical nature have been added to assist in relating these techniques to the theory.

The material is arranged to permit flexibility in the choice of topics for a semester course. Except for Chapters 1, 2, 5, 16 through 18, and either 6 and 7 or 10 and 11, any chapter on ordinary differential equations can be omitted without interfering with the study of later chapters. Parts of chapters can be omitted in many instances.

For a course aimed at reaching power series as rapidly as is consistent with some treatment of more elementary methods, a reasonable set of omissions would be Chapter 4; Chapters 6 and 8 or 10 and 11; Chapter 9; Chapter 15; parts of Chapter 16; and whatever applications the instructor cares to omit.

This book has sufficient material for a full-year course, if the individual topics are taken up with the attention to detail that such a course suggests.

Chapters 1 through 16 of this book appear separately as *A Short Course in Differential Equations*, Fourth Edition. The shorter version is intended for courses that do not include discussion of infinite series methods.

The author is indebted to many persons who have influenced his thinking in many ways. The most profound influence has come from the late Professor Rainville, whose reputation as a superb teacher lives in the minds of all his former students. Especial thanks are also given to Esther Rainville for her interest and encouragement.

I am grateful for the many comments and suggestions made by my students and colleagues at Franklin and Marshall College. I am pleased to acknowledge in particular Professor Paul W. Berg of Stanford University and Professor Howard Sherwood of Illinois Institute of Technology for their very valuable suggestions.

PHILLIP E. BEDIENT

Lancaster, Pennsylvania

Contents

CHAPTER 7   Nonhomogeneous Equations: Undetermined Coefficients

CHAPTER 8   Variation of Parameters

CHAPTER 9   Inverse Differential Operators

CHAPTER 10   The Laplace Transform

CHAPTER 11   Inverse Transforms

CHAPTER 12   Applications

CHAPTER 13   Systems of Equations

CHAPTER 14   Electric Circuits and Networks

CHAPTER 15   The Existence and Uniqueness of Solutions

CHAPTER 16   Nonlinear Equations

CHAPTER 17   The Power Series Method

CHAPTER 18   Solutions near Regular Singular Points

CHAPTER 23 Fourier Series

CHAPTER 24 Boundary Value Problems

CHAPTER 25 Additional Properties of the Laplace Transform

CHAPTER 26 Partial Differential Equations; Transform Methods

Index   **461**

CHAPTER **1**

Definitions, Elimination of Arbitrary Constants

1. Examples of differential equations

A differential equation is one that involves at least one derivative of an unknown function. As in equation (3) below, a derivative may be involved implicitly through the presence of differentials. Our aim is to solve differential equations; that is, to find the unknown function, or functions, which occur.

Differential equations arise frequently in physics, engineering, and chemistry, and on occasion in such subjects as biology, physiology, and economics. The solution of differential equations plays an important role in the study of the motions of heavenly bodies such as planets, moons, and artificial satellites.

The following are examples of differential equations:

$$\frac{dy}{dx} = \cos x, \tag{1}$$

$$\frac{d^2 y}{dx^2} + k^2 y = 0, \tag{2}$$

1

$$(x^2 + y^2)\,dx - 2xy\,dy = 0, \tag{3}$$

$$\frac{\partial u}{\partial t} = h^2\left(\frac{\partial^2 u}{\partial x^2} + \frac{\partial^2 u}{\partial y^2}\right), \tag{4}$$

$$L\frac{d^2 i}{dt^2} + R\frac{di}{dt} + \frac{1}{C}i = E\omega \cos \omega t, \tag{5}$$

$$\frac{\partial^2 V}{\partial x^2} + \frac{\partial^2 V}{\partial y^2} = 0, \tag{6}$$

$$\left(\frac{d^2 w}{dx^2}\right)^3 - xy\frac{dw}{dx} + w = 0, \tag{7}$$

$$\frac{d^3 x}{dy^3} + x\frac{dx}{dy} - 4xy = 0, \tag{8}$$

$$\frac{d^2 y}{dx^2} + 7\left(\frac{dy}{dx}\right)^3 - 8y = 0, \tag{9}$$

$$\frac{d^2 y}{dt^2} + \frac{d^2 x}{dt^2} = x, \tag{10}$$

$$x\frac{\partial f}{\partial x} + y\frac{\partial f}{\partial y} = nf. \tag{11}$$

When an equation involves one or more derivatives with respect to a particular variable, that variable is called an *independent* variable. A variable is called *dependent* if a derivative of that variable occurs.

In the equation

$$L\frac{d^2 i}{dt^2} + R\frac{di}{dt} + \frac{1}{C}i = E\omega \cos \omega t \tag{5}$$

i is the dependent variable, t the independent variable, and L, R, C, E, and ω are called parameters. The equation

$$\frac{\partial^2 V}{\partial x^2} + \frac{\partial^2 V}{\partial y^2} = 0 \tag{6}$$

has one dependent variable V and two independent variables.

Since the equation

$$(x^2 + y^2)\,dx - 2xy\,dy = 0 \tag{3}$$

may be written

$$x^2 + y^2 - 2xy\frac{dy}{dx} = 0 \quad \checkmark$$

or

$$(x^2 + y^2)\frac{dx}{dy} - 2xy = 0, \quad \checkmark$$

we may consider either variable to be dependent, the other being the independent one.

Oral Exercise

Identify the independent variables, the dependent variables, and the parameters in the equations given as examples in this section.

2. Definitions

The *order* of a differential equation is the order of the highest-ordered derivative appearing in the equation. For instance,

$$\frac{d^2y}{dx^2} + 2b\left(\frac{dy}{dx}\right)^3 + y = 0 \tag{1}$$

is an equation of "order two." It is also referred to as a "second-order equation."

More generally, the equation

$$F(x, y, y', \ldots, y^{(n)}) = 0 \tag{2}$$

is called an "nth-order" ordinary differential equation. Under suitable restrictions on the function F, equation (2) can be solved explicitly for $y^{(n)}$ in terms of the other $n + 1$ variables $x, y, y', \ldots, y^{(n-1)}$, to obtain

$$y^{(n)} = f(x, y, y', \ldots, y^{(n-1)}). \tag{3}$$

For the purposes of this book we shall assume that this is always possible. Otherwise, an equation of the form of equation (2) may actually represent more than one equation of the form of equation (3).

For example, the equation

$$x(y')^2 + 4y' - 6x^2 = 0$$

actually represents the two different equations,

$$y' = \frac{-2 + \sqrt{4 + 6x^3}}{x} \quad \text{or} \quad y' = \frac{-2 - \sqrt{4 + 6x^3}}{x}.$$

A function ϕ, defined on an interval $a < x < b$, is called a solution of the differential equation (3) providing the n derivatives of the function exist on the interval $a < x < b$ and

$$\phi^{(n)}(x) = f(x, \phi(x), \phi'(x), \ldots, \phi^{(n-1)}(x)),$$

for every x in $a < x < b$.

For example, let us verify that

$$y = e^{2x}$$

is a solution of the equation

$$\frac{d^2y}{dx^2} + \frac{dy}{dx} - 6y = 0. \tag{4}$$

We substitute our tentative solution into the left member of equation (4) and find that

$$\frac{d^2y}{dx^2} + \frac{dy}{dx} - 6y = 4e^{2x} + 2e^{2x} - 6e^{2x} \equiv 0,$$

which completes the desired verification.

All of the equations we shall consider in Chapter 2 are of order one, and hence may be written

$$\frac{dy}{dx} = f(x, y).$$

For such equations it is sometimes convenient to use the definitions of elementary calculus to write the equation in the form

$$M(x, y)\,dx + N(x, y)\,dy = 0. \tag{5}$$

A very important concept is that of linearity or nonlinearity of a differential equation. An equation

$$F(x, y, y', \ldots, y^{(n)}) = 0$$

is called linear if the function F is a linear function of the variables $y, y', \ldots, y^{(n)}$. Thus the general linear equation of order n may be written

$$b_0(x)\frac{d^n y}{dx^n} + b_1(x)\frac{d^{n-1}y}{dx^{n-1}} + \cdots + b_{n-1}(x)\frac{dy}{dx} + b_n(x)y = R(x). \tag{6}$$

For example, equation (1) above is nonlinear, and equation (4) is linear. The equation

$$x^2 y'' + xy' + (x^2 - n^2)y = 4x^3$$

is also linear. The manner in which the independent variable enters the equation has nothing to do with the property of linearity.

Oral Exercises

For each of the following, state whether the equation is ordinary or partial, linear or nonlinear, and give its order.

1. $\dfrac{d^2x}{dt^2} + k^2x = 0.$

2. $\dfrac{\partial^2 w}{\partial t^2} = a^2 \dfrac{\partial^2 w}{\partial x^2}.$

3. $(x^2 + y^2)\,dx + 2xy\,dy = 0.$

4. $y' + P(x)y = Q(x).$

5. $y''' - 3y' + 2y = 0.$

6. $yy'' = x.$

7. $\dfrac{\partial^2 u}{\partial x^2} + \dfrac{\partial^2 u}{\partial y^2} + \dfrac{\partial^2 u}{\partial z^2} = 0.$

8. $\dfrac{d^4 y}{dx^4} = w(x).$

9. $x\dfrac{d^2 y}{dt^2} - y\dfrac{d^2 x}{dt^2} = c_1.$

10. $L\dfrac{di}{dt} + Ri = E.$

11. $(x + y)\,dx + (3x^2 - 1)\,dy = 0.$

12. $x(y'')^3 + (y')^4 - y = 0.$

13. $\left(\dfrac{d^3 w}{dx^3}\right)^2 - 2\left(\dfrac{dw}{dx}\right)^4 + yw = 0.$

14. $\dfrac{dy}{dx} = 1 - xy + (y^2.$

15. $y'' + 2y' - 8y = x^2 + \cos x.$

16. $a\,da + b\,db = 0.$

3. The elimination of arbitrary constants

In practice, differential equations arise in many ways, some of which we shall encounter later. There is one way of arriving at a differential equation which is useful in that it gives us a feeling for the kinds of solutions to be expected. In this section we shall start with a relation involving arbitrary constants, and, by elimination of those arbitrary constants, come to a differential equation consistent with the original relation. In a sense we start with the answer and find the problem.

Methods for the elimination of arbitrary constants vary with the way in which the constants enter the given relation. A method which is efficient for one problem may be poor for another. One fact persists throughout. Since each differentiation yields a new relation, the number of derivatives that need be used is the same as the number of arbitrary constants to be eliminated. We shall in each case determine the differential equation that is:

(a) Of order equal to the number of arbitrary constants in the given relation;

(b) Consistent with that relation;

(c) Free from arbitrary constants.

EXAMPLE (a): Eliminate* the arbitrary constants c_1 and c_2 from the relation

$$y = c_1 e^{-2x} + c_2 e^{3x}. \tag{1}$$

Since two constants are to be eliminated, obtain the two derivatives,

$$y' = -2c_1 e^{-2x} + 3c_2 e^{3x}, \tag{2}$$

$$y'' = 4c_1 e^{-2x} + 9c_2 e^{3x}. \tag{3}$$

The elimination of c_1 from equations (2) and (3) yields

$$y'' + 2y' = 15c_2 e^{3x};$$

the elimination of c_1 from equations (1) and (2) yields

$$y' + 2y = 5c_2 e^{3x}.$$

Hence

$$y'' + 2y' = 3(y' + 2y),$$

or

$$y'' - y' - 6y = 0.$$

Another method for obtaining the differential equation in this example proceeds as follows. We know from a theorem in elementary algebra that the three equations (1), (2), and (3) considered as equations in the two unknowns c_1 and c_2 can have solutions only if

$$\begin{vmatrix} -y & e^{-2x} & e^{3x} \\ -y' & -2e^{-2x} & 3e^{3x} \\ -y'' & 4e^{-2x} & 9e^{3x} \end{vmatrix} = 0. \tag{4}$$

Since e^{-2x} and e^{3x} cannot be zero, equation (4) may be rewritten, with the factors e^{-2x} and e^{3x} removed, as

$$\begin{vmatrix} y & 1 & 1 \\ y' & -2 & 3 \\ y'' & 4 & 9 \end{vmatrix} = 0$$

$y(-18+12) - 1(9y' - 3y'')$

$+1(-4y' + 2y'')$

from which the differential equation

$$y'' - y' - 6y = 0$$

follows immediately.

This latter method has the advantage of making it easy to see that the elimination of the constants $c_1, c_2, \ldots, c_n$ from a relation of the form

---

* By differentiations and pertinent legitimate mathematical procedures. Elimination by erasure, for instance, is not permitted.

$$y = c_1 e^{m_1 x} + c_2 e^{m_2 x} + \cdots + c_n e^{m_n x}$$

will always lead to a linear differential equation

$$a_0 \frac{d^n y}{dx^n} + a_1 \frac{d^{n-1} y}{dx^{n-1}} + \cdots + a_{n-1} \frac{dy}{dx} + a_n y = 0,$$

in which the coefficients $a_0, a_1, \ldots, a_n$ are constants. The study of such differential equations will receive much of our attention.

E X A M P L E (b):   Eliminate the constant a from the equation

$$(x - a)^2 + y^2 = a^2.$$

Direct differentiation of the relation yields

$$2(x - a) + 2yy' = 0,$$

from which

$$a = x + yy'.$$

Therefore, using the original equation, we find that

$$(yy')^2 + y^2 = (x + yy')^2,$$

or

$$y^2 = x^2 + 2xyy',$$

which may be written in the form

$$(x^2 - y^2)\, dx + 2xy\, dy = 0.$$

Another method will be used in this example as an illustration of a device which is frequently helpful. The method is based upon the isolation of an arbitrary constant.

The equation

$$(x - a)^2 + y^2 = a^2$$

may be put in the form

$$x^2 + y^2 - 2ax = 0,$$

or

$$\frac{x^2 + y^2}{x} = 2a.$$

Then differentiation of both members leads to

$$\frac{x(2x\, dx + 2y\, dy) - (x^2 + y^2)\, dx}{x^2} = 0,$$

or

$$(x^2 - y^2)\, dx + 2xy\, dy = 0,$$

as desired.

It is interesting to speculate here about the significance of $x = 0$ upon the argument just used. The student should draw a few of the members of this family of circles and ask himself what is peculiar about their behavior at $x = 0$.

EXAMPLE (c):   Eliminate B and α from the relation

$$x = B \cos(\omega t + \alpha), \tag{5}$$

in which ω is a parameter (not to be eliminated).

First we obtain two derivatives of x with respect to t:

$$\frac{dx}{dt} = -\omega B \sin(\omega t + \alpha), \tag{6}$$

$$\frac{d^2 x}{dt^2} = -\omega^2 B \cos(\omega t + \alpha). \tag{7}$$

Comparison of equations (5) and (7) shows at once that

$$\frac{d^2 x}{dt^2} + \omega^2 x = 0.$$

EXAMPLE (d):   Eliminate c from the equation

$$cxy + c^2 x + 4 = 0.$$

At once we get

$$c(y + xy') + c^2 = 0.$$

Since $c \neq 0$,

$$c = -(y + xy')$$

and substitution into the original equation leads us to the result

$$x^3 (y')^2 + x^2 yy' + 4 = 0.$$

Our examples suggest that in a certain sense the totality of solutions of an nth-order equation depends on n arbitrary constants. The sense in which this is true will be stated in Sections 5 and 12.

Exercises

In each of the following, eliminate the arbitrary constants.

1. $x^3 - 3x^2y = c$. ANS. $(x - 2y)\,dx - x\,dy = 0$.

2. $y \sin x - xy^2 = c$. ANS. $y(\cos x - y)\,dx + (\sin x - 2xy)\,dy = 0$.

3. $PV = C$.

4. $x^2y = 1 + cx$. ANS. $(x^2y + 1)\,dx + x^3\,dy = 0$.

5. $cy^2 = x^2 + y$. ANS. $2xy\,dx - (y + 2x^2)\,dy = 0$.

6. $x = A \sin(\omega t + \beta)$: ω a parameter, not to be eliminated.

$$\text{ANS.} \quad \frac{d^2x}{dt^2} + \omega^2 x = 0.$$

7. $x = c_1 \cos \omega t + c_2 \sin \omega t$; ω a parameter. $$\text{ANS.} \quad \frac{d^2x}{dt^2} + \omega^2 x = 0.$$

8. $y = cx + c^2 + 1$. ANS. $y = xy' + (y')^2 + 1$.

9. $y = mx + \dfrac{h}{m}$; h a parameter, m to be eliminated. ANS. $y = xy' + \dfrac{h}{y'}$.

10. $y^2 = 4ax$. ANS. $2x\,dy - y\,dx = 0$.

11. $y = ax^2 + bx + c$. ANS. $y''' = 0$.

12. $y = c_1 + c_2 e^{2x}$. ANS. $y'' - 2y' = 0$.

13. $y = 4 + c_1 e^{2x}$. ANS. $y' - 2y = -8$.

14. $y = c_1 + c_2 e^{-3x}$. ANS. $y'' + 3y' = 0$.

15. $y = c_1 e^{-x} + c_2 e^{-3x}$. ANS. $y'' + 4y' + 3y = 0$.

16. $y = x + c_1 e^{-x} + c_2 e^{-3x}$. ANS. $y'' + 4y' + 3y = 4 + 3x$.

17. $y = c_1 e^x + c_2 e^{-2x}$. ANS. $y'' + y' - 2y = 0$.

18. $y = x^2 + c_1 e^x + c_2 e^{-2x}$. ANS. $y'' + y' - 2y = 2(1 + x - x^2)$.

19. $y = c_1 e^{-x} + c_2 x e^{-x}$. ANS. $y'' + 2y' + y = 0$.

20. $y = A e^{2x} + B x e^{2x}$. ANS. $y'' - 4y' + 4y = 0$.

21. $y = c_1 e^{2x} \cos 3x + c_2 e^{2x} \sin 3x$. ANS. $y'' - 4y' + 13y = 0$.

22. $y = c_1 e^{ax} \cos bx + c_2 e^{ax} \sin bx$; a and b are parameters. *Do not eliminate* ANS. $y'' - 2ay' + (a^2 + b^2)y = 0$.

23. $y = c_1 x + c_2 e^{-x}$. ANS. $(x + 1)y'' + xy' - y = 0$.

24. $y = x^2 + c_1 x + c_2 e^{-x}$. ANS. $(x + 1)y'' + xy' - y = x^2 + 2x + 2$.

25. $y = c_1 x^2 + c_2 e^{2x}$. ANS. $x(1 - x)y'' + (2x^2 - 1)y' - 2(2x - 1)y = 0$.

4. Families of curves

A relation involving a parameter, as well as one or both of the coordinates of a point in a plane, represents a family of curves, one curve corresponding to each value of the parameter. For instance, the equation

$$(x - c)^2 + (y - c)^2 = 2c^2, \tag{1}$$

or

$$x^2 + y^2 - 2c(x + y) = 0, \tag{2}$$

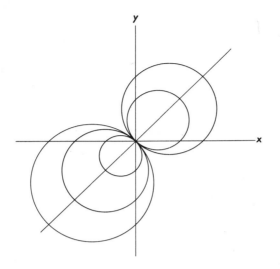

FIGURE 1

may be interpreted as the equation of a family of circles, each having its center on the line $y = x$ and each passing through the origin. Figure 1 shows several elements, or members, of this family.

If the constant c in equation (1) or in equation (2) is treated as an arbitrary constant and eliminated as in the preceding section, the result is called the *differential equation of the family represented by equation* (1). In this example, the elimination of c is easily performed by isolating c, then differentiating throughout the equation with respect to x. Thus, from

$$\frac{x^2 + y^2}{x + y} = 2c$$

we find that

$$\frac{(x + y)(2x\,dx + 2y\,dy) - (x^2 + y^2)(dx + dy)}{(x + y)^2} = 0.$$

Therefore

$$(x^2 + 2xy - y^2)\,dx - (x^2 - 2xy - y^2)\,dy = 0 \qquad (3)$$

is the differential equation of the family of circles represented by equation (1).

Note that equation (3) associates with each point (x, y) in the plane a definite slope

$$\frac{dy}{dx} = \frac{x^2 + 2xy - y^2}{x^2 - 2xy - y^2}, \qquad (4)$$

except where the denominator on the right in (4) vanishes. An examination of the method that was used to get (4) from (1) shows that at any point (x, y), equation (4) gives the slope of that curve of the family (1) which passes through the point in question.

A simple and convenient check is now revealed. When the denominator on the right of equation (4) vanishes, the curve passing through that point must have a vertical tangent. From

$$x^2 - 2xy - y^2 = 0$$

we see that

$$y = (\sqrt{2} - 1)x \tag{5}$$

or

$$y = -(\sqrt{2} + 1)x. \tag{6}$$

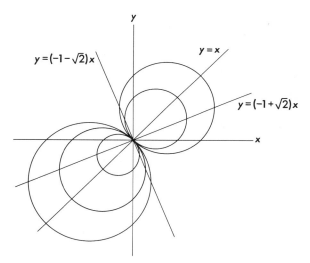

FIGURE 2

In Figure 2, the straight lines (5) and (6) appear along with the family (1). It is seen that the lines (5) and (6) cut the members of the family of circles in precisely those points of vertical tangency.

For a two-parameter family of curves, the differential equation will be of order two, and such a simple geometric interpretation is not available.

EXAMPLE (a): Find the differential equation of the family of parabolas (Figure 3), having their vertices at the origin and their foci on the y-axis.

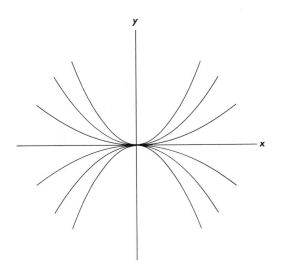

FIGURE 3

From analytic geometry, we find the equation of this family of parabolas to be

$$x^2 = 4ay. \tag{7}$$

Then from

$$\frac{x^2}{y} = 4a$$

the a may be eliminated by differentiation. Thus it follows that

$$2xy \, dx - x^2 \, dy = 0. \tag{8}$$

We may write the differential equation of the family (7) as

$$2y \, dx - x \, dy = 0, \tag{9}$$

because $x = 0$ is still a solution of (9), and nothing is lost in removing the factor x from the left member of (8).

EXAMPLE (b): Find the differential equation of the family of circles (Figure 4) having their centers on the y-axis.

Since a member of the family of circles of this example may have its center anywhere on the *y*-axis and its radius of any magnitude, we are dealing with the two-parameter family

$$x^2 + (y - b)^2 = r^2. \tag{10}$$

$$2x + 2(y-b)y' = 0$$

We shall eliminate both *b* and *r* and arrive, of course, at a second-order differential equation for the family (10).

At once

$$x + (y - b)y' = 0,$$

from which

$$\frac{x + yy'}{y'} = b.$$

Then

$$\frac{y'[1 + yy'' + (y')^2] - y''(x + yy')}{(y')^2} = 0,$$

so the desired differential equation is

$$xy'' - (y')^3 - y' = 0.$$

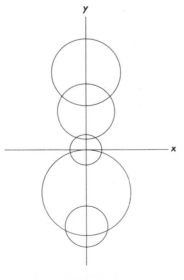

FIGURE 4

Exercises

In each exercise, obtain the differential equation of the family of plane curves described and sketch several representative members of the family.

1. Straight lines through the origin.   ANS. $y\,dx - x\,dy = 0$.

2. Straight lines through the fixed point (h, k). The h and k are not to be eliminated.
          ANS. $(y - k)\,dx - (x - h)\,dy = 0$.

3. Straight lines with slope and y-intercept equal.
          ANS. $y\,dx - (x + 1)\,dy = 0$.

4. Straight lines with slope and x-intercept equal.   ANS. $(y')^2 = xy' - y$.

5. Straight lines with algebraic sum of the intercepts fixed as k.
          ANS. $(xy' - y)(y' - 1) + ky' = 0$.

6. Straight lines at a fixed distance p from the origin.
          ANS. $(xy' - y)^2 = p^2[1 + (y')^2]$.

7. Circles with center at the origin.   ANS. $x\,dx + y\,dy = 0$.

8. Circles with center on the x-axis.   ANS. $yy'' + (y')^2 + 1 = 0$.

9. Circles with fixed radius r and tangent to the x-axis.
          ANS. $(y \pm r)^2(y')^2 + y^2 \pm 2ry = 0$.

10. Circles tangent to the x-axis.   ANS. $[1 + (y')^2]^3 = [yy'' + 1 + (y')^2]^2$.

11. Circles with center on the line $y = -x$, and passing through the origin.
          ANS. $(x^2 - 2xy - y^2)\,dx + (x^2 + 2xy - y^2)\,dy = 0$.

12. Circles of radius unity. Use the fact that the radius of curvature is one.
          ANS. $(y'')^2 = [1 + (y')^2]^3$.

13. All circles. Use the curvature.   ANS. $y'''[1 + (y')^2] = 3y'(y'')^2$.

14. Parabolas with vertex on the x-axis, with axis parallel to the y-axis, and with distance from focus to vertex fixed as a.   ANS. $a(y')^2 = y$.

15. Parabolas with vertex on the y-axis, with axis parallel to the x-axis, and with distance from focus to vertex fixed as a.   ANS. $x(y')^2 = a$.

16. Parabolas with axis parallel to the y-axis and with distance from vertex to focus fixed as a.   ANS. $2ay'' = 1$.

17. Parabolas with axis parallel to the x-axis and with distance from vertex to focus fixed as a.   ANS. $2ay'' + (y')^3 = 0$.

18. Work Ex. 17, using differentiation with respect to y.   ANS. $2a\,\dfrac{d^2x}{dy^2} = 1$.

19. Use the fact that

$$\frac{d^2x}{dy^2} = \frac{d}{dy}\left(\frac{dx}{dy}\right) = \frac{dx}{dy}\frac{d}{dx}\left(\frac{dx}{dy}\right) = \frac{dx}{dy}\frac{d}{dx}\left(\frac{dy}{dx}\right)^{-1} = \frac{-y''}{(y')^3}$$

to prove that the answers to Exs. 17 and 18 are equivalent.

20. Parabolas with vertex and focus on the x-axis.   ANS. $yy'' + (y')^2 = 0$.

21. Parabolas with axis parallel to the x-axis.   ANS. $y'y''' - 3(y'')^2 = 0$.

22. Central conics with center at the origin and vertices on the coordinate axes.
          ANS. $xyy'' + x(y')^2 - yy' = 0$.

23. The confocal central conics

$$\frac{x^2}{a^2 + \lambda} + \frac{y^2}{b^2 + \lambda} = 1$$

with a and b held fixed.   ANS. $(xy' - y)(yy' + x) = (a^2 - b^2)y'$.

24. The cubics $cy^2 = x^2(x - a)$ with a held fixed.

   ANS. $2x(x - a)y' = y(3x - 2a)$.

25. The cubics of Ex. 24 with c held fixed and a to be eliminated.

   ANS. $2cy(xy' - y) = x^3$.

26. The quartics $c^2y^2 = x(x - a)^3$ with a held fixed.

   ANS. $2x(x - a)y' = y(4x - a)$.

27. The quartics of Ex. 26 with c held fixed and a to be eliminated.

   ANS. $c^2(2xy' - y)^3 = 27x^4y$.

28. The strophoids $y^2 = \dfrac{x^2(a + x)}{a - x}$.   ANS. $(x^4 - 4x^2y^2 - y^4)\, dx + 4x^3y\, dy = 0$.

29. The cissoids $y^2 = \dfrac{x^3}{a - x}$.   ANS. $2x^3y' = y(y^2 + 3x^2)$.

30. The trisectrices of Maclaurin $y^2(a + x) = x^2(3a - x)$.

   ANS. $(3x^4 - 6x^2y^2 - y^4)\, dx + 8x^3y\, dy = 0$.

31. Circles through the intersections of the circle $x^2 + y^2 = 1$ and the line $y = x$. Use the "$u + kv$" form; that is, the equation

$$x^2 + y^2 - 1 + k(y - x) = 0.$$

   ANS. $(x^2 - 2xy - y^2 + 1)\, dx + (x^2 + 2xy - y^2 - 1)\, dy = 0$.

32. Circles through the fixed points $(a, 0)$ and $(-a, 0)$. Use the method of Ex. 31.

   ANS. $2xy\, dx + (y^2 + a^2 - x^2)\, dy = 0$.

33. The circles $r = 2a(\sin \theta - \cos \theta)$.

   ANS. $(\cos \theta - \sin \theta)\, dr + r(\cos \theta + \sin \theta)\, d\theta = 0$.

34. The cardioids $r = a(1 - \sin \theta)$.   ANS. $(1 - \sin \theta)\, dr + r \cos \theta\, d\theta = 0$.

35. The cissoids $r = a \sin \theta \tan \theta$. (See Ex. 29.)

   ANS. $\sin \theta \cos \theta\, dr - r(1 + \cos^2 \theta)\, d\theta = 0$.

36. The strophoids $r = a(\sec \theta + \tan \theta)$.   ANS. $\dfrac{dr}{d\theta} = r \sec \theta$.

37. The trisectrices of Maclaurin $r = a(4 \cos \theta - \sec \theta)$. (See Ex. 30.)

   ANS. $\cos \theta(4 \cos^2 \theta - 1)\, dr + r \sin \theta(4 \cos^2 \theta + 1)\, d\theta = 0$.

CHAPTER 2

Equations of Order One

5. An existence theorem for equations of order one

In this chapter we shall study several elementary methods for solving first-order differential equations. To make what we do more plausible, we now state an important theorem which will be discussed in more detail in Chapter 15.

Consider the equation of order one

$$\frac{dy}{dx} = f(x, y). \tag{1}$$

Let T denote the rectangular region defined by

$$|x - x_0| \le a \quad \text{and} \quad |y - y_0| \le b,$$

a region with the point (x_0, y_0) at its center. Suppose that f and $\partial f / \partial y$ are continuous functions of x and y in T.

Under the conditions imposed on $f(x, y)$ above, there exists an interval about x_0, $|x - x_0| \leq h$, and a function $y(x)$ which has the properties:

  (a) $y = y(x)$ is a solution of equation (1) on the interval $|x - x_0| \leq h$;

  (b) On the interval $|x - x_0| \leq h$, $y(x)$ satisfies the inequality $|y(x) - y_0| \leq b$;

  (c) At $x = x_0$, $y = y(x_0) = y_0$;

  (d) $y(x)$ is unique on the interval $|x - x_0| \leq h$ in the sense that it is the only function that has all of the properties (a), (b), and (c).

The interval $|x - x_0| \leq h$ may or may not need to be smaller than the interval $|x - x_0| \leq a$ over which conditions were imposed upon $f(x, y)$.

In rough language, the theorem states that if $f(x, y)$ is sufficiently well behaved near the point (x_0, y_0) then the differential equation

$$\frac{dy}{dx} = f(x, y) \tag{1}$$

has a solution that passes through the point (x_0, y_0) and that solution is unique near (x_0, y_0).

6. Separation of variables

We begin our study of the methods for solving first-order equations by studying an equation of the form

$$M \, dx + N \, dy = 0,$$

where M and N may be functions of both x and y. Some equations of this type are so simple that they can be put in the form

$$A(x) \, dx + B(y) \, dy = 0; \tag{1}$$

that is, the variables can be separated. Then a solution can be written at once. For it is only a matter of finding a function F whose total differential is the left member of (1). Then $F = c$, where c is an arbitrary constant, is the desired result.

EXAMPLE (a): Solve the equation

$$\frac{dy}{dx} = \frac{2y}{x}, \qquad \text{for} \quad x > 0 \quad \text{and} \quad y > 0. \tag{2}$$

We note that for the function in equation (2), the theorem of the previous section applies and assures the existence of a unique continuous solution through any point in the first quadrant. By separating the variables we can write

$$\frac{dy}{y} = \frac{2\,dx}{x}.$$

Hence we obtain a family of solutions

$$\ln|y| = 2\ln|x| + c \tag{3}$$

or, because we are in the first quadrant,

$$y = e^c x^2. \tag{4}$$

If we now put $c_1 = e^c$, we can write

$$y = c_1 x^2, \qquad c_1 > 0. \tag{5}$$

EXAMPLE (b): Solve the equation of the previous example for $x \neq 0$.

The argument now must be taken in two parts. First, if $y \neq 0$, we can proceed as before to equation (3). However, equation (5) must be written

$$|y| = c_1 x^2, \qquad c_1 > 0. \tag{6}$$

Second, if $y = 0$, we see immediately that since $x \neq 0$, $y = 0$ is a solution of the differential equation (2).

As a matter of convenience the solutions given by equation (6) are usually written

$$y = c_2 x^2, \tag{7}$$

where c_2 is taken to be an arbitrary real number. Indeed this form for the solutions incorporates the special case $y = 0$. Thus we say that the family of curves given in Figure 5 represents a family of solution curves for the differential equation (2).

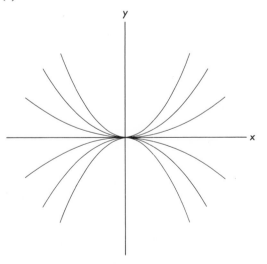

FIGURE 5

We must be cautious, however, The function defined by

$$g(x) = x^2, \qquad x > 0$$
$$= -4x^2, \qquad x \leq 0,$$

obtained by piecing together two different parabolic arcs could also be considered a solution of the differential equation even though this function is not included in the family of equation (7). The uniqueness statement in the theorem of Section 5, indicates that as long as we restrict our attention to a point (x_0, y_0) with $x_0 \neq 0$ and consider a rectangle with center at (x_0, y_0) containing no points at which $x = 0$, then in that rectangle there is a unique solution that passes through (x_0, y_0) and is continuous in the rectangle.

EXAMPLE (c):   Solve the equation

$$(1 + y^2) \, dx + (1 + x^2) \, dy = 0, \tag{8}$$

with the "initial condition" that when $x = 0$, $y = -1$.

From the differential equation we get

$$\frac{dx}{1 + x^2} + \frac{dy}{1 + y^2} = 0$$

from which it follows at once that

$$\text{Arctan } x + \text{Arctan } y = c. \tag{9}$$

In the set of solutions (9), each "Arctan" stands for the principal value of the inverse tangent and is subject to the restriction

$$-\tfrac{1}{2}\pi < \text{Arctan } x < \tfrac{1}{2}\pi.$$

The initial condition that $y = -1$ when $x = 0$ permits us to determine the value of c that must be used to obtain the particular solution desired here. Since Arctan $0 = 0$ and Arctan $(-1) = -\tfrac{1}{4}\pi$, the solution of the initial value problem is

$$\text{Arctan } x + \text{Arctan } y = -\tfrac{1}{4}\pi. \tag{10}$$

Suppose next that we wish to sketch the graph of (10). Resorting to a device of trigonometry, we take the tangent of each side of (10). Since

$$\tan (\text{Arctan } x) = x$$

and

$$\tan (A + B) = \frac{\tan A + \tan B}{1 - \tan A \tan B},$$

we are led to the equation

$$\frac{x+y}{1-xy} = -1,$$

or

$$xy - x - y - 1 = 0. \tag{11}$$

Now (11) is the equation of an equilateral hyperbola with asymptotes $x = 1$ and $y = 1$. But if we turn to (10), we see from

$$\text{Arctan } x = -\tfrac{1}{4}\pi - \text{Arctan } y$$

that, since $(-\text{Arctan } y) < \tfrac{1}{2}\pi,$

$$\text{Arctan } x < \tfrac{1}{4}\pi.$$

Hence $x < 1$, and equation (10) represents only one branch of the hyperbola (11). In Figure 6, the solid curve is the graph of equation (10); the solid curve and the dotted curve together are the graph of equation (11).

Each branch of the hyperbola (11) represents a solution of the differential equation, one branch for $x < 1$, the other for $x > 1$. In this problem we were forced onto the left branch, equation (10), by the initial condition that $y = -1$ when $x = 0$.

One distinction between the equations (10) and (11) can be seen by noting that a computing machine, given the differential equation (8) and seeking a

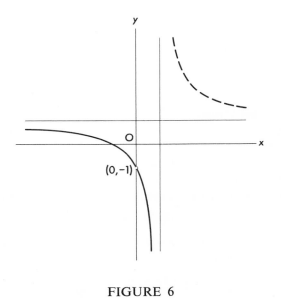

FIGURE 6

solution that passes through the point $(0, -1)$, would draw only the left branch of the curve in Figure 6. The barrier (asymptote) at $x = 1$ would prevent the machine from learning of the existence of the other branch of the hyperbola (11).

EXAMPLE (d): Solve the initial value problem

$$2x(y + 1)\, dx - y\, dy = 0, \tag{12}$$

where $x = 0$ and $y = -2$.

Separating the variables in equation (12), we obtain

$$2x\, dx = \left(1 - \frac{1}{y + 1}\right) dy, \qquad y \neq -1.$$

Integrating, we get a family of solutions given implicitly by

$$x^2 = y - \ln|y + 1| + c. \tag{13}$$

Since we seek a member of this family that passes through the point $(0, -2)$, we must have

$$0 = -2 - \ln|-1| + c,$$

or

$$c = 2.$$

Thus the solution to the problem is given implicitly by

$$x^2 = y - \ln|y + 1| + 2.$$

The reader should note how the theorem of Section 5 applies to this problem to indicate that we have found implicitly the unique solution to the initial value problem which is continuous for $y < -1$.

7. The exp *u* notation

The function e^u enters our work frequently, and sometimes the exponent u is complicated. Even a simple example such as $e^{x^{\frac{1}{4}} y^2}$ may be undesirable in print, because exponents are usually set in small type. It is customary in advanced mathematics to use the notation

$$\exp u = e^u. \tag{1}$$

That is, exp is used to denote the exponential function in much the same way that sin is used to denote the sine function.

EXAMPLE (a): For $e^{x^{\frac{1}{4}} y^2}$ we write $\exp(x^{\frac{1}{2}} y^2)$.

EXAMPLE (b): The meaning of the following relation should be clear:

$$(y + 1) \exp (x^2) = c_3 \exp (y). \tag{2}$$

Most people retain the notation e^u when u simple, even though in the same equation the exp notation may have been used elsewhere. Equation (2) is sometimes written in the form

$$(y + 1) \exp (x^2) = c_3 e^y. \tag{3}$$

A few minutes of practice should make the reader feel at home with the symbol exp u. Some familiarity with this notation will result from verification of simple identities such as the following:

$$\exp (x) \cdot \exp (y) = \exp (x + y), \tag{4}$$

$$[\exp (x)]^k = \exp (kx), \tag{5}$$

$$\exp (\ln y) = y, \tag{6}$$

$$\exp \left(\frac{x}{y}\right) \exp \left(\frac{y}{x}\right) = \exp \left(\frac{x^2 + y^2}{xy}\right), \tag{7}$$

$$\exp (3 \ln x) = [\exp (\ln x^3)] = x^3, \tag{8}$$

$$\exp (x - 2 \ln x) = x^{-2} e^x. \tag{9}$$

We shall use the exp notation whenever it seems to add to the clarity of the printed result.

Exercises

In Exs. 1–26, obtain a family of solutions and indicate for what values of x they are valid.

1. $(4 + x)y' = y^3$.   ANS. $2y^2 \ln |c(4 + x)| = -1$.
2. $\exp (y^2) dx + x^2 y \, dy = 0$.   ANS. $x \exp (-y^2) + 2 = cx$.
3. $\cos x \cos y \, dx + \sin x \sin y \, dy = 0$.   ANS. $\sin x = c \cos y$.
4. $3y \, dx = 2x \, dy$.   ANS. $x^3 = cy^2$.
5. $my \, dx = nx \, dy$.   ANS. $x^m = cy^n$.
6. $y' = xy^2$.   ANS. $y(x^2 + c) + 2 = 0$.
7. $\dfrac{dV}{dP} = \dfrac{-V}{P}$.   ANS. $PV = C$.
8. $e^x(y - 1) dx + 2(e^x + 4) dy = 0$.   ANS. $(y - 1)^2(e^x + 4) = c^2$.
9. $dr = e(r \sin \theta \, d\theta - \cos \theta \, dr)$.   ANS. $r(1 + e \cos \theta) = c$.
10. $(xy - x) dx + (xy + y) dy = 0$.   ANS. $(y - 1) \exp (x + y) = c(x + 1)$.
11. $(y + 1) dx = 2xy \, dy$.   ANS. $e^{2y} = cx(y + 1)^2$.
12. $x^2 \, dx + y(x - 1) \, dy = 0$.
13. $(xy + x) dx = (x^2y^2 + x^2 + y^2 + 1) \, dy$.   ANS. $\ln (x^2 + 1) = y^2 - 2y + 4 \ln |c(y + 1)|$.
14. $x \cos^2 y \, dx + \tan y \, dy = 0$.   ANS. $x^2 + \tan^2 y = c^2$.

15. $x^2yy' = e^y$. ANS. $x(y + 1) = (1 + cx)e^y$.

16. $\tan^2 y \, dy = \sin^3 x \, dx$. ANS. $\cos^3 x - 3 \cos x = 3(\tan y - y + c)$.

17. $y' = \cos^2 x \cos y$. ANS. $4 \ln |\sec y + \tan y| = 2x + \sin 2x + c$.

18. $y' = y \sec x$. ANS. $y = c(\sec x + \tan x)$.

19. $dx = t(1 + t^2) \sec^2 x \, dt$. ANS. $2x + \sin 2x = c + (1 + t^2)^2$.

20. $(e^{2x} + 4)y' = y$. ANS. $y^8(1 + 4e^{-2x}) = c^2$.

21. $\alpha \, d\beta + \beta \, d\alpha + \alpha\beta(3 \, d\alpha + d\beta) = 0$. ANS. $c\alpha\beta = \exp(-3\alpha - \beta)$.

22. $(1 + \ln x) \, dx + (1 + \ln y) \, dy = 0$. ANS. $x \ln x + y \ln y = c$.

23. $x \, dx - \sqrt{a^2 - x^2} \, dy = 0$.

ANS. $y - c = -\sqrt{a^2 - x^2}$, the lower half of the circle $x^2 + (y - c)^2 = a^2$.

24. $x \, dx + \sqrt{a^2 - x^2} \, dy = 0$.

ANS. $y - c = \sqrt{a^2 - x^2}$, the upper half of the circle $x^2 + (y - c)^2 = a^2$.

25. $a^2 \, dx = x\sqrt{x^2 - a^2} \, dy$. ANS. $x = a \sec \dfrac{y + c}{a}$.

26. $y \ln x \ln y \, dx + dy = 0$. ANS. $x \ln x + \ln |\ln y| = x + c$.

In Exs. 27–33, obtain the particular solution satisfying the initial condition indicated.

27. $\dfrac{dr}{dt} = -4rt$; when $t = 0$, $r = r_0$. ANS. $r = r_0 \exp(-2t^2)$.

28. $2xyy' = 1 + y^2$; when $x = 2$, $y = 3$. ANS. $y^2 = 5x - 1$.

29. $xyy' = 1 + y^2$; when $x = 2$, $y = 3$. ANS. $5x^2 - 2y^2 = 2$.

30. $y' = x \exp(y - x^2)$; when $x = 0$, $y = 0$. ANS. $2e^{-y} = 1 + \exp(-x^2)$.

31. $xy^2 \, dx + e^x \, dy = 0$; when $x \to \infty$, $y \to \frac{1}{2}$. ANS. $y = e^x/(2e^x - x - 1)$.

32. $(2a^2 - r^2) \, dr = r^3 \sin \theta \, d\theta$; when $\theta = 0$, $r = a$.

33. $v \dfrac{dv}{dx} = g$; when $x = x_0$, $v = v_0$. ANS. $v^2 - v_0^2 = 2g(x - x_0)$.

8. Homogeneous functions

Polynomials in which all terms are of the same degree, such as

$$x^2 - 3xy + 4y^2,$$
$$x^3 + y^3, \tag{1}$$
$$x^4y + 7y^5,$$

are called *homogeneous* polynomials. We wish now to extend that concept of homogeneity so it will apply to functions other than polynomials.

If we assign a physical dimension, say length, to each variable x and y in the polynomials in (1), then each polynomial itself also has a physical dimension, length to some power. This suggests the desired generalization, If, when certain variables are thought of as lengths, a function has physical dimension length to the kth power, then we shall call that function homogeneous of degree k in those variables. For example, the function

$$f(x, y) = 2y^3 \exp\left(\frac{y}{x}\right) - \frac{x^4}{x + 3y} \tag{2}$$

is of dimension (length)^3 when x and y are lengths. Therefore that function is said to be homogeneous of degree 3 in x and y.

We permit the degree k to be any number. The function $\sqrt{x + 4y}$ is called homogeneous of degree $\frac{1}{2}$ in x and y. The function

$$\frac{x}{\sqrt{x^2 + y^2}}$$

is homogeneous of degree zero in x and y.

A formal definition of homogeneity is: *The function $f(x, y)$ is said to be homogeneous of degree k in x and y if, and only if,*

$$f(\lambda x, \lambda y) = \lambda^k f(x, y). \tag{3}$$

The definition is easily extended to functions of more than two variables.

For the function $f(x, y)$ of equation (2), the formal definition of homogeneity leads us to consider

$$f(\lambda x, \lambda y) = 2\lambda^3 y^3 \exp\left(\frac{\lambda y}{\lambda x}\right) - \frac{\lambda^4 x^4}{\lambda x + 3\lambda y}.$$

But we see at once that

$$f(\lambda x, \lambda y) = \lambda^3 f(x, y);$$

hence $f(x, y)$ is homogeneous of degree 3 in x and y, as stated previously.

The following theorems prove useful in the next section.

THEOREM 1: *If $M(x, y)$ and $N(x, y)$ are both homogeneous and of the same degree, the function $M(x, y)/N(x, y)$ is homogeneous of degree zero.*

THEOREM 2: *If $f(x, y)$ is homogeneous of degree zero in x and y, $f(x, y)$ is a function of y/x alone.*

Proof of Theorem 1 is left to the student.

Proof of Theorem 2: Let us put $y = vx$. Then Theorem 2 states that if $f(x, y)$ is homogeneous of degree zero, $f(x, y)$ is a function of v alone. Now

$$f(x, y) = f(x, vx) = x^0 f(1, v) = f(1, v), \tag{4}$$

in which the x is now playing the role taken by λ in the definition (3) above. By (4), $f(x, y)$ depends on v alone as stated in Theorem 2.

Oral Exercises

Determine in each exercise whether the function is homogeneous or not. If it is homogeneous, state the degree of the function.

1. $4x^2 - 3xy + y^2$. H, 2

2. $x^3 - xy + y^3$. N.H. 3

3. $2y + \sqrt{x^2 + y^2}$. H, 1

4. $\sqrt{x} - y$. H, ½

5. e^x. N.H. 1

6. $\tan x$. H, 0

7. $\exp\left(\dfrac{x}{y}\right)$. N.H. 0

8. $\tan \dfrac{3y}{x}$. N.H., 0

9. $(x^2 + y^2) \exp\left(\dfrac{2x}{y}\right) + 4xy$. H, 2

10. $x \sin \dfrac{y}{x} - y \sin \dfrac{x}{y}$. H, 1

11. $\dfrac{x^2 + 3xy}{x - 2y}$. H, 1

12. $\dfrac{x^5}{x^2 + 2y^2}$. λ^3 H. 3

13. $(u^2 + v^2)^{3/2}$. N, H. 2

14. $(u^2 - 4v^2)^{-1/2}$. H 2

15. $y^2 \tan \dfrac{x}{y}$. $= f(x,y)$ H, 2

16. $\dfrac{(x^2 + y^2)^{1/2}}{(x^2 - y^2)^{1/2}}$. H, 0

17. $\dfrac{a + 4b}{a - 4b}$. $= f(x,y)$ N, H. 0

18. $\ln \dfrac{x}{y}$. NH 0

19. $x \ln x - y \ln y$. H. 0

$\dfrac{x \ln x}{y \ln y}$

20. $x \ln x - x \ln y$. H. 0

$\dfrac{x \ln x}{x \ln y}$ H. 0

9. Equations with homogeneous coefficients

Suppose the coefficients M and N in an equation of order one,

$$M(x, y)\, dx + N(x, y)\, dy = 0, \tag{1}$$

are both homogeneous functions and are of the *same degree* in x and y. By Theorems 1 and 2 of Section 8, the ratio M/N is a function of y/x alone. Hence equation (1) may be put in the form

$$\frac{dy}{dx} + g\left(\frac{y}{x}\right) = 0. \tag{2}$$

This suggests the introduction of a new variable v by putting $y = vx$. Then (2) becomes

$$x \frac{dv}{dx} + v + g(v) = 0, \tag{3}$$

in which the variables are separable. We can obtain the solution of (3) by the method of Section 6, insert y/x for v, and thus arrive at the solution of (1). We have shown that the substitution $y = vx$ will transform equation (1) into an equation in v and x in which the variables are separable.

The above method would have been equally successful had we used $x = vy$ to obtain from (1) an equation in y and v. See Example (b) below.

EXAMPLE (a): Solve the equation

$$(x^2 - xy + y^2)\, dx - xy\, dy = 0. \tag{4}$$

Since the coefficients in (4) are both homogeneous and of degree two in x and y, let us put $y = vx$. Then (4) becomes

$$(x^2 - x^2v + x^2v^2)\, dx - x^2v(v\, dx + x\, dv) = 0,$$

from which the factor x^2 should be removed at once. That done, we have to solve

$$(1 - v + v^2)\, dx - v(v\, dx + x\, dv) = 0,$$

or

$$(1 - v)\, dx - xv\, dv = 0.$$

Hence we separate variables to get

$$\frac{dx}{x} + \frac{v\, dv}{v - 1} = 0.$$

Then from

$$\frac{dx}{x} + \left[1 + \frac{1}{v - 1} \right] dv = 0$$

a family of solutions is seen to be

$$\ln|x| + v + \ln|v - 1| = \ln|c|,$$

or

$$x(v - 1)e^v = c.$$

In terms of the original variables, these solutions are given by

$$x\left(\frac{y}{x} - 1 \right) \exp\left(\frac{y}{x} \right) = c,$$

or

$$(y - x) \exp\left(\frac{y}{x} \right) = c.$$

EXAMPLE (b): Solve the equation

$$xy\, dx + (x^2 + y^2)\, dy = 0. \tag{5}$$

Again the coefficients in the equation are homogeneous and of degree two. We could use $y = vx$, but the relative simplicity of the dx term in (5) suggests that we put

$$x = vy.$$

Then $dx = v\, dy + y\, dv$, and equation (5) is replaced by

$$vy^2(v\, dy + y\, dv) + (v^2y^2 + y^2)\, dy = 0,$$

or

$$v(v\,dy + y\,dv) + (v^2 + 1)\,dy = 0.$$

Hence we need to solve

$$vy\,dv + (2v^2 + 1)\,dy = 0, \tag{6}$$

which leads at once to

$$\ln(2v^2 + 1) + 4\ln|y| = \ln c,$$

or

$$y^4(2v^2 + 1) = c.$$

Thus the desired solutions are

$$y^4\left(\frac{2x^2}{y^2} + 1\right) = c;$$

that is,

$$y^2(2x^2 + y^2) = c. \tag{7}$$

Since the left member of equation (7) cannot be negative, we may, for symmetry's sake, change the arbitrary constant to $c_1{}^4$, writing

$$y^2(2x^2 + y^2) = c_1{}^4.$$

It is worth-while for the student to attack equation (5) using $y = vx$. That method leads directly to the equation

$$(v^3 + 2v)\,dx + x(v^2 + 1)\,dv = 0.$$

Frequently in equations with homogeneous coefficients, it is quite immaterial whether one uses $y = vx$ or $x = vy$. However, it is sometimes easier to substitute for the variable whose differential has the simpler coefficient.

Exercises

In Exs. 1–19 obtain a family of solutions.

- **1.** $(x - 2y)\,dx + (2x + y)\,dy = 0.$ ANS. $\ln(x^2 + y^2) + 4\,\text{Arctan}\,(y/x) = c.$
- **2.** $2(2x^2 + y^2)\,dx - xy\,dy = 0.$ ANS. $x^4 = c^2(4x^2 + y^2).$
- **3.** $xy\,dx - (x^2 + 3y^2)\,dy = 0.$ ANS. $x^2 = 6y^2\ln|y/c|.$
- **4.** $x^2y' = 4x^2 + 7xy + 2y^2.$ ANS. $x^2(y + 2x) = c(y + x).$
- **5.** $3xy\,dx + (x^2 + y^2)\,dy = 0.$
- **6.** $(x - y)(4x + y)\,dx + x(5x - y)\,dy = 0.$ ANS. $x(y + x)^2 = c(y - 2x).$

7. $(5v - u)\,du + (3v - 7u)\,dv = 0.$ ANS. $(3v + u)^2 = c(v - u).$

8. $(x^2 + 2xy - 4y^2)\,dx - (x^2 - 8xy - 4y^2)\,dy = 0.$

            ANS. $x^2 + 4y^2 = c(x + y).$

9. $(x^2 + y^2)\,dx - xy\,dy = 0.$ ANS. $y^2 = 2x^2 \ln |x/c|.$

10. $v^2\,dx + x(v - 4x)\,dv = 0.$ ANS. $xv^2 = c(v - 2x).$

11. $(2x + y)^2\,dx = xy\,dy.$ ANS. $x^3(x + y) = c \exp (y/x).$

12. $y\,dx = (x + \sqrt{y^2 - x^2})\,dy.$ ANS. $\text{Arcsin} (x/y) = \ln |y/c|.$

13. $(3x^2 - 2xy + 3y^2)\,dx = 4xy\,dy.$ ANS. $(y - x)(y + 3x)^3 = cx^3.$

14. $[x \csc (y/x) - y]\,dx + x\,dy = 0.$ ANS. $\ln |x/c| = \cos (y/x).$

15. $x\,dx + \sin^2 (y/x)[y\,dx - x\,dy] = 0.$

         ANS. $4x \ln |x/c| - 2y + x \sin (2y/x) = 0.$

16. $(x - y \ln y + y \ln x)\,dx + x(\ln y - \ln x)\,dy = 0.$

            ANS. $(x - y) \ln x + y \ln y = cx + y.$

17. $[x - y \,\text{Arctan} (y/x)]\,dx + x \,\text{Arctan} (y/x)\,dy = 0.$

         ANS. $2y \,\text{Arctan} (y/x) = x \ln [c^2(x^2 + y^2)/x^4].$

18. $v(v^2 + u^2)\,du + u(v^2 - u^2)\,dv = 0.$

19. $(y^3 - 4xy^2 - 2x^3)\,dx + x^2(2y + x)\,dy = 0.$

         ANS. $x^2(y - 2x)^2 = c^2(x^2 + y^2).$

20. Prove that with the aid of the substitution $y = vx$, you can solve any equation of the form

$$y^n f(x)\,dx + H(x, y)(y\,dx - x\,dy) = 0,$$

where $H(x, y)$ is homogeneous in x and y.

In Exs. 21–33 find the solution indicated.

21. $(x - y)\,dx + (3x + y)\,dy = 0;$ when $x = 2, y = -1.$

         ANS. $2(x + 2y) + (x + y) \ln |x + y| = 0.$

22. $(y - \sqrt{x^2 + y^2})\,dx - x\,dy = 0;$ when $x = \sqrt{3}, y = 1.$ ANS. $x^2 = 9 - 6y.$

23. $(y + \sqrt{x^2 + y^2})\,dx - x\,dy = 0;$ when $x = \sqrt{3}, y = 1.$ ANS. $x^2 = 2y + 1.$

24. $[x \cos^2 (y/x) - y]\,dx + x\,dy = 0;$ when $x = 1, y = \pi/4.$

         ANS. $\tan (y/x) = \ln (e/x).$

25. $(y^2 + 7xy + 16x^2)\,dx + x^2\,dy = 0;$ when $x = 1, y = 1.$

         ANS. $x - y = 5(y + 4x) \ln x.$

26. $y^2\,dx + (x^2 + 3xy + 4y^2)\,dy = 0;$ when $x = 2, y = 1.$

         ANS. $4(2y + x) \ln y = 2y - x.$

27. $xy\,dx + 2(x^2 + 2y^2)\,dy = 0;$ when $x = 0, y = 1.$ ANS. $y^4(3x^2 + 4y^2) = 4.$

28. $y(2x^2 - xy + y^2)\,dx - x^2(2x - y)\,dy = 0;$ when $x = 1, y = \tfrac{1}{2}.$

         ANS. $y^2 \ln x = 2y^2 + xy - x^2.$

29. $y(9x - 2y)\,dx - x(6x - y)\,dy = 0;$ when $x = 1, y = 1.$

         ANS. $3x^3 - x^2y - 2y^2 = 0.$

30. $y(x^2 + y^2)\,dx + x(3x^2 - 5y^2)\,dy = 0;$ when $x = 2, y = 1.$

         ANS. $2y^5 - 2x^2y^3 + 3x = 0.$

31. $(16x + 5y)\,dx + (3x + y)\,dy = 0;$ the curve to pass through the point $(1, -3).$

         ANS. $y + 3x = (y + 4x) \ln (y + 4x).$

32. $v(3x + 2v)\,dx - x^2\,dv = 0;$ when $x = 1, v = 2.$ ANS. $2x^3 + 2x^2v - 3v = 0.$

33. $(3x^2 - 2y^2)y' = 2xy;$ when $x = 0, y = -1.$ ANS. $x^2 = 2y^2(y + 1).$

34. From Theorems 1 and 2, page 24, it follows that if F is homogeneous of degree k in x and y, F can be written in the form

$$F = x^k \varphi\left(\frac{y}{x}\right). \tag{A}$$

Use (A) to prove Euler's theorem that if F is a homogeneous function of degree k in x and y,

$$x\frac{\partial F}{\partial x} + y\frac{\partial F}{\partial y} = kF.$$

10. Exact equations

In Section 6 it was noted that when an equation can be put in the form

$$A(x)\,dx + B(y)\,dy = 0,$$

a set of solutions can be determined by integration; that is, by finding a function whose differential is $A(x)\,dx + B(y)\,dy$.

That idea can be extended to some equations of the form

$$M(x, y)\,dx + N(x, y)\,dy = 0 \tag{1}$$

in which separation of variables may not be possible. Suppose that a function $F(x, y)$ can be found that has for its total differential the expression $M\,dx + N\,dy$; that is,

$$dF = M\,dx + N\,dy. \tag{2}$$

Then certainly

$$F(x, y) = c \tag{3}$$

is a set of solutions of (1). For, from (3) it follows that

$$dF = 0,$$

or, in view of (2),

$$M\,dx + N\,dy = 0,$$

as desired.

Two things, then, are needed: first, to find out under what conditions on M and N a function F exists such that its total differential is exactly $M\,dx + N\,dy$; second, if those conditions are satisfied, actually to determine the function F. If there exists a function F such that

$$M\,dx + N\,dy$$

is exactly the total differential of F, we call equation (1) an *exact equation*.

If the equation

$$M \, dx + N \, dy = 0 \tag{1}$$

is exact, then by definition F exists such that

$$dF = M \, dx + N \, dy.$$

But, from calculus,

$$dF = \frac{\partial F}{\partial x} \, dx + \frac{\partial F}{\partial y} \, dy,$$

so

$$M = \frac{\partial F}{\partial x}, \quad N = \frac{\partial F}{\partial y}.$$

These two equations lead to

$$\frac{\partial M}{\partial y} = \frac{\partial^2 F}{\partial y \, \partial x}$$

and

$$\frac{\partial N}{\partial x} = \frac{\partial^2 F}{\partial x \, \partial y}.$$

Again from calculus

$$\frac{\partial^2 F}{\partial y \, \partial x} = \frac{\partial^2 F}{\partial x \, \partial y},$$

provided these partial derivatives are continuous. Therefore, if (1) is an exact equation, then

$$\frac{\partial M}{\partial y} = \frac{\partial N}{\partial x}. \tag{4}$$

Thus, for (1) to be exact it is necessary that (4) be satisfied.

Let us now show that if condition (4) is satisfied, then (1) is an exact equation. Let $\phi(x, y)$ be a function for which

$$\frac{\partial \phi}{\partial x} = M.$$

The function ϕ is the result of integrating $M \, dx$ with respect to x while holding y constant. Now

$$\frac{\partial^2 \phi}{\partial y \, \partial x} = \frac{\partial M}{\partial y} \, ;$$

hence, if (4) is satisfied, then also

$$\frac{\partial^2 \phi}{\partial x\, \partial y} = \frac{\partial N}{\partial x}.$$ (5)

Let us integrate both sides of this last equation with respect to x, holding y fixed. In the integration with respect to the x, the "arbitrary constant" may be any function of y. Let us call it $B'(y)$, for ease in indicating its integral. Then integration of (5) with respect to x yields

$$\frac{\partial \phi}{\partial y} = N + B'(y).$$ (6)

Now a function F can be exhibited, namely,

$$F = \phi(x, y) - B(y),$$

for which

$$dF = \frac{\partial \phi}{\partial x}\, dx + \frac{\partial \phi}{\partial y}\, dy - B'(y)\, dy$$

$$= M\, dx + [N + B'(y)]\, dy - B'(y)\, dy$$

$$= M\, dx + N\, dy.$$

Hence, equation (1) is exact. We have completed a proof of the theorem stated below.

THEOREM 3:   *If M, N, $\partial M/\partial y$, and $\partial N/\partial x$ are continuous functions of x and y, then a necessary and sufficient condition that*

$$M\, dx + N\, dy = 0$$ (1)

be an exact equation is that

$$\frac{\partial M}{\partial y} = \frac{\partial N}{\partial x}.$$ (4)

Furthermore, the proof contains the germ of a method for obtaining a set of solutions, a method used in Examples (a) and (b) below.

EXAMPLE (a):   Solve the equation

$$3x(xy - 2)\, dx + (x^3 + 2y)\, dy = 0.$$ (7)

First, from the fact that

$$\frac{\partial M}{\partial y} = 3x^2 \quad \text{and} \quad \frac{\partial N}{\partial x} = 3x^2,$$

we conclude that equation (7) is exact. Therefore, its solution is $F = c$, where

$$\frac{\partial F}{\partial x} = M = 3x^2 y - 6x, \tag{8}$$

and

$$\frac{\partial F}{\partial y} = N = x^3 + 2y. \tag{9}$$

Let us attempt to determine F from equation (8). Integration of both sides of (8) with respect to x, holding y constant, yields

$$F = x^3 y - 3x^2 + T(y), \tag{10}$$

where the usual arbitrary constant in indefinite integration is now necessarily a function $T(y)$, as yet unknown. To determine $T(y)$, we use the fact that the function F of equation (10) must also satisfy equation (9). Hence

$$x^3 + T'(y) = x^3 + 2y, \quad \text{—GIVES ANSWER}$$
$$T'(y) = 2y.$$

No arbitrary constant is needed in obtaining $T(y)$, since one is being introduced on the right in the solution $F = c$. Then

$$T(y) = y^2,$$

and from (10)

$$F = x^3 y - 3x^2 + y^2.$$

Finally, a set of solutions of equation (7) is defined by

$$x^3 y - 3x^2 + y^2 = c.$$

EXAMPLE (b):   Solve the equation

$$(2x^3 - xy^2 - 2y + 3) \, dx - (x^2 y + 2x) \, dy = 0. \tag{11}$$

Here

$$\frac{\partial M}{\partial y} = -2xy - 2 = \frac{\partial N}{\partial x},$$

so equation (11) is exact.

A set of solutions of (11) is $F = c$, where

$$\frac{\partial F}{\partial x} = 2x^3 - xy^2 - 2y + 3 \tag{12}$$

and

$$\frac{\partial F}{\partial y} = -x^2 y - 2x. \tag{13}$$

Because (13) is simpler than (12), and for variety's sake, let us start the determination of F from equation (13).

At once, from (13)

$$F = -\tfrac{1}{2}x^2 y^2 - 2xy + Q(x),$$

where $Q(x)$ will be determined from (12). The latter yields

$$-xy^2 - 2y + Q'(x) = 2x^3 - xy^2 - 2y + 3,$$
$$Q'(x) = 2x^3 + 3.$$

Therefore

$$Q(x) = \tfrac{1}{2}x^4 + 3x,$$

and the desired set of solutions of (11) is

$$-\tfrac{1}{2}x^2 y^2 - 2xy + \tfrac{1}{2}x^4 + 3x = \tfrac{1}{2}c,$$

or

$$x^4 - x^2 y^2 - 4xy + 6x = c.$$

Exercises

Test each of the following equations for exactness and solve the equation. The equations that are not exact may, of course, be solved by methods discussed in the preceding sections.

1. $(x + y)\,dx + (x - y)\,dy = 0.$ ANS. $x^2 + 2xy - y^2 = c.$

2. $(6x + y^2)\,dx + y(2x - 3y)\,dy = 0.$ ANS. $3x^2 + xy^2 - y^3 = c.$

3. $(2xy - 3x^2)\,dx + (x^2 + y)\,dy = 0.$ ANS. $x^2 y - x^3 + \tfrac{1}{2}y^2 = c.$

4. $(y^2 - 2xy + 6x)\,dx - (x^2 - 2xy + 2)\,dy = 0.$

         ANS. $xy^2 - x^2 y + 3x^2 - 2y = c.$

5. $(2xy + y)\,dx + (x^2 - x)\,dy = 0.$ ANS. $y = cx(x - 1)^{-3}.$

6. $(x - 2y)\,dx + 2(y - x)\,dy = 0.$ ANS. $x^2 + 2y^2 = 4xy + c.$

7. Do Ex. 6 by another method.

8. $(2x - 3y)\,dx + (2y - 3x)\,dy = 0.$ ANS. $x^2 + y^2 = 3xy + c.$

9. Do Ex. 8 by another method.

10. $v(2uv^2 - 3)\,du + (3u^2 v^2 - 3u + 4v)\,dv = 0.$

         ANS. $v(u^2 v^2 - 3u + 2v) = c.$

11. $(\cos 2y - 3x^2 y^2)\,dx + (\cos 2y - 2x \sin 2y - 2x^3 y)\,dy = 0.$

         ANS. $\tfrac{1}{2}\sin 2y + x \cos 2y - x^3 y^2 = c.$

12. $(1 + y^2)\,dx + (x^2 y + y)\,dy = 0.$ ANS. $2\,\text{Arctan}\,x + \ln(1 + y^2) = c.$

13. $(1 + y^2 + xy^2)\,dx + (x^2 y + y + 2xy)\,dy = 0.$ ANS. $2x + y^2(1 + x)^2 = c.$

14. $(w^3 + wz^2 - z)\,dw + (z^3 + w^2 z - w)\,dz = 0.$ ANS. $(w^2 + z^2)^2 = 4wz + c.$

15. $(2xy - \tan y)\,dx + (x^2 - x \sec^2 y)\,dy = 0.$ ANS. $x^2 y - x \tan y = c.$

16. $(\cos x \cos y - \cot x)\,dx - \sin x \sin y\,dy = 0.$

         ANS. $\sin x \cos y = \ln |c \sin x|.$

17. $(r + \sin \theta - \cos \theta) \, dr + r(\sin \theta + \cos \theta) \, d\theta = 0.$

ANS. $r^2 + 2r(\sin \theta - \cos \theta) = c.$

18. $x(3xy - 4y^3 + 6) \, dx + (x^3 - 6x^2y^2 - 1) \, dy = 0.$

ANS. $x^3y - 2x^2y^3 + 3x^2 - y = c.$

19. $(\sin \theta - 2r \cos^2 \theta) \, dr + r \cos \theta (2r \sin \theta + 1) \, d\theta = 0.$

ANS. $r \sin \theta - r^2 \cos^2 \theta = c.$

20. $[2x + y \cos (xy)] \, dx + x \cos (xy) \, dy = 0.$ ANS. $x^2 + \sin (xy) = c.$

21. $2xy \, dx + (y^2 + x^2) \, dy = 0.$ ANS. $y(3x^2 + y^2) = c.$

22. $2xy \, dx + (y^2 - x^2) \, dy = 0.$ ANS. $x^2 + y^2 = cy.$

23. $(xy^2 + y - x) \, dx + x(xy + 1) \, dy = 0.$ ANS. $x^2y^2 + 2xy - x^2 = c.$

24. $3y(x^2 - 1) \, dx + (x^3 + 8y - 3x) \, dy = 0;$ when $x = 0, y = 1.$

ANS. $xy(x^2 - 3) = 4(1 - y^2).$

25. $(1 - xy)^{-2} \, dx + [y^2 + x^2(1 - xy)^{-2}] \, dy = 0;$ when $x = 2, y = 1.$

ANS. $xy^4 - y^3 + 5xy - 3x = 5.$

26. $(3 + y + 2y^2 \sin^2 x) \, dx + (x + 2xy - y \sin 2x) \, dy = 0.$

ANS. $y^2 \sin 2x = c + 2x(3 + y + y^2).$

27. $2x[3x + y - y \exp(-x^2)] \, dx + [x^2 + 3y^2 + \exp(-x^2)] \, dy = 0.$

ANS. $x^2y + y^3 + 2x^3 + y \exp(-x^2) = c.$

28. $(xy^2 + x - 2y + 3) \, dx + x^2y \, dy = 2(x + y) \, dy;$ when $x = 1, y = 1.$

ANS. $(xy - 2)^2 + (x + 3)^2 = 2y^2 + 15.$

11. The linear equation of order one

In Section 10 we studied first-order differential equations that were exact. If an equation is not exact, it is natural to attempt to make it exact by the introduction of an appropriate factor, which is then called an integrating factor. Indeed, in Section 6 we multiplied by an integrating factor to separate the variables and thereby obtain an exact equation.

In general, very little can be said about the theory of integrating factors for first-order equations. In Chapter 4, we shall prove some theorems that will give some assistance in a few isolated situations. There is one important class of equations, however where the existence of an integrating factor can be demonstrated. This is the class of linear equations of order one.

An equation that is linear and of order one in the dependent variable y must by definition (Section 2) be of the form

$$A(x)\frac{dy}{dx} + B(x)y = C(x). \tag{1}$$

By dividing each member of equation (1) by $A(x)$, we obtain

$$\frac{dy}{dx} + P(x)y = Q(x), \tag{2}$$

which we choose as the standard form for the linear equation of order one.

For the moment, suppose that there exists for equation (2) a positive integrating factor $v(x) > 0$, a function of x alone. Then

$$v(x)\left[\frac{dy}{dx} + P(x)y\right] = v(x) \cdot Q(x) \tag{3}$$

must be an exact equation. But (3) is easily put into the form

$$M \, dx + N \, dy = 0$$

with

$$M = vPy - vQ,$$

and

$$N = v,$$

in which v, P, and Q are functions of x alone.

Therefore, if equation (3) is to be exact, it follows from the requirement

$$\frac{\partial M}{\partial y} = \frac{\partial N}{\partial x}$$

that v must satisfy the equation

$$vP = \frac{dv}{dx}. \tag{4}$$

From (4), v may be obtained readily, for

$$P \, dx = \frac{dv}{v},$$

so

$$\ln v = \int P \, dx,$$

or

$$v = \exp\left(\int P \, dx\right). \tag{5}$$

That is if equation (2) has a positive integrating factor independent of y, then that factor must be as given by equation (5).

It remains to be shown that the v given by equation (5) is actually an integrating factor of

$$\frac{dy}{dx} + P(x)y = Q(x). \tag{2}$$

Let us apply the factor throughout (2), obtaining

$$\exp\left(\int P\,dx\right)\frac{dy}{dx} + P\exp\left(\int P\,dx\right)y = Q\exp\left(\int P\,dx\right). \tag{6}$$

The left member of (6) is the derivative of the product

$$y\exp\left(\int P\,dx\right);$$

the right member of (6) is a function of x only. Hence equation (6) is exact, which is what we wanted to show.

Of course one integrating factor is sufficient. Hence we may use in the exponent $\left(\int P\,dx\right)$ any function whose derivative is P.

Because of the great importance of the ideas just discussed and the frequent occurrence of linear equations of first order, we summarize the steps involved in solving such equations:

(a) Put the equation into standard form:

$$\frac{dy}{dx} + Py = Q;$$

(b) Obtain the integrating factor $\exp\left(\int P\,dx\right)$;
(c) Apply the integrating factor to the equation in its standard form;
(d) Solve the resultant exact equation.

Note in integrating the exact equation, that *the integral of the left member is always the product of the dependent variable and the integrating factor used.*

EXAMPLE (a):   Solve the equation

$$2(y - 4x^2)\,dx + x\,dy = 0.$$

The equation is linear in y. When put in standard form it becomes

$$\frac{dy}{dx} + \frac{2}{x}y = 8x, \qquad \text{when} \quad x \neq 0. \tag{7}$$

Then an integrating factor is

$$\exp\left(\int\frac{2\,dx}{x}\right) = \exp\left(2\ln|x|\right) = \exp\left(\ln x^2\right) = x^2.$$

Next apply the integrating factor to (7), thus obtaining the exact equation

$$x^2\frac{dy}{dx} + 2xy = 8x^3, \tag{8}$$

which may be immediately rewritten as

$$\frac{d}{dx}(x^2 y) = 8x^3. \tag{9}$$

By integrating (9) we find that

$$x^2y = 2x^4 + c. \tag{10}$$

This can be checked. From (10) we get (8) by differentiation. Then the original differential equation follows from (8) by a simple adjustment. Hence (10) defines a set of solutions of the original equation.

EXAMPLE (b):   Solve the equation

$$y\,dx + (3x - xy + 2)\,dy = 0.$$

Since the product $y\,dy$ occurs here, the equation is not linear in y. It is, however, linear in x. Therefore we arrange the terms as in

$$y\,dx + (3 - y)x\,dy = -2\,dy$$

and pass to the standard form,

$$\frac{dx}{dy} + \left(\frac{3}{y} - 1\right)x = \frac{-2}{y}, \qquad \text{for} \quad y \neq 0. \tag{11}$$

Now

$$\wp = \int \left(\frac{3}{y} - 1\right)dy = 3\ln|y| - y + c_1,$$

so that an integrating factor for equation (11) is

$$\begin{aligned} \exp(3\ln|y| - y) &= \exp(3\ln|y|) \cdot e^{-y} \\ &= \exp(\ln|y|^3) \cdot e^{-y} \\ &= |y|^3 e^{-y}. \end{aligned}$$

It follows that for $y > 0$, $y^3 e^{-y}$ is an integrating factor for equation (11) and for $y < 0$, $-y^3 e^{-y}$ serves as an integrating factor. In either case we are led to the exact equation

$$y^3 e^{-y}\,dx + y^2(3 - y)e^{-y}x\,dy = -2y^2 e^{-y}\,dy$$

from which we get $d(xy^3 e^{-y})$

$$\begin{aligned} xy^3 e^{-y} &= -2\int y^2 e^{-y}\,dy \\ &= 2y^2 e^{-y} + 4ye^{-y} + 4e^{-y} + c. \end{aligned}$$

Thus a family of solutions is defined implicitly by

$$xy^3 = 2y^2 + 4y + 4 + ce^y.$$

12. The general solution of a linear equation

At the beginning of this chapter we stated an existence and uniqueness theorem for first-order differential equations. If the differential equation in that theorem happens to be a linear equation we can prove a somewhat stronger statement.

Consider the linear differential equation

$$\frac{dy}{dx} + P(x)y = Q(x). \tag{1}$$

Suppose that P and Q are continuous functions on the interval $a < x < b$, and that $x = x_0$ is any number in that interval. If y_0 is an arbitrary real number, there exists a unique solution $y = y(x)$ of the differential equation (1) that also satisfies the initial condition

$$y(x_0) = y_0.$$

Moreover, this solution satisfies equation (1) throughout the entire interval $a < x < b$.

The proof of this theorem has essentially been obtained in Section 11. Multiplication of equation (1) by the integrating factor $v = \exp\left(\int P\,dx\right)$ and integration gives

$$yv = \int vQ\,dx + c.$$

Since $v \neq 0$, we can write

$$y = v^{-1} \int vQ\,dx + cv^{-1}. \tag{2}$$

It is a simple matter to show that since $v \neq 0$ and v is continuous on $a < x < b$, (2) is a family of solutions of equation (1).

It is also easy to see that given any x_0 on the interval $a < x < b$ together with any number y_0, we can choose the constant c so that $y = y_0$ when $x = x_0$.

The effect of our argument is that every equation of the form of equation (1), for which P and Q have some common interval of continuity, will have a unique set of solutions containing one constant of integration, and which can be obtained by introducing the appropriate integrating factor. Because we are assured of the uniqueness of these solutions, we know that any other solution obtained by any other method must be one of the functions in our one parameter family of solutions. It is for this reason that this set of solutions is called the *general solution* of equation (1). The word "general" is intended to mean that we have found all possible solutions that satisfy the differential equation on the interval $a < x < b$.

Exercises

In Exs. 1–25, find the general solution.

1. $(x^5 + 3y)\,dx - x\,dy = 0.$ ANS. $2y = x^5 + cx^3.$

2. $2(2xy + 4y - 3)\,dx + (x + 2)^2\,dy = 0.$ ANS. $y = 2(x + 2)^{-1} + c(x + 2)^{-4}.$

3. $y' = x - 2y.$ ANS. $4y = 2x - 1 + ce^{-2x}.$

4. $(y + 1)\,dx + (4x - y)\,dy = 0.$ ANS. $20x = 4y - 1 + c(y + 1)^{-4}.$

5. $u\,dx + (1 - 3u)x\,du = 3u^2 e^{3u}\,du.$ ANS. $xu = (u^3 + c)e^{3u}.$

6. $u\,dx + (1 - 3u)x\,du = 3u\,du.$ ANS. $xu = ce^{3u} - u - \frac{1}{3}.$

7. $y' = x - 4xy.$ Solve by two methods.   ANS. $4y = 1 + c\exp(-2x^2).$

8. $y' = \csc x + y\cot x.$ ANS. $y = c\sin x - \cos x.$

9. $y' = \csc x - y\cot x.$ ANS. $y\sin x = x + c.$

10. $(2xy + x^2 + x^4)\,dx - (1 + x^2)\,dy = 0.$

       ANS. $y = (1 + x^2)(c + x - \text{Arctan } x).$

11. $(y - \cos^2 x)\,dx + \cos x\,dy = 0.$ ANS. $y(\sec x + \tan x) = c + x - \cos x.$

12. $y' = x - 2y\cot 2x.$ ANS. $4y\sin 2x = c + \sin 2x - 2x\cos 2x.$

13. $(y - x + xy\cot x)\,dx + x\,dy = 0.$ ANS. $xy\sin x = c + \sin x - x\cos x.$

14. $\dfrac{dy}{dx} - my = c_1 e^{mx}$, where c_1 and m are constants.   ANS. $y = (c_1 x + c_2)e^{mx}.$

15. $\dfrac{dy}{dx} - m_2 y = c_1 e^{m_1 x}$, where c_1, m_1, m_2 are constants and $m_1 \neq m_2$.

       ANS. $y = c_3 e^{m_1 x} + c_2 e^{m_2 x}$, where $c_3 = \dfrac{c_1}{m_1 - m_2}.$

16. $v\,dx + (2x + 1 - vx)\,dv = 0.$ ANS. $xv^2 = v + 1 + ce^v.$

17. $x(x^2 + 1)y' + 2y = (x^2 + 1)^3.$ ANS. $x^2 y = \frac{1}{4}(x^2 + 1)^3 + c(x^2 + 1).$

18. $2y(y^2 - x)\,dy = dx.$ ANS. $x = y^2 - 1 + c\exp(-y^2).$

19. $(1 + xy)\,dx - (1 + x^2)\,dy = 0.$ ANS. $y = x + c(1 + x^2)^{1/2}.$

20. $2y\,dx = (x^2 - 1)(dx - dy).$ ANS. $(x - 1)y = (x + 1)[c + x - 2\ln|x + 1|].$

21. $dx - (1 + 2x\tan y)\,dy = 0.$ ANS. $2x\cos^2 y = y + c + \sin y\cos y.$

22. $(1 + \cos x)y' = \sin x(\sin x + \sin x\cos x - y).$

       ANS. $y = (1 + \cos x)(c + x - \sin x).$

23. $y' = 1 + 3y\tan x.$ ANS. $3y\cos^3 x = c + 3\sin x - \sin^3 x.$

24. $(x + a)y' = bx - ny;\ a, b, n$ are constants with $n \neq 0, n \neq -1.$

       ANS. $n(n + 1)y = b(nx - a) + c(x + a)^{-n}.$

25. Solve the equation of Ex. 24 for the exceptional cases $n = 0$ and $n = -1.$

       ANS.   If $n = 0,\ y = bx + c - ab\ln|x + a|.$

       If $n = -1,\ y = ab + c(x + a) + b(x + a)\ln|x + a|.$

26. In the standard form $dy + Py\,dx = Q\,dx$ put $y = vw$, thus obtaining

$$w(dv + Pv\,dx) + v\,dw = Q\,dx.$$

Then, by first choosing v so that

$$dv + Pv\,dx = 0$$

and later determining w, show how to complete the solution of

$$dy + Py\, dx = Q\, dx.$$

In Exs. 27–33 find the particular solution indicated.

27. $(2x + 3)y' = y + (2x + 3)^{1/2}$; when $x = -1$, $y = 0$.

ANS. $2y = (2x + 3)^{1/2} \ln (2x + 3)$.

28. $y' = x^3 - 2xy$; when $x = 1$, $y = 1$.   ANS. $2y = x^2 - 1 + 2 \exp (1 - x^2)$.

29. $L\dfrac{di}{dt} + Ri = E$, where L, R, and E are constants; when $t = 0$, $i = 0$.

$$\text{ANS.} \quad i = \frac{E}{R}\left[1 - \exp\left(-\frac{Rt}{L}\right)\right].$$

30. $L\dfrac{di}{dt} + Ri = E \sin \omega t$; when $t = 0$, $i = 0$.

ANS.   Let $Z^2 = R^2 + \omega^2 L^2$. Then

$$i = EZ^{-2}\left[R \sin \omega t - \omega L \cos \omega t + \omega L \exp\left(-\frac{Rt}{L}\right)\right].$$

31. Find that solution of $y' = 2(2x - y)$ which passes through the point $(0, -1)$.

ANS. $y = 2x - 1$.

32. Find that solution of $y' = 2(2x - y)$ which passes through the point $(0, 1)$.

ANS. $y = 2x - 1 + 2e^{-2x}$.

33. $(1 + t^2)\, ds + 2t[st^2 - 3(1 + t^2)^2]\, dt = 0$; when $t = 0$, $s = 2$.

ANS. $s = (1 + t^2)[3 - \exp (-t^2)]$.

Miscellaneous Exercises

In each exercise, find a set of solutions, unless the statement of the exercise stipulates otherwise.

1. $y' = \exp (2x - y)$.   ANS. $2e^y = e^{2x} + c$.
2. $(x + y)\, dx + x\, dy = 0$.   ANS. $x(x + 2y) = c$.
3. $y^2\, dx - x(2x + 3y)\, dy = 0$.   ANS. $y^2(x + y) = cx$.
4. $(x^2 + 1)\, dx + x^2 y^2\, dy = 0$.   ANS. $xy^3 = 3(1 + cx - x^2)$.
5. $(x^3 + y^3)\, dx + y^2(3x + ky)\, dy = 0$; k is constant.

ANS. $ky^4 + 4xy^3 + x^4 = c$.

6. $y' = x^3 - 2xy$; when $x = 1$, $y = 2$.   ANS. $2y = x^2 - 1 + 4 \exp (1 - x^2)$.

7. $\dfrac{dy}{dx} - \cos x = \cos x \tan^2 y$.   ANS. $2 \sin x = y + \sin y \cos y + c$.

8. $\cos x \dfrac{dy}{dx} = 1 - y - \sin x$.   ANS $y(1 + \sin x) = (x + c) \cos x$.

9. $\sin \theta \dfrac{dr}{d\theta} = -1 - 2r \cos \theta$. ANS. $r \sin^2 \theta = c + \cos \theta$.

10. $y(x + 3y)\, dx + x^2\, dy = 0$.   ANS. $x^2 y = c(2x + 3y)$.

11. $\dfrac{dy}{dx} = \sec^2 x \sec^3 y.$ ANS. $3 \tan x + c = 3 \sin y - \sin^3 y.$

12. $y(2x^3 - x^2 y + y^3)\,dx - x(2x^3 + y^3)\,dy = 0.$ ANS. $2x^2 y \ln|cx| = 4x^3 - y^3.$

13. $(1 + x^2)y' = x^4 y^4.$ ANS. $x^3 y^3 + 1 = y^3(c + 3x - 3 \text{ Arctan } x).$

14. $y(3 + 2xy^2)\,dx + 3(x^2 y^2 + x - 1)\,dy = 0.$ ANS. $x^2 y^3 = 3(c + y - xy).$

15. $(2x^2 - 2xy - y^2)\,dx + xy\,dy = 0.$ ANS. $x^3 = c(y - x)\exp(y/x).$

16. $y(x^2 + y^2)\,dx + x(3x^2 - 5y^2)\,dy = 0$; when $x = 2,\ y = 1.$

ANS. $2y^5 - 2x^2 y^3 + 3x = 0.$

17. $y' + ay = b$; a and b are constants. Solve by two methods.

ANS. $y = b/a + ce^{-ax}.$

18. $(x - y)\,dx - (x + y)\,dy = 0.$ Solve by two methods.

ANS. $x^2 - 2xy - y^2 = c.$

19. $\dfrac{dx}{dt} = \cos x \cos^2 t.$ ANS. $4 \ln|\sec x + \tan x| = 2t + \sin 2t + c.$

20. $(\sin y - y \sin x)\,dx + (\cos x + x \cos y)\,dy = 0.$ ANS. $x \sin y + y \cos x = c.$

21. $(1 + 4xy - 4x^2 y)\,dx + (x^2 - x^3)\,dy = 0$; when $x = 2,\ y = \tfrac{1}{4}.$

ANS. $2x^4 y = x^2 + 2x + 2 \ln(x - 1).$

22. $3x^3 y' = 2y(y - 3).$ ANS. $y = c(y - 3)\exp(x^{-2}).$

23. $(2y \cos x + \sin^4 x)\,dx = \sin x\,dy$; when $x = \tfrac{1}{2}\pi,\ y = 1.$

ANS. $y = 2 \sin^2 x \sin^2 \tfrac{1}{2}x.$

24. $xy(dx - dy) = x^2\,dy + y^2\,dx.$ ANS. $x = y \ln|cxy|.$

25. $a^2(dy - dx) = x^2\,dy + y^2\,dx$; a is constant.

ANS. $2 \text{ Arctan } (y/a) = \ln|c(x + a)/(x - a)|.$

26. $(y - \sin^2 x)\,dx + \sin x\,dy = 0.$ ANS. $y(\csc x - \cot x) = x + c - \sin x.$

27. $(x - y)\,dx + (3x + y)\,dy = 0$; when $x = 2,\ y = -1.$

ANS. $2(x + 2y) + (x + y)\ln(x + y) = 0.$

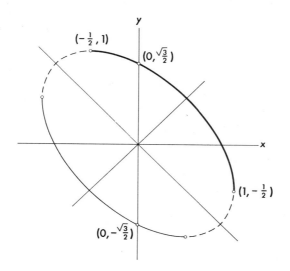

FIGURE 7

28. $y\,dx = (2x + 1)(dx - dy)$. ANS. $3y = (2x + 1) + c(2x + 1)^{-1/2}$.

In solving Exs. 29–33, recall that the principal value Arcsin x of the inverse sine function is restricted as follows:

$$-\tfrac{1}{2}\pi \leqq \text{Arcsin } x \leqq \tfrac{1}{2}\pi.$$

29. $\sqrt{1 - y^2}\,dx + \sqrt{1 - x^2}\,dy = 0$.

ANS. Arcsin x + Arcsin $y = c$, or a part of the ellipse
$x^2 + 2c_1xy + y^2 + c_1{}^2 - 1 = 0$, where $c_1 = \cos c$.

30. Solve the equation of Ex. 29 with the added condition that when $x = 0$, $y = \tfrac{1}{2}\sqrt{3}$. ANS. Arcsin x + Arcsin $y = \tfrac{1}{3}\pi$, or that arc of the ellipse $x^2 + xy + y^2 = \tfrac{3}{4}$ that is indicated by a heavy solid line in Figure 7.

31. Solve the equation of Ex. 29 with the added condition that when $x = 0$, $y = -\tfrac{1}{2}\sqrt{3}$. ANS. Arcsin x + Arcsin $y = -\tfrac{1}{3}\pi$, or that arc of the ellipse $x^2 + xy + y^2 = \tfrac{3}{4}$, that is indicated by a light solid line in Figure 7.

32. Show that after the answers to Exs. 30 and 31 have been deleted, the remaining arcs of the ellipse

$$x^2 + xy + y^2 = \tfrac{3}{4}$$

are not solutions of the differential equation

$$\sqrt{1 - y^2}\,dx + \sqrt{1 - x^2}\,dy = 0.$$

For this purpose consider the sign of the slope of the curve.

33. For the equation

$$\sqrt{1 - y^2}\,dx - \sqrt{1 - x^2}\,dy = 0$$

state and solve four problems analogous to Exs. 29–32 above.

34. $v\,du = (e^v + 2uv - 2u)\,dv$. ANS. $v^2u = ce^{2v} - (v + 1)e^v$.

35. $y\,dx = (3x + y^3 - y^2)\,dy$; when $x = 1, y = -1$. ANS. $x = y^2[1 + y \ln (-y)]$.

36. $y^2\,dx - (xy + 2)\,dy = 0$. ANS. $xy = cy^2 - 1$.

37. $(x^2 - 2xy - y^2)\,dx - (x^2 + 2xy - y^2)\,dy = 0$.

ANS. $(x + y)(x^2 - 4xy + y^2) = c^3$.

38. $y^2\,dx + (xy + y^2 - 1)\,dy = 0$; when $x = -1, y = 1$.

ANS. $y^2 + 2xy + 1 = 2 \ln y$.

39. $y(y^2 - 3x^2)\,dx + x^3\,dy = 0$. ANS. $2x^6 = y^2(x^4 + c)$.

40. $y' = \cos x - y \sec x$; when $x = 0, y = 1$.

ANS. $y(1 + \sin x) = \cos x(x + 2 - \cos x)$.

41. Find that solution of $y' = 3x + y$ which passes through the point $(-1, 0)$.

ANS. $y = -3(x + 1)$.

42. Find that solution of $y' = 3x + y$ which passes through the point $(-1, 1)$.

ANS. $y = \exp (x + 1) - 3(x + 1)$.

43. $y' = y \tan x + \cos x$. ANS. $2y = \sin x + (x + c) \sec x$.

44. $(x^2 - 1 + 2y)\,dx + (1 - x^2)\,dy = 0$; when $x = 2, y = 1$.

ANS. $(x + 1)y = (x - 1)[x + 1 + 2 \ln (x - 1)]$.

45. $(x^3 - 3xy^2)\,dx + (y^3 - 3x^2y)\,dy = 0$. ANS. $x^4 - 6x^2y^2 + y^4 = c$.

46. $(1 - x^2)y' = 1 - xy - 3x^2 + 2x^4$. ANS. $y = x - x^3 + c(1 - x^2)^{1/2}$.

47. $(y^2 + y)\,dx - (y^2 + 2xy + x)\,dy = 0$; when $x = 3, y = 1$. ANS. $2y^2 + y = x$.

48. $(y^3 - x^3)\,dx = xy(x\,dx + y\,dy).$ ANS. $2x^2 \ln|x + y| = cx^2 + 2xy - y^2.$

49. $y' = \sec x - y \tan x.$ ANS. $y = \sin x + c \cos x.$

50. $x^2 y' = y(1 - x).$ ANS. $x \ln|cxy| = -1.$

51. $xy' = x - y + xy \tan x.$ ANS. $xy \cos x = c + \cos x + x \sin x.$

52. $(3x^4 y - 1)\,dx + x^5\,dy = 0;$ when $x = 1, y = 1.$ ANS. $x^4 y = 2x - 1.$

53. $y^2\,dx + x^2\,dy = 2xy\,dy.$ ANS. $y^2 = x(y + c).$

54. $(\sin x \sin y + \tan x)\,dx - \cos x \cos y\,dy = 0.$ ANS. $\cos x \sin y = \ln|c \sec x|.$

55. $(3xy - 4y - 1)\,dx + x(x - 2)\,dy = 0;$ when $x = 1, y = 2.$

ANS. $2x^2(x - 2)y = x^2 - 5.$

CHAPTER **3**

Elementary Applications

13. Velocity of escape from the earth

Many physical problems involve differential equations of order one.

Consider the problem of determining the velocity of a particle projected in a radial direction outward from the earth and acted upon by only one force, the gravitational attraction of the earth.

We shall assume an initial velocity in a radial direction so that the motion of the particle takes place entirely on a line through the center of the earth.

According to the Newtonian law of gravitation, the acceleration of the particle will be inversely proportional to the square of the distance from the particle to the center of the earth. Let r be that variable distance, and let R be the radius of the earth. If t represents time, v the velocity of the particle, a its acceleration, and k the constant of proportionality in the Newtonian law, then

$$a = \frac{dv}{dt} = \frac{k}{r^2}.$$

The acceleration is negative because the velocity is decreasing. Hence the constant k is negative. When $r = R$, then $a = -g$, the acceleration of gravity at the surface of the earth. Thus

$$-g = \frac{k}{R^2},$$

from which

$$a = -\frac{gR^2}{r^2}.$$

We wish to express the acceleration in terms of the velocity and the distance. We have $a = \dfrac{dv}{dt}$ and $v = \dfrac{dr}{dt}$. Hence

$$a = \frac{dv}{dt} = \frac{dr}{dt}\frac{dv}{dr} = v\frac{dv}{dr},$$

so the differential equation for the velocity is now seen to be

$$v\frac{dv}{dr} = -\frac{gR^2}{r^2}. \qquad (1)$$

The method of separation of variables applies to equation (1) and leads at once to the set of solutions

$$v^2 = \frac{2gR^2}{r} + C.$$

Suppose the particle leaves the earth's surface with the velocity v_0. Then $v = v_0$ when $r = R$, from which the constant C is easily determined to be

$$C = v_0{}^2 - 2gR.$$

Thus a particle projected in a radial direction outward from the earth's surface with an initial velocity v_0 will travel with a velocity v given by the equation

$$v^2 = \frac{2gR^2}{r} + v_0{}^2 - 2gR. \qquad (2)$$

It is of considerable interest to determine whether the particle will escape from the earth. Now at the surface of the earth, at $r = R$, the velocity is positive, $v = v_0$. An examination of the right member of equation (2) shows that the velocity of the particle will remain positive if, and only if,

$$v_0{}^2 - 2gR \geqq 0. \qquad (3)$$

For, if the inequality (3) is satisfied, the velocity given by equation (2) will remain positive, since it cannot vanish, is continuous, and is positive at $r = R$. On the other hand, if (3) is not satisfied, then $v_0{}^2 - 2gR < 0$, and there will be a critical value of r for which the right member of equation (2) is zero. That is, the particle would stop, the velocity would change from positive to negative, and the particle would return to the earth.

A particle projected from the earth with a velocity v_0 such that $v_0 \geqq \sqrt{2gR}$ will escape from the earth. Hence, the minimum such velocity of projection,

$$v_e = \sqrt{2gR}, \tag{4}$$

is called the *velocity of escape*.

The radius of the earth is approximately $R = 3960$ miles. The acceleration of gravity at the surface of the earth is approximately $g = 32.16$ feet per second per second, or $g = 6.09(10)^{-3}$ miles per second per second. For the earth, the velocity of escape is easily found to be $v_e = 6.95$ miles per second.

Of course, the gravitational pull of other celestial bodies, the moon, the sun, Mars, Venus, etc. has been neglected in the idealized problem treated here. It is not difficult to see that such approximations are justified, since we are interested in only the critical initial velocity v_e. Whether the particle actually recedes from the earth forever or becomes, for instance, a satellite of some heavenly body, is of no consequence in the present problem.

If in this study we happen to be thinking of the particle as an idealization of a ballistic-type rocket, then other elements must be considered. Air resistance in the first few miles may not be negligible. Methods for overcoming such difficulties are not suitable topics for discussion here.

It must be realized that the formula $v_e = \sqrt{2gR}$ applies equally well for the velocity of escape from the other members of the solar system, as long as R and g are given their appropriate values.

14. Newton's law of cooling

Experiment has shown that under certain conditions, a good approximation to the temperature of an object can be obtained by using Newton's law of cooling: The temperature of a body changes at a rate which is proportional to the difference in temperature between the outside medium and the body itself. We shall assume here that the constant of proportionality is the same whether the temperature is increasing or decreasing.

Suppose, for instance, that a thermometer, which has been at the reading 70°F inside a house, is placed outside where the air temperature is 10°F.

Three minutes later it is found that the thermometer reading is 25°F. We wish to predict the thermometer reading at various later times.

Let u (°F) represent the temperature of the thermometer at time t (min.), the time being measured from the instant the thermometer is placed outside. We are given that when $t = 0$, $u = 70$ and when $t = 3$, $u = 25$.

According to Newton's law, the time rate of change of temperature, du/dt, is proportional to the temperature difference $(u - 10)$. Since the thermometer temperature is decreasing, it is convenient to choose $(-k)$ as the constant of proportionality. Thus the u is to be determined from the differential equation

$$\frac{du}{dt} = -k(u - 10), \tag{1}$$

and the conditions that

$$\text{when } t = 0, \ u = 70 \tag{2}$$

and

$$\text{when } t = 3, \ u = 25. \tag{3}$$

We need to know the thermometer reading at two different times because there are two constants to be determined, the k in equation (1) and the "arbitrary" constant that occurs in the solution of the differential equation (1).

From equation (1) it follows at once that

$$u = 10 + Ce^{-kt}.$$

Then condition (2) yields $70 = 10 + C$ from which $C = 60$, so we have

$$u = 10 + 60e^{-kt}. \tag{4}$$

The value of k will be determined now by using the condition (3). Putting $t = 3$ and $u = 25$ into equation (4) we get

$$25 = 10 + 60e^{-3k},$$

from which $e^{-3k} = \frac{1}{4}$, so $k = \frac{1}{3} \ln 4$.

Thus, the temperature is given by the equation

$$u = 10 + 60 \exp\left(-\tfrac{1}{3}t \ln 4\right). \tag{5}$$

Since $\ln 4 = 1.39$, equation (5) may be replaced by

$$u = 10 + 60 \exp\left(-0.46t\right), \tag{6}$$

which is convenient when a table of values of e^{-x} is available.

15. Simple chemical conversion

It is known from the results of chemical experimentation that, in certain reactions in which a substance A is being converted into another substance, the time rate of change of the amount x of unconverted substance is proportional to x.

Let the amount of unconverted substance be known at some specified time; that is, let $x = x_0$ at $t = 0$. Then the amount x at any time $t > 0$ is determined by the differential equation

$$\frac{dx}{dt} = -kx \qquad (1)$$

and the condition that $x = x_0$ when $t = 0$. Since the amount x is decreasing as time increases, the constant of proportionality in equation (1) is taken to be $(-k)$.

From equation (1) it follows that

$$x = Ce^{-kt}.$$

But $x = x_0$ when $t = 0$. Hence $C = x_0$. Thus we have the result

$$x = x_0 e^{-kt}. \qquad (2)$$

Let us now add another condition, which will enable us to determine k. Suppose it is known that at the end of half a minute, at $t = 30$ (sec.), two-thirds of the original amount x_0 has already been converted. Let us determine how much unconverted substance remains at $t = 60$ (sec.).

When two-thirds of the substance has been converted, one-third remains unconverted. Hence $x = \frac{1}{3}x_0$ when $t = 30$. Equation (2) now yields the relation

$$\tfrac{1}{3}x_0 = x_0 e^{-30k}$$

from which k is easily found to be $\frac{1}{30} \ln 3$. Then with t measured in seconds, the amount of unconverted substance is given by the equation

$$x = x_0 \exp\left(-\tfrac{1}{30}t \ln 3\right). \qquad (3)$$

At $t = 60$,

$$x = x_0 \exp\left(-2 \ln 3\right) = x_0(3)^{-2} = \tfrac{1}{9}x_0.$$

Exercises

1. The radius of the moon is roughly 1080 miles. The acceleration of gravity at the surface of the moon is about $0.165g$, where g is the acceleration of gravity at the surface of the earth. Determine the velocity of escape for the moon.

                                                        ANS.   1.5 mi./sec.

2. Determine to two significant figures the velocity of escape for each of the celestial bodies listed below. The data given are rough and g may be taken to be $6.1(10)^{-3}$ mi./sec.^{2}.

	Accel. of gravity at surface	Radius in miles	Ans. in mi./sec.
Venus	$0.85g$	3,800	6.3
Mars	$0.38g$	2,100	3.1
Jupiter	$2.6g$	43,000	37
Sun	$28g$	432,000	380
Ganymede	$0.12g$	1,780	1.6

3. A thermometer reading 18°F is brought into a room the temperature of which is 70°F. One minute later the thermometer reading is 31°F. Determine the temperature reading as a function of time and in particular, find the temperature reading five minutes after the thermometer is first brought into the room.

ANS. $u = 70 - 52 \exp(-0.29t)$; when $t = 5$, $u = 58$.

4. A thermometer reading 75°F is taken out where the temperature is 20°F. The reading is 30°F four minutes later. Find (a) the thermometer reading seven minutes after the thermometer was brought outside, and (b) the time taken for the reading to drop from 75°F to within a half degree of the air temperature.

ANS.   (a) 23°F; (b) 11.5 min.

5. At 1:00 P.M., a thermometer reading 70°F is taken outside where the air temperature is -10°F, ten below zero. At 1:02 P.M., the reading is 26°F. At 1:05 P.M., the thermometer is taken back indoors where the air is at 70°F. What is the thermometer reading at 1:09 P.M.?

6. At 9 A.M., a thermometer reading 70°F is taken outdoors where the temperature is 15°F. At 9:05 A.M., the thermometer reading is 45°F. At 9:10 A.M., the thermometer is taken back indoors where the temperature is fixed at 70°F. Find (a) the reading at 9:20 A.M. and (b) when the reading, to the nearest degree, will show the correct (70°F) indoor temperature.   ANS.   (a) 58°F; (b) 9:46 A.M.

7. At 2:00 P.M., a thermometer reading 80°F is taken outside where the air temperature is 20°F. At 2:03 P.M., the temperature reading yielded by the thermometer is 42°F. Later, the thermometer is brought inside where the air is at 80°F. At 2:10 P.M., the reading is 71°F. When was the thermometer brought indoors?

ANS.   At 2:05 P.M.

8. Suppose that a chemical reaction proceeds according to the law given in Section 15 above. If half the substance A has been converted at the end of ten seconds, find when nine-tenths of the substance will have been converted.

ANS.   33 sec.

9. The conversion of a substance B follows the law used in Section 15 above. If only a fourth of the substance has been converted at the end of ten seconds, find when nine-tenths of the substance will have been converted.

ANS.   80 sec.

10. For a substance C, the time rate of conversion is proportional to the square of the amount x of unconverted substance. Let k be the numerical value of the constant of proportionality and let the amount of unconverted substance be x_0 at time $t = 0$. Determine x for all $t \geq 0$.   ANS. $x = x_0/(1 + x_0 kt)$.

11. Two substances, *A* and *B*, are being converted into a single compound *C*. In the laboratory it has been shown that, for these substances, the following law of conversion holds: the time rate of change of the amount *x* of compound *C* is proportional to the product of the amounts of unconverted substances *A* and *B*. Assume the units of measure so chosen that one unit of the compound *C* is formed from the combination of one unit of *A* with one unit of *B*. If at time $t = 0$ there are *a* units of substance *A*, *b* units of substance *B*, and none of the compound *C*, present, show that the law of conversion may be expressed by the equation

$$\frac{dx}{dt} = k(a - x)(b - x).$$

Solve this equation with the given initial condition.

ANS.   If $b \neq a$, $x = \dfrac{ab[\exp (b - a)kt - 1]}{b \exp (b - a)kt - a}$; if $b = a$, $x = a^2kt/(akt + 1)$.

12. In the solution of Ex. 11 above, assume that $k > 0$ and investigate the behavior of *x* as $t \to \infty$.   ANS.   If $b \geq a$, $x \to a$; if $b \leq a$, $x \to b$.

13. Radium decomposes at a rate proportional to the quantity of radium present. Suppose that it is found that in 25 years approximately 1.1 per cent of a certain quantity of radium has decomposed. Determine approximately how long it will take for one-half the original amount of radium to decompose.

ANS.   1600 years.

14. A certain radioactive substance has a half-life of 38 hours. Find how long it takes for 90% of the radioactivity to be dissipated.   ANS.   126 hrs

15. A bacterial population *B* is known to have a rate of growth proportional to *B* itself. If between noon and 2 P.M. the population triples, at what time, no controls being exerted, should *B* become 100 times what it was at noon?

ANS.   About 8:22 P.M.

16. In the motion of an object through a certain medium (air at certain pressures is an example), the medium furnishes a resisting force proportional to the square of the velocity of the moving object. Suppose a body falls, due to the action of gravity, through such a medium. Let *t* represent time, and *v* represent velocity, positive downward. Let *g* be the usual constant acceleration of gravity and let *w* be the weight of the body. Use Newton's law, force equals mass times acceleration, to conclude that the differential equation of the motion is

$$\frac{w}{g}\frac{dv}{dt} = w - kv^2,$$

where kv^2 is the magnitude of the resisting force furnished by the medium.

17. Solve the differential equation of Ex. 16 with the initial condition that $v = v_0$ when $t = 0$. Introduce the constant $a^2 = w/k$ to simplify the formulas.

ANS. $\dfrac{a + v}{a - v} = \dfrac{a + v_0}{a - v_0} \exp \left(\dfrac{2gt}{a}\right).$

18. List a consistent set of units for the dimensions of the variables and parameters of Exs. 16–17 above.   ANS.   *t* in sec.   *g* in ft./sec.^{2}
v in ft./sec.   *k* in (lb.)(sec.^{2})/(ft.^{2})
w in lb.   *a* in ft./sec.

19. There are mediums that resist motion through them with a force proportional to the first power of the velocity. For such a medium, state and solve problems analogous to Exs. 16–18 above, except that for convenience a constant $b = w/k$ may be introduced to replace the a^2 of Ex. 17. Show that b has the dimensions of a velocity.

ANS. $v = b + (v_0 - b) \exp\left(-\dfrac{gt}{b}\right).$

FIGURE 8

20. Figure 8 shows a weight, w pounds, sliding down an inclined plane which makes an angle α with the horizontal. Assume that no force other than gravity is acting on the weight; that is, there is no friction, no air resistance, etc. At time $t = 0$, let $x = x_0$ and let the initial velocity be v_0. Determine x for $t > 0$.

ANS. $x = \tfrac{1}{2}gt^2 \sin \alpha + v_0 t + x_0.$

21. A long, very smooth board is inclined at an angle of $10°$ with the horizontal. A weight starts from rest ten feet from the bottom of the board and slides downward under the action of gravity alone. Find how long it will take the weight to reach the bottom of the board and determine the terminal speed.

ANS.   1.9 sec. and 10.5 ft./sec.

22. Add to the conditions of Ex. 20 above a retarding force of magnitude kv, where v is the velocity. Determine v and x under the assumption that the weight starts from rest with $x = x_0$. Use the notation $a = kg/w$.

ANS. $v = a^{-1}g \sin \alpha \,(1 - e^{-at}); \; x = x_0 + a^{-2}g \sin \alpha \,(-1 + e^{-at} + at).$

23. A man, standing at O in Figure 9, holds a rope of length a to which a weight is attached, initially at W_0. The man walks to the right dragging the weight after him. When the man is at M, the weight is at W. Find the differential equation of the path (called the tractrix) of the weight and solve the equation.

ANS. $x = a \ln \dfrac{a + \sqrt{a^2 - y^2}}{y} - \sqrt{a^2 - y^2}.$

24. A tank contains 80 gallons of pure water. A brine solution with 2 pounds of salt per gallon enters at 2 gallons per minute, and the well-stirred mixture leaves at the same rate. Find (a) the amount of salt in the tank at any time, and (b) the time at which the brine leaving will contain 1 pound of salt per gallon.

ANS.   (a) $s = 160[1 - \exp(-t/40)]$; (b) $t = 40 \ln 2$ min.

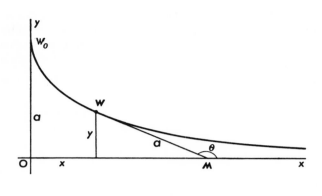

FIGURE 9

25. For the tank in the previous problem, determine the limiting value for the amount of salt in the tank after a long time. How much time must pass before the amount of salt in the tank reaches 80% of this limiting value?

26. A certain sum of money P draws interest compounded continuously. If at a certain time there is P_0 dollars in the account, determine the time when the principal attains the value $2P_0$ dollars, if the annual interest rate is (a) 2%, or (b) 4%.   ANS.   (a) 50 ln 2 years; (b) 100 ln 2 years.

16. Orthogonal trajectories; rectangular coordinates

Suppose that we have a family of curves given by

$$f(x, y, c) = 0, \tag{1}$$

one curve corresponding to each c in some range of values of the parameter c. In certain applications it is found desirable to know what curves have the property that wherever any one of them intersects a curve of the family (1) it does so at right angles.

That is, we wish to determine a family of curves with equations

$$g(x, y, k) = 0 \tag{2}$$

such that at any intersection of a curve of the family (2) with a curve of the family (1) the tangents to the two curves are perpendicular. The families (1) and (2) are then said to be *orthogonal trajectories** of each other.

If two curves are to be orthogonal, then at each point of intersection the

---

* The word orthogonal comes from the Greek ορθη (right) and γωνια (angle); the word trajectory comes from the Latin *trajectus* (cut across). Hence a curve that cuts across certain others at right angles is called an orthogonal trajectory of those others.

slopes of the curves must be negative reciprocals of each other. That fact leads us to a method for finding orthogonal trajectories of a given family of curves. First we find the differential equation of the given family. Then replacing dy/dx by $-dx/dy$ in that equation yields the differential equation of the orthogonal trajectories to the given curves. It remains only to solve the latter differential equation.

So far we have solved differential equations of only one form,

$$M\,dx + N\,dy = 0.$$

For such an equation

$$\frac{dy}{dx} = -\frac{M}{N},$$

so the differential equation of the orthogonal trajectories is

$$\frac{dy}{dx} = \frac{N}{M}$$

or

$$N\,dx - M\,dy = 0.$$

EXAMPLE: Find the orthogonal trajectories of all parabolas with vertices at the origin and foci on the x-axis.

The algebraic equation of such parabolas is

$$y^2 = 4ax. \tag{3}$$

Hence, from

$$\frac{y^2}{x} = 4a,$$

we find the differential equation of the family (3) to be

$$2x\,dy - y\,dx = 0. \tag{4}$$

Therefore the orthogonal trajectories of the family (3) must satisfy the equation

$$2x\,dx + y\,dy = 0. \tag{5}$$

From (5) it follows that

$$2x^2 + y^2 = b^2, \tag{6}$$

where b is the arbitrary constant. Thus the orthogonal trajectories of (3) are certain ellipses (6) with centers at the origin. See Figure 10.

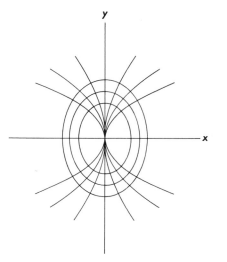

FIGURE 10

Exercises

In each exercise, find the orthogonal trajectories of the given family of curves. Draw a few representative curves of each family whenever a figure is requested.

1. $x - 4y = c$. Draw the figure.   ANS. $4x + y = k$.
2. $x^2 + y^2 = c^2$. Draw the figure.   ANS. $y = kx$.
3. $x^2 - y^2 = c_1$. Draw the figure.   ANS. $xy = c_2$.
4. Circles through the origin with centers on the x-axis. Draw the figure.
                         ANS.   Circles through the origin with centers on the y-axis.
5. Straight lines with slope and y-intercept equal. Draw the figure.
                                                              ANS. $(x + 1)^2 + y^2 = a^2$.
6. $y^2 = cx^3$. Draw the figure.   ANS. $2x^2 + 3y^2 = k^2$.
7. $e^x + e^{-y} = c_1$.   ANS. $e^y - e^{-x} = c_2$.
8. $y = c_1(\sec x + \tan x)$.   ANS. $y^2 = 2(c_2 - \sin x)$.
9. $x^3 = 3(y - c)$. Draw the figure.   ANS. $x(y - k) = 1$.
10. $x = c \exp(y^2)$.   ANS. $y = c_1 \exp(-x^2)$.
11. $y = ce^{-mx}$, with m held fixed. Draw the figure.   ANS. $my^2 = 2(x - c_1)$.
12. Ellipses with centers at $(0, 0)$ and two vertices at $(1, 0)$ and $(-1, 0)$.
                                                              ANS. $x^2 + y^2 = 2 \ln |cx|$.
13. $x^2 - y^2 = cx$.   ANS. $y(y^2 + 3x^2) = c_1$.
14. The cissoids, $y^2 = x^3/(a - x)$.   ANS. $(x^2 + y^2)^2 = b(2x^2 + y^2)$.
15. The trisectrices of Maclaurin, $(a + x)y^2 = x^2(3a - x)$.
                                                       ANS. $(x^2 + y^2)^5 = cy^3(5x^2 + y^2)$.
16. $ax^2 + by^2 = c$, with a and b held fixed.   ANS. $y^a = kx^b$.

17. $ax^2 + y^2 = 2acx$, with a held fixed.   ANS.   If $a \neq 2$, $(2 - a)x^2 + y^2 = c_1 y^a$.
If $a = 2$, $x^2 = -y^2 \ln(c_2 y)$.

18. $y(x^2 + c) + 2 = 0$.   ANS. $y^3 = -3 \ln|kx|$.

19. $x^n + y^n = a^n$, with n held fixed and $n \neq 2$.   ANS. $x^{2-n} - y^{2-n} = c$.

20. $y^2 = x^2(1 - cx)$.   ANS. $x^2 + 3y^2 = c_1 y$.

21. $y^2 = 4x^2(1 - cx)$.   ANS. $2x^2 = 3y^2(1 - c_1 y^2)$.

22. $y^2 = ax^2(1 - cx)$, with a held fixed.

ANS.   If $a \neq 2$, $(a - 2)x^2 = 3y^2(1 - c_1 y^{a-2})$.
If $a = 2$, $x^2 = -3y^2 \ln|c_2 y|$.

23. $y(x^2 + 1) = cx$.   ANS. $y^2 = x^2 + 2 \ln|k(x^2 - 1)|$.

24. $y = 3x - 1 + ce^{-3x}$.   ANS. $27x = 9y - 1 + ke^{-9y}$.

25. $y^2(2x^2 + y^2) = c^2$.   ANS. $y^2 = 2x^2 \ln|kx|$.

26. $y^4 = c^2(x^2 + 4y^2)$.   ANS. $x^8(2x^2 + 5y^2) = k^2$.

27. $x^4(4x^2 + 3y^2) = c^2$.   ANS. $y^8 = k^2(3x^2 + 2y^2)$.

28. For the family $x^2 + 3y^2 = cy$, find that member of the orthogonal trajectories which passes through $(1, 2)$.   ANS. $y^2 = x^2(3x + 1)$.

17. Orthogonal trajectories; polar coordinates

Consider a curve whose equation is expressed in polar coordinates. In calculus it is shown that the angle ψ (Figure 11), measured positive in the counterclockwise direction from the radius vector to the tangent line at a point, is given by

$$\tan \psi = r \frac{d\theta}{dr}.$$

If two curves are orthogonal, as they are shown in Figure 12, then $\psi_2 = \psi_1 + \pi/2$ and thus $\tan \psi_2 = - \cot \psi_1 = -1/\tan \psi_1$. Therefore, if two curves are to cut one another at right angles, then at the point of intersection

FIGURE 11

FIGURE 12

the value of the product

$$r \frac{d\theta}{dr}$$

for one curve must be the negative reciprocal of the value of that product for the other curve.

When polar coordinates are used, suppose a family of curves has the differential equation

$$P \, dr + Q \, d\theta = 0. \tag{1}$$

Then

$$\frac{d\theta}{dr} = - \frac{P}{Q}$$

so

$$r \frac{d\theta}{dr} = - \frac{Pr}{Q}. \tag{2}$$

Hence the family of the orthogonal trajectories of the solutions of (1) must be solutions of the equation

$$r \frac{d\theta}{dr} = + \frac{Q}{Pr},$$

or

$$Q \, dr - r^2 P \, d\theta = 0. \tag{3}$$

EXAMPLE: Find the orthogonal trajectories of the family of cardioids $r = a(1 + \cos \theta)$. A few curves of each family are shown in Figure 13.

From

$$\frac{r}{1 + \cos \theta} = a$$

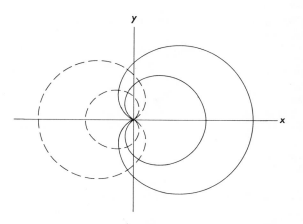

FIGURE 13

the differential equation

$$(1 + \cos \theta)\, dr + r \sin \theta \, d\theta = 0$$

follows at once. Then the differential equation of the orthogonal trajectories is

$$r \sin \theta \, dr - r^2(1 + \cos \theta)\, d\theta = 0$$

or

$$\sin \theta \, dr - r(1 + \cos \theta)\, d\theta = 0.$$

Separating the variables, we use the form

$$\frac{dr}{r} - \frac{(1 + \cos \theta)\, d\theta}{\sin \theta} = 0,$$

or

$$\frac{dr}{r} - \csc \theta \, d\theta - \frac{\cos \theta}{\sin \theta}\, d\theta = 0.$$

Hence

$$\ln |r| - \ln |\csc \theta - \cot \theta| - \ln |\sin \theta| = \ln |b|,$$

so the orthogonal trajectories of the original family of cardioids are seen to be

$$r = b \sin \theta(\csc \theta - \cot \theta),$$

or

$$r = b(1 - \cos \theta).$$

The student should show that this is the same family as the one we started with; that is, the family of cardioids is self-orthogonal.

Exercises

In each exercise, find the orthogonal trajectories of the given family of curves. Draw the figures in Exs. 1–8.

1. $r = a \cos^2 \theta$.   ANS. $r^2 = b \sin \theta$.

2. $r = a \cos 2\theta$.   ANS. $r^4 = b \sin 2\theta$.

3. $r = 2a \sin \theta$.   ANS. $r = 2b \cos \theta$.

4. $r = 2a(\sin \theta + \cos \theta)$.   ANS. $r = 2b(\sin \theta - \cos \theta)$.

5. $r = a(1 + \sin \theta)$.   ANS. $r = b(1 - \sin \theta)$.

6. $r^2 = a \sin 2\theta$.   ANS. $r^2 = b \cos 2\theta$.

7. $r = 4a \sec \theta \tan \theta$.   ANS. $r^2(1 + \sin^2 \theta) = b^2$.

8. $r^2 \cos 2\theta = c_1$.   ANS. $r^2 \sin 2\theta = c_2$.

9. $r = k/(1 + 2 \cos \theta)$.   ANS. $r^2 \sin^3 \theta = b(1 + \cos \theta)$.

10. $r = k/(2 + \cos \theta)$.   ANS. $r \sin^3 \theta = b(1 + \cos \theta)^2$.

11. $r = k/(1 + \varepsilon \cos \theta)$ with ε fixed. What are k and ε geometrically?

     ANS. $r^\varepsilon \sin^{\varepsilon+1} \theta = b(1 + \cos \theta)$.

12. $r = a(1 - 2 \sin \theta)$.   ANS. $r^2 = b \cos \theta(1 + \sin \theta)$.

13. The strophoids, $r = a(\sec \theta + \tan \theta)$.   ANS. $r = be^{-\sin \theta}$.

14. The cissoids, $r = a \sin \theta \tan \theta$.   ANS. $r^2 = b(1 + \cos^2 \theta)$.

15. The trisectrices of Maclaurin, $r = a(4 \cos \theta - \sec \theta)$.

     ANS. $r^5 = b \sin^3 \theta(4 \cos^2 \theta + 1)$.

16. $r = a(1 + \sin^2 \theta)$.   ANS. $r^2 = b \cos \theta \cot \theta$.

CHAPTER 4

Additional Topics on Equations of Order One

18. Integrating factors found by inspection

In Section 11 we found that any linear equation of order one can be solved with the aid of an integrating factor. In Section 19 there is some discussion of tests for the determination of integrating factors.

At present we are concerned with equations that are simple enough to enable us to find integrating factors by inspection. The ability to do this depends largely upon recognition of certain common exact differentials and upon experience.

Below are four exact differentials which occur frequently:

$$d(xy) = x\,dy + y\,dx, \tag{1}$$

$$d\left(\frac{x}{y}\right) = \frac{y\,dx - x\,dy}{y^2}, \tag{2}$$

$$d\left(\frac{y}{x}\right) = \frac{x\,dy - y\,dx}{x^2}, \tag{3}$$

$$d\left(\operatorname{Arctan}\frac{y}{x}\right) = \frac{x\,dy - y\,dx}{x^2 + y^2}. \tag{4}$$

Note the homogeneity of the coefficients of dx and dy in each of these differentials.

A differential involving only one variable, one such as $x^{-2}\,dx$, is an exact differential.

EXAMPLE (a):   Solve the equation

$$y\,dx + (x + x^3y^2)\,dy = 0. \tag{5}$$

Let us group the terms of like degree, writing the equation in the form

$$(y\,dx + x\,dy) + x^3y^2\,dy = 0.$$

Now the combination $(y\,dx + x\,dy)$ attracts attention, so we rewrite the equation, obtaining

$$d(xy) + x^3y^2\,dy = 0. \tag{6}$$

Since the differential of xy is present in equation (6), any factor that is a function of the product xy will not disturb the integrability of that term. But the other term contains the differential dy, hence should contain a function of y alone. Therefore, let us divide by $(xy)^3$ and write

$$\frac{d(xy)}{(xy)^3} + \frac{dy}{y} = 0.$$

The equation above is integrable as it stands. A family of solutions is

$$-\frac{1}{2x^2y^2} + \ln|y| = -\ln|c|,$$

or

$$2x^2y^2 \ln|cy| = 1.$$

EXAMPLE (b):   Solve the equation

$$y(x^3 - y)\,dx - x(x^3 + y)\,dy = 0. \tag{7}$$

Let us regroup the terms of (7) to obtain

$$x^3(y\,dx - x\,dy) - y(y\,dx + x\,dy) = 0. \tag{8}$$

Recalling that

$$d\left(\frac{x}{y}\right) = \frac{y\,dx - x\,dy}{y^2},$$

we divide the terms of equation (8) throughout by y^2 to get

$$x^3 \, d\left(\frac{x}{y}\right) - \frac{d(xy)}{y} = 0. \tag{9}$$

Equation (9) will be made exact by introducing a factor, if it can be found, to make the coefficient of $d(x/y)$ a function of (x/y) and the coefficient of $d(xy)$ a function of (xy). Some skill in obtaining such factors can be developed with a little practice.

There is a straightforward attack on equation (9) which has its good points. Assume that the integrating factor desired is $x^k y^n$, where k and n are to be determined. Applying that factor, we obtain

$$x^{k+3} y^n \, d\left(\frac{x}{y}\right) - x^k y^{n-1} \, d(xy) = 0. \tag{10}$$

Since the coefficient of $d(x/y)$ is to be a function of the ratio (x/y), the exponents of x and y in that coefficient must be numerically equal, but of opposite sign. That is,

$$k + 3 = -n. \tag{11}$$

In a similar manner, from the coefficient of $d(xy)$ it follows that we must put

$$k = n - 1. \tag{12}$$

From equations (11) and (12) we conclude that $k = -2$, $n = -1$. The desired integrating factor is $x^{-2} y^{-1}$ and (10) becomes

$$\frac{x}{y} \, d\left(\frac{x}{y}\right) - \frac{d(xy)}{x^2 y^2} = 0$$

of which a set of solutions is

$$\frac{1}{2}\left(\frac{x}{y}\right)^2 + \frac{1}{xy} = \frac{c}{2}.$$

Finally, we may write the desired solutions of equation (7) as

$$x^3 + 2y = cxy^2.$$

EXAMPLE (c): Solve the equation

$$3x^2 y \, dx + (y^4 - x^3) \, dy = 0.$$

Since two terms in the coefficients of dx and dy are of degree three and the other coefficient is not of degree three, let us regroup the terms to get

$$(3x^2 y \, dx - x^3 \, dy) + y^4 \, dy = 0,$$

or

$$y \, d(x^3) - x^3 \, dy + y^4 \, dy = 0.$$

The form of the first two terms now suggests the numerator in the differential of a quotient, as in

$$d\left(\frac{u}{v}\right) = \frac{v\,du - u\,dv}{v^2}.$$

Therefore, we divide each term of our equation by y^2 and obtain

$$\frac{y\,d(x^3) - x^3\,dy}{y^2} + y^2\,dy = 0,$$

or

$$d\left(\frac{x^3}{y}\right) + y^2\,dy = 0.$$

Hence a solution set of the original equation is

$$\frac{x^3}{y} + \frac{y^3}{3} = \frac{c}{3}$$

or

$$3x^3 + y^4 = cy.$$

Exercises

Except when the exercise indicates otherwise, find a set of solutions.

1. $y(2xy + 1)\,dx - x\,dy = 0.$ ANS. $x(xy + 1) = cy.$
2. $y(y^3 - x)\,dx + x(y^3 + x)\,dy = 0.$ ANS. $2xy^3 - x^2 = cy^2.$
3. $(x^3y^3 + 1)\,dx + x^4y^2\,dy = 0.$ ANS. $x^3y^3 = -3\ln|cx|.$
4. $2t\,ds + s(2 + s^2t)\,dt = 0.$ ANS. $1 + s^2t = cs^2t^2.$
5. $y(x^4 - y^2)\,dx + x(x^4 + y^2)\,dy = 0.$ ANS. $y(3x^4 + y^2) = cx^3.$
6. $y(y^2 + 1)\,dx + x(y^2 - 1)\,dy = 0.$ ANS. $x(y^2 + 1) = cy.$
7. Do Ex. 6 by a second method.
8. $y(x^3 - y^5)\,dx - x(x^3 + y^5)\,dy = 0.$ ANS. $x^4 = y^4(c + 4xy).$
9. $y(x^2 - y^2 + 1)\,dx - x(x^2 - y^2 - 1)\,dy = 0.$ ANS. $x^2 + cxy + y^2 = 1.$
10. $(x^3 + xy^2 + y)\,dx + (y^3 + x^2y + x)\,dy = 0.$

     ANS. $(x^2 + y^2)^2 = c - 4xy.$

11. $y(x^2 + y^2 - 1)\,dx + x(x^2 + y^2 + 1)\,dy = 0.$

     ANS. $xy + \text{Arctan}\,(y/x) = c.$

12. $(x^3 + xy^2 - y)\,dx + (y^3 + x^2y + x)\,dy = 0.$

     ANS. $2\,\text{Arctan}\,(y/x) = c - x^2 - y^2.$

13. $y(x^3e^{xy} - y)\,dx + x(y + x^3e^{xy})\,dy = 0.$ ANS. $2x^2e^{xy} + y^2 = cx^2.$
14. $xy(y^2 + 1)\,dx + (x^2y^2 - 2)\,dy = 0$; when $x = 1, y = 1.$

     ANS. $x^2(y^2 + 1) = 2 + 4\ln y.$

15. $y^2(1 - x^2)\,dx + x(x^2y + 2x + y)\,dy = 0.$ ANS. $x^2y + x + y = cxy^2.$
16. $y(x^2y^2 - 1)\,dx + x(x^2y^2 + 1)\,dy = 0.$ ANS. $x^2y^2 = 2\ln|cx/y|.$
17. $x^4y' = -x^3y - \csc\,(xy).$ ANS. $2x^2\cos\,(xy) = cx^2 - 1.$

18. $[1 + y \tan (xy)] \, dx + x \tan (xy) \, dy = 0.$ ANS. $\cos (xy) = ce^x.$

19. $y(x^2y^2 - m) \, dx + x(x^2y^2 + n) \, dy = 0.$ ANS. $x^2y^2 = 2 \ln |cx^m/y^n|.$

20. $x(x^2 - y^2 - x) \, dx - y(x^2 - y^2) \, dy = 0$; when $x = 2$, $y = 0.$

ANS. $3(x^2 - y^2)^2 = 4(x^3 + 4).$

21. $y(x^2 + y) \, dx + x(x^2 - 2y) \, dy = 0$; when $x = 1$, $y = 2.$

ANS. $x^2y - y^2 + 2x = 0.$

22. $y(x^3y^3 + 2x^2 - y) \, dx + x^3(xy^3 - 2) \, dy = 0$; when $x = 1$, $y = 1.$

ANS. $x^3y^3 + 4x^2 - 7xy + 2y = 0.$

23. $y(2 - 3xy) \, dx - x \, dy = 0.$ ANS. $x^2(1 - xy) = cy.$

24. $y(2x + y^2) \, dx + x(y^2 - x) \, dy = 0.$ ANS. $x(x + y^2) = cy.$

25. $y \, dx + 2(y^4 - x) \, dy = 0.$ ANS. $y^4 + x = cy^2.$

26. $y(3x^3 - x + y) \, dx + x^2(1 - x^2) \, dy = 0.$ ANS. $y \ln |cx| = x(1 - x^2).$

27. $2x^5y' = y(3x^4 + y^2).$ ANS. $x^4 = y^2(1 + cx).$

28. $(x^n y^{n+1} + ay) \, dx + (x^{n+1} y^n + bx) \, dy = 0.$

ANS.   If $n \neq 0$, $x^n y^n = n \ln |cx^{-a}y^{-b}|.$
If $n = 0$, $xy = c_1 x^{-a} y^{-b}.$

29. $(x^{n+1} y^n + ay) \, dx + (x^n y^{n+1} + ax) \, dy = 0.$

ANS.   If $n \neq 1$, $(n - 1)(xy)^{n-1}(x^2 + y^2 - c) = 2a.$
If $n = 1$, $x^2 + y^2 - c = -2a \ln |xy|.$

19. The determination of integrating factors

Let us see what progress can be made on the problem of the determination of an integrating factor for the equation

$$M \, dx + N \, dy = 0. \tag{1}$$

Suppose u, possibly a function of both x and y, is to be an integrating factor of (1). Then the equation

$$uM \, dx + uN \, dy = 0 \tag{2}$$

must be exact. Therefore, by the result of Section 10,

$$\frac{\partial}{\partial y} (uM) = \frac{\partial}{\partial x} (uN).$$

Hence u must satisfy the partial differential equation

$$u \frac{\partial M}{\partial y} + M \frac{\partial u}{\partial y} = u \frac{\partial N}{\partial x} + N \frac{\partial u}{\partial x},$$

or

$$u \left(\frac{\partial M}{\partial y} - \frac{\partial N}{\partial x} \right) = N \frac{\partial u}{\partial x} - M \frac{\partial u}{\partial y}. \tag{3}$$

Furthermore, by reversing the argument above, it can be seen that if u satisfies equation (3), then u is an integrating factor for equation (1). We have "reduced" the problem of solving the ordinary differential equation (1) to the problem of obtaining a particular solution of the partial differential equation (3).

Not much has been gained, since we have developed no methods for attacking an equation such as (3). Therefore, we turn the problem back into the realm of ordinary differential equations by restricting u to be a function of only one variable.

First let u be a function of x alone. Then $\partial u/\partial y = 0$ and $\partial u/\partial x$ becomes du/dx. Then (3) reduces to

$$u\left(\frac{\partial M}{\partial y} - \frac{\partial N}{\partial x}\right) = N\frac{du}{dx},$$

or

$$\frac{1}{N}\left(\frac{\partial M}{\partial y} - \frac{\partial N}{\partial x}\right) dx = \frac{du}{u}. \tag{4}$$

If the left member of the above equation is a function of x alone, then we can determine u at once. Indeed, if

$$\frac{1}{N}\left(\frac{\partial M}{\partial y} - \frac{\partial N}{\partial x}\right) = f(x), \tag{5}$$

then the desired integrating factor is $u = \exp\left(\int f(x)\,dx\right)$.

By a similar argument, assuming that u is a function of y alone, we are led to the conclusion that if

$$\frac{1}{M}\left(\frac{\partial M}{\partial y} - \frac{\partial N}{\partial x}\right) = g(y), \tag{6}$$

then an integrating factor for equation (1) is $u = \exp\left(-\int g(y)\,dy\right)$.

Our two results are expressed in the following rules.

If $\dfrac{1}{N}\left(\dfrac{\partial M}{\partial y} - \dfrac{\partial N}{\partial x}\right) = f(x)$, a function of x alone, then $\exp\left(\int f(x)\,dx\right)$ is an integrating factor for the equation

$$M\,dx + N\,dy = 0. \tag{1}$$

If $\dfrac{1}{M}\left(\dfrac{\partial M}{\partial y} - \dfrac{\partial N}{\partial x}\right) = g(y)$, a function of y alone, then $\exp\left(-\int g(y)\,dy\right)$ is an integrating factor for equation (1).

It should be emphasized that if neither of the preceding criteria is satisfied, we can say only that the equation does not have an integrating factor that is a function of x or y alone. For example, the student should show that the above criteria fail in the case of Example (a) of Section 18, even though $(xy)^{-3}$ is an integrating factor for the differential equation.

EXAMPLE (a):   Solve the equation

$$(4xy + 3y^2 - x)\, dx + x(x + 2y)\, dy = 0. \tag{7}$$

Here $M = 4xy + 3y^2 - x$, $N = x^2 + 2xy$, so

$$\frac{\partial M}{\partial y} - \frac{\partial N}{\partial x} = 4x + 6y - (2x + 2y) = 2x + 4y.$$

Hence

$$\frac{1}{N}\left(\frac{\partial M}{\partial y} - \frac{\partial N}{\partial x}\right) = \frac{2x + 4y}{x(x + 2y)} = \frac{2}{x}.$$

Therefore an integrating factor for equation (7) is

$$\exp\left(2\int\frac{dx}{x}\right) = \exp\left(2\ln|x|\right) = x^2.$$

Returning to the original equation (7), we insert the integrating factor and obtain

$$(4x^3y + 3x^2y^2 - x^3)\, dx + (x^4 + 2x^3y)\, dy = 0, \tag{8}$$

which we know must be an exact equation. The methods of Section 10 apply. We are then led to put equation (8) in the form

$$(4x^3y\, dx + x^4\, dy) + (3x^2y^2\, dx + 2x^3y\, dy) - x^3\, dx = 0,$$

from which the solution set

$$x^4y + x^3y^2 - \tfrac{1}{4}x^4 = \tfrac{1}{4}c,$$

or

$$x^3(4xy + 4y^2 - x) = c$$

follows at once.

EXAMPLE (b):   Solve the equation

$$y(x + y + 1)\, dx + x(x + 3y + 2)\, dy = 0. \tag{9}$$

First we form

$$\frac{\partial M}{\partial y} = x + 2y + 1, \qquad \frac{\partial N}{\partial x} = 2x + 3y + 2.$$

Then we see that

$$\frac{\partial M}{\partial y} - \frac{\partial N}{\partial x} = -x - y - 1,$$

so

$$\frac{1}{N}\left(\frac{\partial M}{\partial y} - \frac{\partial N}{\partial x}\right) = -\frac{x + y + 1}{x(x + 3y + 2)}$$

is not a function of x alone. But

$$\frac{1}{M}\left(\frac{\partial M}{\partial y} - \frac{\partial N}{\partial x}\right) = -\frac{x + y + 1}{y(x + y + 1)} = -\frac{1}{y}.$$

Therefore $\exp(\ln|y|) = |y|$ is the desired integrating factor for (9).

It follows that for $y > 0$, y itself is an integrating factor of equation (9) and for $y < 0$, $-y$ is an integrating factor. In either case (9) becomes

$$(xy^2 + y^3 + y^2)\,dx + (x^2y + 3xy^2 + 2xy)\,dy = 0,$$

or

$$(xy^2\,dx + x^2y\,dy) + (y^3\,dx + 3xy^2\,dy) + (y^2\,dx + 2xy\,dy) = 0.$$

Then a set of solutions of (9) is defined implicitly by

$$\tfrac{1}{2}x^2y^2 + xy^3 + xy^2 = \tfrac{1}{2}c,$$

or

$$xy^2(x + 2y + 2) = c.$$

EXAMPLE (c):   Solve the equation

$$y(x + y)\,dx + (x + 2y - 1)\,dy = 0. \tag{10}$$

From $\dfrac{\partial M}{\partial y} = x + 2y$, $\dfrac{\partial N}{\partial x} = 1$, we conclude at once that

$$\frac{1}{N}\left(\frac{\partial M}{\partial y} - \frac{\partial N}{\partial x}\right) = \frac{x + 2y - 1}{x + 2y - 1} = 1.$$

Hence e^x is an integrating factor for (10). Then

$$(xye^x + y^2e^x)\,dx + (xe^x + 2ye^x - e^x)\,dy = 0$$

is an exact equation. Grouping the terms in the following manner,

$$[xye^x\,dx + (xe^x - e^x)\,dy] + (y^2e^x\,dx + 2ye^x\,dy) = 0,$$

leads us at once to the family of solutions defined by

$$e^x(x - 1)y + y^2e^x = c,$$

or

$$y(x + y - 1) = ce^{-x}.$$

Exercises

Solve each of the following equations.

1. $(x^2 + y^2 + 1) dx + x(x - 2y) dy = 0.$ ANS. $x^2 - y^2 + xy - 1 = cx.$

2. $2y(x^2 - y + x) dx + (x^2 - 2y) dy = 0.$ ANS. $y(x^2 - y) = ce^{-2x}.$

3. $y(2x - y + 1) dx + x(3x - 4y + 3) dy = 0.$ ANS. $xy^3(x - y + 1) = c.$

4. $y(4x + y) dx - 2(x^2 - y) dy = 0.$ ANS. $2x^2 + xy + 2y \ln |y| = cy.$

5. $(xy + 1) dx + x(x + 4y - 2) dy = 0.$ ANS. $xy + \ln |x| + 2y^2 - 2y = c.$

6. $(2y^2 + 3xy - 2y + 6x) dx + x(x + 2y - 1) dy = 0.$

      ANS. $x^2(y^2 + xy - y + 2x) = c.$

7. $y(y + 2x - 2) dx - 2(x + y) dy = 0.$ ANS. $y(2x + y) = ce^x.$

8. $y^2 dx + (3xy + y^2 - 1) dy = 0.$ ANS. $y^2(y^2 + 4xy - 2) = c.$

9. $2y(x + y + 2) dx + (y^2 - x^2 - 4x - 1) dy = 0.$

      ANS. $x^2 + 2xy + y^2 + 4x + 1 = cy.$

10. $2(2y^2 + 5xy - 2y + 4) dx + x(2x + 2y - 1) dy = 0.$

      ANS. $x^4(y^2 + 2xy - y + 2) = c.$

11. $3(x^2 + y^2) dx + x(x^2 + 3y^2 + 6y) dy = 0.$ ANS. $x(x^2 + 3y^2) = ce^{-y}.$

12. $y(8x - 9y) dx + 2x(x - 3y) dy = 0.$ ANS. $x^3y(2x - 3y) = c.$

13. Do Ex. 12 by another method.

14. $y(2x^2 - xy + 1) dx + (x - y) dy = 0.$ ANS. $y(2x - y) = c \exp(-x^2).$

15. Euler's theorem (Ex. 34, page 29) on homogeneous functions states that if F is a homogeneous function of degree k in x and y, then

$$x \frac{\partial F}{\partial x} + y \frac{\partial F}{\partial y} = kF.$$

Use Euler's theorem to prove the result that if M and N are homogeneous functions of the same degree, and if $Mx + Ny \neq 0$, then

$$\frac{1}{Mx + Ny}$$

is an integrating factor for the equation

$$M\, dx + N\, dy = 0. \qquad (1)$$

16. In the result to be proved in Ex. 15 above there is an exceptional case, namely, when $Mx + Ny = 0$. Solve equation (1) when $Mx + Ny = 0$.   ANS. $y = cx.$

Use the integrating factor in the result of Ex. 15 above to solve each of the equations in Exs. 17–20.

17. $xy\, dx - (x^2 + 2y^2) dy = 0.$ ANS. $x^2 = 4y^2 \ln |y/c|.$

18. $v^2 dx + x(x + v) dv = 0.$ ANS. $xv^2 = c(x + 2v).$

19. $v(u^2 + v^2) du - u(u^2 + 2v^2) dv = 0.$ ANS. $u^2 = 2v^2 \ln |cv^2/u|.$

20. $(x^2 + y^2) dx - xy\, dy = 0.$ (Ex. 9, page 28.)

21. Apply the method of this section to the general linear equation of order one.

20. Substitution suggested by the equation

An equation of the form

$$M \, dx + N \, dy = 0$$

may not yield at once (or at all) to the methods of Chapter 2. Even then the usefulness of those methods is not exhausted. It may be possible by some change of variables to transform the equation into one of a type which we know how to solve.

A natural source of suggestions for useful transformations is the differential equation itself. If a particular function of one or both variables stands out in the equation, then it is worth while to examine the equation after that function has been introduced as a new variable. For instance, in the equation

$$(x + 2y - 1) \, dx + 3(x + 2y) \, dy = 0 \tag{1}$$

the combination $(x + 2y)$ occurs twice and so attracts attention. Hence we put

$$x + 2y = v,$$

and since no other function of x and y stands out, we retain either x or y for the other variable. The solution is completed in Example (a) below.

In the equation

$$(1 + 3x \sin y) \, dx - x^2 \cos y \, dy = 0, \tag{2}$$

the presence of both $\sin y$ and its differential $\cos y \, dy$, and the fact that y appears in the equation in no other manner, leads us to put $\sin y = w$ and to obtain the differential equation in w and x. See Example (b) below.

EXAMPLE (a): Solve the equation

$$(x + 2y - 1) \, dx + 3(x + 2y) \, dy = 0. \tag{1}$$

As suggested above, put

$$x + 2y = v.$$

Then

$$dx = dv - 2 \, dy$$

and equation (1) becomes

$$(v - 1)(dv - 2 \, dy) + 3v \, dy = 0,$$

or

$$(v - 1) \, dv + (v + 2) \, dy = 0.$$

Now the variables can be separated. From the equation in the form

$$\frac{v-1}{v+2}\, dv + dy = 0,$$

we get

$$\left[1 - \frac{3}{v+2}\right] dv + dy = 0$$

and then

$$v - 3 \ln |v + 2| + y + c = 0.$$

But $v = x + 2y$, so our final result is

$$x + 3y + c = 3 \ln |x + 2y + 2|.$$

EXAMPLE (b):   Solve the equation

$$(1 + 3x \sin y)\, dx - x^2 \cos y\, dy = 0. \tag{2}$$

Put $\sin y = w$. Then $\cos y\, dy = dw$ and (2) becomes

$$(1 + 3xw)\, dx - x^2\, dw = 0,$$

an equation linear in w. From the standard form

$$dw - \frac{3}{x} w\, dx = \frac{dx}{x^2} \qquad \frac{dw}{dx} - \left(\frac{3}{x}\right)w = \frac{1}{x^2}$$

an integrating factor is seen to be

$$\exp(-3 \ln |x|) = |x|^{-3}.$$

Application of the integrating factor yields the exact equation

$$x^{-3}\, dw - 3x^{-4}w\, dx = x^{-5}\, dx,$$

for either $x > 0$ or $x < 0$, from which we get

$$x^{-3}w = -\tfrac{1}{4}x^{-4} + \tfrac{1}{4}c,$$

or

$$4xw = cx^4 - 1.$$

Hence (2) has the solution set

$$4x \sin y = cx^4 - 1.$$

21. Bernoulli's equation

A well-known equation that fits into the category of Section 20 is Bernoulli's equation,

$$y' + P(x)y = Q(x)y^n. \tag{1}$$

If $n = 1$ in (1), the variables are separable, so we concentrate on the case $n \neq 1$. Equation (1) may be put in the form

$$y^{-n} \, dy + Py^{-n+1} \, dx = Q \, dx. \tag{2}$$

But the differential of y^{-n+1} is $(1 - n)y^{-n} \, dy$, so equation (2) may be simplified by putting

$$y^{-n+1} = z,$$

from which

$$(1 - n)y^{-n} \, dy = dz.$$

Thus the equation in z and x is

$$dz + (1 - n)Pz \, dx = (1 - n)Q \, dx,$$

a linear equation in standard form. Hence any Bernoulli equation can be solved with the aid of the above change of dependent variable (unless $n = 1$, when no substitution is needed).

EXAMPLE (a):   Solve the equation

$$y(6y^2 - x - 1) \, dx + 2x \, dy = 0. \tag{3}$$

First let us group the terms according to powers of y, writing

$$2x \, dy - y(x + 1) \, dx + 6y^3 \, dx = 0.$$

Now it can be seen that the equation is a Bernoulli equation, since it involves only terms containing respectively dy, y, and y^n ($n = 3$ here). Therefore, we divide throughout by y^3, obtaining

$$2xy^{-3} \, dy - y^{-2}(x + 1) \, dx = -6 \, dx.$$

This equation is linear in y^{-2}, so we put $y^{-2} = v$, obtain $dv = -2y^{-3} \, dy$, and need to solve the equation

$$x \, dv + v(x + 1) \, dx = 6 \, dx,$$

or

$$dv = v(1 + x^{-1}) \, dx = 6x^{-1} \, dx. \tag{4}$$

Since

$$\exp(x + \ln|x|) = |x| \, e^x$$

is an integrating factor for (4), the equation

$$xe^x \, dv + ve^x(x + 1) \, dx = 6e^x \, dx$$

is exact. Its solution set

$$xve^x = 6e^x + c,$$

together with $v = y^{-2}$, leads us to the final result

$$y^2(6 + ce^{-x}) = x.$$

EXAMPLE (b):   Solve the equation

$$6y^2\, dx - x(2x^3 + y)\, dy = 0. \tag{5}$$

This is a Bernoulli equation with x as the dependent variable, so it can be treated in the manner used in Example (a). That method of attack is left for the exercises.

Equation (5) can equally well be treated as follows. Note that if each member of (5) be multiplied by x^2, the equation becomes

$$6y^2x^2\, dx - x^3(2x^3 + y)\, dy = 0. \tag{6}$$

In (6), the variable x appears only in the combinations x^3 and its differential $3x^2\, dx$. Hence a reasonable choice for a new variable is $w = x^3$. The equation in w and y is

$$2y^2\, dw - w(2w + y)\, dy = 0,$$

an equation with coefficients homogeneous of degree two in y and w. The further change of variable $w = zy$ leads to the equation

$$2y\, dz - z(2z - 1)\, dy = 0,$$

$$\frac{4\, dz}{2z - 1} - \frac{2\, dz}{z} - \frac{dy}{y} = 0.$$

Therefore, we have

$$2 \ln |2z - 1| - 2 \ln |z| - \ln |y| = \ln |c|,$$

or

$$(2z - 1)^2 = cyz^2.$$

But $z = w/y = x^3/y$, so the solutions we seek are

$$(2x^3 - y)^2 = cyx^6.$$

Exercises

In Exs. 1–21 solve the equation.

1. $(3x - 2y + 1)\, dx + (3x - 2y + 3)\, dy = 0.$
   ANS. $5(x + y + c) = 2 \ln |15x - 10y + 11|.$

2. $\sin y(x + \sin y)\, dx + 2x^2 \cos y\, dy = 0.$
   ANS. $x^3 \sin^2 y = c(3x + \sin y)^2.$

3. $\dfrac{dy}{dx} = (9x + 4y + 1)^2.$
   ANS. $3 \tan (6x + c) = 2(9x + 4y + 1).$

4. $y' = y - xy^3 e^{-2x}$.   ANS. $e^{2x} = y^2(x^2 + c)$.

5. $\dfrac{dy}{dx} = \sin(x + y)$.   ANS. $x + c = \tan(x + y) - \sec(x + y)$.

6. $xy\,dx + (x^2 - 3y)\,dy = 0$.   ANS. $x^2 y^2 = 2y^3 + c$.

7. $(3\tan x - 2\cos y)\sec^2 x\,dx + \tan x \sin y\,dy = 0$.

ANS. $\cos y \tan^2 x = \tan^3 x + c$.

8. $(x + 2y - 1)\,dx + (2x + 4y - 3)\,dy = 0$. Solve by two methods.

ANS. $(x + 2y - 1)^2 = 2y + c$.

9. Solve the equation

$$6y^2\,dx - x(2x^3 + y)\,dy = 0$$

of Example (b) above by treating it as a Bernoulli equation in the dependent variable x.

10. $2x^3 y' = y(y^2 + 3x^2)$. Solve by two methods.   ANS. $y^2(c - x) = x^3$.

11. $(3\sin y - 5x)\,dx + 2x^2 \cot y\,dy = 0$.   ANS. $x^3(\sin y - x)^2 = c \sin^2 y$.

12. $y' = 1 + 6x \exp(x - y)$.   ANS. $\exp(y - x) = 3x^2 + c$.

13. $\dfrac{dv}{du} = (u - v)^2 - 2(u - v) - 2$.   ANS. $(u - v - 3)\exp(4u) = c(u - v + 1)$.

14. $2y\,dx + x(x^2 \ln y - 1)\,dy = 0$.   ANS. $y(1 + x^2 - x^2 \ln y) = cx^2$.

15. $\cos y \sin 2x\,dx + (\cos^2 y - \cos^2 x)\,dy = 0$.

ANS. $\cos^2 x(1 + \sin y) = \cos y(y + c - \cos y)$.

16. $(ke^{2v} - u)\,du = 2e^{2v}(e^{2v} + ku)\,dv$.

ANS. $2k \operatorname{Arctan}(ue^{-2v}) = \ln|c(u^2 + e^{4v})|$.

17. $y' \tan x \sin 2y = \sin^2 x + \cos^2 y$.   ANS. $(\sin^2 x + 3\cos^2 y)\sin x = c$.

18. $(x + 2y - 1)\,dx - (x + 2y - 5)\,dy = 0$.

19. $y(x \tan x + \ln y)\,dx + \tan x\,dy = 0$.   ANS. $\sin x \ln y = x \cos x - \sin x + c$.

20. $xy' - y = x^k y^n$, where $n \neq 1$ and $k + n \neq 1$.

ANS. $(k + n - 1)y^{1-n} = (1 - n)x^k + cx^{1-n}$.

21. The equation of Ex. 20 for the values of k and n not included there.

ANS.   If $n = 1$ and $k \neq 0$, $x^k = k \ln|cy/x|$.

If $n = 1$ and $k = 0$, $y = cx^2$.

If $n \neq 1$ but $k + n = 1$, $y^{1-n} = (1 - n)x^{1-n} \ln|cx|$.

In Exs. 22–27, find the particular solution required.

22. $4(3x + y - 2)\,dx - (3x + y)\,dy = 0$; when $x = 1$, $y = 0$.

ANS. $7(4x - y - 4) = 8 \ln \dfrac{21x + 7y - 8}{13}$.

23. $y' = 2(3x + y)^2 - 1$; when $x = 0$, $y = 1$.   ANS. $4 \operatorname{Arctan}(3x + y) = 8x + \pi$.

24. $2xyy' = y^2 - 2x^3$. Find the solution that passes through the point $(1, 2)$.

ANS. $y^2 = x(5 - x^2)$.

25. $(y^4 - 2xy)\,dx + 3x^2\,dy = 0$; when $x = 2$, $y = 1$.   ANS. $x^2 = y^3(x + 2)$.

26. $(2y^3 - x^3)\,dx + 3xy^2\,dy = 0$; when $x = 1$, $y = 1$. Solve by two methods.

ANS. $5x^2 y^3 = x^5 + 4$.

27. $(x^2 + 6y^2)\,dx - 4xy\,dy = 0$; when $x = 1$, $y = 1$. Solve by three methods.

ANS. $2y^2 = x^2(3x - 1)$.

22. Coefficients linear in the two variables

Consider the equation

$$(a_1 x + b_1 y + c_1) \, dx + (a_2 x + b_2 y + c_2) \, dy = 0, \qquad (1)$$

in which the a's, b's, and c's are constants. We know already how to solve the special case in which $c_1 = 0$ and $c_2 = 0$, for then the coefficients in (1) are each homogeneous and of degree one in x and y. It is reasonable to attempt to reduce equation (1) to that situation.

In connection with (1) consider the lines

$$a_1 x + b_1 y + c_1 = 0, \qquad (2)$$
$$a_2 x + b_2 y + c_2 = 0.$$

They may be parallel or they may intersect. There will not be two lines if a_1 and b_1 are zero, or if a_2 and b_2 are zero, but equation (1) will then be linear in one of its variables.

If the lines (2) intersect, let the point of intersection be (h, k). Then the translation

$$x = u + h, \qquad (3)$$
$$y = v + k$$

will change the equations (2) into equations of lines through the origin of the uv coordinate system, namely,

$$a_1 u + b_1 v = 0, \qquad (4)$$
$$a_2 u + b_2 v = 0.$$

Therefore, since $dx = du$ and $dy = dv$, the change of variables

$$x = u + h,$$
$$y = v + k,$$

where (h, k) is the point of intersection of the lines (2), will transform the differential equation (1) into

$$(a_1 u + b_1 v) \, du + (a_2 u + b_2 v) \, dv = 0, \qquad (5)$$

an equation which we know how to solve.

If the lines (2) do not intersect, there exists a constant k such that

$$a_2 x + b_2 y = k(a_1 x + b_1 y),$$

so that equation (1) appears in the form

$$(a_1 x + b_1 y + c_1) \, dx + [k(a_1 x + b_1 y) + c_2] \, dy = 0. \qquad (6)$$

The recurrence of the expression $(a_1 x + b_1 y)$ in (6) suggests the introduction of a new variable $w = a_1 x + b_1 y$. Then the new equation, in w and x or in w and y, is one with variables separable, since its coefficients contain only w and constants.

EXAMPLE (a): Solve the equation

$$(x + 2y - 4)\, dx - (2x + y - 5)\, dy = 0. \tag{7}$$

The lines

$$x + 2y - 4 = 0,$$
$$2x + y - 5 = 0$$

intersect at the point $(2, 1)$. Hence put

$$x = u + 2,$$
$$y = v + 1.$$

Then equation (7) becomes

$$(u + 2v)\, du - (2u + v)\, dv = 0, \tag{8}$$

which has coefficients homogeneous and of degree one in u and v. Therefore let $u = vz$, which transforms (8) into

$$(z + 2)(z\, dv + v\, dz) - (2z + 1)\, dv = 0,$$

or

$$(z^2 - 1)\, dv + v(z + 2)\, dz = 0.$$

Separation of the variables v and z leads us to the equation

$$\frac{dv}{v} + \frac{(z + 2)\, dz}{z^2 - 1} = 0.$$

[margin: $\dfrac{z+2}{(z-1)(z+1)} = \dfrac{A}{(z-1)} + \dfrac{\beta}{(z+1)}$]

With the aid of partial fractions, we can write the above equation in the form

$$\frac{2\, dv}{v} + \frac{3\, dz}{z - 1} - \frac{dz}{z + 1} = 0.$$

[margin: $z+2 = A(z+1) + \beta(z-1)$]
[margin: $z + 2 = Az + \beta z + A - \beta$]

Hence we get

$$2 \ln |v| + 3 \ln |z - 1| - \ln |z + 1| = \ln|c|$$

[margin: $z = Az + \beta z$, $2 = A - \beta$]

from which it follows that

$$v^2(z - 1)^3 = c(z + 1),$$

[margin: $1 = A + \beta$; $2 = A - \beta$; $3 = 2A$; $\frac{3}{2} = A$; $-\frac{1}{2} = \beta$]

or

$$(vz - v)^3 = c(vz + v).$$

Now $vz = u$, so a set of solutions appears as

$$(u - v)^3 = c(u + v).$$

But $u = x - 2$ and $v = y - 1$. Therefore the desired result in terms of x and y is

$$(x - y - 1)^3 = c(x + y - 3).$$

For other methods of solution of equation (7), see Exs. 23 and 30 below.

EXAMPLE (b):   Solve the equation

$$(2x + 3y - 1)\, dx + (2x + 3y + 2)\, dy = 0, \tag{9}$$

with the condition that $y = 3$ when $x = 1$.

The lines

$$2x + 3y - 1 = 0$$

and

$$2x + 3y + 2 = 0$$

are parallel. Therefore we proceed, as we should have upon first glancing at the equation, to put

$$2x + 3y = v.$$

Then $2\, dx = dv - 3\, dy$, and equation (9) is transformed into

$$(v - 1)(dv - 3\, dy) + 2(v + 2)\, dy = 0,$$

or

$$(v - 1)\, dv - (v - 7)\, dy = 0. \tag{10}$$

Equation (10) is easily solved, leading us to the relation

$$v - y + c + 6 \ln |v - 7| = 0.$$

Therefore a solution set of (9) is

$$2x + 2y + c = -6 \ln |2x + 3y - 7|.$$

But $y = 3$ when $x = 1$, so $c = -8 - 6 \ln 4$. Hence the particular solution required is

$$x + y - 4 = -3 \ln \left[\tfrac{1}{4}(2x + 3y - 7)\right].$$

Exercises

In Exs. 1–18 solve the equations.

1. $(y - 2)\, dx - (x - y - 1)\, dy = 0.$ ANS. $x - 3 = (2 - y) \ln |c(y - 2)|.$

2. $(x - 4y - 9)\, dx + (4x + y - 2)\, dy = 0.$

ANS. $\ln [(x - 1)^2 + (y + 2)^2] - 8 \operatorname{Arctan} \dfrac{x - 1}{y + 2} = c.$

3. $(2x - y) dx + (4x + y - 6) dy = 0.$ ANS. $(x + y - 3)^3 = c(2x + y - 4)^2.$
4. $(x - 4y - 3) dx - (x - 6y - 5) dy = 0.$

ANS. $(x - 2y - 1)^2 = c(x - 3y - 2).$

5. $(2x + 3y - 5) dx + (3x - y - 2) dy = 0.$ Solve by two methods.

6. $2 dx + (2x - y + 3) dy = 0.$ Use a change of variable.

ANS. $y + c = -\ln |2x - y + 4|.$

7. Solve the equation of Ex. 6 by using the fact that the equation is linear in x.

8. $(x - y + 2) dx + 3 dy = 0.$ ANS. $x + c = 3 \ln |x - y + 5|.$

9. Solve Ex. 8 by another method.

10. $(x + y - 1) dx + (2x + 2y + 1) dy = 0.$ ANS. $x + 2y + c = 3 \ln |x + y + 2|.$

11. $(3x + 2y + 7) dx + (2x - y) dy = 0.$ Solve by two methods.

12. $(x - 2) dx + 4(x + y - 1) dy = 0.$

ANS. $2(y + 1) = -(x + 2y) \ln |c(x + 2y)|.$

13. $(x - 3y + 2) dx + 3(x + 3y - 4) dy = 0.$

ANS. $\ln [(x - 1)^2 + 9(y - 1)^2] - 2 \operatorname{Arctan} \dfrac{x - 1}{3(y - 1)} = c.$

14. $(6x - 3y + 2) dx - (2x - y - 1) dy = 0.$

ANS. $3x - y + c = 5 \ln |2x - y + 4|.$

15. $(9x - 4y + 4) dx - (2x - y + 1) dy = 0.$

ANS. $y - 1 = 3(y - 3x - 1) \ln |c(3x - y + 1)|.$

16. $(x + 3y - 4) dx + (x + 4y - 5) dy = 0.$

ANS. $y - 1 = (x + 2y - 3) \ln |c(x + 2y - 3)|.$

17. $(x + 2y - 1) dx - (2x + y - 5) dy = 0.$ ANS. $(x - y - 4)^3 = c(x + y - 2).$
18. $(x - 1) dx - (3x - 2y - 5) dy = 0.$ ANS. $(2y - x + 3)^2 = c(y - x + 2).$

In Exs. 19–22 obtain the particular solution indicated.

19. $(2x - 3y + 4) dx + 3(x - 1) dy = 0;$ when $x = 3, y = 2.$

ANS. $3(y - 2) = -2(x - 1) \ln \dfrac{x - 1}{2}.$

20. The equation of Ex. 19 but with the condition: when $x = -1, y = 2.$

ANS. $3(y - 2) = -2(x - 1) \ln \dfrac{1 - x}{2}.$

21. $(x + y - 4) dx - (3x - y - 4) dy = 0;$ when $x = 4, y = 1.$

ANS. $2(x + 2y - 6) = 3(x - y) \ln \dfrac{x - y}{3}.$

22. The equation of Ex. 21 but with the condition: when $x = 3, y = 7.$

ANS. $y - 5x + 8 = 2(y - x) \ln \dfrac{y - x}{4}.$

23. Prove that the change of variables

$$x = \alpha_1 u + \alpha_2 v, \qquad y = u + v$$

will transform the equation

$$(a_1 x + b_1 y + c_1) dx + (a_2 x + b_2 y + c_2) dy = 0 \qquad \text{(A)}$$

into an equation in which the variables u and v are separable, if α_1 and α_2 are roots of the equation

$$a_1 \alpha^2 + (a_2 + b_1)\alpha + b_2 = 0, \qquad \text{(B)}$$

and if $\alpha_2 \neq \alpha_1$.

Note that this method of solution of (A) is not practical for us unless the roots of equation (B) are real and distinct.

Solve Exs. 24–29 by the method indicated in Ex. 23.

24. Ex. 4 above. As a check, the equation (B) for this case is

$$\alpha^2 - 5\alpha + 6 = 0,$$

so we may choose $\alpha_1 = 2$ and $\alpha_2 = 3$.

The equation in u and v turns out to be

$$(v - 1)\, du - 2(u + 2)\, dv = 0.$$

25. Ex. 3 above.   **26.** Ex. 10 above.
27. Ex. 17 above.   **28.** Ex. 18 above.
29. Example (a) in the text of this section.
30. Prove that the change of variables

$$x = \alpha_1 u + \beta v, \qquad y = u + v$$

will transform the equation

$$(a_1 x + b_1 y + c_1)\, dx + (a_2 x + b_2 y + c_2)\, dy = 0 \qquad \text{(A)}$$

into an equation that is linear in the variable u, if α_1 is a root of the equation

$$a_1 \alpha^2 + (a_2 + b_1)\alpha + b_2 = 0, \qquad \text{(B)}$$

and if β is any number such that $\beta \neq \alpha_1$.

Note that this method is not practical for us unless the roots of equation (B) are real. But they need not be distinct as they had to be in the theorem of Ex. 23. The method of this exercise is particularly useful when the roots of (B) are equal.

Solve Exs. 31–35 by the method indicated in Ex. 30.

31. Ex. 16 above. The only possible α_1 is (-2). Then β may be chosen to be anything else.
32. Ex. 12 above.   **33.** Ex. 15 above.   **34.** Ex. 18 above.
35. Ex. 4 above. As seen in Ex. 24, the roots of the "α-equation" are 2 and 3. If you choose $\alpha_1 = 2$, for example, then you make β anything except 2. Of course, if you choose $\alpha_1 = 2$ and $\beta = 3$, then you are reverting to the method of Ex. 23.

23. Solutions involving nonelementary integrals

In solving differential equations we frequently are confronted with the need for integrating an expression that is not the differential of any elementary*

---

* By an elementary function we mean a function studied in the ordinary beginning calculus course. For example, polynomials, exponentials, logarithms, trigonometric, and inverse trigonometric functions are elementary. All functions obtained from them by a finite number of applications of the elementary operations of addition, subtraction, multiplication, division, extraction of roots, and raising to powers are elementary. Finally, we include such functions as $\sin (\sin x)$, in which the argument in a function previously classed as elementary is replaced by an elementary function.

function. Following is a short list of nonelementary integrals:

$$\int \exp(-x^2)\, dx \qquad \int \frac{e^{-x}}{x}\, dx \qquad \int x \tan x\, dx$$

$$\int \sin x^2\, dx \qquad \int \frac{\sin x}{x}\, dx \qquad \int \frac{dx}{\ln x}$$

$$\int \cos x^2\, dx \qquad \int \frac{\cos x}{x}\, dx \qquad \int \frac{dx}{\sqrt{1-x^3}}.$$

Integrals involving the square root of a polynomial of degree greater than two are, in general, nonelementary. In special instances they may degenerate into elementary integrals.

The following example presents two ways of dealing with problems in which nonelementary integrals arise.

EXAMPLE: Solve the equation

$$y' - 2xy = 1$$

with the initial condition that when $x = 0$, $y = 1$.

The equation being linear in y, we write

$$dy - 2xy\, dx = dx,$$

obtain the integrating factor $\exp(-x^2)$, and prepare to solve

$$\exp(-x^2)\, dy - 2xy \exp(-x^2)\, dx = \exp(-x^2)\, dx. \tag{1}$$

The left member is, of course, the differential of $y \exp(-x^2)$. But the right member is not the differential of any elementary function; that is, $\int \exp(-x^2)\, dx$ is a nonelementary integral.

Let us turn to power series for help. From the series

$$\exp(-x^2) = \sum_{n=0}^{\infty} \frac{(-1)^n x^{2n}}{n!},$$

obtained in calculus, it follows that

$$\int \exp(-x^2)\, dx = c + \sum_{n=0}^{\infty} \frac{(-1)^n x^{2n+1}}{n!(2n+1)}.$$

Thus the differential equation (1) has the general solution

$$y \exp(-x^2) = c + \sum_{n=0}^{\infty} \frac{(-1)^n x^{2n+1}}{n!(2n+1)}.$$

Since $y = 1$ when $x = 0$, c may be found from

$$1 = c + 0.$$

Therefore, the particular solution desired is

$$y \exp(-x^2) = 1 + \sum_{n=0}^{\infty} \frac{(-1)^n x^{2n+1}}{n!(2n+1)}. \tag{2}$$

An alternative procedure is the introduction of a definite integral. In calculus, the error function defined by

$$\text{erf } x = \frac{2}{\sqrt{\pi}} \int_0^x \exp(-\beta^2)\, d\beta \tag{3}$$

is sometimes studied. Since, from (3),

$$\frac{d}{dx} \text{erf } x = \frac{2}{\sqrt{\pi}} \exp(-x^2),$$

we may integrate the exact equation (1) as follows:

$$y \exp(-x^2) = \tfrac{1}{2}\sqrt{\pi}\, \text{erf } x + c. \tag{4}$$

Since erf $0 = 0$, the condition that $y = 1$ when $x = 0$ yields $c = 1$. Hence, as an alternative to (2) we obtain

$$y \exp(-x^2) = 1 + \tfrac{1}{2}\sqrt{\pi}\, \text{erf } x. \tag{5}$$

Equation (5) means the same as

$$y \exp(-x^2) = 1 + \int_0^x \exp(-\beta^2)\, d\beta. \tag{6}$$

Writing a solution in the form of (6) implies that the definite integral is to be evaluated by power series, approximate integration such as Simpson's rule, mechanical quadrature, or any other available tool. If it happens, as in this case, that the definite integral is itself a tabulated function, that is a great convenience, but it is not vital. The essential thing is to reduce the solution to a computable form.

Exercises

In each exercise, express the solution with the aid of power series or definite integrals.

1. $y' = y[1 - \exp(-x^2)]$.   ANS. $\ln |cy| = x - \tfrac{1}{2}\sqrt{\pi}\, \text{erf } x.$

2. $(xy - \sin x)\, dx + x^2\, dy = 0$.   ANS. $xy = c + \displaystyle\int_0^x \frac{\sin w}{w}\, dw,$

$$\text{or } y = cx^{-1} + \sum_{n=0}^{\infty} (-1)^n \frac{x^{2n}}{(2n+1)(2n+1)!}.$$

3. $y' = 1 - 4x^3 y$.   ANS. $y = \exp(-x^4)\left[c + \displaystyle\int_0^x \exp(\beta^4)\, d\beta \right].$

4. $(y \cos^2 x - x \sin x) \, dx + \sin x \cos x \, dy = 0.$

ANS. $y \sin x = c + \int_0^x \beta \tan \beta \, d\beta.$

5. $(1 + xy) \, dx - x \, dy = 0;$ when $x = 1, y = 0.$ ANS. $y = e^x \int_1^x \frac{e^{-\beta}}{\beta} \, d\beta.$

6. $\left[x \exp\left(\frac{y^2}{x^2}\right) - y \right] dx + x \, dy = 0;$ when $x = 1, y = 2.$

ANS. $\ln x = \int_{y/x}^2 \exp(-\beta^2) \, d\beta.$

7. $x(2y + x) \, dx - dy = 0;$ when $x = 0, y = 1.$

ANS. $2y = 2 \exp(x^2) - x + \tfrac{1}{2}\sqrt{\pi} \exp(x^2) \operatorname{erf} x.$

Miscellaneous exercises

In each exercise, find a set of solutions unless the statement of the exercise stipulates otherwise.

1. $(y^2 - 3y - x) \, dx + (2y - 3) \, dy = 0.$ ANS. $y^2 - 3y - x + 1 = ce^{-x}.$
2. $(y^3 + y + 1) \, dx + x(x - 3y^2 - 1) \, dy = 0.$ ANS. $y^3 - xy + y + 1 = cx.$
3. $(x + 3y - 5) \, dx - (x - y - 1) \, dy = 0.$

ANS. $2(y - 1) = (x + y - 3) \ln|c(x + y - 3)|.$

4. $(x^5 - y^2) \, dx + 2xy \, dy = 0.$ ANS. $x^5 + 4y^2 = cx.$
5. $(2x + y - 4) \, dx + (x - 3y + 12) \, dy = 0.$

ANS. $2x^2 + 2xy - 3y^2 - 8x + 24y = c.$

6. Solve in two ways the equation $y' = ax + by + c$ with $b \neq 0.$

ANS. $b^2 y = c_1 e^{bx} - abx - a - cb.$

7. $y^3 \sec^2 x \, dx - (1 - 2y^2 \tan x) \, dy = 0.$ ANS. $y^2 \tan x = \ln|cy|.$
8. $x^3 y \, dx + (3x^4 - y^3) \, dy = 0.$ ANS. $15x^4 y^{12} = 4y^{15} + c.$
9. $(a_1 x + ky + c_1) \, dx + (kx + b_2 y + c_2) \, dy = 0.$

ANS. $a_1 x^2 + 2kxy + b_2 y^2 + 2c_1 x + 2c_2 y = c.$

10. $(x - 4y + 7) \, dx + (x + 2y + 1) \, dy = 0.$

ANS. $(x - y + 4)^3 = c(x - 2y + 5)^2.$

11. $xy \, dx + (y^4 - 3x^2) \, dy = 0.$ ANS. $x^2 = y^4(1 + cy^2).$
12. $(x + 2y - 1) \, dx - (2x + y - 5) \, dy = 0.$
13. $(5x + 3e^y) \, dx + 2xe^y \, dy = 0.$ ANS. $x^3(x + e^y)^2 = c.$
14. $(3x + y - 2) \, dx + (3x + y + 4) \, dy = 0.$ ANS. $x + y + c = 3 \ln|3x + y + 7|.$
15. $(x - 3y + 4) \, dx + 2(x - y - 2) \, dy = 0.$ ANS. $(x + y - 8)^4 = c(x - 2y + 1).$
16. $(x - 2) \, dx + 4(x + y - 1) \, dy = 0.$

ANS. $2(y + 1) = -(x + 2y) \ln|c(x + 2y)|.$

17. $y \, dx = x(1 + xy^4) \, dy.$ ANS. $y(5 + xy^4) = cx.$
18. $2x \, dv + v(2 + v^2 x) \, dx = 0;$ when $x = 1, v = \tfrac{1}{2}.$ ANS. $xv^2(5x - 1) = 1.$
19. $2(x - y) \, dx + (3x - y - 1) \, dy = 0.$ ANS. $(x + y - 1)^4 = c(4x - 2y - 1).$
20. $(2x - 5y + 12) \, dx + (7x - 4y + 15) \, dy = 0.$

ANS. $(x + 2y - 3)^3 = c(x - y + 3).$

21. $y \, dx + x(x^2 y - 1) \, dy = 0.$ ANS. $y^2(2x^2 y - 3) = cx^2.$
22. $dy/dx = \tan y \cot x - \sec y \cos x.$ ANS. $\sin y + \sin x \ln|c \sin x| = 0.$

23. $[1 + (x + y)^2] dx + [1 + x(x + y)] dy = 0.$

ANS. $y^2 = (x + y)^2 + 2 \ln |x + y| + c.$

24. $(x - 2y - 1) dx - (x - 3) dy = 0.$ Solve by two methods.

ANS. $(x - 3)^2(x - 3y) = c.$

25. $(2x - 3y + 1) dx - (3x + 2y - 4) dy = 0.$ Solve by two methods.

ANS. $x^2 + x - 3xy - y^2 + 4y = c.$

26. $(4x + 3y - 7) dx + (4x + 3y + 1) dy = 0.$

ANS. $x + y + c = 8 \ln |4x + 3y + 25|.$

27. Find a change of variables that will reduce any equation of the form

$$xy' = yf(xy)$$

to an equation in which the variables are separable.

28. $(x + 4y + 3) dx - (2x - y - 3) dy = 0.$

ANS. $3(y + 1) = (x + y) \ln |c(x + y)|.$

29. $(3x - 3y - 2) dx - (x - y + 1) dy = 0.$

ANS. $2(y - 3x + c) = 5 \ln |2x - 2y - 3|.$

30. $(x - 6y + 2) dx + 2(x + 2y + 2) dy = 0.$

ANS. $4y = -(x - 2y + 2) \ln |c(x - 2y + 2)|.$

31. $(x^4 - 4x^2y^2 - y^4) dx + 4x^3y \, dy = 0;$ when $x = 1, y = 2.$

ANS. $y^2(5 - 3x) = x^2(5 + 3x).$

32. $(x - y - 1) dx - 2(y - 2) dy = 0.$ ANS. $(x + y - 5)^2(x - 2y + 1) = c.$

33. $(x - 3y + 3) dx + (3x + y + 9) dy = 0.$

ANS. $\ln [(x + 3)^2 + y^2] = c + 6 \operatorname{Arctan} [(x + 3)/y].$

34. $(2x + 4y - 1) dx - (x + 2y - 3) dy = 0.$ ANS. $\ln |x + 2y - 1| = y - 2x + c.$

35. $4y \, dx + 3(2x - 1)(dy + y^4 \, dx) = 0;$ when $x = 1, y = 1.$

ANS. $y^3(2x - 1)(5x - 4) = 1.$

36. $y(x - 1) dx - (x^2 - 2x - 2y) dy = 0.$ ANS. $x^2 - 2x - 4y = cy^2.$

37. $(6xy - 3y^2 + 2y) dx + 2(x - y) dy = 0.$ ANS. $y(2x - y) = ce^{-3x}.$

38. $y' = x - y + 2.$ Solve by two methods. ANS. $\ln |x - y + 1| = c - x.$

39. $(x + y - 2) dx - (x - 4y - 2) dy = 0.$

ANS. $\ln [(x - 2)^2 + 4y^2] + \operatorname{Arctan} \dfrac{x - 2}{2y} = c.$

40. $4 \, dx + (x - y + 2)^2 \, dy = 0.$ ANS. $y + 2 \operatorname{Arctan} \dfrac{x - y + 2}{2} = c.$

CHAPTER 5

Linear Differential Equations

24. The general linear equation

The general linear differential equation of order n is an equation which can be written

$$b_0(x)\frac{d^n y}{dx^n} + b_1(x)\frac{d^{n-1}y}{dx^{n-1}} + \cdots + b_{n-1}(x)\frac{dy}{dx} + b_n(x)y = R(x). \qquad (1)$$

The functions $R(x)$ and $b_i(x)$; $i = 0, 1, \ldots, n$, are to be independent of the variable y. If $R(x)$ is identically zero, equation (1) is said to be linear and homogeneous*; if $R(x)$ is not identically zero, equation (1) is called linear and nonhomogeneous. In this chapter we shall obtain some fundamental and important properties of linear equations.

First we prove that if y_1 and y_2 are solutions of the homogeneous equation

$$b_0(x)y^{(n)} + b_1(x)y^{(n-1)} + \cdots + b_{n-1}(x)y' + b_n(x)y = 0, \qquad (2)$$

* It is perhaps unfortunate that the word homogeneous as it is used here has a very different meaning from that in Sections 9 and 10.

82

and if c_1 and c_2 are constants, then

$$y = c_1 y_1 + c_2 y_2$$

is a solution of equation (2).

The statement that y_1 and y_2 are solutions of (2) means that

$$b_0 y_1^{(n)} + b_1 y_1^{(n-1)} + \cdots + b_{n-1} y_1' + b_n y_1 = 0 \tag{3}$$

and

$$b_0 y_2^{(n)} + b_1 y_2^{(n-1)} + \cdots + b_{n-1} y_2' + b_n y_2 = 0. \tag{4}$$

Now let us multiply each member of (3) by c_1, each member of (4) by c_2, and add the results. We get

$$b_0[c_1 y_1^{(n)} + c_2 y_2^{(n)}] + b_1[c_1 y_1^{(n-1)} + c_2 y_2^{(n-1)}] + \cdots$$
$$+ b_{n-1}[c_1 y_1' + c_2 y_2'] + b_n[c_1 y_1 + c_2 y_2] = 0. \tag{5}$$

Since $c_1 y_1' + c_2 y_2' = (c_1 y_1 + c_2 y_2)'$, etc., equation (5) is neither more nor less than the statement that $c_1 y_1 + c_2 y_2$ is a solution of equation (2). The proof is completed. The special case $c_2 = 0$ is worth noting; that is, for a homogeneous linear equation any constant times a solution is also a solution.

In a similar manner, or by iteration of the above result, it can be seen that if y_i; $i = 1, 2, \ldots, k$, are solutions of equation (2), and if c_i; $i = 1, 2, \ldots, k$, are constants, then

$$y = c_1 y_1 + c_2 y_2 + \cdots + c_k y_k \tag{6}$$

is a solution of equation (2).

The expression in equation (6) is called a linear combination of the functions $y_1, y_2, \ldots, y_n$. The theorem just proved can thus be stated: *Any linear combination of solutions of a linear homogeneous differential equation is also a solution.*

25. Linear independence

Given the functions $f_1, \ldots, f_n$, if constants $c_1, c_2, \ldots, c_n$, not all zero, exist such that

$$c_1 f_1(x) + c_2 f_2(x) + \cdots + c_n f_n(x) = 0 \tag{1}$$

identically in some interval $a \leq x \leq b$, then the functions $f_1, f_2, \ldots, f_n$ are said to be *linearly dependent*. If no such relation exists, the functions are said to be *linearly independent*. That is, the functions $f_1, f_2, \ldots, f_n$ are linearly independent when equation (1) implies that $c_1 = c_2 = \cdots = c_n = 0$.

It should be clear that if the functions of a set are linearly dependent, then at least one of them is a linear combination of the others; if they are linearly independent, then none of them is a linear combination of the others.

26. An existence and uniqueness theorem

In Section 12 we stated an existence theorem for an initial value problem involving a first-order linear differential equation. The generalization of this theorem to nth order linear equations can be stated as follows:

Let $P_1, P_2, \ldots, P_n$, and R be functions that are continuous on an interval $a < x < b$. Suppose that x_0 is a real number in the interval and that $y_0, y_1, \ldots, y_{n-1}$ are n arbitrary real numbers. Then there exists a unique function $y = y(x)$ defined on the interval $a < x < b$, which is a solution of the equation

$$y^{(n)} + P_1 y^{(n-1)} + \cdots + P_n y = R \tag{1}$$

on the interval and which satisfies the initial conditions

$$y(x_0) = y_0, y'(x_0) = y_1, \ldots, y^{(n-1)}(x_0) = y_{n-1}.$$

EXAMPLE: Find the unique solution of the initial value problem

$$y'' + y = 0, y(0) = 0, y'(0) = 1. \tag{2}$$

We observe that $\sin x$ and $\cos x$ are solutions of (2), so that for arbitrary c_1 and c_2

$$y = c_1 \sin x + c_2 \cos x$$

is also a solution by the theorem of Section 24.

Because of the initial conditions in (2), we are led to choose c_1 and c_2 so that $c_1 \sin 0 + c_2 \cos 0 = 0$ and $c_1 \cos 0 - c_2 \sin 0 = 1$. This can be done in only one way, namely by choosing $c_1 = 1$ and $c_2 = 0$. We find that the function $\sin x$ is a solution of the initial value problem (2). Moreover, since the problem satisfies the conditions required in the foregoing theorem, no matter what interval we choose, $\sin x$ is the only solution to the problem given in (2).

27. The Wronskian

With the definitions of Section 25 in mind, we shall now obtain a sufficient condition that n functions be linearly independent over an interval $a \leq x \leq b$.

Let us assume that each of the functions $f_1, f_2, \ldots, f_n$ is differentiable at least $(n-1)$ times in the interval $a \leq x \leq b$. Then from the equation

$$c_1 f_1 + c_2 f_2 + \cdots + c_n f_n = 0, \tag{1}$$

it follows by successive differentiation that

$$c_1 f_1' + c_2 f_2' + \cdots + c_n f_n' = 0,$$
$$c_1 f_1'' + c_2 f_2'' + \cdots + c_n f_n'' = 0,$$
$$\cdots$$
$$c_1 f_1^{(n-1)} + c_2 f_2^{(n-1)} + \cdots + c_n f_n^{(n-1)} = 0.$$

Considered as a system of equations in $c_1, c_2, \ldots, c_n$, the n linear equations directly above will have no solution except the one with each of the c's equal to zero, if the determinant of the system does not vanish. That is, if

$$\begin{vmatrix} f_1 & f_2 & \cdots & f_n \\ f_1' & f_2' & \cdots & f_n' \\ f_1'' & f_2'' & \cdots & f_n'' \\ \cdots & & & \\ f_1^{(n-1)} & f_2^{(n-1)} & \cdots & f_n^{(n-1)} \end{vmatrix} \neq 0, \tag{2}$$

INDEPENDENT

then the functions $f_1, f_2, \ldots, f_n$ are linearly independent. The determinant in (2) is called the *Wronskian* of the n functions involved. We have shown that the nonvanishing of the Wronskian is a sufficient condition that the functions be linearly independent.

The nonvanishing of the Wronskian on an interval is not a necessary condition for linear independence. The Wronskian may vanish even when the functions are linearly independent, as exhibited in Ex. 9 below.

If the n functions involved are solutions of a homogeneous linear differential equation, the situation is simplified as is shown by Theorem 4. A proof of this theorem in the case $n = 2$, is suggested in Exs. 10–13 below.

THEOREM 4: *If, on the interval $a \leq x \leq b$, $b_0(x) \neq 0$, $b_0, b_1, \ldots, b_n$ are continuous, and $y_1, y_2, \ldots, y_n$ are solutions of the equation*

$$b_0 y^{(n)} + b_1 y^{(n-1)} + \cdots + b_{n-1} y' + b_n y = 0, \tag{3}$$

then a necessary and sufficient condition that $y_1, \ldots, y_n$ be linearly independent is the nonvanishing of the Wronskian of $y_1, \ldots, y_n$ on the interval $a \leq x \leq b$.

The functions $\cos \omega t$, $\sin \omega t$, $\sin(\omega t + \alpha)$, in which t is the variable and ω and α are constants, are linearly dependent because there exist constants c_1, c_2, c_3 such that

$$c_1 \cos \omega t + c_2 \sin \omega t + c_3 \sin(\omega t + \alpha) = 0$$

for all t. Indeed, one set of such constants is $c_1 = \sin \alpha$, $c_2 = \cos \alpha$, $c_3 = -1$.

One of the best-known sets of n linearly independent functions of x is the set $1, x, x^2, \ldots, x^{n-1}$. The linear independence of the powers of x follows at once from the fact that if $c_1, c_2, \ldots, c_n$ are not all zero, the equation

$$c_1 + c_2 x + \cdots + c_n x^{n-1} = 0$$

can have, at most, $(n-1)$ distinct roots and so cannot vanish identically in any interval. See also Ex. 1 below.

Exercises

1. Obtain the Wronskian of the functions

$$1, x, x^2, \ldots, x^{n-1} \text{ for } n > 1.$$

ANS. $W = 0! \, 1! \, 2! \cdots (n-1)!$.

2. Show that the functions e^x, e^{2x}, e^{3x} are linearly independent.

ANS. $W = 2e^{6x} \neq 0$.

3. Show that the functions e^x, $\cos x$, $\sin x$ are linearly independent.

ANS. $W = 2e^x \neq 0$.

4. By determining constants c_1, c_2, c_3, c_4, not all zero and which are such that $c_1 f_1 + c_2 f_2 + c_3 f_3 + c_4 f_4 = 0$ identically, show that the functions

$$f_1 = x, f_2 = e^x, f_3 = xe^x, f_4 = (2 - 3x)e^x$$

are linearly dependent.

ANS.   One such set of c's is: $c_1 = 0$, $c_2 = -2$, $c_3 = 3$, $c_4 = 1$.

5. Show that $\cos(\omega t - \beta)$, $\cos \omega t$, $\sin \omega t$ are linearly dependent functions of t.

6. Show that 1, $\sin x$, $\cos x$ are linearly independent.

7. Show that 1, $\sin^2 x$, $\cos^2 x$ are linearly dependent.

8. Show that two nonvanishing differentiable functions of x are linearly dependent if, and only if, their Wronskian vanishes identically. This statement is not true for more than two functions.

9. Let $f_1(x) = 1 + x^3$ for $x \leq 0$, $f_1(x) = 1$ for $x \geq 0$;
$\qquad f_2(x) = 1$ for $x \leq 0$, $f_2(x) = 1 + x^3$ for $x \geq 0$;
$\qquad f_3(x) = 3 + x^3$ for all x.
Show that (a) f, f', f'' are continuous for all x for each of f_1, f_2, f_3;
$\qquad$ (b) the Wronskian of f_1, f_2, f_3 is zero for all x;
$\qquad$ (c) f_1, f_2, f_3 are linearly independent over the interval $-1 \leq x \leq 1$.
In part (c) you must show that if $c_1 f_1(x) + c_2 f_2(x) + c_3 f_3(x) = 0$ for all x in $-1 \leq x \leq 1$, $c_1 = c_2 = c_3 = 0$. Use $x = -1$, 0, 1 successively to obtain three equations to solve for c_1, c_2, and c_3.

10. Given any interval $a < x < b$ with x_0 a fixed number in the interval and suppose y is a solution of the homogeneous equation

$$y'' + Py' + Qy = 0. \tag{A}$$

Further, suppose that $y(x_0) = y'(x_0) = 0$. Use the existence and uniqueness theorem of Section 26 to prove that $y(x) = 0$ for every x in the interval $a < x < b$.

11. Suppose that y_1 and y_2 are solutions of equation (A) of Ex. 10 and suppose the Wronskian of y_1 and y_2 is identically zero on $a < x < b$. Show that for x_0 in the interval $a < x < b$, there must exist constants $\bar{c}_1$ and $\bar{c}_2$ not both zero such that

$$\bar{c}_1 y_1(x_0) + \bar{c}_2 y_2(x_0) = 0,$$

and

$$\bar{c}_1 y_1'(x_0) + \bar{c}_2 y_2'(x_0) = 0.$$

12. Consider the function defined by

$$y(x) = \bar{c}_1 y_1(x) + \bar{c}_2 y_2(x),$$

where $\bar{c}_1$ and $\bar{c}_2$ are the constants determined in Ex. 11. Show that this function is a solution of equation (A) above and that it follows that $y(x) \equiv 0$ on $a < x < b$. (Use the results of Ex. 10.)

13. Combine the results of Exs. 10–12 to obtain a proof of the necessity condition of Theorem 4 in the case when $n = 2$. Also note that the sufficiency condition was established in the text of this section.

28. General solution of a homogeneous equation

Let $y_1, y_2, \ldots, y_n$ be linearly independent solutions of the homogeneous equation

$$b_0(x)y^{(n)} + b_1(x)y^{(n-1)} + \cdots + b_{n-1}(x)y' + b_n(x)y = 0. \tag{1}$$

Then the *general solution* of equation (1) is

$$y = c_1 y_1 + c_2 y_2 + \cdots + c_n y_n, \tag{2}$$

where $c_1, c_2, \ldots, c_n$ are arbitrary constants.

In a sense each particular solution of the linear differential equation (1) is a special case (some choice of the c's) of the general solution (2). The basic ideas needed for a proof of this important result are exhibited here for the equation of order two. No additional complications enter for equations of higher order.

Consider the equation

$$b_0(x)y'' + b_1(x)y' + b_2(x)y = 0. \tag{3}$$

Let the function

$$y = f(x) \tag{4}$$

be any particular solution of equation (3), the solution being valid in some interval $a < x < b$ in which $b_0(x)$ does not vanish and in which the functions b_1/b_0 and b_2/b_0 possess derivatives of all orders.

We assume (it can be proved) that at $x = \alpha$, within the stipulated interval, $f(x)$ is sufficiently well behaved to insure that the Taylor series for $f(x)$,

$$f(x) = \sum_{k=0}^{\infty} \frac{f^{(k)}(\alpha)(x - \alpha)^k}{k!}, \tag{5}$$

converges to $f(x)$ in some interval about $x = \alpha$.

Then the solution $f(x)$ is completely determined by knowledge of $f(\alpha)$ and $f'(\alpha)$, the values of f and f' taken at some point α within the interval. For, since we can divide by $b_0(x)$, equation (3) yields y'' in terms of y, y', and the known coefficients in the equation. Then $y''(\alpha) = f''(\alpha)$ can be determined. Successive differentiation of the equation for y'' will yield the higher derivatives. Thus $f^{(k)}(\alpha)$ can be computed for $k = 2, 3, \ldots$, from the values of $f(\alpha)$ and $f'(\alpha)$. Then, using Taylor's series (5), we see that $f(x)$ is determined by the differential equation and the two values $f(\alpha)$ and $f'(\alpha)$.

Now let $y_1(x)$, $y_2(x)$ be any two linearly independent solutions of equation (3). Further, let α be chosen as some point in the interval, $a < \alpha < b$, where the Wronskian of y_1 and y_2 does not vanish,

$$\begin{vmatrix} y_1(\alpha) & y_2(\alpha) \\ y_1'(\alpha) & y_2'(\alpha) \end{vmatrix} \neq 0. \tag{6}$$

Consider the solution

$$y = c_1 y_1(x) + c_2 y_2(x), \tag{7}$$

from which

$$y' = c_1 y_1'(x) + c_2 y_2'(x).$$

We wish to choose c_1 and c_2 so that the y of equation (7) will become the solution $f(x)$. But we can surely force that y to be such that $y(\alpha) = f(\alpha)$ and $y'(\alpha) = f'(\alpha)$. That is, the equations

$$c_1 y_1(\alpha) + c_2 y_2(\alpha) = f(\alpha), \tag{8}$$

$$c_1 y_1'(\alpha) + c_2 y_2'(\alpha) = f'(\alpha),$$

can be solved for c_1 and c_2 because of the inequality (6), the nonvanishing of the Wronskian. Then $f(x)$ and $y(x)$ have the same initial values, so that by the uniqueness theorem of Section 26 they are identical.

It is necessary to keep in mind that the above discussion used the fact that $b_0(x) \neq 0$ in the interval $a < x < b$. It is easy to see that the linear equation

$$xy' - 2y = 0$$

has the general solution $y = cx^2$ and also such particular solutions as

$$y_1 = x^2, \qquad 0 \leq x,$$
$$= -4x^2, \qquad x < 0.$$

The solution y_1 is not a special case of the general solution. But in any interval throughout which $b_0(x) = x \neq 0$, this particular solution is a special case of the general solution. It was, of course, made up by piecing together at $x = 0$ two parts, each drawn from the general solution.

29. General solution of a nonhomogeneous equation

Let y_p be any particular solution (not necessarily involving any arbitrary constants) of the equation

$$b_0 y^{(n)} + b_1 y^{(n-1)} + \cdots + b_{n-1} y' + b_n y = R(x) \tag{1}$$

and let y_c be a solution of the corresponding homogeneous equation

$$b_0 y^{(n)} + b_1 y^{(n-1)} + \cdots + b_{n-1} y' + b_n y = 0. \tag{2}$$

Then

$$y = y_c + y_p \tag{3}$$

is a solution of equation (1). For, using the y of equation (3) we see that

$$b_0 y^{(n)} + \cdots + b_n y = (b_0 y_c^{(n)} + \cdots + b_n y_c)$$
$$+ (b_0 y_p^{(n)} + \cdots + b_n y_p) = 0 + R(x) = R(x).$$

If $y_1, y_2, \ldots, y_n$ are linearly independent solutions of equation (2), then

$$y_c = c_1 y_1 + c_2 y_2 + \cdots + c_n y_n, \tag{4}$$

in which the c's are arbitrary constants, is the general solution of equation (2). The right member of equation (4) is called the *complementary function* for equation (1).

The general solution of the nonhomogeneous equation (1) is the sum of the complementary function and any particular solution. To justify this usage of the term "general solution" we must show that if f is any solution of equation (1) then $f \equiv y_c + y_p$ for some particular choice of the $c_1, \ldots, c_n$. We note that since f and y_p are both solutions of the nonhomogeneous equation (1), $f - y_p$ is a solution of the homogeneous equation (2). Hence by the theorem of Section 28

$$f - y_p \equiv c_1 y_1 + c_2 y_2 + \cdots + c_n y_n$$

for some particular choice of the $c_1, \ldots, c_n$. This establishes what we wished to show.

EXAMPLE (a):   Find the general solution of

$$y'' = 4. \qquad y''-q=0 \tag{5}$$

We first observe that the functions 1 and x are linearly independent on any interval and are solutions of the homogeneous equation $y'' = 0$. Hence, the complementary function for equation (5) is

$$y_c = c_1 + c_2 x.$$

On the other hand, the function $2x^2$ is a particular solution of equation (5). Hence, the general solution of equation (5) is

$$y = c_1 + c_2 x + 2x^2.$$

EXAMPLE (b):   Find the general solution of the equation

$$y'' - y = 4. \tag{6}$$

It is easily seen that $y = -4$ is a solution of equation (6). Therefore the y_p in equation (3) may be taken to be (-4). As we shall see later, the homogeneous equation

$$y'' - y = 0$$

has as its general solution

$$y_c = c_1 e^x + c_2 e^{-x}.$$

Thus the complementary function for equation (6) is $c_1 e^x + c_2 e^{-x}$ and a particular solution of (6) is $y_p = -4$. Hence the general solution of equation (6) is

$$y = c_1 e^x + c_2 e^{-x} - 4,$$

in which c_1 and c_2 are arbitrary constants.

30. Differential operators

Let D denote differentiation with respect to x, D^2 differentiation twice with respect to x, and so on; that is, for positive integral k,

$$D^k y = \frac{d^k y}{dx^k}.$$

The expression

$$A = a_0 D^n + a_1 D^{n-1} + \cdots + a_{n-1} D + a_n \tag{1}$$

is called a differential operator of order n. It may be defined as that operator which, when applied to any function* y, yields the result

$$Ay = a_0 \frac{d^n y}{dx^n} + a_1 \frac{d^{n-1} y}{dx^{n-1}} + \cdots + a_{n-1} \frac{dy}{dx} + a_n y. \tag{2}$$

* The function y is assumed to possess as many derivatives as may be encountered in whatever operations take place.

The coefficients $a_0, a_1, \ldots, a_n$ in the operator A may be functions of x, but in this book the only operators used will be those with constant coefficients.

Two operators A and B are said to be equal if, and only if, the same result is produced when each acts upon the function y. That is, $A = B$ if, and only if, $Ay = By$ for all functions y possessing the derivatives necessary for the operations involved.

The product AB of two operators A and B is defined as that operator which produces the same result as is obtained by using the operator B followed by the operator A. Thus $ABy = A(By)$. The product of two differential operators always exists and is a differential operator. For operators with *constant coefficients*, but not usually for those with variable coefficients, it is true that $AB = BA$.

EXAMPLE (a):   Let $A = D + 2$ and $B = 3D - 1$.
   Then

$$By = (3D - 1)y = 3\frac{dy}{dx} - y$$

and

$$A(By) = (D + 2)\left(3\frac{dy}{dx} - y\right)$$

$$= 3\frac{d^2y}{dx^2} - \frac{dy}{dx} + 6\frac{dy}{dx} - 2y$$

$$= 3\frac{d^2y}{dx^2} + 5\frac{dy}{dx} - 2y$$

$$= (3D^2 + 5D - 2)y.$$

Hence $AB = (D + 2)(3D - 1) = 3D^2 + 5D - 2$.

   Now consider BA. Acting upon y, the operator BA yields

$$B(Ay) = (3D - 1)\left(\frac{dy}{dx} + 2y\right)$$

$$= 3\frac{d^2y}{dx^2} + 6\frac{dy}{dx} - \frac{dy}{dx} - 2y$$

$$= 3\frac{d^2y}{dx^2} + 5\frac{dy}{dx} - 2y.$$

Hence

$$BA = 3D^2 + 5D - 2 = AB.$$

EXAMPLE (b):   Let $G = xD + 2$, and $H = D - 1$. Then

$$G(Hy) = (xD + 2)\left(\frac{dy}{dx} - y\right)$$

$$= x\frac{d^2y}{dx^2} - x\frac{dy}{dx} + 2\frac{dy}{dx} - 2y$$

$$= x\frac{d^2y}{dx^2} + (2 - x)\frac{dy}{dx} - 2y,$$

so

$$GH = xD^2 + (2 - x)D - 2.$$

On the other hand

$$H(Gy) = (D - 1)\left(x\frac{dy}{dx} + 2y\right)$$

$$= \frac{d}{dx}\left(x\frac{dy}{dx} + 2y\right) - \left(x\frac{dy}{dx} + 2y\right)$$

$$= x\frac{d^2y}{dx^2} + \frac{dy}{dx} + 2\frac{dy}{dx} - x\frac{dy}{dx} - 2y$$

$$= x\frac{d^2y}{dx^2} + (3 - x)\frac{dy}{dx} - 2y;$$

that is,

$$HG = xD^2 + (3 - x)D - 2.$$

It is worthy of notice that here we have two operators G and H (one of them with variable coefficients), the product of which is dependent on the order of the factors. On this topic see also Exs. 17–22 in the next section.

The sum of two differential operators is obtained by expressing each in the form

$$a_0 D^n + a_1 D^{n-1} + \cdots + a_{n-1}D + a_n$$

and adding corresponding coefficients. For instance, if

$$A = 3D^2 - D + x - 2$$

and

$$B = x^2 D^2 + 4D + 7,$$

then

$$A + B = (3 + x^2)D^2 + 3D + x + 5.$$

Differential operators are linear operators; that is, if A is any differential operator, if c_1 and c_2 are constants, and if f_1 and f_2 are any functions of x each possessing the required number of derivatives, then

$$A(c_1 f_1 + c_2 f_2) = c_1 A f_1 + c_2 A f_2.$$

31. The fundamental laws of operation

Let A, B, and C be any differential operators as defined in Section 30. With the above definitions of addition and multiplication, it follows that differential operators satisfy the following:
(1) The commutative law of addition:

$$A + B = B + A.$$

(2) The associative law of addition:

$$(A + B) + C = A + (B + C).$$

(3) The associative law of multiplication:

$$(AB)C = A(BC).$$

(4) The distributive law of multiplication with respect to addition:

$$A(B + C) = AB + AC.$$

If A and B are operators with *constant coefficients*, then they also satisfy
(5) The commutative law of multiplication:

$$AB = BA.$$

Therefore, differential operators with constant coefficients satisfy all the laws of the algebra of polynomials with respect to the operations of addition and multiplication.

If m and n are any two positive integers, then

$$D^m D^n = D^{m+n},$$

a useful result which follows immediately from the definitions.

Since for purposes of addition and multiplication the operators with constant coefficients behave just as algebraic polynomials behave, it is legitimate to use the tools of elementary algebra. In particular, synthetic division may be used to factor operators with constant coefficients.

Exercises

Perform the indicated multiplications in Exs. 1–4.

1. $(4D + 1)(D - 2)$.   ANS. $4D^2 - 7D - 2$.
2. $(2D - 3)(2D + 3)$.   ANS. $4D^2 - 9$.
3. $(D + 2)(D^2 - 2D + 5)$.   ANS. $D^3 + D + 10$.
4. $(D - 2)(D + 1)^2$.   ANS. $D^3 - 3D - 2$.

In Exs. 5–16, factor each of the operators.

5. $2D^2 + 3D - 2$.   ANS. $(D + 2)(2D - 1)$.

6. $2D^2 - 5D - 12$.
7. $D^3 - 2D^2 - 5D + 6$.   ANS. $(D - 1)(D + 2)(D - 3)$.
8. $4D^3 - 4D^2 - 11D + 6$.
9. $D^4 - 4D^2$.   ANS. $D^2(D - 2)(D + 2)$.
10. $D^3 - 3D^2 + 4$.
11. $D^3 - 21D + 20$.   ANS. $(D - 1)(D - 4)(D + 5)$.
12. $2D^3 - D^2 - 13D - 6$.
13. $2D^4 + 11D^3 + 18D^2 + 4D - 8$.   ANS. $(D + 2)^3(2D - 1)$.
14. $8D^4 + 36D^3 - 66D^2 + 35D - 6$.
15. $D^4 + D^3 - 2D^2 + 4D - 24$.   ANS. $(D - 2)(D + 3)(D^2 + 4)$.
16. $D^3 - 11D - 20$.   ANS. $(D - 4)(D^2 + 4D + 5)$.

Perform the indicated multiplications in Exs. 17–22.

17. $(D - x)(D + x)$.   ANS. $D^2 + 1 - x^2$.
18. $(D + x)(D - x)$.   ANS. $D^2 - 1 - x^2$.
19. $D(xD - 1)$.   ANS. xD^2.
20. $(xD - 1)D$.   ANS. $xD^2 - D$.
21. $(xD + 2)(xD - 1)$.   ANS. $x^2D^2 + 2xD - 2$.
22. $(xD - 1)(xD + 2)$.   ANS. $x^2D^2 + 2xD - 2$.

32. Some properties of differential operators

Since for constant m and positive integral k,

$$D^k e^{mx} = m^k e^{mx},$$ (1)

it is easy to find the effect an operator has upon e^{mx}. Let $f(D)$ be a polynomial in D,

$$f(D) = a_0 D^n + a_1 D^{n-1} + \cdots + a_{n-1}D + a_n.$$ (2)

Then

$$f(D)e^{mx} = a_0 m^n e^{mx} + a_1 m^{n-1}e^{mx} + \cdots + a_{n-1}me^{mx} + a_n e^{mx},$$

so

$$f(D)e^{mx} = e^{mx}f(m).$$ (3)

If m is a root of the equation $f(m) = 0$, then in view of equation (3),

$$f(D)e^{mx} = 0.$$

Next consider the effect of the operator $D - a$ on the product of e^{ax} and a function y. We have

$$(D - a)(e^{ax}y) = D(e^{ax}y) - ae^{ax}y$$

$$= e^{ax} Dy,$$

and

$$(D - a)^2(e^{ax}y) = (D - a)(e^{ax}Dy)$$
$$= e^{ax}D^2y.$$

Repeating the operation, we are led to

$$(D - a)^n(e^{ax}y) = e^{ax}D^ny. \tag{4}$$

Using the linearity of differential operators, we conclude that when $f(D)$ is a polynomial in D with constant coefficients, then

$$e^{ax}f(D)y = f(D - a)[e^{ax}y]. \tag{5}$$

The relation (5) shows us how to shift an exponential factor from the left of a differential operator to the right of the operator. This relation has many uses, some of which we will examine in Chapter 6.

EXAMPLE (a):   Let $f(D) = 2D^2 + 5D - 12$. Then the equation $f(m) = 0$ is

$$2m^2 + 5m - 12 = 0,$$

or

$$(m + 4)(2m - 3) = 0,$$

of which the roots are $m_1 = -4$ and $m_2 = \frac{3}{2}$.

With the aid of equation (3) above it can be seen that

$$(2D^2 + 5D - 12)e^{-4x} = 0$$

and that

$$(2D^2 + 5D - 12) \exp(\tfrac{3}{2}x) = 0.$$

In other words, $y_1 = e^{-4x}$ and $y_2 = \exp(\tfrac{3}{2}x)$ are solutions of

$$(2D^2 + 5D - 12)y = 0.$$

EXAMPLE (b):   Show that

$$(D - m)^n(x^k e^{mx}) = 0 \quad \text{for} \quad k = 0, 1, \ldots, (n - 1). \tag{6}$$

In equation (5) we let $f(D) = (D - m)^n$ and $y = x^k$. Then using the exponential shift we obtain

$$(D - m)^n(x^k e^{mx}) = e^{mx}D^n x^k.$$

But $D^n x^k = 0$ for $k = 0, 1, 2, \ldots, n - 1$, which gives us equation (6) directly.

The results obtained in equations (3), (5), and (6) are of fundamental importance to the solving of linear differential equations with constant coefficients which we consider in Chapter 6.

EXAMPLE (c): As an illustration of the use of the exponential shift we solve the differential equation

$$(D + 3)^4 y = 0. \tag{7}$$

First we multiply equation (7) by e^{3x} to obtain

$$e^{3x}(D + 3)^4 y = 0.$$

Applying the exponential shift as in equation (5) leads to

$$D^4(e^{3x}y) = 0.$$

Integrating four times gives us

$$e^{3x}y = c_1 + c_2 x + c_3 x^2 + c_4 x^3,$$

and finally,

$$y = (c_1 + c_2 x + c_3 x^2 + c_4 x^3)e^{-3x}. \tag{8}$$

Note that each of the four functions e^{-3x}, xe^{-3x}, $x^2 e^{-3x}$, and $x^3 e^{-3x}$ is a solution of equation (7). This of course is assured by the theorem of equation (6) of Example (b).

If we now show that the four functions are linearly independent, equation (8) gives the general solution of equation (7). See Ex. 5 below.

Exercises

In Exs. 1–4 use the exponential shift as in Example (c) above to find the general solution.

1. $(D - 2)^3 y = 0.$ ANS. $y = (c_1 + c_2 x + c_3 x^2)e^{2x}.$
2. $(D + 1)^2 y = 0.$
3. $(2D - 1)^2 y = 0.$ ANS. $y = (c_1 + c_2 x) \exp(\tfrac{1}{2}x).$
4. $(D + 7)^6 y = 0.$
5. To show that the four functions in Example (c) above are linearly independent on any interval, assume that they are linearly dependent, and show that this leads to a contradiction of the results obtained in Ex. 1 of Sec. 27.
6. Prove that the set of functions

$$e^{ax}, xe^{ax}, x^2 e^{ax}, \ldots, x^{n-1}e^{ax}$$

is a linearly independent set on any interval. See Ex. 5.

Whereas $(2m-1)^2 = 0$

$m = \frac{1}{2}, \frac{1}{2}$ a root

$y = c_1 e^{\frac{1}{2}x} + c_2 x e^{\frac{1}{2}}$

CHAPTER **6**

Linear Equations
with Constant Coefficients

33. Introduction

Two methods for solving linear differential equations with constant coefficients are presented in this book. A classical technique is treated in this and the next chapter. Chapters 10 and 11 contain a development of the Laplace transform and its use in solving differential equations. Each method has its advantages and its disadvantages. Each is theoretically sufficient; both are necessary for maximum efficiency.

34. The auxiliary equation; distinct roots

Any linear homogeneous differential equation with constant coefficients,

$$a_0 \frac{d^n y}{dx^n} + a_1 \frac{d^{n-1} y}{dx^{n-1}} + \cdots + a_{n-1} \frac{dy}{dx} + a_n y = 0, \tag{1}$$

may be written in the form

$$f(D)y = 0, \tag{2}$$

where $f(D)$ is a linear differential operator. As we saw in the preceding chapter, if m is any root of the algebraic equation $f(m) = 0$, then

$$f(D)e^{mx} = 0,$$

which means simply that $y = e^{mx}$ is a solution of equation (2). The equation

$$f(m) = 0 \tag{3}$$

is called the *auxiliary equation* associated with (1) or (2).

The auxiliary equation for (1) is of degree n. Let its roots be $m_1, m_2, \ldots, m_n$. If these roots are all real and distinct, then the n solutions

$$y_1 = \exp(m_1 x), \; y_2 = \exp(m_2 x), \ldots, y_2 = \exp(m_n x)$$

are linearly independent and the general solution of (1) can be written at once. It is

$$y = c_1 \exp(m_1 x) + c_2 \exp(m_2 x) + \cdots + c_n \exp(m_n x),$$

in which $c_1, c_2, \cdots, c_n$ are arbitrary constants.

Repeated roots of the auxiliary equation will be treated in the next section. Imaginary roots will be avoided until Section 37, where the corresponding solutions will be put into a desirable form.

EXAMPLE (a):   Solve the equation

$$\frac{d^3 y}{dx^3} - 4\frac{d^2 y}{dx^2} + \frac{dy}{dx} + 6y = 0.$$

First write the auxiliary equation

$$m^3 - 4m^2 + m + 6 = 0,$$

whose roots $m = -1, 2, 3$ may be obtained by synthetic division. Then the general solution is seen to be

$$y = c_1 e^{-x} + c_2 e^{2x} + c_3 e^{3x}.$$

EXAMPLE (b):   Solve the equation

$$(3D^3 + 5D^2 - 2D)y = 0.$$

The auxiliary equation is

$$3m^3 + 5m^2 - 2m = 0$$

and its roots are $m = 0, -2, \frac{1}{3}$. Using the fact that $e^{0x} = 1$, the desired solution may be written

$$y = c_1 + c_2 e^{-2x} + c_3 \exp(\tfrac{1}{3}x).$$

EXAMPLE (c):   Solve the equation

$$\frac{d^2x}{dt^2} - 4x = 0$$

with the conditions that when $t = 0$, $x = 0$ and $dx/dt = 3$.
    The auxiliary equation is

$$m^2 - 4 = 0,$$

with roots $m = 2, -2$. Hence the general solution of the differential equation is

$$x = c_1 e^{2t} + c_2 e^{-2t}.$$

It remains to enforce the conditions at $t = 0$. Now

$$\frac{dx}{dt} = 2c_1 e^{2t} - 2c_2 e^{-2t}.$$

Thus the condition that $x = 0$ when $t = 0$ requires that

$$0 = c_1 + c_2,$$

and the condition that $dx/dt = 3$ when $t = 0$ requires that

$$3 = 2c_1 - 2c_2.$$

From the simultaneous equations for c_1 and c_2 we conclude that $c_1 = \frac{3}{4}$ and $c_2 = -\frac{3}{4}$. Therefore

$$x = \tfrac{3}{4}(e^{2t} - e^{-2t}),$$

which can also be put in the form

$$x = \tfrac{3}{2} \sinh(2t).$$

Exercises

In Exs. 1–22, find the general solution. When the operator D is used, it is implied that the independent variable is x.

1. $(D^2 + 2D - 3)y = 0.$ ANS. $y = c_1 e^x + c_2 e^{-3x}.$
2. $(D^2 + 2D)y = 0.$
3. $(D^2 + D - 6)y = 0.$ ANS. $y = c_1 e^{2x} + c_2 e^{-3x}.$
4. $(D^2 - 5D + 6)y = 0.$
5. $(D^3 + 3D^2 - 4D)y = 0.$ ANS. $y = c_1 + c_2 e^x + c_3 e^{-4x}.$

6. $(D^3 - 3D^2 - 10D)y = 0.$

7. $(D^3 + 6D^2 + 11D + 6)y = 0.$ ANS. $y = c_1 e^{-x} + c_2 e^{-2x} + c_3 e^{-3x}.$

8. $(D^3 + 3D^2 - 4D - 12)y = 0.$

9. $(4D^3 - 7D + 3)y = 0.$ ANS. $y = c_1 e^x + c_2 \exp(\tfrac{1}{2}x) + c_3 \exp(-\tfrac{3}{2}x).$

10. $(4D^3 - 13D - 6)y = 0.$

11. $\dfrac{d^3x}{dt^3} + \dfrac{d^2x}{dt^2} - 2\dfrac{dx}{dt} = 0.$ ANS. $x = c_1 + c_2 e^t + c_3 e^{-2t}.$

12. $\dfrac{d^3x}{dt^3} - 19\dfrac{dx}{dt} + 30x = 0.$

13. $(9D^3 - 7D + 2)y = 0.$ ANS. $y = c_1 e^{-x} + c_2 \exp(\tfrac{1}{3}x) + c_3 \exp(\tfrac{2}{3}x).$

14. $(4D^3 - 21D - 10)y = 0.$

15. $(D^3 - 14D + 8)y = 0.$

ANS. $y = c_1 e^{-4x} + c_2 \exp[(2 + \sqrt{2})x] + c_3 \exp[(2 - \sqrt{2})x].$

16. $(D^3 - D^2 - 4D - 2)y = 0.$

17. $(4D^4 - 8D^3 - 7D^2 + 11D + 6)y = 0.$

ANS. $y = c_1 e^{-x} + c_2 e^{2x} + c_3 \exp(-\tfrac{1}{2}x) + c_4 \exp(\tfrac{3}{2}x).$

18. $(4D^4 - 16D^3 + 7D^2 + 4D - 2)y = 0.$

19. $(4D^4 + 4D^3 - 13D^2 - 7D + 6)y = 0.$

20. $(4D^5 - 8D^4 - 17D^3 + 12D^2 + 9D)y = 0.$

21. $(D^2 - 4aD + 3a^2)y = 0,\ a$ real $\neq 0.$

22. $[D^2 - (a + b)D + ab]y = 0,\ a$ and b real and unequal.

In Exs. 23–24, find the particular solution indicated.

23. $(D^2 - 2D - 3)y = 0$; when $x = 0$, $y = 0$, and $y' = -4$.   ANS. $y = e^{-x} - e^{3x}.$

24. $(D^2 - D - 6)y = 0$; when $x = 0$, $y = 0$, and when $x = 1$, $y = e^3$.

ANS. $y = (e^{3x} - e^{-2x})/(1 - e^{-5}).$

In Exs. 25–29, find for $x = 1$ the y value for the particular solution required.

25. $(D^2 - 2D - 3)y = 0$; when $x = 0$, $y = 4$ and $y' = 0$.

ANS.   When $x = 1$, $y = e^3 + 3e^{-1} = 21.2.$

26. $(D^3 - 4D)y = 0$; when $x = 0$, $y = 0$, $y' = 0$, and $y'' = 2$.

ANS.   When $x = 1$, $y = \sinh^2 1.$

27. $(D^2 - D - 6)y = 0$; when $x = 0$, $y = 3$ and $y' = -1$.

ANS.   When $x = 1$, $y = 20.4.$

28. $(D^2 + 3D - 10)y = 0$; when $x = 0$, $y = 0$, and when $x = 2$, $y = 1$.

ANS.   When $x = 1$, $y = 0.135.$

29. $(D^3 - 2D^2 - 5D + 6)y = 0$; when $x = 0$, $y = 1$, $y' = -7$, and $y'' = -1$.

ANS.   When $x = 1$, $y = -19.8.$

35. The auxiliary equation; repeated roots

Suppose that in the equation

$$f(D)y = 0 \tag{1}$$

the operator $f(D)$ has repeated factors; that is, the auxiliary equation $f(m) = 0$ has repeated roots. Then the method of the previous section does not yield the general solution. Let the auxiliary equation have three equal roots $m_1 = b$, $m_2 = b$, $m_3 = b$. The corresponding part of the solution yielded by the method of Section 34 is

$$y = c_1 e^{bx} + c_2 e^{bx} + c_3 e^{bx},$$
$$y = (c_1 + c_2 + c_3)e^{bx}. \tag{2}$$

Now (2) can be replaced by

$$y = c_4 e^{bx} \tag{3}$$

with $c_4 = c_1 + c_2 + c_3$. Thus, corresponding to the three roots under consideration, this method has yielded only the solution (3). The difficulty is present, of course, because the three solutions corresponding to the roots $m_1 = m_2 = m_3 = b$ are not linearly independent.

What is needed is a method for obtaining n linearly independent solutions corresponding to n equal roots of the auxiliary equation. Suppose the auxiliary equation $f(m) = 0$ has the n equal roots

$$m_1 = m_2 = \cdots = m_n = b.$$

Then the operator $f(D)$ must have a factor $(D - b)^n$. We wish to find n linearly independent y's for which

$$(D - b)^n y = 0. \tag{4}$$

Turning to the result (6) near the end of Section 32 and writing $m = b$, we find that

$$(D - b)^n(x^k e^{bx}) = 0 \text{ for } k = 0, 1, 2, \ldots, (n - 1). \tag{5}$$

The functions $y_k = x^k e^{bx}$; $k = 0, 1, 2, \ldots, (n - 1)$ are linearly independent because aside from the common factor e^{bx} they contain only the respective powers $x^0, x^1, x^2, \ldots, x^{n-1}$. (See Ex. 4, Sec. 32.)

The general solution of equation (4) is

$$y = c_1 e^{bx} + c_2 x e^{bx} + \cdots + c_n x^{n-1} e^{bx}. \tag{6}$$

Furthermore, if $f(D)$ contains the factor $(D - b)^n$, then the equation

$$f(D)y = 0 \tag{1}$$

can be written

$$g(D)(D - b)^n y = 0 \tag{7}$$

where $g(D)$ contains all the factors of $f(D)$ except $(D - b)^n$. Then any solution of

$$(D - b)^n y = 0 \tag{4}$$

is also a solution of (7) and therefore of (1).

Now we are in a position to write the solution of equation (1) whenever the auxiliary equation has only real roots. Each root of the auxiliary equation is either distinct from all the other roots or it is one of a set of equal roots. Corresponding to a root m_i distinct from all others, there is the solution

$$y_i = c_i \exp(m_i x), \tag{8}$$

and corresponding to n equal roots $m_1, m_2, \ldots, m_n$, each equal to b, there are the solutions

$$c_1 e^{bx}, c_2 x e^{bx}, \ldots, c_n x^{n-1} e^{bx}. \tag{9}$$

The collection of solutions (9) has the proper number of elements, a number equal to the order of the differential equation, because there is one solution corresponding to each root of the auxiliary equation. The solutions thus obtained can be proved to be linearly independent.

EXAMPLE (a):   Solve the equation

$$(D^4 - 7D^3 + 18D^2 - 20D + 8)y = 0. \tag{10}$$

With the aid of synthetic division, it is easily seen that the auxiliary equation

$$m^4 - 7m^3 + 18m^2 - 20m + 8 = 0$$

has the roots $m = 1, 2, 2, 2$. Then the general solution of equation (10) is

$$y = c_1 e^x + c_2 e^{2x} + c_3 x e^{2x} + c_4 x^2 e^{2x},$$

or

$$y = c_1 e^x + (c_2 + c_3 x + c_4 x^2)e^{2x}.$$

EXAMPLE (b):   Solve the equation

$$\frac{d^4 y}{dx^4} + 2\frac{d^3 y}{dx^3} + \frac{d^2 y}{dx^2} = 0.$$

The auxiliary equation is

$$m^4 + 2m^3 + m^2 = 0,$$

with roots $m = 0, 0, -1, -1$. Hence the desired solution is

$$y = c_1 + c_2 x + c_3 e^{-x} + c_4 x e^{-x}.$$

Exercises

In Exs. 1–20 find the general solution.

1. $(D^2 - 6D + 9)y = 0.$ ANS. $y = (c_1 + c_2 x)e^{3x}.$
2. $(D^2 + 4D + 4)y = 0.$
3. $(4D^3 + 4D^2 + D)y = 0.$ ANS. $y = c_1 + (c_2 + c_3 x) \exp(-\tfrac{1}{2}x).$

4. $(D^3 - 8D^2 + 16D)y = 0.$
5. $(D^4 + 6D^3 + 9D^2)y = 0.$ ANS. $\quad y = c_1 + c_2 x + (c_3 + c_4 x)e^{-3x}.$
6. $(D^3 - 3D^2 + 4)y = 0.$
7. $(4D^3 - 3D + 1)y = 0.$ ANS. $\quad y = c_1 e^{-x} + (c_2 + c_3 x) \exp(\tfrac{1}{2}x).$
8. $(D^4 - 3D^3 - 6D^2 + 28D - 24)y = 0.$
9. $(4D^4 - 4D^3 - 23D^2 + 12D + 36)y = 0.$

     ANS. $\quad y = (c_1 + c_2 x)e^{2x} + (c_3 + c_4 x)\exp(-\tfrac{3}{2}x).$

10. $(D^3 + 6D^2 + 12D + 8)y = 0.$
11. $(D^5 - D^3)y = 0.$

     ANS. $\quad y = c_1 + c_2 x + c_3 x^2 + c_4 e^x + c_5 e^{-x};$
     or $y = c_1 + c_2 x + c_3 x^2 + c_6 \cosh x + c_7 \sinh x.$

12. $(D^5 - 16D^3)y = 0.$
13. $(4D^4 + 4D^3 - 3D^2 - 2D + 1)y = 0.$
14. $(54D^4 - 27D^3 - 9D^2 + 7D - 1)y = 0.$
15. $(D^4 - 2D^3 - 3D^2 + 4D + 4)y = 0.$ ANS. $\quad y = (c_1 + c_2 x)e^{-x} + (c_3 + c_4 x)e^{2x}.$
16. $(27D^4 - 18D^2 + 8D - 1)y = 0.$
17. $(4D^5 + 4D^4 - 9D^3 - 11D^2 + D + 3)y = 0.$
18. $(D^5 - 15D^3 + 10D^2 + 60D - 72)y = 0.$
19. $(D^4 + 2D^3 - 6D^2 - 16D - 8)y = 0.$

     ANS. $\quad y = (c_1 + c_2 x)e^{-2x} + c_3 \exp[(1 + \sqrt{3})x] + c_4 \exp[(1 - \sqrt{3})x].$
20. $(D^4 - 2D^3 - 5D^2 + 2)y = 0.$

In Exs. 21–26, find the particular solution indicated.

21. $(D^2 + 4D + 4)y = 0$; when $x = 0$, $y = 1$ and $y' = -1$.

     ANS. $\quad y = (1 + x)e^{-2x}.$
22. The equation of Ex. 21 with the condition that the graph of the solution pass through the points $(0, 2)$ and $(2, 0)$.   ANS. $\quad y = (2 - x)e^{-2x}.$
23. $(D^3 - 3D - 2)y = 0$; when $x = 0$, $y = 0$, $y' = 9$, $y'' = 0$.

     ANS. $\quad y = 2e^{2x} + (3x - 2)e^{-x}.$
24. $(D^4 + 3D^3 + 2D^2)y = 0$; when $x = 0$, $y = 0$, $y' = 4$, $y'' = -6$, $y''' = 14$.

     ANS. $\quad y = 2(x + e^{-x} - e^{-2x}).$
25. The equation of Ex. 24 with the conditions: when $x = 0$, $y = 0$, $y' = 3$, $y'' = -5$, $y''' = 9$.   ANS. $\quad y = 2 - e^{-x} - e^{-2x}.$
26. $(D^3 + D^2 - D - 1)y = 0$; when $x = 0$, $y = 1$, when $x = 2$, $y = 0$, and also as $x \to \infty$, $y \to 0$.   ANS. $\quad y = \tfrac{1}{4}(2 - x)e^{-x}.$

In Exs. 27–29, find for $x = 2$ the y value for the particular solution required.

27. $(4D^2 - 4D + 1)y = 0$; when $x = 0$, $y = -2$, $y' = 2$.

     ANS. When $x = 2$, $y = 4e.$
28. $(D^3 + 2D^2)y = 0$; when $x = 0$, $y = -3$, $y' = 0$, $y'' = 12$.

     ANS. When $x = 2$, $y = 3e^{-4} + 6.$
29. $(D^3 + 5D^2 + 3D - 9)y = 0$; when $x = 0$, $y = -1$, when $x = 1$, $y = 0$, and also as $x \to \infty$, $y \to 0$.   ANS. When $x = 2$, $y = e^{-6}.$

36. A definition of exp z for imaginary z

Since the auxiliary equation may have imaginary roots, we need now to lay down a definition of exp z for imaginary z.

Let $z = \alpha + i\beta$ with α and β real. Since it is desirable to have the ordinary laws of exponents remain valid, it is wise to require that

$$\exp(\alpha + i\beta) = e^{\alpha} \cdot e^{i\beta}. \tag{1}$$

To e^{α} with α real, we attach the usual meaning.

Now consider $e^{i\beta}$, β real. In calculus it is shown that for all real x

$$e^x = 1 + \frac{x}{1!} + \frac{x^2}{2!} + \frac{x^3}{3!} + \cdots + \frac{x^n}{n!} + \cdots, \tag{2}$$

or

$$e^x = \sum_{n=0}^{\infty} \frac{x^n}{n!}. \tag{2}$$

If we now tentatively put $x = i\beta$ in (2) as a definition of $e^{i\beta}$, we get

$$e^{i\beta} = 1 + \frac{i\beta}{1!} + \frac{i^2\beta^2}{2!} + \frac{i^3\beta^3}{3!} + \frac{i^4\beta^4}{4!} + \cdots + \frac{i^n\beta^n}{n!} + \cdots. \tag{3}$$

Separating the even powers of β from the odd powers of β in (3) yields

$$e^{i\beta} = 1 + \frac{i^2\beta^2}{2!} + \frac{i^4\beta^4}{4!} + \cdots + \frac{i^{2k}\beta^{2k}}{(2k)!} + \cdots$$
$$+ \frac{i\beta}{1!} + \frac{i^3\beta^3}{3!} + \cdots + \frac{i^{2k+1}\beta^{2k+1}}{(2k+1)!} + \cdots, \tag{4}$$

or

$$e^{i\beta} = \sum_{k=0}^{\infty} \frac{i^{2k}\beta^{2k}}{(2k)!} + \sum_{k=0}^{\infty} \frac{i^{2k+1}\beta^{2k+1}}{(2k+1)!}. \tag{4}$$

Now $i^{2k} = (-1)^k$, so we may write

$$e^{i\beta} = 1 - \frac{\beta^2}{2!} + \frac{\beta^4}{4!} + \cdots + \frac{(-1)^k\beta^{2k}}{(2k)!} + \cdots$$
$$+ i\left[\frac{\beta}{1!} - \frac{\beta^3}{3!} + \cdots + \frac{(-1)^k\beta^{2k+1}}{(2k+1)!} + \cdots\right], \tag{5}$$

or

$$e^{i\beta} = \sum_{k=0}^{\infty} \frac{(-1)^k\beta^{2k}}{(2k)!} + i\sum_{k=0}^{\infty} \frac{(-1)^k\beta^{2k+1}}{(2k+1)!}. \tag{5}$$

But the series on the right in (5) are precisely those for $\cos \beta$ and $\sin \beta$ as developed in calculus. Hence we are led to the tentative result

$$e^{i\beta} = \cos \beta + i \sin \beta. \tag{6}$$

The student should realize that the manipulations above have no meaning in themselves at this stage (assuming that infinite series with complex terms are not a part of the content of elementary mathematics). What has been accomplished is this: the formal manipulations above have suggested the meaningful definition (6). Combining (6) with (1) we now put forward a reasonable *definition* of exp $(\alpha + i\beta)$, namely,

$$\exp(\alpha + i\beta) = e^{\alpha}(\cos\beta + i\sin\beta), \quad \alpha \text{ and } \beta \text{ real.} \tag{7}$$

Replacing β by $(-\beta)$ in (7) yields a result which is of value to us in the next section,

$$\cos(-\beta) = \cos\beta$$

$$\exp(\alpha - i\beta) = e^{\alpha}(\cos\beta - i\sin\beta).$$

It is interesting and important that with the definition (7), the function e^z for complex z retains many of the properties possessed by the function e^x for real x. Such matters are often studied in detail in books on complex variables.[*]

Here we need in particular to know that if

$$y = \exp(a + ib)x,$$

with a, b, and x real, then

$$(D - a - ib)y = 0.$$

The result desired follows at once by differentiation, with respect to x, of the function

$$y = e^{ax}(\cos bx + i\sin bx).$$

37. The auxiliary equation; imaginary roots

Consider a differential equation $f(D)y = 0$ for which the auxiliary equation $f(m) = 0$ has real coefficients. From elementary algebra we know that if the auxiliary equation has any imaginary roots, those roots must occur in conjugate pairs. Thus if

$$m_1 = a + ib$$

is a root of the equation $f(m) = 0$, with a and b real and $b \neq 0$, then

$$m_2 = a - ib$$

is also a root of $f(m) = 0$. It must be kept in mind that this result is a consequence of the reality of the coefficients in the equation $f(m) = 0$. Imaginary roots do not necessarily appear in pairs in an algebraic equation whose coefficients involve imaginaries.

---

[*] For example, R. V. Churchill, *Complex Variables and Applications* (2nd edition; New York: McGraw-Hill Book Co., 1960), pp. 46–50.

We can now construct in usable form solutions of

$$f(D)y = 0 \tag{1}$$

corresponding to imaginary roots of $f(m) = 0$. For, since $f(m)$ is assumed to have real coefficients, any imaginary roots appear in conjugate pairs

$$m_1 = a + ib \text{ and } m_2 = a - ib.$$

Then, according to the preceding section, equation (1) is satisfied by

$$y = c_1 \exp[(a + ib)x] + c_2 \exp[(a - ib)x]. \tag{2}$$

Taking x to be real along with a and b, we get from (2) the result

$$y = c_1 e^{ax}(\cos bx + i \sin bx) + c_2 e^{ax}(\cos bx - i \sin bx). \tag{3}$$

Now (3) may be written $\quad c_3 = (c_1 + c_2) \quad c_4 = i(c_1 - c_2)$

$$y = (c_1 + c_2)e^{ax}\cos bx + i(c_1 - c_2)e^{ax}\sin bx.$$

Finally, let $c_1 + c_2 = c_3$, and $i(c_1 - c_2) = c_4$, where c_3 and c_4 are new arbitrary constants. Then equation (1) is seen to have the solutions

$$y = c_3 e^{ax}\cos bx + c_4 e^{ax}\sin bx, \tag{4}$$

corresponding to the two roots $m_1 = a + ib$ and $m_2 = a - ib$, $(b \neq 0)$ of the auxiliary equation.

The reduction of the solution (2) above to the desirable form (4) has been done once and that is enough. Whenever a pair of conjugate imaginary roots of the auxiliary equation appears, we write down at once in the form given on the right in equation (4) the particular solution corresponding to those two roots.

EXAMPLE (a):   Solve the equation

$$(D^3 - 3D^2 + 9D + 13)y = 0.$$

For the auxiliary equation

$$m^3 - 3m^2 + 9m + 13 = 0,$$

one root, $m_1 = -1$, is easily found. When the factor $(m + 1)$ is removed by synthetic division, it is seen that the other two roots are solutions of the quadratic equation

$$m^2 - 4m + 13 = 0.$$

Those roots are found to be $m_2 = 2 + 3i$ and $m_3 = 2 - 3i$. The auxiliary equation has the roots $m = -1, 2 \pm 3i$. Hence the general solution of the differential equation is

$$y = c_1 e^{-x} + c_2 e^{2x}\cos 3x + c_3 e^{2x}\sin 3x$$

Repeated imaginary roots lead to solutions analogous to those brought in by repeated real roots. For instance, if the roots $m = a \pm ib$ occur three times, then the corresponding six linearly independent solutions of the differential equation are those appearing in the expression

$$(c_1 + c_2 x + c_3 x^2)e^{ax} \cos bx + (c_4 + c_5 x + c_6 x^2)e^{ax} \sin bx.$$

EXAMPLE (b):   Solve the equation

$$(D^4 + 8D^2 + 16)y = 0.$$

The auxiliary equation $m^4 + 8m^2 + 16 = 0$ may be written

$$(m^2 + 4)^2 = 0,$$

so its roots are seen to be $m = \pm 2i, \pm 2i$. The roots $m_1 = 2i$ and $m_2 = -2i$ occur twice each. Thinking of $2i$ as $0 + 2i$ and recalling that $e^{0x} = 1$, we write the solution of the differential equation as

$$y = (c_1 + c_2 x) \cos 2x + (c_3 + c_4 x) \sin 2x.$$

In such exercises as those below a fine check can be obtained by direct substitution of the result and its appropriate derivatives into the differential equation. The verification is particularly effective because the operations performed in the check are so different from those performed in obtaining the solution.

Exercises

Find the general solution except when the exercise stipulates otherwise.

1. Verify directly that the relation

$$y = c_3 e^{ax} \cos bx + c_4 e^{ax} \sin bx$$

satisfies the equation

$$[(D - a)^2 + b^2]y = 0.$$

2. $(D^2 - 2D + 5)y = 0$. Verify your answer.

   ANS. $y = c_1 e^x \cos 2x + c_2 e^x \sin 2x.$

3. $(D^2 - 2D + 2)y = 0.$

4. $(D^2 + 9)y = 0$. Verify your answer.

   ANS. $y = c_1 \cos 3x + c_2 \sin 3x.$

5. $(D^2 - 9)y = 0.$

   ANS. $y = c_1 \cosh 3x + c_2 \sinh 3x.$

6. $(D^2 + 4D + 5)y = 0$. Verify your answer.

7. $(D^2 - 6D + 25)y = 0.$

   ANS. $y = e^{3x}(c_1 \cos 4x + c_2 \sin 4x).$

8. $(D^3 + D^2 + 4D + 4)y = 0$. Verify your answer.

9. $(D^2 - 1)y = 0$; when $x = 0$, $y = y_0$ and $y' = 0.$

10. $(D^2 + 1)y = 0$; when $x = 0$, $y = y_0$ and $y' = 0.$

   ANS. $y = y_0 \cosh x.$

   ANS. $y = y_0 \cos x.$

11. $(D^4 + 2D^3 - 11D^2 - 52D)y = 0.$

12. $(D^3 + 5D^2 + 17D + 13)y = 0$; when $x = 0$, $y = 0$, $y' = 1$, and $y'' = 6.$

   ANS. $y = e^{-x} - e^{-2x} \cos 3x.$

13. $(D^5 - 2D^3 - 2D^2 - 3D - 2)y = 0.$

14. $(D^4 - 2D^3 + 2D^2 - 2D + 1)y = 0.$ Verify your answer.

15. $(D^4 + 18D^2 + 81)y = 0.$ ANS. $y = (c_1 + c_2 x)\cos 3x + (c_3 + c_4 x)\sin 3x.$

16. $(2D^4 + 11D^3 - 4D^2 - 69D + 34)y = 0.$ Verify your answer.

17. $(D^6 + 6D^4 + 9D^2 + 4)y = 0.$

18. $(16D^3 - 11D - 5)y = 0.$

19. $\dfrac{d^2x}{dt^2} + k^2x = 0,$ k real; when $t = 0,$ $x = 0$ and $\dfrac{dx}{dt} = v_0.$ Verify your result completely.   ANS. $x = (v_0/k)\sin kt.$

20. $(D^3 + D^2 + 4D + 4)y = 0;$ when $x = 0,$ $y = 0,$ $y' = -1,$ and $y'' = 5.$

                                            ANS. $y = e^{-x} - \cos 2x.$

21. $\dfrac{d^2x}{dt^2} + 2b\dfrac{dx}{dt} + k^2x = 0, k > b > 0;$ when $t = 0,$ $x = 0$ and $\dfrac{dx}{dt} = v_0.$

    $D^2 \quad 2bD$ ANS. $x = (v_0/a)e^{-bt}\sin at,$ where $a = \sqrt{k^2 - b^2}.$

Miscellaneous exercises

Obtain the general solution unless otherwise instructed. Your answer can be checked by direct substitution.

1. $(9D^4 + 6D^3 + D^2)y = 0.$

2. $(4D^3 - 13D + 6)y = 0.$

3. $(D^3 + 2D^2 - 15D)y = 0.$

4. $(D^3 + 2D^2 + D + 2)y = 0.$

5. $(D^3 - 2D^2 - 3D)y = 0.$

6. $(D^3 + 3D^2 - 4)y = 0.$

7. $(4D^3 - 27D + 27)y = 0.$

8. $(10D^3 + D^2 - 7D + 2)y = 0.$

9. $(D^3 + 7D^2 + 19D + 13)y = 0;$ when $x = 0,$ $y = 0,$ $y' = 2,$ and $y'' = -12.$

10. $(D^2 - D - 6)y = 0;$ when $x = 0,$ $y = 2$ and $y' = 1.$

11. $(D^4 + 6D^3 + 9D^2)y = 0;$ when $x = 0,$ $y = 0,$ $y' = 0,$ and $y'' = 6,$ and as $x \to \infty,$ $y' \to 1.$ For this particular solution, find the value of y when $x = 1.$

                                            ANS. $y = 1 - e^{-3}.$

12. $(D^3 + 6D^2 + 12D + 8)y = 0;$ when $x = 0,$ $y = 1,$ $y' = -2,$ and $y'' = 2.$

13. $(D^3 + 3D^2 + 3D + 1)y = 0.$

14. $(D^4 - 2D^3 - 13D^2 + 38D - 24)y = 0.$

15. $(D^6 + 9D^4 + 24D^2 + 16)y = 0.$

16. $(8D^3 - 4D^2 - 2D + 1)y = 0.$

17. $(D^4 + D^3 - 4D^2 - 4D)y = 0.$

18. $(D^4 - 2D^3 + 5D^2 - 8D + 4)y = 0.$

19. $(D^4 + 2D^2 + 1)y = 0.$

20. $(D^4 + 5D^2 + 4)y = 0.$

21. $(D^4 + 3D^3 - 4D)y = 0.$

22. $(D^5 + D^4 - 9D^3 - 13D^2 + 8D + 12)y = 0.$

23. $(D^4 - 11D^3 + 36D^2 - 16D - 64)y = 0.$

24. $(D^2 + 2D + 5)y = 0.$

25. $(D^4 + 4D^3 + 2D^2 - 8D - 8)y = 0.$

26. $(4D^4 - 24D^3 + 35D^2 + 6D - 9)y = 0.$

27. $(4D^4 + 20D^3 + 35D^2 + 25D + 6)y = 0.$

28. $(D^4 - 7D^3 + 11D^2 + 5D - 14)y = 0.$

29. $(D^3 + 5D^2 + 7D + 3)y = 0.$

30. $(D^3 - 2D^2 + D - 2)y = 0.$

31. $(D^3 - D^2 + D - 1)y = 0.$

32. $(D^3 + 4D^2 + 5D)y = 0.$

33. $(D^4 - 13D^2 + 36)y = 0.$

34. $(D^4 - 5D^3 + 5D^2 + 5D - 6)y = 0.$

35. $(4D^3 + 8D^2 - 11D + 3)y = 0.$

36. $(D^3 + D^2 - 16D - 16)y = 0.$

37. $(D^4 - D^3 - 3D^2 + D + 2)y = 0.$

38. $(D^3 - 2D^2 - 3D + 10)y = 0.$

39. $(D^5 + D^4 - 6D^3)y = 0.$

40. $(4D^3 + 28D^2 + 61D + 37)y = 0.$

41. $(4D^3 + 12D^2 + 13D + 10)y = 0.$

42. $(18D^3 - 33D^2 + 20D - 4)y = 0.$

43. $(4D^4 - 15D^2 + 5D + 6)y = 0.$

44. $(D^5 + D^4 - 7D^3 - 11D^2 - 8D - 12)y = 0.$

45. $(D^4 + 3D^3 - 6D^2 - 28D - 24)y = 0.$

46. $(4D^4 - 4D^3 - 23D^2 + 12D + 36)y = 0.$

47. $(4D^5 - 23D^3 - 33D^2 - 17D - 3)y = 0.$

CHAPTER **7**

Nonhomogeneous Equations:
Undetermined Coefficients

38. Construction of a homogeneous equation from a specified solution

In Section 29 we saw that the general solution of the equation

$$(b_0 D^n + b_1 D^{n-1} + \cdots + b_{n-1}D + b_n)y = R(x) \tag{1}$$

is

$$y = y_c + y_p,$$

where y_c, the complementary function, is the general solution of the homogeneous equation

$$(b_0 D^n + b_1 D^{n-1} + \cdots + b_{n-1}D + b_n)y = 0 \tag{2}$$

and y_p is any particular solution of the original equation (1).

Various methods for getting a particular solution of (1) when the b_0,

110

$b_1, \ldots, b_n$ are constants will be presented. In preparation for the method of undetermined coefficients it is wise to obtain proficiency in writing a homogeneous differential equation of which a given function of proper form is a solution.

Recall that in solving homogeneous equations with constant coefficients, a term such as $c_1 e^{ax}$ occurred only when the auxiliary equation $f(m) = 0$ had a root $m = a$, and then the operator $f(D)$ had a factor $(D - a)$. In like manner, $c_2 x e^{ax}$ appeared only when $f(D)$ contained the factor $(D - a)^2$, $c_3 x^2 e^{ax}$ only when $f(D)$ contained $(D - a)^3$, etc. Such terms as $c e^{ax} \cos bx$ or $c e^{ax} \sin bx$ correspond to roots $m = a \pm ib$, or to a factor $[(D - a)^2 + b^2]$.

EXAMPLE (a):   Find a homogeneous linear equation, with constant coefficients, which has as a particular solution

$$y = 7e^{3x} + 2x.$$

First note that the coefficients (7 and 2) are quite irrelevant for the present problem, so long as they are not zero. We shall obtain an equation satisfied by $y = c_1 e^{3x} + c_2 x$, no matter what the constants c_1 and c_2 may be.

A term $c_1 e^{3x}$ occurs along with a root $m = 3$ of the auxiliary equation. The term $c_2 x$ will appear if the auxiliary equation has $m = 0, 0$; that is, a double root $m = 0$. We have recognized that the equation

$$D^2(D - 3)y = 0,$$

or

$$(D^3 - 3D^2)y = 0,$$

has $y = c_1 e^{3x} + c_2 x + c_3$ as its general solution, and therefore that it also has $y = 7e^{3x} + 2x$ as a particular solution.

EXAMPLE (b):   Find a homogeneous linear equation with real, constant coefficients that is satisfied by

$$y = 6 + 3xe^x - \cos x. \tag{3}$$

The term 6 is associated with $m = 0$, the term $3xe^x$ with a double root $m = 1, 1$, and the term $(-\cos x)$ with the pair of imaginary roots $m = 0 \pm i$. Hence the auxiliary equation is

$$m(m - 1)^2(m^2 + 1) = 0,$$

or

$$m^5 - 2m^4 + 2m^3 - 2m^2 + m = 0.$$

Therefore the function in (3) is a solution of the differential equation

$$(D^5 - 2D^4 + 2D^3 - 2D^2 + D)y = 0. \tag{4}$$

That is, from the general solution

$$y = c_1 + (c_2 + c_3 x)e^x + c_4 \cos x + c_5 \sin x$$

of equation (4), the relation (3) follows by an appropriate choice of the constants: $c_1 = 6$, $c_2 = 0$, $c_3 = 3$, $c_4 = -1$, $c_5 = 0$.

EXAMPLE (c):   Find a homogeneous linear equation with real, constant coefficients which is satisfied by

$$y = 4xe^x \sin 2x.$$

The desired equation must have its auxiliary equation with roots $m = 1 \pm 2i$, $1 \pm 2i$. The roots $m = 1 \pm 2i$ correspond to factors $(m - 1)^2 + 4$, so the auxiliary equation must be

$$[(m - 1)^2 + 4]^2 = 0,$$

or

$$m^4 - 4m^3 + 14m^2 - 20m + 25 = 0.$$

Hence the desired equation is

$$(D^4 - 4D^3 + 14D^2 - 20D + 25)y = 0.$$

Note that in all such problems, a correct (but undesirable) solution may be obtained by inserting additional roots of the auxiliary equation.

Oral exercises

In Exs. 1–14, obtain in factored form a linear differential equation, with real, constant coefficients and which is satisfied by the given function.

1. $y = 4e^{2x} + 3e^{-x}$.   ANS. $(D - 2)(D + 1)y = 0$.
2. $y = 7 - 2x + \frac{1}{2}e^{4x}$.   ANS. $D^2(D - 4)y = 0$.
3. $y = -2x + \frac{1}{2}e^{4x}$.   ANS. $D^2(D - 4)y = 0$.
4. $y = x^2 - 5 \sin 3x$.   ANS. $D^3(D^2 + 9)y = 0$.
5. $y = 2e^x \cos 3x$.   ANS. $(D - 1 - 3i)(D - 1 + 3i)y = 0$;
or $[(D - 1)^2 + 9]y = 0$; or $(D^2 - 2D + 10)y = 0$.
6. $y = x^2 + 4e^x$.
7. $y = 3xe^x - 2e^{-x}$.
8. $y = 6 + 2e^{3x}$.
9. $y = 2x^2 + 1$.
10. $y = \sin 2x$.
11. $y = \sin 2x + 3 \cos 2x$.
12. $y = \cos kx$.
13. $y = x \sin 2x$.
14. $y = 2 \sinh x$.

In Exs. 15–36, list the roots of the auxiliary equation for a homogeneous linear equation with real, constant coefficients and having the given function as a particular solution.

15. $y = 3xe^{2x}$.   2,2

16. $y = x^2 e^{-x} + 4e^x$.   ANS. $m = 2, 2$.

17. $y = e^{-x} \cos 4x$.   ANS. $m = -1, -1, -1, 1$.

18. $y = 3e^{-x} \cos 4x + 15e^{-x} \sin 4x$.   ANS. $m = -1 \pm 4i$.

19. $y = x(e^{2x} + 4)$.   2,2,0,0   ANS. $m = -1 \pm 4i$.

20. $y = 3 + 8e^{-2x}$.   ANS. $m = 0, 0, 2, 2$.

21. $y = 2x^2 - e^{-3x}$.

22. $y = 4 + 2x^2 - e^{-3x}$.

23. $y = xe^x$.

24. $y = xe^x + 5e^x$.

25. $y = 4 \cos 2x$.

26. $y = 4 \cos 2x - 3 \sin 2x$.

27. $y = x \cos 2x - 3 \sin 2x$.

28. $y = x \cos 2x$.

29. $y = e^{-2x} \cos 3x$.

30. $y = e^{-2x}(\cos 3x + \sin 3x)$.

31. $y = x^2 - x + e^{-x}(x + \cos x)$.

32. $y = x^2 \sin x$.

33. $y = x^2 \sin x + x \cos x$.

34. $y = 8 \cos 4x + \sin 3x$.

35. $y = \sin^3 x$. Use the fact that $\sin^3 x = \frac{1}{4}(3 \sin x - \sin 3x)$.

36. $y = \cos^2 x$.

$0 \pm i$, $0 \pm 3i$

39. Solution of a nonhomogeneous equation

Before proceeding to the theoretical basis and the actual working technique of the useful method of undetermined coefficients, let us examine the underlying ideas as applied to a simple numerical example.

Consider the equation

$$D^2(D - 1)y = 3e^x + \sin x. \tag{1}$$

The complementary function may be determined at once from the roots

$$m = 0, 0, 1 \tag{2}$$

of the auxiliary equation. The complementary function is

$$y_c = c_1 + c_2 x + c_3 e^x. \tag{3}$$

Since the general solution of (1) is

$$y = y_c + y_p$$

where y_c is as given in (3) and y_p is any particular solution of (1), all that remains for us to do is to find a particular solution of (1).

The right-hand member of (1),

$$R(x) = 3e^x + \sin x, \tag{4}$$

is a particular solution of a homogeneous linear differential equation whose auxiliary equation has the roots

$$m' = 1, \pm i. \tag{5}$$

Therefore the function R is a particular solution of the equation

$$(D - 1)(D^2 + 1)R = 0. \tag{6}$$

We wish to convert (1) into a homogeneous linear differential equation with constant coefficients, because we know how to solve any such equation. But, by (6), the operator $(D - 1)(D^2 + 1)$ will annihilate the right member of (1). Therefore, we apply that operator to both sides of equation (1) and get

$$(D - 1)(D^2 + 1)D^2(D - 1)y = 0. \tag{7}$$

Any solution of (1) must be a particular solution of (7). The general solution of (7) can be written at once from the roots of its auxiliary equation, those roots being the values $m = 0, 0, 1$ from (2) and the values $m' = 1, \pm i$ from (5). Thus the general solution of (7) is

$$y = c_1 + c_2 x + c_3 e^x + c_4 xe^x + c_5 \cos x + c_6 \sin x. \tag{8}$$

But the desired general solution of (1) is

$$y = y_c + y_p, \tag{9}$$

where

$$y_c = c_1 + c_2 x + c_3 e^x,$$

the c_1, c_2, c_3 being arbitrary constants as in (8). Thus there must exist a particular solution of (1) containing at most the remaining terms in (8). Using different letters as coefficients to emphasize that they are not arbitrary, we conclude that (1) has a particular solution

$$y_p = Axe^x + B \cos x + C \sin x. \tag{10}$$

We now have only to determine the numerical coefficients A, B, C by direct use of the original equation

$$D^2(D - 1)y = 3e^x + \sin x. \tag{1}$$

From (10) it follows that

$$Dy_p = A(xe^x + e^x) - B \sin x + C \cos x,$$

$$D^2y_p = A(xe^x + 2e^x) - B \cos x - C \sin x,$$

$$D^3y_p = A(xe^x + 3e^x) + B \sin x - C \cos x.$$

Substitution of y_p into (1) then yields

$$Ae^x + (B + C) \sin x + (B - C) \cos x = 3e^x + \sin x. \tag{11}$$

Since (11) is to be an identity and since e^x, $\sin x$, and $\cos x$ are linearly independent, the corresponding coefficients in the two members of (11) must be equal; that is,

$$A = 3$$
$$B + C = 1$$
$$B - C = 0.$$

Therefore $A = 3$, $B = \frac{1}{2}$, $C = \frac{1}{2}$. Returning to (10), we find that a particular solution of equation (1) is

$$y_p = 3xe^x + \frac{1}{2} \cos x + \frac{1}{2} \sin x.$$

The general solution of the original equation

$$D^2(D - 1)y = 3e^x + \sin x \tag{1}$$

is therefore obtained by adding to the complementary function the y_p found above:

$$y = c_1 + c_2 x + c_3 e^x + 3xe^x + \frac{1}{2} \cos x + \frac{1}{2} \sin x. \tag{12}$$

A careful analysis of the ideas behind the process used shows that to arrive at the solution (12), we need perform only the following steps:

(a) From (1) find the values of m and m' as exhibited in (2) and (5);
(b) From the values of m and m' write y_c and y_p as in (3) and (10);
(c) Substitute y_p into (1), equate corresponding coefficients, and obtain the numerical values of the coefficients in y_p;
(d) Write the general solution of (1).

40. The method of undetermined coefficients

Let us examine the general problem of the type treated in the preceding section. Let $f(D)$ be a polynomial in the operator D. Consider the equation

$$f(D)y = R(x). \tag{1}$$

Let the roots of the auxiliary equation $f(m) = 0$ be

$$m = m_1, m_2, \ldots, m_n. \tag{2}$$

The general solution of (1) is

$$y = y_c + y_p \tag{3}$$

where y_c can be obtained at once from the values of m in (2) and where $y = y_p$ is any particular solution (yet to be obtained) of (1).

Now suppose that the right member $R(x)$ of (1) is *itself a particular solution of some homogeneous linear differential equation with constant coefficients*,

$$g(D)R = 0, \tag{4}$$

whose auxiliary equation has the roots

$$m' = m'_1, m'_2, \cdots, m'_k. \tag{5}$$

Recall that the values of m' in (5) can be obtained by inspection from $R(x)$.

The differential equation

$$g(D)f(D)y = 0 \tag{6}$$

has as the roots of its auxiliary equation the values of m from (2) and m' from (5). Hence the general solution of (6) contains the y_c of (3) and so is of the form

$$y = y_c + y_q.$$

But also any particular solution of (1) must satisfy (6). Now, if

$$f(D)(y_c + y_q) = R(x),$$

then $f(D)y_q = R(x)$ because $f(D)y_c = 0$. Then deleting the y_c from the general solution of (6) leaves a function y_q which for some numerical values of its coefficients must satisfy (1); that is, the coefficients in y_q can be determined so that $y_q = y_p$. The determination of those numerical coefficients may be accomplished as in the examples below.

It must be kept in mind that the method of this section is applicable when, and only when, the right member of the equation is itself a particular solution of some homogeneous linear differential equation with constant coefficients.

EXAMPLE (a):   Solve the equation

$$(D^2 + D - 2)y = 2x - 40 \cos 2x. \tag{7}$$

Here we have

$$m = 1, -2$$

and

$$m' = 0, 0, \pm 2i.$$

Therefore we may write

$$y_c = c_1 e^x + c_2 e^{-2x},$$
$$y_p = A + Bx + C \cos 2x + E \sin 2x,$$

in which c_1 and c_2 are arbitrary constants, while A, B, C, and E are to be determined numerically so y_p will satisfy the equation (7).

Since

$$Dy_p = B - 2C \sin 2x + 2E \cos 2x$$

and

$$D^2y_p = -4C \cos 2x - 4E \sin 2x,$$

direct substitution of y_p into (7) yields

$$-4C \cos 2x - 4E \sin 2x + B - 2C \sin 2x + 2E \cos 2x - 2A$$
$$- 2Bx - 2C \cos 2x - 2E \sin 2x = 2x - 40 \cos 2x. \quad (8)$$

But (8) is to be an identity in x, so we must equate coefficients of each of the set of linearly independent functions $\cos 2x$, $\sin 2x$, x, 1 appearing in the identity. Thus it follows that

$$-6C + 2E = -40,$$
$$-6E - 2C = 0,$$
$$-2B = 2,$$
$$B - 2A = 0.$$

The above equations determine A, B, C, and E. Indeed, they lead to

$$A = -\tfrac{1}{2}, \qquad C = 6,$$
$$B = -1, \qquad E = -2.$$

Since the general solution of (7) is $y = y_c + y_p$, we can now write the desired result,

$$y = c_1 e^x + c_2 e^{-2x} - \tfrac{1}{2} - x + 6 \cos 2x - 2 \sin 2x.$$

EXAMPLE (b):   Solve the equation

$$(D^2 + 1)y = \sin x. \quad (9)$$

At once $m = \pm i$ and $m' = \pm i$. Therefore

$$y_c = c_1 \cos x + c_2 \sin x,$$
$$y_p = Ax \cos x + Bx \sin x.$$

Now

$$y_p'' = A(-x \cos x - 2 \sin x) + B(-x \sin x + 2 \cos x),$$

so the requirement that y_p satisfy equation (9) yields

$$-2A \sin x + 2B \cos x = \sin x,$$

from which $A = -\tfrac{1}{2}$ and $B = 0$.
    The general solution of (9) is

$$y = c_1 \cos x + c_2 \sin x - \tfrac{1}{2}x \cos x.$$

EXAMPLE (c):   Determine y so that it will satisfy the equation

$$y''' - y' = 4e^{-x} + 3e^{2x} \tag{10}$$

with the conditions that when $x = 0$, $y = 0$, $y' = -1$, and $y'' = 2$.

First we note that $m = 0, 1, -1$, and $m' = -1, 2$. Thus

$$y_c = c_1 + c_2 e^x + c_3 e^{-x},$$

$$y_p = Axe^{-x} + Be^{2x}.$$

Now

$$y_p' = A(-xe^{-x} + e^{-x}) + 2Be^{2x},$$

$$y_p'' = A(xe^{-x} - 2e^{-x}) + 4Be^{2x},$$

$$y_p''' = A(-xe^{-x} + 3e^{-x}) + 8Be^{2x}.$$

Then

$$y_p''' - y_p' = 2Ae^{-x} + 6Be^{2x},$$

so that from (10) we may conclude that $A = 2$ and $B = \frac{1}{2}$.

The general solution of (10) is therefore

$$y = c_1 + c_2 e^x + c_3 e^{-x} + 2xe^{-x} + \tfrac{1}{2}e^{2x}. \tag{11}$$

We must determine c_1, c_2, c_3 so (11) will satisfy the conditions that when $x = 0$, $y = 0$, $y' = -1$, and $y'' = 2$.

From (11) it follows that

$$y' = c_2 e^x - c_3 e^{-x} - 2xe^{-x} + 2e^{-x} + e^{2x} \tag{12}$$

and

$$y'' = c_2 e^x + c_3 e^{-x} + 2xe^{-x} - 4e^{-x} + 2e^{2x}. \tag{13}$$

We put $x = 0$ in each of (11), (12), and (13) to get the equations for the determination of c_1, c_2, and c_3. These are

$$0 = c_1 + c_2 + c_3 + \tfrac{1}{2},$$

$$-1 = c_2 - c_3 + 3,$$

$$2 = c_2 + c_3 - 2,$$

from which $c_1 = -\frac{9}{2}$, $c_2 = 0$, $c_3 = 4$. Therefore, the final result is

$$y = -\tfrac{9}{2} + 4e^{-x} + 2xe^{-x} + \tfrac{1}{2}e^{2x}.$$

An important point, sometimes overlooked by students, is that it is the general solution, the y of (11), that must be made to satisfy the initial conditions.

Exercises

In Exs. 1–35, obtain the general solution.

1. $(D^2 + D)y = -\cos x.$ ANS. $y = c_1 + c_2 e^{-x} + \frac{1}{2}\cos x - \frac{1}{2}\sin x.$

2. $(D^2 - 6D + 9)y = e^x.$ ANS. $y = (c_1 + c_2 x)e^{3x} + \frac{1}{4}e^x.$

3. $(D^2 + 3D + 2)y = 12x^2.$ ANS. $y = c_1 e^{-x} + c_2 e^{-2x} + 6x^2 - 18x + 21.$

4. $(D^2 + 3D + 2)y = 1 + 3x + x^2.$ ANS. $y = c_1 e^{-x} + c_2 e^{-2x} + \frac{1}{2}x^2.$

5. $(D^2 + 9)y = 5e^x - 162x.$ ANS. $y = c_1 \cos 3x + c_2 \sin 3x + \frac{1}{2}e^x - 18x.$

6. $(D^2 + 9)y = 5e^x - 162x^2.$ ANS. $y = c_1 \cos 3x + c_2 \sin 3x + \frac{1}{2}e^x - 18x^2 + 4.$

7. $y'' - 3y' - 4y = 30e^x.$ ANS. $y = c_1 e^{4x} + c_2 e^{-x} - 5e^x.$

8. $y'' - 3y' - 4y = 30e^{4x}.$ ANS. $y = (c_1 + 6x)e^{4x} + c_2 e^{-x}.$

9. $(D^2 - 4)y = e^{2x} + 2.$ ANS. $y = c_1 e^{-2x} + (c_2 + \frac{1}{4}x)e^{2x} - \frac{1}{2}.$

10. $(D^2 - D - 2)y = 6x + 6e^{-x}.$ ANS. $y = c_1 e^{-x} + c_2 e^{2x} - 3x + 3/2 - 2xe^{-x}.$

11. $y'' - 4y' + 3y = 20 \cos x.$ ANS. $y = c_1 e^x + c_2 e^{3x} + 2\cos x - 4\sin x.$

12. $y'' - 4y' + 3y = 2\cos x + 4\sin x.$ ANS. $y = c_1 e^x + c_2 e^{3x} + \cos x.$

13. $y'' + 2y' + y = 7 + 75\sin 2x.$

ANS. $y = e^{-x}(c_1 + c_2 x) + 7 - 12\cos 2x - 9\sin 2x.$

14. $(D^2 + 4D + 5)y = 50x + 13e^{3x}.$

ANS. $y = e^{-2x}(c_1 \cos x + c_2 \sin x) + 10x - 8 + \frac{1}{2}e^{3x}.$

15. $(D^2 + 1)y = \cos x.$ ANS. $y = c_1 \cos x + c_2 \sin x + \frac{1}{2}x \sin x.$

16. $(D^2 - 4D + 4)y = e^{2x}.$ ANS. $y = e^{2x}(c_1 + c_2 x + \frac{1}{2}x^2).$

17. $(D^2 - 1)y = e^{-x}(2\sin x + 4\cos x).$

18. $(D^2 - 1)y = 8xe^x.$ ANS. $y = c_1 e^{-x} + e^x(c_2 - 2x + 2x^2).$

19. $(D^3 - D)y = x.$ ANS. $y = c_1 + c_2 e^x + c_3 e^{-x} - \frac{1}{2}x^2.$

20. $(D^3 - D^2 + D - 1)y = 4\sin x.$

ANS. $y = c_1 e^x + (c_2 + x)\cos x + (c_3 - x)\sin x.$

21. $(D^3 + D^2 - 4D - 4)y = 3e^{-x} - 4x - 6.$

ANS. $y = c_1 e^{2x} + c_2 e^{-2x} + (c_3 - x)e^{-x} + x + \frac{1}{2}.$

22. $(D^4 - 1)y = 7x^2.$

23. $(D^4 - 1)y = e^{-x}.$ ANS. $y = c_1 e^x + (c_2 - \frac{1}{4}x)e^{-x} + c_3 \cos x + c_4 \sin x.$

24. $(D^2 - 1)y = 10\sin^2 x.$ Use the identity $\sin^2 x = \frac{1}{2}(1 - \cos 2x).$

ANS. $y = c_1 e^x + c_2 e^{-x} - 5 + \cos 2x.$

25. $(D^2 + 1)y = 12\cos^2 x.$ ANS. $y = c_1 \cos x + c_2 \sin x + 6 - 2\cos 2x.$

26. $(D^2 + 4)y = 4\sin^2 x.$ ANS. $y = c_1 \cos 2x + c_2 \sin 2x + \frac{1}{4}(1 - x\sin 2x).$

27. $y'' - 3y' - 4y = 16x - 50\cos 2x.$

28. $(D^3 - 3D - 2)y = 100\sin 2x.$

29. $y'' + 4y' + 3y = 15e^{2x} + e^{-x}.$

30. $y'' - y = e^x - 4.$

31. $y'' - y' - 2y = 6x + 6e^{-x}.$

32. $y'' + 6y' + 13y = 60\cos x + 26.$

33. $(D^3 - 3D^2 + 4)y = 6 + 80\cos 2x.$

34. $(D^3 + D - 10)y = 29e^{4x}.$

35. $(D^3 + D^2 - 4D - 4)y = 8x + 8 + 6e^{-x}.$

In Exs. 36–44, find the particular solution indicated.

36. $(D^2 + 1)y = 10e^{2x};$ when $x = 0,$ $y = 0$ and $y' = 0.$

ANS. $y = 2(e^{2x} - \cos x - 2\sin x).$

37. $(D^2 - 4)y = 2 - 8x$; when $x = 0$, $y = 0$ and $y' = 5$.

ANS. $y = e^{2x} - \frac{1}{2}e^{-2x} + 2x - \frac{1}{2}$.

38. $(D^2 + 3D)y = -18x$; when $x = 0$, $y = 0$ and $y' = 5$.

ANS. $y = 1 + 2x - 3x^2 - e^{-3x}$.

39. $(D^2 + 4D + 5)y = 10e^{-3x}$; when $x = 0$, $y = 4$ and $y' = 0$.

40. $\dfrac{d^2x}{dt^2} + 4\dfrac{dx}{dt} + 5x = 10$; when $t = 0$, $x = 0$ and $\dfrac{dx}{dt} = 0$.

ANS. $x = 2(1 - e^{-2t}\cos t - 2e^{-2t}\sin t)$.

41. $\ddot{x} + 4\dot{x} + 5x = 8\sin t$; when $t = 0$, $x = 0$ and $\dot{x} = 0$. Note that $\dot{x} = \dfrac{dx}{dt}$, $\ddot{x} = \dfrac{d^2x}{dt^2}$

is a common notation when the independent variable is time.

ANS. $x = (1 + e^{-2t})\sin t - (1 - e^{-2t})\cos t$.

42. $y'' + 9y = 81x^2 + 14\cos 4x$; when $x = 0$, $y = 0$ and $y' = 3$.

43. $(D^3 + 4D^2 + 9D + 10)y = -24e^x$; when $x = 0$, $y = 0$, $y' = -4$ and $y'' = 10$.

44. $y'' + 2y' + 5y = 8e^{-x}$; when $x = 0$, $y = 0$ and $y' = 8$.

In Exs. 45–48, obtain from the particular solution indicated the value of y and the value of y' at $x = 2$.

45. $y'' + 2y' + y = x$; at $x = 0$, $y = -3$, and at $x = 1$, $y = -1$.

ANS.   At $x = 2$, $y = e^{-2}$ and $y' = 1$.

46. $y'' + 2y' + y = x$; at $x = 0$, $y = -2$ and $y' = 2$.

ANS.   At $x = 2$, $y = 2e^{-2}$ and $y' = 1 - e^{-2}$.

47. $4y'' + y = 2$; at $x = \pi$, $y = 0$ and $y' = 1$.

ANS.   At $x = 2$, $y = -0.7635$ and $y' = +0.3012$.

48. $2y'' - 5y' - 3y = -9x^2 - 1$; at $x = 0$, $y = 1$ and $y' = 0$.

ANS.   At $x = 2$, $y = 5.64$ and $y' = 5.68$.

49. $(D^2 + D)y = x + 1$; when $x = 0$, $y = 1$, and when $x = 1$, $y = \frac{1}{4}$.   Compute   the value of y at $x = 4$.   ANS.   At $x = 4$, $y = 8 - e^{-1} - e^{-2} - e^{-3}$.

50. $(D^2 + 1)y = x^3$; when $x = 0$, $y = 0$, and when $x = \pi$, $y = 0$. Show that this initial value problem has no solution.

51. $(D^2 + 1)y = 2\cos x$; when $x = 0$, $y = 0$, and when $x = \pi$, $y = 0$. Show that this initial value problem has an unlimited number of solutions and obtain them.

ANS. $y = (c + x)\sin x$.

52. For the equation $(D^3 + D^2)y = 4$, find the solution whose graph has at the origin a point of inflection with a horizontal tangent line.

ANS. $y = 4 - 4x + 2x^2 - 4e^{-x}$.

53. For the equation $(D^2 - D)y = 2 - 2x$, find a particular solution which has at some point (to be determined) on the x-axis an inflection point with a horizontal tangent line.

ANS.   The point is $(1, 0)$; the solution is $y = x^2 + 1 - 2\exp(x - 1)$.

41. Solution by inspection

It is frequently easy to obtain a particular solution of a nonhomogeneous equation

$$(b_0 D^n + b_1 D^{n-1} + \cdots + b_{n-1}D + b_n)y = R(x) \tag{1}$$

by inspection.

For example, if $R(x)$ is a constant R_0 and if $b_n \neq 0$,

$$y_p = \frac{R_0}{b_n} \tag{2}$$

is a solution of

$$(b_0 D^n + b_1 D^{n-1} + \cdots + b_n)y = R_0 ; b_n \neq 0, R_0 \text{ constant}, \tag{3}$$

because all derivatives of y_p are zero, so

$$(b_0 D^n + b_1 D^{n-1} + \cdots + b_n)y_p = b_n R_0/b_n = R_0 .$$

Suppose that $b_n = 0$ in equation (3). Let $D^k y$ be the lowest-ordered derivative that actually appears in the differential equation. Then the equation may be written

$$(b_0 D^n + \cdots + b_{n-k} D^k)y = R_0 ; b_{n-k} \neq 0, R_0 \text{ constant}. \tag{4}$$

Now $D^k x^k = k!$, a constant, so that all higher derivatives of x^k are zero. Thus it becomes evident that (4) has a solution

$$y_p = \frac{R_0 x^k}{k! \, b_{n-k}}, \tag{5}$$

for then $(b_0 D^n + \cdots + b_{n-k} D^k)y_p = b_{n-k} R_0 k!/(k! b_{n-k}) = R_0 .$

EXAMPLE (a):   Solve the equation

$$(D^2 - 3D + 2)y = 16. \tag{6}$$

By the methods of Chapter 6 we obtain the complementary function,

$$y_c = c_1 e^x + c_2 e^{2x}.$$

By inspection a particular solution of the original equation is

$$y_p = \tfrac{16}{2} = 8.$$

Hence the general solution of (6) is

$$y = c_1 e^x + c_2 e^{2x} + 8.$$

EXAMPLE (b):   Solve the equation

$$\frac{d^5 y}{dx^5} + 4\frac{d^3 y}{dx^3} = 7. \tag{7}$$

From the auxiliary equation $m^5 + 4m^3 = 0$ we get $m = 0, 0, 0, \pm 2i$. Hence

$$y_c = c_1 + c_2 x + c_3 x^2 + c_4 \cos 2x + c_5 \sin 2x.$$

A particular solution of (7) is

$$y_p = \frac{7x^3}{3! \cdot 4} = \frac{7x^3}{24}.$$

As a check, note that

$$(D^5 + 4D^3)\frac{7x^3}{24} = 0 + 4 \cdot \frac{7 \cdot 6}{24} = 7.$$

The general solution of equation (7) is

$$y = c_1 + c_2 x + c_3 x^2 + \tfrac{7}{24}x^3 + c_4 \cos 2x + c_5 \sin 2x,$$

in which the $c_1, \ldots, c_5$ are arbitrary constants.

Examination of

$$(D^2 + 4)y = \sin 3x \tag{8}$$

leads us to search for a solution proportional to $\sin 3x$, because if y is proportional to $\sin 3x$, so is $D^2 y$. Indeed, from

$$y = A \sin 3x \tag{9}$$

we get

$$D^2 y = -9A \sin 3x,$$

so (9) is a solution of (8) if

$$(-9 + 4)A = 1; A = -\tfrac{1}{5}.$$

Thus (8) has the general solution

$$y = c_1 \cos 2x + c_2 \sin 2x - \tfrac{1}{5} \sin 3x,$$

a result easily obtained mentally.

For equation (8), the general method of undetermined coefficients leads us to write

$$m = \pm 2i, m' = \pm 3i,$$

and so to write

$$y_p = A \sin 3x + B \cos 3x. \tag{10}$$

When the y_p of (10) is substituted into (8), it is found, of course, that

$$A = -\tfrac{1}{5}, B = 0.$$

In contrast, consider the equation

$$(D^2 + 4D + 4)y = \sin 3x. \tag{11}$$

Here any attempt to find a solution proportional to $\sin 3x$ is doomed to failure because, although $D^2 y$ will also be proportional to $\sin 3x$, the term Dy will involve $\cos 3x$. There is no other term on either side of (11) to compensate for this cosine term, so no solution of the form $y = A \sin 3x$ is possible. For this equation, $m = -2, -2, m' = \pm 3i$, and in the particular solution

$$y_p = A \sin 3x + B \cos 3x,$$

it must turn out that $B \neq 0$. No labor has been saved by the inspection.
In more complicated situations such as

$$(D^2 + 4)y = x \sin 3x - 2 \cos 3x,$$

the method of inspection will save no work.
For the equation

$$(D^2 + 4)y = e^{5x}, \tag{12}$$

we see, since $(D^2 + 4)e^{5x} = 29e^{5x}$, that

$$y_p = \tfrac{1}{29}e^{5x}$$

is a solution.
Finally, note that if y_1 is a solution of

$$f(D)y = R_1(x)$$

and y_2 is a solution of

$$f(D)y = R_2(x),$$

then

$$y_p = y_1 + y_2$$

is a solution of

$$f(D)y = R_1(x) + R_2(x).$$

It follows readily that the task of obtaining a particular solution of

$$f(D)y = R(x)$$

may be split into parts by treating separate terms of $R(x)$ independently, if convenient. See the examples below. This is the basis of the "method of superposition," which plays a useful role in applied mathematics.

EXAMPLE (c):   Find a particular solution of

$$(D^2 - 9)y = 3e^x + x - \sin 4x. \tag{13}$$

Since $(D^2 - 9)e^x = -8e^x$, we see by inspection that

$$y_1 = -\tfrac{3}{8}e^x$$

is a particular solution of

$$(D^2 - 9)y_1 = 3e^x.$$

In a similar manner, we see that $y_2 = -\frac{1}{9}x$ satisfies

$$(D^2 - 9)y_2 = x$$

and that

$$y_3 = \frac{1}{25} \sin 4x$$

satisfies

$$(D^2 - 9)y_3 = -\sin 4x.$$

Hence

$$y_p = -\frac{3}{8}e^x - \frac{1}{9}x + \frac{1}{25} \sin 4x$$

is a solution of equation (13).

EXAMPLE (d):   Find a particular solution of

$$(D^2 + 4)y = \sin x + \sin 2x. \tag{14}$$

At once we see that $y_1 = \frac{1}{3} \sin x$ is a solution of

$$(D^2 + 4)y_1 = \sin x.$$

Then we seek a solution of

$$(D^2 + 4)y_2 = \sin 2x \tag{15}$$

by the method of undetermined coefficients. Since $m = \pm 2i$ and

$$m' = \pm 2i,$$

we put

$$y_2 = Ax \sin 2x + Bx \cos 2x$$

into (15) and easily determine that

$$4A \cos 2x - 4B \sin 2x = \sin 2x,$$

from which $A = 0$, $B = -\frac{1}{4}$.

Thus a particular solution of (14) is

$$y_p = \frac{1}{3} \sin x - \frac{1}{4}x \cos 2x.$$

(handwritten: $(D+1)y = \sin x$, $m = \pm i$)

(handwritten: $(D)y = \cos x$)

Exercises

1. Show that if $b \neq a$, then

$$(D^2 + a^2)y = \sin bx$$

has the particular solution $y = (a^2 - b^2)^{-1} \sin bx$.

2. Show that the equation *(handwritten: $(D^2 + a^2)y = \cos ax$)*

$$(D^2 + a^2)y = \sin ax$$

has no solution of the form $y = A \sin ax$, with A constant. Find a particular solution of the equation.　　　　　ANS.　$y = -\dfrac{x}{2a} \cos ax$.

In Exs. 3–50, find a particular solution by inspection. Verify your solution.

3. $(D^2 + 4)y = 12.$ *(handwritten: $y_p = 3$)*
4. $(D^2 + 9)y = 18.$
5. $(D^2 + 4D + 4)y = 8.$
6. $(D^2 + 2D - 3)y = 6.$
7. $(D^3 - 3D + 2)y = -7.$
8. $(D^4 + 4D^2 + 4)y = -20.$
9. $(D^2 + 4D)y = 12.$
10. $(D^3 - 9D)y = 27.$
11. $(D^3 + D)y = 15.$
12. $(D^3 + D)y = -8.$ *(handwritten: $-\frac{12x^2}{2}$)*
13. $(D^4 - 4D^2)y = 24.$ *(handwritten: $= -3x^2$)*
14. $(D^4 + D^2)y = -12.$
15. $(D^5 - D^3)y = 24.$ *(handwritten: $2 \sin t$)*
16. $(D^5 - 9D^3)y = 27.$
17. $(D^2 + 4)y = 6 \sin x.$ *(handwritten: $+2\sin t$)*　　　　ANS.　$y = 2 \sin x.$
18. $(D^2 + 4)y = 10 \cos 3x.$　　　　ANS.　$y = -2 \cos 3x.$
19. $(D^2 + 4)y = 8x + 1 - 15e^x.$　　　　ANS.　$y = 2x + \frac{1}{4} - 3e^x.$
20. $(D^2 + D)y = 6 + 3e^{2x}.$　　　　ANS.　$y = 6x + \frac{1}{2}e^{2x}.$
21. $(D^2 + 3D - 4)y = 18e^{2x}.$　　　　ANS.　$y = 3e^{2x}.$
22. $(D^2 + 2D + 5)y = 4e^x - 10.$　　　　ANS.　$y = \frac{1}{2}e^x - 2.$
23. $(D^2 - 1)y = 2e^{3x}.$
24. $(D^2 - 1)y = 2x + 3.$
25. $(D^2 - 1)y = \cos 2x.$
26. $(D^2 - 1)y = \sin 2x.$ *(handwritten: $= -\frac{1}{5} \sin 2x$)*
27. $(D^2 + 1)y = e^x + 3x.$
28. $(D^2 + 1)y = 5e^{-3x}.$ *(handwritten: $= \frac{5e^{-3x}}{10} = \frac{1}{2}e^{-3x}$)*
29. $(D^2 + 1)y = -2x + \cos 2x.$
30. $(D^2 + 1)y = 4e^{-2x}.$ *(handwritten: $\frac{4}{10}$)*
31. $(D^2 + 1)y = 10 \sin 4x.$
32. $(D^2 + 1)y = -6e^{-3x}.$
33. $(D^2 + 2D + 1)y = 12e^x.$
34. $(D^2 + 2D + 1)y = 7e^{-2x}.$
35. $(D^2 - 2D + 1)y = 12e^{-x}.$
36. $(D^2 - 2D + 1)y = 6e^{-2x}.$
37. $(D^2 - 2D - 3)y = e^x.$
38. $(D^2 - 2D - 3)y = e^{2x}.$
39. $(4D^2 + 1)y = 12 \sin x.$
40. $(4D^2 + 1)y = -12 \cos x.$ *(handwritten: $= 4 \cos x$)*
41. $(4D^2 + 4D + 1)y = 18e^x - 5.$
42. $(4D^2 + 4D + 1)y = 7e^{-x} + 2.$
43. $(D^3 - 1)y = e^{-x}.$
44. $(D^3 - 1)y = 4 - 3x^2.$ *(handwritten: $= -4 + 3x^2$)*
45. $(D^3 - D)y = e^{2x}.$
46. $(D^4 + 4)y = 5e^{2x}.$ *(handwritten: $= \frac{5}{20}e^{2x}$)*
47. $(D^4 + 4)y = 6 \sin 2x.$
48. $(D^4 + 4)y = \cos 2x.$
49. $(D^3 - D)y = 5 \sin 2x.$
50. $(D^3 - D)y = 5 \cos 2x.$ *(handwritten: $y_p = -\frac{1}{2} \sin 2x$)*

(handwritten bottom left: $\cos 2x$ / $-\sin 2x$ / $-\cos 2x$　　　$\frac{1}{2}\cos 2x$)

(handwritten bottom center-right: $-\sin$ / $-\cos$ / $\sin$)

(handwritten: Quiz – thru 41)

CHAPTER 8

Variation of Parameters

42. Introduction

In Chapter 7 we solved the nonhomogeneous linear equation with constant coefficients

$$(b_0 D^n + b_1 D^{n-1} + \cdots + b_{n-1} D + b_n)y = R(x) \tag{1}$$

by the method of undetermined coefficients. We saw that this method would be applicable only for a certain class of differential equations: those for which $R(x)$ itself was a solution of a homogeneous linear equation with constant coefficients.

In this chapter we shall study two methods that carry no such restrictions. In fact, much of what we do will be applicable to linear equations with variable coefficients.

We begin with a procedure by D'Alembert that is often called the method of reduction of order.

43. Reduction of order

Consider the general second-order linear equation

$$y'' + py' + qy = R. \tag{1}$$

Suppose we know a solution $y = y_1$ of the corresponding homogeneous equation

$$y'' + py' + qy = 0. \tag{2}$$

Then the introduction of a new dependent variable v by the substitution

$$y = y_1 v \tag{3}$$

will lead to a solution of equation (1) in the following way.

From (3) it follows that

$$y' = y_1 v' + y_1' v,$$
$$y'' = y_1 v'' + 2y_1' v' + y_1'' v,$$

so substitution of (3) into (1) yields

$$y_1 v'' + 2y_1' v' + y_1'' v + py_1 v' + py_1' v + qy_1 v = R,$$

or

$$y_1 v'' + (2y_1' + py_1)v' + (y_1'' + py_1' + qy_1)v = R. \tag{4}$$

But $y = y_1$ is a solution of (2). That is,

$$y_1'' + py_1' + qy_1 = 0$$

and equation (4) reduces to

$$y_1 v'' + (2y_1' + py_1)v' = R. \tag{5}$$

Now let $v' = w$ so equation (5) becomes

$$y_1 w' + (2y_1' + py_1)w = R, \tag{6}$$

a linear equation of the first order in w.

By the usual method (integrating factor) we can find w from (6). Then we can get v from $v' = w$ by an integration. Finally $y = y_1 v$.

Note that the method is not restricted to equations with constant coefficients. It depends only upon our knowing a particular solution of equation (2); that is, upon our knowledge of the complementary function. For practical purposes, the method depends also upon our being able to effect the integrations.

EXAMPLE (a):   Solve the equation

$$y'' - y = e^x. \qquad (7)$$

The complementary function of (7) is

$$y_c = c_1 e^x + c_2 e^{-x}.$$

We shall take the particular solution e^x and use the method of reduction of order by setting

$$y = ve^x.$$

Then

$$y' = ve^x + v'e^x,$$

and

$$y'' = ve^x + 2v'e^x + v''e^x.$$

Substituting into equation (7) gives

$$v'' + 2v' = 1. \qquad (8)$$

Equation (8) is a first-order linear equation in the variable v'. Applying the integrating factor e^{2x} yields

$$e^{2x}(v'' + 2v') = e^{2x}.$$

Thus

$$e^{2x}v' = \tfrac{1}{2}e^{2x} + c, \qquad (9)$$

where c is an arbitrary constant. Equation (9) readily gives

$$v' = \tfrac{1}{2} + ce^{-2x},$$

and hence

$$v = c_1 e^{-2x} + c_2 + \tfrac{1}{2}x,$$

where c_1 and c_2 are arbitrary constants.

Remembering that $y = ve^x$, we finally have

$$y = c_1 e^{-x} + c_2 e^x + \tfrac{1}{2}xe^x.$$

Of course, the solution to equation (7) could have been obtained by the method of undetermined coefficients. Let us now solve a problem not solvable by that method.

EXAMPLE (b):   Solve the equation

$$(D^2 + 1)y = \csc x \qquad (10)$$

The complementary function is

$$y_c = c_1 \cos x + c_2 \sin x. \qquad (11)$$

We may use any special case of (11) as the y_1 in the theory above. Let us then put

$$y = v \sin x.$$

We find that

$$y' = v' \sin x + v \cos x$$

and

$$y'' = v'' \sin x + 2v' \cos x - v \sin x.$$

The equation for v is

$$v'' \sin x + 2v' \cos x = \csc x, \qquad \div \frac{1}{\sin x}$$

or

$$v'' + 2v' \cot x = \csc^2 x. \tag{12}$$

Put $v' = w$; then equation (12) becomes

$$w' + 2w \cot x = \csc^2 x, \qquad \frac{dw}{dx} + (2\cot x)\, w = \csc^2 x$$

for which an integrating factor is $\sin^2 x$. Thus

$$= e^{2\int \cot x\, dx}$$

$$\sin^2 x\, dw + 2w \sin x \cos x\, dx = dx \tag{13}$$

is exact. From (13) we get

$$= e^{2\int \frac{\cos x}{\sin x}\, dx}$$

$$w \sin^2 x = x,$$

$$= e^{2\ln \sin x}$$

and if we seek only a particular solution, we have

$$w = x \csc^2 x \qquad = \sin^2 x$$

or

$$w = \frac{x}{\sin^2 x}$$

$$v' = x \csc^2 x.$$

$$= x \csc^2 x$$

Hence

$$v = \int x \csc^2 x\, dx, \qquad \text{by parts}$$

or

$$v = -x \cot x + \ln |\sin x|,$$

a result easily obtained using integration by parts.

Now

$$y = v \sin x,$$

so the particular solution which we sought is

$$y_p = -x \cos x + \sin x \ln |\sin x|.$$

Finally, the complete solution of (10) is seen to be

$$y = c_1 \cos x + c_2 \sin x - x \cos x + \sin x \ln |\sin x|.$$

Exercises

Use the method of reduction of order to solve the following equations.

1. $(D^2 - 1)y = x.$ ANS. $y = c_1 e^x + c_2 e^{-x} - x.$

2. $(D^2 - 3D + 2)y = e^x.$ ANS. $y = c_1 e^{2x} + c_2 e^x - xe^x.$

3. $(D^2 - 6D + 9)y = e^x.$ ANS.   See Ex. 2, Section 40.

4. $(D^2 + 9)y = \sin x.$

5. Use the substitution $y = v \cos x$ to solve the equation of Example (b) above.

6. Use $y = ve^{-x}$ to solve the equation of Example (a) above.

7. $(D^2 + 1)y = \sec x.$

8. $(D^2 + 1)y = \sec^3 x.$ Use $y = v \sin x.$

9. $(D^2 + 1)y = \csc^3 x.$ Take a hint from Ex. 8.

10. $(D^2 + 2D + 1)y = (e^x - 1)^{-2}.$ ANS. $y = e^{-x}[c_1 + c_2 x - \ln|1 - e^{-x}|].$

11. $(D^2 - 3D + 2)y = (1 + e^{2x})^{-1/2}.$

12. Verify that $y = e^x$ is a solution of the equation

$$(x - 1)y'' - xy' + y = 0.$$

Use this fact to find the general solution of

$$(x - 1)y'' - xy' + y = 1.$$

     ANS. $y = c_1 x + c_2 e^x + 1.$

13. Observe that $y = x$ is a particular solution of the equation

$$2x^2 y'' + xy' - y = 0$$

and find the general solution. For what values of x is the solution valid?

     ANS. $y = c_1 x + c_2 x^{-1/2}.$

14. In Chapter 19 we shall study Bessel's differential equation of index zero

$$xy'' + y' + xy = 0.$$

Suppose that one solution of this equation is given the name $J_0(x)$. Show that a second solution takes the form

$$J_0(x) \int \frac{dx}{x[J_0(x)]^2}.$$

15. One solution of the Legendre differential equation

$$(1 - x^2)y'' - 2xy' + 2y = 0$$

is $y = x.$ Find a second solution.   ANS. $y = -2 + \ln\left|\dfrac{1 + x}{1 - x}\right|.$

44. Variation of parameters

In the previous section we saw that if y_1 is a solution of the homogeneous equation

$$y'' + p(x)y' + q(x)y = 0, \tag{1}$$

then we can use it to determine the general solution of the nonhomogeneous equation

$$y'' + p(x)y' + q(x)y = R(x). \tag{2}$$

In using the method of reduction of order we proceeded as follows. Since y_1 is a solution of (1), the function $c_1 y_1$ is also a solution for an arbitrary constant c_1. We replaced the constant c_1 by a function $v(x)$ and considered the possibility of the existence of a solution of equation (2) of the form $v \cdot y_1$. This led us to a first-order linear equation in the variable v' that we were able to solve.

Suppose now that we know the general solution of the homogeneous equation (1). That is, suppose

$$y_c = c_1 y_1 + c_2 y_2 \tag{3}$$

is a solution of (1), where y_1 and y_2 are linearly independent on an interval $a < x < b$. Let us see what happens if we replace both of the constants in (3) with functions of x. That is, we consider

$$y = Ay_1 + By_2 \tag{4}$$

and try to determine $A(x)$ and $B(x)$ so that $Ay_1 + By_2$ is a solution of equation (2).

Note that we are involved with two unknown functions $A(x)$ and $B(x)$ and that we have only insisted that these functions satisfy one condition: the function in (4) is to be a solution of equation (2). We may therefore expect to impose a second condition on $A(x)$ and $B(x)$ in some way which would be to our advantage. Indeed, if we simply impose the condition $B(x) \equiv 0$, then we will be dealing with the method of reduction of order. Actually we impose a somewhat different condition on A and B.

From (4) it follows that

$$y' = Ay_1' + By_2' + A'y_1 + B'y_2. \tag{5}$$

Rather than become involved with derivatives of A and B of higher order than the first, we now choose some particular function for the expression

$$A'y_1 + B'y_2.$$

Technically, we could let this function be $\sin x$, e^x, or any other suitable function. For simplicity we choose

$$A'y_1 + B'y_2 = 0. \tag{6}$$

It then follows from (5) that

$$y'' = Ay_1'' + By_2'' + A'y_1' + B'y_2'. \tag{7}$$

Since y was to be a solution of (2) we substitute from (4), (5), and (7) into equation (2) to obtain

$$A(y_1'' + py_1' + qy_1) + B(y_2'' + py_2' + qy_2) + A'y_1' + B'y_2' = R(x).$$

But y_1 and y_2 are solutions of the homogeneous equation (1), so that finally

$$A'y_1' + B'y_2' = R(x). \tag{8}$$

Equations (6) and (8) now give us two equations that we wish to solve for A' and B'. This solution exists providing the determinant

$$\begin{vmatrix} y_1 & y_2 \\ y_1' & y_2' \end{vmatrix}$$

does not vanish. But this determinant is precisely the Wronskian of the functions y_1 and y_2, which were presumed to be linearly independent on the interval $a < x < b$. Therefore, the Wronskian does not vanish on that interval and we can find A' and B'. By integration we can now find A and B. Once A and B are known, equation (4) gives us the desired y.

This argument can easily be extended to equations of order higher than two, but no essentially new ideas appear. Moreover, there is nothing in the method that prohibits the linear differential equation involved from having variable coefficients.

EXAMPLE (a):   Solve the equation

$$(D^2 + 1)y = \sec x \tan x. \tag{9}$$

Of course,

$$y_c = c_1 \cos x + c_2 \sin x.$$

Let us seek a particular solution by variation of parameters. Put

$$y = A \cos x + B \sin x, \tag{10}$$

from which

$$y' = -A \sin x + B \cos x + A' \cos x + B' \sin x.$$

Next set

$$A' \cos x + B' \sin x = 0, \tag{11}$$

so

$$y' = -A \sin x + B \cos x.$$

Then

$$y'' = -A \cos x - B \sin x - A' \sin x + B' \cos x. \tag{12}$$

Next we eliminate y by combining equations (10) and (12) with the original equation (9). Thus we get the relation

$$-A' \sin x + B' \cos x = \sec x \tan x. \tag{13}$$

From (13) and (11), A' is easily eliminated. The result is

$$B' = \tan x,$$

so

$$B = \ln |\sec x|, \tag{14}$$

in which the arbitrary constant has been disregarded because we are seeking only a particular solution to add to our previously determined complementary function y_c.

From equations (13) and (11) it also follows easily that

$$A' = - \sin x \sec x \tan x,$$

or

$$A' = - \tan^2 x.$$

Then

$$A = - \int \tan^2 x \, dx = \int (1 - \sec^2 x) \, dx,$$

so

$$A = x - \tan x, \tag{15}$$

again disregarding the arbitrary constant.

Returning to equation (10) with the known A from (15) and the known B from (14), we write the particular solution

$$y_p = (x - \tan x) \cos x + \sin x \ln |\sec x|,$$

or

$$y_p = x \cos x - \sin x + \sin x \ln |\sec x|.$$

Then the general solution of (9) is

$$y = c_1 \cos x + c_3 \sin x + x \cos x + \sin x \ln |\sec x|, \tag{16}$$

where the term $(- \sin x)$ in y_p has been absorbed in the complementary function term $c_3 \sin x$, since c_3 is an arbitrary constant.

The solution (16) can, as usual, be verified by direct substitution into the original differential equation.

EXAMPLE (b): Solve the equation

$$(D^2 - 3D + 2)y = \frac{1}{1 + e^{-x}} \tag{17}$$

Here

$$y_c = c_1 e^x + c_2 e^{2x},$$

so we put

$$y = Ae^x + Be^{2x}. \tag{18}$$

Since

$$y' = Ae^x + 2Be^{2x} + A'e^x + B'e^{2x},$$

we impose the condition

$$A'e^x + B'e^{2x} = 0. \tag{19}$$

Then

$$y' = Ae^x + 2Be^{2x}, \tag{20}$$

from which it follows that

$$y'' = Ae^x + 4Be^{2x} + A'e^x + 2B'e^{2x}. \tag{21}$$

Combining (18), (20), (21), and the original equation (17), we find that

$$A'e^x + 2B'e^{2x} = \frac{1}{1 + e^{-x}}. \qquad (22)$$

Elimination of B' from equations (19) and (22) yields

$$A'e^x = -\frac{1}{1 + e^{-x}},$$

$$A' = -\frac{e^{-x}}{1 + e^{-x}}.$$

Then

$$A = \ln(1 + e^{-x}).$$

Similarly,

$$B'e^{2x} = \frac{1}{1 + e^{-x}}$$

so

$$B = \int \frac{e^{-2x}}{1 + e^{-x}} dx = \int \left[e^{-x} - \frac{e^{-x}}{1 + e^{-x}} \right] dx,$$

or

$$B = -e^{-x} + \ln(1 + e^{-x}).$$

Then, from (18),

$$y_p = e^x \ln(1 + e^{-x}) - e^x + e^{2x} \ln(1 + e^{-x}).$$

The term $(-e^x)$ in y_p can be absorbed into the complementary function. The general solution of equation (17) is

$$y = c_3 e^x + c_2 e^{2x} + (e^x + e^{2x}) \ln(1 + e^{-x}).$$

45. Solution of $y'' + y = f(x)$

Consider next the equation

$$(D^2 + 1)y = f(x), \tag{1}$$

in which all that we require of $f(x)$ is that it be integrable in the interval on which we seek a solution. For instance, $f(x)$ may be any continuous function or any function with only a finite number of finite discontinuities on the interval $a \leqq x \leqq b$.

The method of variation of parameters will now be applied to the solution of (1). Put

$$y = A \cos x + B \sin x. \tag{2}$$

Then

$$y' = -A \sin x + B \cos x + A' \cos x + B' \sin x,$$

and if we choose

$$A' \cos x + B' \sin x = 0, \tag{3}$$

we obtain

$$y'' = -A \cos x - B \sin x - A' \sin x + B' \cos x. \tag{4}$$

From (1), (2), and (4) it follows that

$$-A' \sin x + B' \cos x = f(x). \tag{5}$$

Equations (3) and (5) may be solved for A' and B', yielding

$$A' = -f(x) \sin x, \quad B' = f(x) \cos x.$$

We may now write

$$A = -\int_a^x f(\beta) \sin \beta \, d\beta, \tag{6}$$

$$B = \int_a^x f(\beta) \cos \beta \, d\beta, \tag{7}$$

for any x in $a \leqq x \leqq b$. It is here that we use the integrability of $f(x)$ on the interval $a \leqq x \leqq b$.

The A and B of (6) and (7) may be inserted in (2) to give us the particular solution

$$y_p = -\cos x \int_a^x f(\beta) \sin \beta \, d\beta + \sin x \int_a^x f(\beta) \cos \beta \, d\beta$$

$$= \int_a^x f(\beta)[\sin x \cos \beta - \cos x \sin \beta] \, d\beta. \tag{8}$$

Hence we have

$$y_p = \int_a^x f(\beta) \sin (x - \beta) \, d\beta, \qquad (9)$$

and we can now write the general solution of equation (1):

$$y = c_1 \cos x + c_2 \sin x + \int_a^x f(\beta) \sin (x - \beta) \, d\beta. \qquad (10)$$

Exercises

In Exs. 1–18, use variation of parameters.

1. $(D^2 + 1)y = \csc x \cot x.$
     ANS. $y = c_1 \cos x + c_2 \sin x - x \sin x - \cos x \ln |\sin x|.$

2. $(D^2 + 1)y = \cot x.$
     ANS. $y = y_c - \sin x \ln |\csc x + \cot x|.$

3. $(D^2 + 1)y = \sec x.$
     ANS. $y = c_1 \cos x + c_2 \sin x + x \sin x + \cos x \ln |\cos x|.$
     ANS. $y = y_c - 1 + \sin x \ln |\sec x + \tan x|.$

4. $(D^2 + 1)y = \sec^2 x.$

5. $(D^2 + 1)y = \sec^3 x.$
     ANS. $y = y_c + \tfrac{1}{2} \sec x.$

6. $(D^2 + 1)y = \sec^4 x.$
     ANS. $y = y_c - \tfrac{1}{2} + \tfrac{1}{6} \sec^2 x + \tfrac{1}{2} \sin x \ln |\sec x + \tan x|.$

7. $(D^2 + 1)y = \tan x.$
     ANS. $y = y_c - \cos x \ln |\sec x + \tan x|.$

8. $(D^2 + 1)y = \tan^2 x.$
     ANS. $y = y_1 - 1$, where y_1 is the solution of Ex. 4 above.

9. $(D^2 + 1)y = \sec x \csc x.$
     ANS. $y = y_c - \cos x \ln |\sec x + \tan x| - \sin x \ln |\csc x + \cot x|.$

10. $(D^2 + 1)y = \sec^2 x \csc x.$
     ANS. $y = y_c - \sin x \ln |\csc 2x + \cot 2x|.$

11. $(D^2 - 2D + 1)y = e^{2x}(e^x + 1)^{-2}.$
     ANS. $y = y_c + e^x \ln (1 + e^x).$

12. $(D^2 - 3D + 2)y = e^{2x}/(1 + e^{2x}).$
     ANS. $y = y_c + e^x \operatorname{Arctan} (e^{-x}) - \tfrac{1}{2} e^{2x} \ln (1 + e^{-2x}).$

13. $(D^2 - 3D + 2)y = \cos (e^{-x}).$
     ANS. $y = y_c - e^{2x} \cos (e^{-x}).$

14. $(D^2 - 1)y = 2(1 - e^{-2x})^{-1/2}.$
     ANS. $y = c_1 e^x + c_2 e^{-x} - e^x \operatorname{Arcsin} (e^{-x}) - (1 - e^{-2x})^{1/2}.$

15. $(D^2 - 1)y = e^{-2x} \sin e^{-x}.$
     ANS. $y = y_c - \sin e^{-x} - e^x \cos e^{-x}.$

16. $(D - 1)(D - 2)(D - 3)y = e^x.$
     ANS. $y = y_c + \tfrac{1}{2} x e^x.$

17. $y''' - y' = x.$

18. $y''' + y' = \tan x.$

19. Observe that x and e^x are solutions of the homogeneous equation associated with

$$(1 - x)y'' + xy' - y = 2(x - 1)^2 e^{-x}.$$

Use this fact to solve the nonhomogeneous equation.

20. Solve the equation

$$y'' - y = e^x$$

by the method of variation of parameters, but instead of setting $A'y_1 + B'y_2 = 0$ as in equation (6), Section 44, choose $A'y_1 + B'y_2 = k$, for constant k.

21. Apply the suggestion of Ex. 20 to Ex. 5 above.

22. Let y_1 and y_2 be solutions of the homogeneous equation associated with

$$y'' + p(x)y' + q(x)y = f(x). \qquad \text{(A)}$$

Let $W(x)$ be the Wronskian of y_1 and y_2, and assume $W(x) \neq 0$ on the interval $a < x < b$. Show that a particular solution of equation (A) is given by

$$y_p = \int_a^x \frac{f(\beta)[y_1(\beta)y_2(x) - y_1(x)y_2(\beta)]\, d\beta}{W(\beta)}. \qquad \text{(B)}$$

23. The conditions of Ex. 22 imply that

$$y_1'' + py_1' + qy_1 = 0 \qquad \text{(C)}$$

and

$$y_2'' + py_2' + qy_2 = 0. \qquad \text{(D)}$$

If we multiply equation (C) by y_2 and equation (D) by y_1 and then subtract the two equations, we obtain

$$(y_2 y_1'' - y_1 y_2'') + p(y_2 y_1' - y_1 y_2') = 0.$$

From this equation show that the Wronskian of y_1 and y_2 can be written

$$W(x) = c \exp\left[-\int p\, dx\right], \qquad \text{(E)}$$

where c is constant. Equation (E) is known as Abel's formula.

24. Conclude from Ex. 23 that if $W(x_0) = 0$ for some x_0 on the interval $a < x < b$, then $W(x) \equiv 0$ for all $a < x < b$.

25. Solve the initial value problem

$$y'' + y = f(x); \quad \text{when } x = x_0,\ y = y_0,\ \text{and } y' = y_0'.$$

Hint: Show that the constant a in equations (6) and (7) above could have been chosen to be x_0. Determine the c_1 and c_2 of equation (10) by using the form of y_p in equation (8).

ANS. $y = y_0 \cos(x - x_0) + y_0' \sin(x - x_0) + \int_{x_0}^x f(\beta) \sin(x - \beta)\, d\beta.$

Miscellaneous exercises

1. $(D^2 - 1)y = 2e^{-x}(1 + e^{-2x})^{-2}.$ ANS. $y = y_c - xe^{-x} - \tfrac{1}{2}e^{-x}\ln(1 + e^{-2x}).$

2. $(D^2 - 1)y = (1 - e^{2x})^{-3/2}.$ ANS. $y = y_c - (1 - e^{2x})^{1/2}.$

3. $(D^2 - 1)y = e^{2x}(3\tan e^x + e^x \sec^2 e^x).$ ANS. $y = y_c + e^x \ln|\sec e^x|.$

4. $(D^2 + 1)y = \sec^2 x \tan x.$

ANS. $y = y_c + \tfrac{1}{2}\tan x + \tfrac{1}{2}\cos x \ln|\sec x + \tan x|.$

5. Do Ex. 4 by another method.

6. $(D^2 + 1)y = \csc x.$ Use variation of parameters.

ANS. See Example (b) of Section 43.

7. $(D^2 - 3D + 2)y = \sec^2(e^{-x}).$ ANS. $y = c_1 e^x + c_2 e^{2x} + e^{2x}\ln|\sec(e^{-x})|.$

8. Do Ex. 7 by another method.

9. $(D^2 - 1)y = 2/(1 + e^x)$.

ANS. $y = y_c - 1 - xe^x + (e^x - e^{-x}) \ln (1 + e^x)$.

10. $(D^3 + D)y = \sec^2 x$. *Hint:* integrate once first.

ANS. $y = c_1 + c_2 \cos x + c_3 \sin x - \cos x \ln |\sec x + \tan x|$.

11. $(D^2 - 1)y = 2/(e^x - e^{-x})$.

ANS. $y = y_c - xe^{-x} + \frac{1}{2}(e^x - e^{-x}) \ln |1 - e^{-2x}|$.

12. $(D^2 - 3D + 2)y = \sin e^{-x}$. ANS. $y = y_c - e^{2x} \sin e^{-x}$.

13. $(D^2 - 1)y = 1/(e^{2x} + 1)$. ANS. $y = y_c - \frac{1}{2} - \cosh x \operatorname{Arctan} e^{-x}$.

14. $y'' + y = \sec^3 x \tan x$. ANS. $y = y_c + \frac{1}{6} \sec x \tan x$.

15. $y'' + y = \sec x \tan^2 x$. Verify your answer.

16. $y'' + 4y' + 3y = \sin e^x$. ANS. $y = y_c - e^{-2x} \sin e^x - e^{-3x} \cos e^x$.

17. $y'' + y = \csc^3 x \cot x$. ANS. $y = y_c + \frac{1}{6} \cot x \csc x$.

CHAPTER 9

Inverse Differential Operators

46. The exponential shift

In Chapter 5 we studied some of the properties of the algebra of linear differential operators with constant coefficients. We found this algebra useful in finding solutions of homogeneous linear equations. In this chapter we show briefly how differential operators may be used to find particular solutions for nonhomogeneous linear equations.

As a first illustration we make use of the exponential shift theorem that was derived in Section 32:

$$e^{ax}f(D)y = f(D - a)[e^{ax}y], \qquad (1)$$

where $f(D)$ is a linear differential operator with constant coefficients.

EXAMPLE (a): Solve the equation

$$(D^2 - 2D + 5)y = 16x^3e^{3x}. \qquad (2)$$

Note that the complementary function is

$$y_c = c_1 e^x \cos 2x + c_2 e^x \sin 2x. \tag{3}$$

We can conclude also that there is a particular solution,

$$y_p = Ax^3 e^{3x} + Bx^2 e^{3x} + Cx e^{3x} + E e^{3x}, \tag{4}$$

which can be obtained by the method of Chapter 7. But the task of obtaining the derivatives of y_p and finding the numerical values of A, B, C, and E is a little tedious. It can be made easier by using the exponential shift (1).

Let us write (2) in the form

$$e^{-3x}(D^2 - 2D + 5)y = 16x^3,$$

and then apply the relation (1), with $a = -3$. In shifting the exponential e^{-3x} from the left to the right of the differential operator, we must replace D by $(D + 3)$ throughout, thus obtaining

$$[(D + 3)^2 - 2(D + 3) + 5](e^{-3x}y) = 16x^3,$$

or

$$(D^2 + 4D + 8)(e^{-3x}y) = 16x^3. \tag{5}$$

In equation (5), the dependent variable is $(e^{-3x}y)$. We know at once that (5) has a particular solution of the form

$$e^{-3x}y_p = Ax^3 + Bx^2 + Cx + E. \tag{6}$$

Successive differentiations of (6) are simple. Indeed,

$$D(e^{-3x}y_p) = 3Ax^2 + 2Bx + C,$$

$$D^2(e^{-3x}y_p) = 6Ax + 2B,$$

so from (5) we get

$$6Ax + 2B + 12Ax^2 + 8Bx + 4C + 8Ax^3 + 8Bx^2 + 8Cx + 8E = 16x^3.$$

Hence

$$8A = 16,$$
$$12A + 8B = 0,$$
$$6A + 8B + 8C = 0,$$
$$2B + 4C + 8E = 0,$$

from which $A = 2$, $B = -3$, $C = \tfrac{3}{2}$, $E = 0$.

Therefore

$$e^{-3x}y_p = 2x^3 - 3x^2 + \tfrac{3}{2}x,$$

or

$$y_p = (2x^3 - 3x^2 + \tfrac{3}{2}x)e^{3x},$$

and the general solution of the original equation (2) is

$$y = c_1 e^x \cos 2x + c_2 e^x \sin 2x + (2x^3 - 3x^2 + \tfrac{3}{2}x)e^{3x}.$$

The complementary function could also have been obtained from (5).

EXAMPLE (b): Solve the equation

$$(D^2 - 2D + 1)y = xe^x + 7x - 2. \tag{7}$$

Here the immediate use of the exponential shift would do no good, because removing the e^x factor from the first term on the right would only insert a factor e^{-x} in the second and third terms on the right. The terms $7x - 2$ on the right give us no trouble as they stand. Therefore we break (7) into two problems, obtaining a particular solution for each of the equations

$$(D^2 - 2D + 1)y_1 = xe^x \tag{8}$$

and

$$(D^2 - 2D + 1)y_2 = 7x - 2. \tag{9}$$

On (8) we use the exponential shift, passing from

$$e^{-x}(D - 1)^2 y_1 = x$$

to

$$D^2(e^{-x}y_1) = x. \tag{10}$$

A particular solution of (10) is easily obtained:

$$e^{-x}y_1 = \tfrac{1}{6}x^3,$$

so

$$y_1 = \tfrac{1}{6}x^3 e^x. \tag{11}$$

Equation (9) is treated as in Chapter 7. Put

$$y_2 = Ax + B.$$

Then $Dy_2 = A$, and from (9) it is easily found that $A = 7$, $B = 12$. Thus a particular solution of (9) is

$$y_2 = 7x + 12. \tag{12}$$

Using (11), (12), and the roots of the auxiliary equation for (7), the general solution of (7) can now be written. It is

$$y = (c_1 + c_2 x)e^x + \tfrac{1}{6}x^3 e^x + 7x + 12.$$

EXAMPLE (c): Solve the equation

$$D^2(D + 4)^2 y = 96e^{-4x}. \tag{13}$$

At once we have $m = 0, 0, -4, -4$ and $m' = -4$. We seek first a particular solution. Therefore we integrate each member of (13) twice before using the exponential shift. From (13) it follows that

$$(D + 4)^2 y_p = 6e^{-4x}, \tag{14}$$

the constants of integration being disregarded because only a particular solution is sought. Equation (14) yields

$$e^{4x}(D + 4)^2 y_p = 6,$$

$$D^2(y_p e^{4x}) = 6,$$

$$y_p e^{4x} = 3x^2,$$

$$y_p = 3x^2 e^{-4x}.$$

Thus the general solution of (13) is seen to be

$$y = c_1 + c_2 x + (c_3 + c_4 x + 3x^2)e^{-4x}.$$

The exponential shift is particularly helpful when applied in connection with terms for which the values of m' (using the notations of Chapter 7) are repetitions of values of m.

Exercises

In Exs. 1–12, use the exponential shift to find a particular solution.

1. $(D - 3)^2 y = e^{3x}$.   ANS. $y = \frac{1}{2}x^2 e^{3x}$.

2. $(D - 1)^2 y = e^x$.

3. $(D + 2)^2 y = 12xe^{-2x}$.   ANS. $y = 2x^3 e^{-2x}$.

4. $(D + 1)^2 y = 3xe^{-x}$.

5. $(D - 2)^3 y = 6xe^{2x}$.   ANS. $y = \frac{1}{4}x^4 e^{2x}$.

6. $(D + 4)^3 y = 8xe^{-4x}$.

7. $(D + 3)^3 y = 15x^2 e^{-3x}$.   ANS. $y = \frac{1}{4}x^5 e^{-3x}$.

8. $(D - 4)^3 y = 15x^2 e^{4x}$.

9. $D^2(D - 2)^2 y = 16e^{2x}$.   ANS. $y = 2x^2 e^{2x}$.

10. $D^2(D + 3)^2 y = 9e^{-3x}$.

11. $(D^2 - D - 2)y = 18xe^{-x}$.   ANS. $y = -(3x^2 + 2x)e^{-x}$.

12. $(D^2 - D - 2)y = 36xe^{2x}$.

In Exs. 13–18, find a particular solution, using the exponential shift in part of your work, as in Example (b) above.

13. $(D - 2)^2 y = 20 - 3xe^{2x}$.   ANS. $y = 5 - \frac{1}{2}x^3 e^{2x}$.

14. $(D - 2)^2 y = 4 - 8x + 6xe^{2x}$.

15. $y'' - 9y = 9(2x - 3 + 4xe^{3x})$.   ANS. $y = 3 - 2x + (3x^2 - x)e^{3x}$.

16. $y'' + 4y' + 4y = 4x - 6e^{-2x} + 3e^x$.

17. $(D + 1)^2 y = e^{-x} + 3x$.   ANS. $y = \frac{1}{2}x^2 e^{-x} + 3x - 6$.

18. $(D^2 - 4)y = 16xe^{-2x} + 8x + 4$.   ANS. $y = -(2x + 1)(xe^{-2x} + 1)$.

In Exs. 19–28, find the general solution.

19. $y'' - 4y = 8xe^{2x}$.   ANS. $y = c_1e^{-2x} + (c_2 - \frac{1}{2}x + x^2)e^{2x}$.
20. $y'' - 9y = -72xe^{-3x}$.
21. $D(D + 1)^2y = e^{-x}$.   ANS. $y = c_1 + (c_2 + c_3x - \frac{1}{2}x^2)e^{-x}$.
22. $D^2(D - 2)^2y = 2e^{2x}$.
23. $y'' + 2y' + y = 48e^{-x} \cos 4x$.   ANS. $y = (c_1 + c_2x - 3 \cos 4x)e^{-x}$.
24. $y'' + 4y' + 4y = 18e^{-2x} \cos 3x$.
25. $(D - 1)^2y = e^x \sec^2 x \tan x$.   ANS. $y = e^x(c_1 + c_2x + \frac{1}{2} \tan x)$.
26. $(D^2 + 4D + 4)y = -x^{-2}e^{-2x}$.   ANS. $y = e^{-2x}(c_1 + c_2x + \ln|x|)$.
27. $(D - a)^2y = e^{ax}f''(x)$.   ANS. $y = e^{ax}[c_1 + c_2x + f(x)]$.
28. $(D^2 + 7D + 12)y = e^{-3x} \sec^2 x(1 + 2 \tan x)$.
                                                  ANS. $y = c_1e^{-4x} + e^{-3x}(c_2 + \tan x)$.

47. The operator $1/f(D)$

In seeking a particular solution of

$$f(D)y = R(x),\qquad (1)$$

it is natural to write

$$y = \frac{1}{f(D)}R(x)\qquad (2)$$

and to try to define an operator $1/f(D)$ so that the function y of (2) will have meaning and will satisfy equation (1).

Instead of building a theory of such inverse differential operators, we shall adopt the following method of attack. Purely formal (unjustified) manipulations of the symbols will be performed, thus leading to a tentative evaluation of

$$\frac{1}{f(D)}R(x).$$

After all, the only thing that we require of our evaluation is that

$$f(D) \cdot \frac{1}{f(D)}R(x) = R(x).\qquad (3)$$

Hence the burden of proof will be placed on a direct verification of the condition (3) in each instance.

48. Evaluation of $[1/f(D)]e^{ax}$

We proved (Section 32) with slightly different notation that

$$f(D)e^{ax} = e^{ax}f(a)\qquad (1)$$

and
$$(D - a)^n(x^n e^{ax}) = n!\, e^{ax}. \tag{2}$$

Equation (1) suggests

$$\frac{1}{f(D)} e^{ax} = \frac{e^{ax}}{f(a)}, \quad f(a) \neq 0. \tag{3}$$

Now from (1) it follows that

$$f(D)\frac{e^{ax}}{f(a)} = \frac{f(a)e^{ax}}{f(a)} = e^{ax}.$$

Hence (3) is verified.

Now suppose that $f(a) = 0$. Then $f(D)$ contains the factor $(D - a)$. Suppose that the factor occurs precisely n times in $f(D)$; that is, let

$$f(D) = \phi(D)(D - a)^n; \quad \phi(a) \neq 0.$$

With the aid of (2) we obtain

$$\phi(D)(D - a)^n(x^n e^{ax}) = \phi(D)n!\, e^{ax},$$

from which, by (1), it follows that

$$\phi(D)(D - a)^n(x^n e^{ax}) = n!\,\phi(a)e^{ax}. \tag{4}$$

Therefore we write

$$\frac{1}{\phi(D)(D - a)^n} e^{ax} = \frac{x^n e^{ax}}{n!\,\phi(a)}, \quad \phi(a) \neq 0, \tag{5}$$

which is easily verified. Indeed,

$$\phi(D)(D - a)^n \frac{x^n e^{ax}}{n!\,\phi(a)} = \frac{n!\,\phi(a)e^{ax}}{n!\,\phi(a)} = e^{ax}.$$

Note that formula (3) is included in formula (5) as the special case, $n = 0$. See also Ex. 19, page 147.

EXAMPLE (a):   Solve the equation
$$(D^2 + 1)y = e^{2x}. \tag{6}$$

Here the roots of the auxiliary equation are $m = \pm i$. Further,
$$f(D) = (D^2 + 1)$$
and
$$f(2) \neq 0.$$

Hence, using (3),
$$y_p = \frac{1}{D^2 + 1} e^{2x} = \frac{e^{2x}}{2^2 + 1} = \frac{1}{5} e^{2x},$$

so the solution of (6) is

$$y = c_1 \cos x + c_2 \sin x + \tfrac{1}{5}e^{2x}.$$

EXAMPLE (b): Solve the equation

$$D^2(D-1)^3(D+1)y = e^x. \tag{7}$$

Here $m = 0, 0, 1, 1, 1, -1$. To get a particular solution of (7), we use formula (5) with $a = 1$, $n = 3$, $\phi(D) = D^2(D+1)$. Then

$$\phi(1) = 1^2 \cdot 2$$

and a particular solution of (7) is given by

$$y_p = \frac{1}{(D-1)^3 D^2(D+1)} e^x = \frac{x^3 e^x}{3! \, 1^2 \cdot 2} = \frac{1}{12} x^3 e^x.$$

Then the general solution of (7) is

$$y = c_1 + c_2 x + c_3 e^{-x} + (c_4 + c_5 x + c_6 x^2 + \tfrac{1}{12}x^3)e^x.$$

49. Evaluation of $(D^2 + a^2)^{-1} \sin ax$ and $(D^2 + a^2)^{-1} \cos ax$

No special device is needed for the evaluation of

$$(D^2 + a^2)^{-1} \sin bx$$

when $b \neq a$. In fact, it is easy to show that

$$\frac{1}{D^2 + a^2} \sin bx = \frac{\sin bx}{a^2 - b^2}; \quad b \neq a,$$

and a similar result holds for the expression $(D^2 + a^2)^{-1} \cos bx$, when $b \neq a$.

Consider next the evaluation of

$$\frac{1}{D^2 + a^2} \sin ax. \tag{1}$$

The formulas of the preceding section can be put to good use here, since

$$\sin ax = \frac{e^{aix} - e^{-aix}}{2i}.$$

Then

$$\frac{1}{D^2 + a^2} \sin ax = \frac{1}{2i} \frac{1}{(D - ai)(D + ai)} (e^{aix} - e^{-aix})$$

$$= \frac{1}{2i} \left(\frac{xe^{aix}}{1! \, 2ai} - \frac{xe^{-aix}}{1!(-2ai)} \right)$$

$$= -\frac{x}{2a} \frac{e^{aix} + e^{-aix}}{2},$$

so

$$\frac{1}{D^2 + a^2} \sin ax = -\frac{x}{2a} \cos ax. \tag{2}$$

The verification of (2) is left as an exercise.

Another useful result,

$$\frac{1}{D^2 + a^2} \cos ax = \frac{x}{2a} \sin ax, \tag{3}$$

can be obtained in the same way.

Oral Exercises

Give the general solution of each equation.

1. $(D^2 - 1)y = e^{2x}$.   ANS. $y = c_1 e^x + c_2 e^{-x} + \frac{1}{3}e^{2x}$.

2. $(D^2 - 1)y = e^x$.   ANS. $y = c_1 e^x + c_2 e^{-x} + \frac{1}{2}xe^x$.

3. $(D^2 + 1)y = \sin x$.   ANS. $y = c_1 \cos x + c_2 \sin x - \frac{1}{2}x \cos x$.

4. $(D^2 + 4)y = \cos 2x$.   ANS. $y = c_1 \cos 2x + c_2 \sin 2x + \frac{1}{4}x \sin 2x$.

5. $(D^2 + 9)y = e^{2x}$.   **6.** $(D^2 + 4)y = e^{3x}$.

7. $(4D^2 + 1)y = e^{-2x}$.   **8.** $D(D - 2)y = e^{-x}$.

9. $D(D - 2)^2 y = e^{2x}$.   **10.** $D(D + 3)^2 y = e^{-3x}$.

11. $(D^2 + 4)y = \cos 3x$.   **12.** $(D^2 + 9)y = \cos 3x$.

13. $(D^2 + 4)y = \sin 2x$.   **14.** $(D^2 + 36)y = \sin 6x$.

15. $(D^2 + 9)y = \sin 3x$.   **16.** $(D^2 + 36)y = \cos 6x$.

Exercises

1. Verify formula (2) of Section 49.

2. Obtain and verify formula (3) of Section 49.

In Exs. 3–18, find the general solution.

3. $(D^2 + 3D - 4)y = 12e^{2x}$.   ANS. $y = c_1 e^{-4x} + c_2 e^x + 2e^{2x}$.

4. $(D^2 + 3D - 4)y = 21e^{3x}$.

5. $(D^2 + 3D - 4)y = 15e^x$.   ANS. $y = c_1 e^{-4x} + (c_2 + 3x)e^x$.

6. $(D^2 + 3D - 4)y = 20e^{-4x}$.

7. $(D^2 - 3D + 2)y = e^x + e^{2x}$.   ANS. $y = (c_1 - x)e^x + (c_2 + x)e^{2x}$.

8. $(4D^2 - 1)y = e^{x/2} + 12e^x$.

9. $D^2(D - 2)^3 y = 48e^{2x}$.   ANS. $y = c_1 + c_2 x + (c_3 + c_4 x + c_5 x^2 + 2x^3)e^{2x}$.

10. $(D^4 - 18D^2 + 81)y = 36e^{3x}$.

11. $(D^2 + 16)y = 14 \cos 3x$.   ANS. $y = c_1 \cos 4x + c_2 \sin 4x + 2 \cos 3x$.

12. $(4D^2 + 1)y = 33 \sin 3x$.

13. $y'' + 16y = 24 \sin 4x$.   ANS. $y = (c_1 - 3x) \cos 4x + c_2 \sin 4x$.

14. $y'' + 16y = 48 \cos 4x$.

15. $y'' + y = 12 \cos 2x - \sin x$.   ANS. $y = (c_1 + \frac{1}{2}x) \cos x + c_2 \sin x - 4 \cos 2x$.

16. $y'' + y = \sin 3x + 4 \cos x.$

17. $(D^2 - 2D + 5)y = e^x \cos 2x.$ *Hint:* use the exponential shift followed by formula (3) of Section 49.

ANS. $y = e^x(c_1 \cos 2x + c_2 \sin 2x) + \tfrac{1}{4}xe^x \sin 2x.$

18. $(D^2 + 2D + 5)y = e^{-x} \sin 2x.$

ANS. $y = e^{-x}(c_1 \cos 2x + c_2 \sin 2x) - \tfrac{1}{4}xe^{-x} \cos 2x.$

19. Prove that if $f(x) = (x - a)^n \phi(x)$, then $f^{(n)}(a) = n!\,\phi(a)$. Then use equation (5) of Section 48 above to prove that

$$\frac{1}{f(D)}\,e^{ax} = \frac{x^n e^{ax}}{f^{(n)}(a)},$$

where n is the smallest non-negative integer for which $f^{(n)}(a) \neq 0$. See C. A. Hutchinson, "Another Note on Linear Operators," *Amer. Math. Monthly*, **46** (1939), 161.

In Exs. 20–23, use the formula of Ex. 19 above.

20. Ex. 5.   **21.** Ex. 6.
22. Ex. 9.   **23.** Ex. 10.

In Exs. 24–29, verify the formulas* stated.

24. $\dfrac{1}{f(D)} \sin ax = \dfrac{f(-D) \sin ax}{f(ai)f(-ai)}$; $f(ai)f(-ai) \neq 0.$

25. $\dfrac{1}{f(D)} \cos ax = \dfrac{f(-D) \cos ax}{f(ai)f(-ai)}$; $f(ai)f(-ai) \neq 0.$

26. $\dfrac{1}{f(D)} \sinh ax = \dfrac{f(-D) \sinh ax}{f(a)f(-a)}$; $f(a)f(-a) \neq 0.$

27. $\dfrac{1}{f(D)} \cosh ax = \dfrac{f(-D) \cosh ax}{f(a)f(-a)}$; $f(a)f(-a) \neq 0.$

28. $\dfrac{1}{(D^2 + a^2)^n} \sin ax = \dfrac{x^n}{(2a)^n n!} \sin (ax - \tfrac{1}{2}n\pi).$

29. $\dfrac{1}{(D^2 + a^2)^n} \cos ax = \dfrac{x^n}{(2a)^n n!} \cos (ax - \tfrac{1}{2}n\pi).$

In Exs. 30–33 use the formulas of Exs. 24–25 above.

30. Ex. 1, page 119.   **31.** Ex. 11, page 119.
32. Ex. 12, page 119.   **33.** Ex. 32, page 119.

* The formulas of Exs. 24–27 were obtained by C. A. Hutchinson, "An Operational Formula," *Amer. Math. Monthly*, **40** (1933), 482–483; those of Exs. 28–29 were given by C. A. Hutchinson, "Note on an Operational Formula," *Amer. Math. Monthly*, **44** (1937), 371–372.

CHAPTER 10

The Laplace Transform

50. The transform concept

The reader is already familiar with some operators that transform functions into functions. An outstanding example is the differential operator D which transforms each function of a large class (those possessing a derivative) into another function.

We have already found that the operator D is useful in the treatment of linear differential equations with constant coefficients. In this chapter we study another transformation (a mapping of functions onto functions) which has played an increasingly important role in both pure and applied mathematics in the past few decades. The operator L, to be introduced in Section 51, is particularly effective in the study of initial value problems involving linear differential equations with constant coefficients.

One class of transformations, which are called integral transforms, may be defined by

$$T\{F(t)\} = \int_{-\infty}^{\infty} K(s, t)F(t)\, dt = f(s). \tag{1}$$

148

Given a function $K(s, t)$, called the kernel of the transformation, equation (1) associates with each $F(t)$ of the class of functions for which the above integral exists a function $f(s)$ defined by (1). Generalizations and abstractions of (1), as well as studies of special cases, are to be found in profusion in mathematical literature.

Various particular choices of $K(s, t)$ in (1) have led to special transforms, each with its own properties to make it useful in specific circumstances. The transform defined by choosing

$$K(s, t) = 0, \qquad \text{for } t < 0,$$
$$= e^{-st}, \qquad \text{for } t \geq 0,$$

is the one to which this chapter is devoted.

51. Definition of the Laplace transform

Let $F(t)$ be any function such that the integrations encountered may be legitimately performed on $F(t)$. The *Laplace transform* of $F(t)$ is denoted by $L\{F(t)\}$ and is defined by

$$L\{F(t)\} = \int_0^\infty e^{-st} F(t) \, dt. \tag{1}$$

The integral in (1) is a function of the parameter s; call that function $f(s)$. We may write

$$L\{F(t)\} = \int_0^\infty e^{-st} F(t) \, dt = f(s). \tag{2}$$

It is customary to refer to $f(s)$, as well as to the symbol $L\{F(t)\}$, as the transform, or the Laplace transform, of $F(t)$.

We may also look upon (2) as a definition of a Laplace operator L, which transforms each function $F(t)$ of a certain set of functions into some function $f(s)$.

It is easy to show that if the integral in (2) does converge, it will do so for all s greater than* some fixed value s_0. That is, equation (2) will define $f(s)$ for $s > s_0$. In extreme cases the integral may converge for all finite s.

It is important that the operator L, like the differential operator D, is a linear operator. If $F_1(t)$ and $F_2(t)$ have Laplace transforms and if c_1 and c_2 are any constants,

$$L\{c_1 F_1(t) + c_2 F_2(t)\} = c_1 L\{F_1(t)\} + c_2 L\{F_2(t)\}. \tag{3}$$

---

* If s is not to be restricted to real values, the convergence takes place for all s with real part greater than some fixed value.

Using elementary properties of definite integrals, the student can easily show the validity of equation (3).

We shall hereafter employ the relation (3) without restating the fact that the operator L is a linear one.

52. Transforms of elementary functions

The transforms of certain exponential and trigonometric functions and of polynomials will now be obtained. These results enter our work frequently.

EXAMPLE (a): Find $L\{e^{kt}\}$.

We proceed as follows:

$$L\{e^{kt}\} = \int_0^\infty e^{-st} \cdot e^{kt}\, dt = \int_0^\infty e^{-(s-k)t}\, dt.$$

For $s \leq k$, the exponent on e is positive or zero and the integral diverges. For $s > k$, the integral converges.

Indeed, for $s > k$,

$$L\{e^{kt}\} = \int_0^\infty e^{-(s-k)t}\, dt$$

$$= \left[\frac{-e^{-(s-k)t}}{s-k}\right]_0^\infty$$

$$= 0 + \frac{1}{s-k}.$$

Thus we find that

$$L\{e^{kt}\} = \frac{1}{s-k}, \qquad s > k. \tag{1}$$

Note the special case $k = 0$:

$$L\{1\} = \frac{1}{s}, \qquad s > 0. \tag{2}$$

EXAMPLE (b): Obtain $L\{\sin kt\}$.

From elementary calculus we obtain

$$\int e^{ax} \sin mx\, dx = \frac{e^{ax}(a \sin mx - m \cos mx)}{a^2 + m^2} + C.$$

Since

$$L\{\sin kt\} = \int_0^\infty e^{-st} \sin kt\, dt,$$

it follows that

$$L\{\sin kt\} = \left[\frac{e^{-st}(-s \sin kt - k \cos kt)}{s^2 + k^2}\right]_0^\infty \tag{3}$$

For positive s, $e^{-st} \to 0$ as $t \to \infty$. Furthermore, $\sin kt$ and $\cos kt$ are bounded as $t \to \infty$. Therefore (3) yields

$$L\{\sin kt\} = 0 - \frac{1(0 - k)}{s^2 + k^2},$$

or

$$L\{\sin kt\} = \frac{k}{s^2 + k^2}, \qquad s > 0. \tag{4}$$

The result

$$L\{\cos kt\} = \frac{s}{s^2 + k^2}, \qquad s > 0, \tag{5}$$

can be obtained in a similar manner.

EXAMPLE (c):   Obtain $L\{t^n\}$ for n a positive integer.
By definition

$$L\{t^n\} = \int_0^\infty e^{-st} t^n \, dt.$$

Let us attack the integral using integration by parts with the choice exhibited in the table.

t^n	$e^{-st} \, dt$
$nt^{n-1} \, dt$	$-\dfrac{1}{s} e^{-st}$

We thus obtain

$$\int_0^\infty e^{-st} t^n \, dt = \left[\frac{-t^n e^{-st}}{s}\right]_0^\infty + \frac{n}{s} \int_0^\infty e^{-st} t^{n-1} \, dt. \tag{6}$$

For $s > 0$ and $n > 0$, the first term on the right in (6) is zero, and we are left with

$$\int_0^\infty e^{-st} t^n \, dt = \frac{n}{s} \int_0^\infty e^{-st} t^{n-1} \, dt, \qquad s > 0,$$

or

$$L\{t^n\} = \frac{n}{s} L\{t^{n-1}\}, \qquad s > 0. \tag{7}$$

From (7) we may conclude that, for $n > 1$,

$$L\{t^{n-1}\} = \frac{n-1}{s} L\{t^{n-2}\}$$

so

$$L\{t^n\} = \frac{n(n-1)}{s^2} L\{t^{n-2}\}. \tag{8}$$

Iteration of this process yields

$$L\{t^n\} = \frac{n(n-1)(n-2)\cdots 2\cdot 1}{s^n} L\{t^0\}.$$

From Example (a) above, we have

$$L\{t^0\} = L\{1\} = s^{-1}.$$

Hence, for n a positive integer,

$$L\{t^n\} = \frac{n!}{s^{n+1}}, \qquad s > 0. \tag{9}$$

The Laplace transform of $F(t)$ will exist even if the object function $F(t)$ is discontinuous, provided the integral in the definition of $L\{F(t)\}$ exists. Little will be done at this time with specific discontinuous $F(t)$, because more efficient methods for obtaining such transforms are to be developed later.

EXAMPLE (d):   Find the Laplace transform of $H(t)$ where

$$H(t) = t, \qquad 0 < t < 4,$$

$$= 5, \qquad t > 4.$$

Note that the fact that $H(t)$ is not defined at $t = 0$ and $t = 4$ has no bearing whatever on the existence, or the value, of $L\{H(t)\}$. We turn to the definition of $L\{H(t)\}$ to obtain

$$L\{H(t)\} = \int_0^\infty e^{-st} H(t)\, dt$$

$$= \int_0^4 e^{-st} t\, dt + \int_4^\infty e^{-st} 5\, dt.$$

Using integration by parts on the next-to-last integral above, we soon arrive, for $s > 0$, at

$$L\{H(t)\} = \left[-\frac{t}{s} e^{-st} - \frac{1}{s^2} e^{-st} \right]_0^4 + \left[-\frac{5}{s} e^{-st} \right]_4^\infty.$$

Thus

$$L\{H(t)\} = -\frac{4e^{-4s}}{s} - \frac{e^{-4s}}{s^2} + 0 + \frac{1}{s^2} - 0 + \frac{5e^{-4s}}{s}$$

$$= \frac{1}{s^2} + \frac{e^{-4s}}{s} - \frac{e^{-4s}}{s^2}.$$

Exercises

1. Show that $\qquad L\{\cos kt\} = \dfrac{s}{s^2 + k^2}, s > 0.$

2. Obtain $L\{t^2 - 3t + 5\}$.

ANS. $\dfrac{2}{s^3} - \dfrac{3}{s^2} + \dfrac{5}{s}, s > 0.$

3. Obtain $L\{\tfrac{1}{2}t^3 + t^2 - 1\}$.

ANS. $\dfrac{3}{s^4} + \dfrac{2}{s^3} - \dfrac{1}{s}, s > 0.$

4. Evaluate $L\{e^{-4t} + 3e^{-2t}\}$.

ANS. $\dfrac{2(2s + 7)}{(s + 2)(s + 4)}, s > -2.$

5. Evaluate $L\{2e^{3t} - e^{-3t}\}$.

ANS. $\dfrac{s + 9}{s^2 - 9}, s > 3.$

6. Show that $L\{\cosh kt\} = \dfrac{s}{s^2 - k^2}, s > |k|.$

7. Show that $L\{\sinh kt\} = \dfrac{k}{s^2 - k^2}, s > |k|.$

8. Use the trigonometric identity $\cos^2 A = \tfrac{1}{2}(1 + \cos 2A)$ and equation (5), Section 52, to evaluate $L\{\cos^2 kt\}$.

ANS. $\dfrac{s^2 + 2k^2}{s(s^2 + 4k^2)}, s > 0.$

9. Parallel the method suggested in Ex. 8 to obtain $L\{\sin^2 kt\}$.

ANS. $\dfrac{2k^2}{s(s^2 + 4k^2)}, s > 0.$

10. Obtain $L\{\sin^2 kt\}$ directly from the answer to Ex. 8.

11. Evaluate $L\{\sin kt \cos kt\}$ with the aid of a trigonometric identity.

ANS. $\dfrac{k}{s^2 + 4k^2}, s > 0.$

12. Evaluate $L\{e^{-at} - e^{-bt}\}$.

ANS. $\dfrac{b - a}{(s + a)(s + b)}, s > \text{Max}(-a, -b).$

13. Find $L\{\psi(t)\}$ where

$$\psi(t) = 4, \qquad 0 < t < 1,$$
$$= 3, \qquad\qquad t > 1.$$

ANS. $\dfrac{1}{s}(4 - e^{-s}), s > 0.$

14. Find $L\{\phi(t)\}$ where

$$\phi(t) = 1, \quad 0 < t < 2,$$
$$= t, \quad t > 2.$$

ANS. $\dfrac{1}{s} + \dfrac{e^{-2s}}{s} + \dfrac{e^{-2s}}{s^2}, \; s > 0.$

15. Find $L\{A(t)\}$ where

$$A(t) = 0, \quad 0 < t < 1,$$
$$= t, \quad 1 < t < 2,$$
$$= 0, \quad t > 2.$$

ANS. $\left(\dfrac{1}{s^2} + \dfrac{1}{s}\right)e^{-s} - \left(\dfrac{1}{s^2} + \dfrac{2}{s}\right)e^{-2s}, \; s > 0.$

16. Find $L\{B(t)\}$ where

$$B(t) = \sin 2t, \quad 0 < t < \pi,$$
$$= 0, \quad t > \pi.$$

ANS. $\dfrac{2(1 - e^{-\pi s})}{s^2 + 4}, \; s > 0.$

53. Transforming initial value problems

Because our major interest lies in the applicability of the Laplace transformation to the solving of differential equations, it seems natural to seek information about the transforms of functions that are derivatives of other functions.

Suppose, for example, we wish to solve the initial value problem

$$\frac{dy}{dt} = e^{2t}, \qquad y(0) = \tfrac{1}{2}. \tag{1}$$

Multiplying equation (1) by e^{-st} and integrating on the interval $0 < t < \infty$ gives

$$L\!\left\{\frac{dy}{dt}\right\} = L\{e^{2t}\}. \tag{2}$$

We need information about the Laplace transform of dy/dx.

By definition, we have

$$L\!\left\{\frac{dy}{dt}\right\} = \int_0^\infty e^{-st}\frac{dy}{dt}\,dt, \tag{3}$$

if this integral exists. An integration by parts performed on the integral in (3) yields

$$L\!\left\{\frac{dy}{dt}\right\} = \left[ye^{-st}\right]_0^\infty + s\int_0^\infty e^{-st}y(t)\,dt.$$

Now if ye^{-st} approaches zero as $t \to \infty$, we have

$$L\left\{\frac{dy}{dt}\right\} = sL\{y(t)\} - y(0). \tag{4}$$

In Section 55 we establish sufficient conditions on the function y for the existence of $L\{y(t)\}$. We shall also see that under the same kinds of conditions, equation (4) is valid.

For the moment, we shall accept (4) and apply it to equation (2). We obtain

$$sL\{y(t)\} - y(0) = L\{e^{2t}\}.$$

Referring now to equation (1) of Section 52 and remembering that $y(0) = \frac{1}{2}$, we find that

$$sL\{y(t)\} - \frac{1}{2} = \frac{1}{s-2}, \qquad s > 2,$$

or

$$L\{y(t)\} = \frac{1}{2} \cdot \frac{1}{s-2}, \qquad s > 2. \tag{5}$$

The foregoing example demonstrates the essence of the Laplace transformation as it applies to linear initial value problems. The problem (1) has been replaced by a new problem, posed in (5). Instead of looking for a function that satisfies (1), we seek a function whose Laplace transform is given in (5). Hopefully these two functions will be one and the same.

In the present example, we can again call upon equation (1) of Section 52 to see that one function that satisfies equation (5) is

$$y(t) = \frac{1}{2}e^{2t}. \tag{6}$$

It is a simple matter to prove that this function is indeed the solution of the initial value problem of (1).

An extension of these ideas to equations of order two can easily be made by replacing the function y in equation (4) with the function dy/dt. We thus have

$$L\left\{\frac{d^2y}{dt^2}\right\} = sL\left\{\frac{dy}{dt}\right\} - y'(0).$$

Another application of (4) yields

$$L\left\{\frac{d^2y}{dt^2}\right\} = s[sL\{y(t)\} - y(0)] - y'(0),$$

or

$$L\left\{\frac{d^2y}{dt^2}\right\} = s^2L\{y(t)\} - sy(0) - y'(0). \tag{7}$$

EXAMPLE (a): Solve the initial value problem

$$y'' + y = 0; \quad y(0) = 0, \quad y'(0) = 1. \tag{8}$$

We shall presume throughout that a solution of (8) exists and that the solution and its derivatives are sufficiently well behaved to insure the existence of the needed transforms. Of course, we will need to prove that the function we obtain on the basis of these assumptions actually is a solution of (8).

Applying the linear operator L to (8) gives

$$L\{y'' + y\} = 0,$$

or

$$L\{y''\} + L\{y\} = 0.$$

An application of equation (7) above gives us

$$s^2 L\{y(t)\} - 1 + L\{y(t)\} = 0,$$

an equation that can easily be solved for $L\{y(t)\}$. We have

$$L\{y(t)\} = \frac{1}{s^2 + 1}. \tag{9}$$

From equation (4) of Section 52 we find that $y = \sin t$ is a function that satisfies (9), and it is easy to verify that $\sin t$ is indeed the solution of the initial value problem (8).

EXAMPLE (b): Solve the initial value problem

$$y'' + y = 1; \quad y(0) = 2, \quad y'(0) = 0. \tag{10}$$

Applying the Laplace operator L to equation (10) gives

$$s^2 L\{y\} - 2s + L\{y\} = \frac{1}{s}, \qquad s > 0. \tag{11}$$

We solve (11) for $L\{y\}$ and find that

$$L\{y(t)\} = \frac{2s^2 + 1}{s(s^2 + 1)} = \frac{1}{s} + \frac{s}{s^2 + 1}. \tag{12}$$

Equations (2) and (5) of Section 52 lead us to

$$y(t) = 1 + \cos t. \tag{13}$$

Again it is a simple matter to show that $1 + \cos t$ is the desired solution of the initial value problem (10).

The observant student will note that the ability to find the unknown function y in equation (12) depended to a great extent on our breaking a rational function of s into a sum of two simpler rational functions. The process is commonly used in elementary calculus and is often referred to as a partial fractions expansion. In some of the following exercises the student will find the use of such expansions helpful.

Exercises

In Exs. 1–10, solve the problem by the Laplace transform method. Verify that your solution satisfies the differential equation and the initial conditions.

1. $y' = e^t$; $y(0) = 1$.   ANS. $y = e^t$.

2. $y' = 3e^t$; $y(0) = 7$.   ANS. $y = 4 + 3e^t$.

3. $y' - y = -e^{-t}$; $y(0) = 1$.   ANS. $y = \dfrac{e^t + e^{-t}}{2}$.

4. $y' + y = e^t$; $y(0) = 0$.   ANS. $y = \dfrac{e^t - e^{-t}}{2}$.

5. $y'' + k^2 y = 0$; $y(0) = 1$, $y'(0) = 0$.   ANS. $y = \cos kt$.

6. $y'' + k^2 y = 0$; $y(0) = 0$, $y'(0) = k$.   ANS. $y = \sin kt$.

7. $y'' - 3y' + 2y = e^{3t}$; $y(0) = y'(0) = 0$.   ANS. $y = \frac{1}{2}e^t - 4e^{2t} + \frac{9}{2}e^{3t}$.

8. $y'' + y = e^t$; $y(0) = y'(0) = 0$.   ANS. $-\frac{1}{2}(\sin t + \cos t - e^t)$.

9. $y'' + y' - 2y = -4$; $y(0) = 2$, $y'(0) = 3$.   ANS. $y = 2 + e^t - e^{-2t}$.

10. $y'' - 2y' = -4$; $y(0) = 0$, $y'(0) = 4$.   ANS. $y = e^{2t} + 2^t + 2t - 1$.

54. Sectionally continuous functions

It should be apparent that if we are to find problems for which the Laplace transform method is useful, we must learn a good deal more about the transforms of more complicated functions than those we considered in the previous sections. Indeed each of the initial value problems in Section 53 is easily solved by methods studied previously.

Our approach will be to prove a number of useful properties of the Laplace transform and then consider initial value problems in which we can make use of those properties.

In Section 51 we began this study by actually determining the transforms of some simple functions. However, it soon becomes tiresome to test each $F(t)$ we encounter to determine whether the integral

$$\int_0^\infty e^{-st} F(t)\, dt \tag{1}$$

exists for some range of values of s. We therefore seek a fairly large class of functions for which we can prove once and for all that the integral (1) exists.

One of our avowed interests in the Laplace transform is in its usefulness as a tool in solving problems in more or less elementary applications, particularly initial value problems in differential equations. Therefore we do not hesitate to restrict our study to functions $F(t)$ that are continuous or even differentiable, except possibly at a discrete set of points, in the semi-infinite range $t \geqq 0$.

For such functions, the existence of the integral (1) can be endangered only at points of discontinuity of $F(t)$ or by divergence due to behavior of the integrand as $t \to \infty$.

In elementary calculus we found that finite discontinuities, or finite jumps, of the integrand did not interfere with the existence of the integral. We therefore introduce a term to describe functions that are continuous except for such jumps.

DEFINITION: *The function $F(t)$ is said to be sectionally continuous over the closed interval $a \leqq t \leqq b$ if that interval can be divided into a finite number of subintervals $c \leqq t \leqq d$ such that in each subinterval:*

1. *$F(t)$ is continuous in the open interval $c < t < d$,*
2. *$F(t)$ approaches a limit as t approaches each endpoint from within the interval; that is, $\underset{t \to c^+}{\text{Lim }} F(t)$ and $\underset{t \to d^-}{\text{Lim }} F(t)$ exist.*

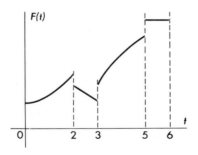

FIGURE 14

Figure 14 shows the graph of a function $F(t)$ that is sectionally continuous over the interval

$$0 \leqq t \leqq 6.$$

The student should realize that there is no implication that $F(t)$ must be sectionally continuous for $L\{F(t)\}$ to exist. Indeed, we shall meet several counterexamples to any such notion. The concept of sectionally continuous functions will, in Section 56, play a role in a set of conditions sufficient for the existence of the transform.

55. Functions of exponential order

If the integral of $e^{-st}F(t)$ between the limits 0 and t_0 exists for every finite positive t_0, the only remaining threat to the existence of the transform

$$\int_0^\infty e^{-st}F(t)\, dt \tag{1}$$

is the behavior of the integrand as $t \to \infty$.

We know that

$$\int_0^\infty e^{-ct}\, dt \tag{2}$$

converges for $c > 0$. This arouses our interest in functions $F(t)$ that are, for large $t(t \geqq t_0)$, essentially bounded by some exponential e^{bt} so that the integrand in (1) will behave like the integrand in (2) for s large enough.

DEFINITION: *The function $F(t)$ is said to be of exponential order as $t \to \infty$ if there exist constants M and b and a fixed t-value t_0 such that*

$$|F(t)| < Me^{bt}, \qquad \text{for } t \geqq t_0. \tag{3}$$

If b is to be emphasized, we say that $F(t)$ is of the order of e^{bt} as $t \to \infty$. We also write

$$F(t) = O(e^{bt}), \qquad t \to \infty, \tag{4}$$

to mean that $F(t)$ is of exponential order, the exponential being e^{bt}, as $t \to \infty$. That is, (4) is another way of expressing (3).

The integral in (1) may be split into parts as follows:

$$\int_0^\infty e^{-st}F(t)\, dt = \int_0^{t_0} e^{-st}F(t)\, dt + \int_{t_0}^\infty e^{-st}F(t)\, dt. \tag{5}$$

If $F(t)$ is of exponential order, $F(t) = O(e^{bt})$, the last integral in equation (5) exists because from the inequality (3) it follows that for $s > b$,

$$\int_{t_0}^\infty |e^{-st}F(t)|\, dt < M \int_{t_0}^\infty e^{-st} \cdot e^{bt}\, dt = \frac{M \exp[-t_0(s-b)]}{s-b}. \tag{6}$$

For $s > b$, the last member of (6) approaches zero as $t_0 \to \infty$. Therefore the last integral in (5) is absolutely convergent* for $s > b$. We have proved the following result.

---

* If complex s is to be used, the integral converges for $\text{Re}(s) > b$.

THEOREM 5: *If the integral of $e^{-st}F(t)$ between the limits 0 and t_0 exists for every finite positive t_0, and if $F(t)$ is of exponential order, $F(t) = O(e^{bt})$ as $t \to \infty$, the Laplace transform*

$$L\{F(t)\} = \int_0^\infty e^{-st}F(t)\,dt = f(s) \tag{7}$$

exists for $s > b$.

We know that a function that is sectionally continuous over an interval is integrable over that interval. This leads us to the following useful special case of Theorem 5.

THEOREM 6: *If $F(t)$ is sectionally continuous over every finite interval in the range $t \geqq 0$, and if $F(t)$ is of exponential order, $F(t) = O(e^{bt})$ as $t \to \infty$, the Laplace transform $L\{F(t)\}$ exists for $s > b$.*

Functions of exponential order play a dominant role throughout our work. It is therefore wise to develop proficiency in determining whether or not a specified function is of exponential order.

Surely if a constant b exists such that

$$\underset{t \to \infty}{\text{Lim}} \,[e^{-bt}|F(t)|] \tag{8}$$

exists, the function $F(t)$ is of exponential order, indeed of the order of e^{bt}. To see this, let the value of the limit (8) be $K \neq 0$. Then, for t large enough, $|e^{-bt}F(t)|$ can be made as close to K as is desired, so certainly

$$|e^{-bt}F(t)| < 2K.$$

Therefore, for t sufficiently large,

$$|F(t)| < Me^{bt}, \tag{9}$$

with $M = 2K$. If the limit in (8) is zero, we may write (9) with $M = 1$.

On the other hand, if for every fixed c,

$$\underset{t \to \infty}{\text{Lim}} \,[e^{-ct}|F(t)|] = \infty, \tag{10}$$

the function $F(t)$ is not of exponential order. For, assume b exists such that

$$|F(t)| < Me^{bt}, \qquad t \geqq t_0; \tag{11}$$

then the choice $c = 2b$ would yield, by (11),

$$|e^{-2bt}F(t)| < Me^{-bt},$$

so $e^{-2bt}F(t) \to 0$ as $t \to \infty$, which disagrees with (10).

EXAMPLE (a): Show that t^3 is of exponential order as $t \to \infty$.
We consider, with b as yet unspecified,

$$\text{Lim}_{t \to \infty} (e^{-bt}t^3) = \text{Lim}_{t \to \infty} \frac{t^3}{e^{bt}}. \tag{12}$$

If $b > 0$, the limit in (12) is of a type treated in calculus. In fact,

$$\text{Lim}_{t \to \infty} \frac{t^3}{e^{bt}} = \text{Lim}_{t \to \infty} \frac{3t^2}{be^{bt}} = \text{Lim}_{t \to \infty} \frac{6t}{b^2 e^{bt}} = \text{Lim}_{t \to \infty} \frac{6}{b^3 e^{bt}} = 0.$$

Therefore t^3 is of exponential order,

$$t^3 = O(e^{bt}), \qquad t \to \infty,$$

for any fixed positive b.

EXAMPLE (b): Show that $\exp(t^2)$ is not of exponential order as $t \to \infty$.
Consider

$$\text{Lim}_{t \to \infty} \frac{\exp(t^2)}{\exp(bt)}. \tag{13}$$

If $b \leq 0$, the limit in (13) is infinite. If $b > 0$,

$$\text{Lim}_{t \to \infty} \frac{\exp(t^2)}{\exp(bt)} = \text{Lim}_{t \to \infty} \exp[t(t-b)] = \infty.$$

Thus, no matter what fixed b we use, the limit in (13) is infinite and $\exp(t^2)$ cannot be of exponential order.

The exercises at the end of the next section give additional opportunities for practice in determining whether or not a function is of exponential order.

56. Functions of class A

For brevity we shall hereafter use the term "a function of class A" for any function that

(a) is sectionally continuous over every finite interval in the range $t \geq 0$ and

(b) is of exponential order as $t \to \infty$.

We may then reword Theorem 6 as follows.

THEOREM 7: *If $F(t)$ is a function of class A, $L\{F(t)\}$ exists.*

It is important to realize that Theorem 7 states only that for $L\{F(t)\}$ to exist, it is sufficient that $F(t)$ be of class A. The condition is not necessary. A classic example showing that functions other than those of class A do have Laplace transforms is

$$F(t) = t^{-\frac{1}{2}}.$$

This function is not sectionally continuous in every finite interval in the range $t \geq 0$, because $F(t) \to \infty$ as $t \to 0^+$. But $t^{-1/2}$ is integrable from 0 to any positive t_0. Also $t^{-1/2} \to 0$ as $t \to \infty$, so $t^{-1/2}$ is of exponential order, with $M = 1$ and $b = 0$ in the inequality (3), page 159. Hence, by Theorem 5, page 160, $L\{t^{-1/2}\}$ exists.

Indeed, for $s > 0$,

$$L\{t^{-1/2}\} = \int_0^\infty e^{-st} t^{-1/2} \, dt,$$

in which the change of variable $st = y^2$ leads to

$$L\{t^{-1/2}\} = 2s^{-1/2} \int_0^\infty \exp(-y^2) \, dy, \qquad s > 0.$$

In elementary calculus we found that $\int_0^\infty \exp(-y^2) \, dy = \frac{1}{2}\sqrt{\pi}.$

Therefore

$$L\{t^{-1/2}\} = 2s^{-1/2} \cdot \frac{1}{2}\sqrt{\pi} \tag{1}$$

$$= \left(\frac{\pi}{s}\right)^{1/2}, \qquad s > 0,$$

even though $t^{-1/2} \to \infty$ as $t \to 0^+$. Additional examples are easily constructed and we shall meet some of them later in the book.

If $F(t)$ is of class A, $F(t)$ is bounded over the range $0 \leq t \leq t_0$,

$$|F(t)| < M_1, \qquad 0 \leq t \leq t_0. \tag{2}$$

But $F(t)$ is also of exponential order,

$$|F(t)| < M_2 e^{bt}, \qquad t \geq t_0. \tag{3}$$

If we choose M as the larger of M_1 and M_2 and c as the larger of b and zero, we may write

$$|F(t)| < Me^{ct}, \qquad t \geq 0. \tag{4}$$

Therefore, for any function $F(t)$ of class A,

$$\left| \int_0^\infty e^{-st} F(t) \, dt \right| < M \int_0^\infty e^{-st} \cdot e^{ct} \, dt = \frac{M}{s - c}, \qquad s > c. \tag{5}$$

Since the right member of (5) approaches zero as $s \to \infty$, we have proved the following useful result.

THEOREM 8:   *If $F(t)$ is of class A and if $L\{F(t)\} = f(s)$,*

$$\lim_{s \to \infty} f(s) = 0.$$

From (5) we may also conclude the stronger result that the transform $f(s)$ of a function $F(t)$ of class A must be such that $sf(s)$ is bounded as $s \to \infty$.

Exercises

1. Prove that if $F_1(t)$ and $F_2(t)$ are each of exponential order as $t \to \infty$, then $F_1(t) \cdot F_2(t)$ and $F_1(t) + F_2(t)$ are also of exponential order as $t \to \infty$.
2. Prove that if $F_1(t)$ and $F_2(t)$ are of class A, page 161, then $F_1(t) + F_2(t)$ and $F_1(t) \cdot F_2(t)$ are also of class A.
3. Show that t^x is of exponential order as $t \to \infty$ for all real x.

In Exs. 4–17, show that the given function is a class A. In these excercises, n denotes a non-negative integer, k any real number.

4. $\sin kt$.
5. $\cos kt$.
6. $\cosh kt$.
7. $\sinh kt$.
8. t^n.
9. $t^n e^{kt}$.
10. $t^n \sin kt$.
11. $t^n \cos kt$.
12. $t^n \sinh kt$.
13. $t^n \cosh kt$.
14. $\dfrac{\sin kt}{t}$.
15. $\dfrac{1 - \exp(-t)}{t}$.
16. $\dfrac{1 - \cos kt}{t}$.
17. $\dfrac{\cos t - \cosh t}{t}$.

57. Transforms of derivatives

Any function of class A, page 161, has a Laplace transform, but the derivative of such a function may or may not be of class A. For the function

$$F_1(t) = \sin[\exp(t)]$$

with derivative

$$F_1'(t) = \exp(t) \cos[\exp(t)],$$

both F_1 and F_1' are of exponential order as $t \to \infty$. Here F_1 is bounded so it is of the order of $\exp(0 \cdot t)$; F_1' is of the order of $\exp(t)$. On the other hand, the function

$$F_2(t) = \sin[\exp(t^2)]$$

with derivative

$$F_2'(t) = 2t \exp(t^2) \cos[\exp(t^2)]$$

is such that F_2 is of the order of exp $(0 \cdot t)$, but F_2' is not of exponential order. From Example (b), page 161,

$$\operatorname*{Lim}_{t \to \infty} \frac{\exp (t^2)}{\exp (bt)} = \infty$$

for any real b. Since the factors $2t \cos [\exp (t^2)]$ do not even approach zero as $t \to \infty$, the product $F_2' \exp (-ct)$ cannot be bounded as $t \to \infty$ no matter how large a fixed c is chosen.

Therefore, in studying the transforms of derivatives, we shall stipulate that the derivatives themselves be of class A.

If $F(t)$ is continuous for $t \geq 0$ and of exponential order as $t \to \infty$, and if $F'(t)$ is of class A, the integral in

$$L\{F'(t)\} = \int_0^\infty e^{-st}F'(t) \, dt \tag{1}$$

may be simplified by integration by parts with the choice exhibited in the table.

$$
\begin{array}{c|c}
e^{-st} & F'(t) \, dt \\
\hline
-se^{-st} \, dt & F(t)
\end{array}
$$

We thus obtain, for s greater than some fixed s_0,

$$\int_0^\infty e^{-st}F'(t) \, dt = \left[e^{-st}F(t) \right]_0^\infty + s \int_0^\infty e^{-st}F(t) \, dt,$$

or

$$L\{F'(t)\} = -F(0) + sL\{F(t)\}. \tag{2}$$

THEOREM 9: *If $F(t)$ is continuous for $t \geq 0$ and of exponential order as $t \to \infty$, and if $F'(t)$ is of class A, page 161, it follows from $L\{F(t)\} = f(s)$ that*

$$L\{F'(t)\} = sf(s) - F(0). \tag{3}$$

In treating a differential equation of order n, we seek solutions for which the highest-ordered derivative present is reasonably well behaved, say sectionally continuous. The integral of a sectionally continuous function is continuous. Hence, we lose nothing by requiring continuity for all derivatives of order lower than n. The requirement that the various derivatives be of exponential order is forced upon us by our desire to use the Laplace transform as a tool. For our purposes, iteration of Theorem 9 to obtain transforms of higher derivatives makes sense.

From (3) we obtain, if F, F', F'' are suitably restricted,

$$L\{F''(t)\} = sL\{F'(t)\} - F'(0),$$

or

$$L\{F''(t)\} = s^2 f(s) - sF(0) - F'(0), \tag{4}$$

and the process can be repeated as many times as we wish.

THEOREM 10: *If* $F(t)$, $F'(t)$, ..., $F^{(n-1)}(t)$ *are continuous for* $t \geq 0$ *and of exponential order as* $t \to \infty$, *and if* $F^{(n)}(t)$ *is of class A, then from*

$$L\{F(t)\} = f(s)$$

it follows that

$$L\{F^{(n)}(t)\} = s^n f(s) - \sum_{k=0}^{n-1} s^{n-1-k} F^{(k)}(0). \tag{5}$$

Thus

$$L\{F^{(3)}(t)\} = s^3 f(s) - s^2 F(0) - sF'(0) - F''(0),$$
$$L\{F^{(4)}(t)\} = s^4 f(s) - s^3 F(0) - s^2 F'(0) - sF''(0) - F^{(3)}(0), \text{ etc.}$$

Theorem 10 is basic in employing the Laplace transform to solve linear differential equations with constant coefficients. The theorem permits us to transform such differential equations into algebraic ones.

The restriction that $F(t)$ be continuous can be relaxed, but discontinuities in $F(t)$ bring in additional terms in the transform of $F'(t)$. As an example, consider an $F(t)$ that is continuous for $t \geq 0$ except for a finite jump at $t = t_1$, as in Figure 15. If $F(t)$ is also of exponential order as $t \to \infty$, and if $F'(t)$ is of class A, we may write

$$L\{F'(t)\} = \int_0^\infty e^{-st} F'(t)\, dt$$
$$= \int_0^{t_1} e^{-st} F'(t)\, dt + \int_{t_1}^\infty e^{-st} F'(t)\, dt.$$

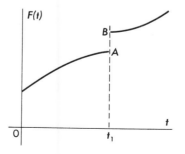

FIGURE 15

Then, integration by parts applied to the last two integrals yields

$$L\{F'(t)\} = \left[e^{-st}F(t)\right]_0^{t_1} + s\int_0^{t_1} e^{-st}F(t)\,dt + \left[e^{-st}F(t)\right]_{t_1}^{\infty} + s\int_{t_1}^{\infty} e^{-st}F(t)\,dt$$

$$= s\int_0^{\infty} e^{-st}F(t)\,dt + \exp(-st_1)F(t_1^-) - F(0) + 0$$

$$- \exp(-st_1)F(t_1^+)$$

$$= sL\{F(t)\} - F(0) - \exp(-st_1)[F(t_1^+) - F(t_1^-)].$$

In Figure 15 the directed distance AB is of length $[F(t_1^+) - F(t_1^-)]$.

THEOREM 11: *If $F(t)$ is of exponential order as $t \to \infty$ and $F(t)$ is continuous for $t \geq 0$ except for a finite jump at $t = t_1$, and if $F'(t)$ is of class A, then from*

$$L\{F(t)\} = f(s)$$

it follows that

$$L\{F'(t)\} = sf(s) - F(0) - \exp(-st_1)[F(t_1^+) - F(t_1^-)]. \tag{6}$$

If $F(t)$ has more than one finite discontinuity, additional terms, similar to the last term in (6), enter the formula for $L\{F'(t)\}$.

58. Derivatives of transforms

For functions of class A, the theorems of advanced calculus show that it is legitimate to differentiate the Laplace transform integral. That is, if $F(t)$ is of class A, from

$$f(s) = \int_0^{\infty} e^{-st}F(t)\,dt \tag{1}$$

it follows that

$$f'(s) = \int_0^{\infty} (-t)e^{-st}F(t)\,dt. \tag{2}$$

The integral on the right in (2) is the transform of the function $(-t)F(t)$.

THEOREM 12: *If $F(t)$ is a function of class A, it follows from*

$$L\{F(t)\} = f(s)$$

that

$$f'(s) = L\{-tF(t)\}. \tag{3}$$

When $F(t)$ is of class A, $(-t)^k F(t)$ is also of class A for any positive integer k.

THEOREM 13:   *If $F(t)$ is of class A, it follows from $L\{F(t)\} = f(s)$ that for any positive integer n,*

$$\frac{d^n}{ds^n} f(s) = L\{(-t)^n F(t)\}. \tag{4}$$

These theorems are useful in several ways. One immediate application is to add to our list of transforms with very little labor. We know that

$$\frac{k}{s^2 + k^2} = L\{\sin kt\}, \tag{5}$$

and therefore, by Theorem 12,

$$\frac{-2ks}{(s^2 + k^2)^2} = L\{-t \sin kt\}.$$

Thus we obtain

$$\frac{s}{(s^2 + k^2)^2} = L\left\{\frac{t}{2k} \sin kt\right\}. \tag{6}$$

From the known formula

$$\frac{s}{s^2 + k^2} = L\{\cos kt\}$$

we obtain, by differentiation with respect to s,

$$\frac{k^2 - s^2}{(s^2 + k^2)^2} = L\{-t \cos kt\}. \tag{7}$$

Let us add to each side of (7) the corresponding member of

$$\frac{1}{s^2 + k^2} = L\left\{\frac{1}{k} \sin kt\right\}$$

to get

$$\frac{s^2 + k^2 + k^2 - s^2}{(s^2 + k^2)^2} = L\left\{\frac{1}{k} \sin kt - t \cos kt\right\},$$

from which it follows that

$$\frac{1}{(s^2 + k^2)^2} = L\left\{\frac{1}{2k^3} (\sin kt - kt \cos kt)\right\}. \tag{8}$$

59. The gamma function

For obtaining the Laplace transform of nonintegral powers of t, we need a function not usually discussed in elementary mathematics.

The Gamma function $\Gamma(x)$ is defined by

$$\Gamma(x) = \int_0^\infty e^{-\beta}\beta^{x-1}\, d\beta, \qquad x > 0. \tag{1}$$

Substitution of $(x + 1)$ for x in (1) gives

$$\Gamma(x + 1) = \int_0^\infty e^{-\beta}\beta^x\, d\beta. \tag{2}$$

An integration by parts, integrating $e^{-\beta}\, d\beta$ and differentiating β^x, yields

$$\Gamma(x + 1) = \left[-e^{-\beta}\beta^x\right]_0^\infty + x \int_0^\infty e^{-\beta}\beta^{x-1}\, d\beta. \tag{3}$$

Since $x > 0$, $\beta^x \to 0$ as $\beta \to 0$. Since x is fixed, $e^{-\beta}\beta^x \to 0$ as $\beta \to \infty$. Thus

$$\Gamma(x + 1) = x \int_0^\infty e^{-\beta}\beta^{x-1}\, d\beta = x\Gamma(x). \tag{4}$$

THEOREM 14:   *For $x > 0$, $\Gamma(x + 1) = x\Gamma(x)$.*

Suppose n is a positive integer. Iteration of Theorem 14 gives us

$$\begin{aligned}
\Gamma(n + 1) &= n\Gamma(n) \\
&= n(n - 1)\Gamma(n - 1) \\
&\quad\cdots \\
&= n(n - 1)(n - 2) \cdots 2 \cdot 1 \cdot \Gamma(1) \\
&= n!\,\Gamma(1).
\end{aligned}$$

But, by definition,

$$\Gamma(1) = \int_0^\infty e^{-\beta}\beta^0\, d\beta = \left[-e^{-\beta}\right]_0^\infty = 1.$$

THEOREM 15:   *For positive integral n, $\Gamma(n + 1) = n!$.*

In the integral for $\Gamma(x + 1)$ in (2), let us put $\beta = st$ with $s > 0$ and t as the new variable of integration. This yields, since $t \to 0$ as $\beta \to 0$ and $t \to \infty$ as $\beta \to \infty$,

$$\Gamma(x + 1) = \int_0^\infty e^{-st}s^x t^x s\, dt = s^{x+1} \int_0^\infty e^{-st}t^x\, dt, \tag{5}$$

which is valid for $x + 1 > 0$. We thus obtain

$$\frac{\Gamma(x+1)}{s^{x+1}} = \int_0^\infty e^{-st} t^x \, dt, \qquad s > 0, x > -1,$$

which in our Laplace transform notation says that

$$L\{t^x\} = \frac{\Gamma(x+1)}{s^{x+1}}, \qquad s > 0, x > -1. \tag{6}$$

If in (6) we put $x = -\frac{1}{2}$, we get

$$L\{t^{-1/2}\} = \frac{\Gamma(\frac{1}{2})}{s^{1/2}}.$$

But we already know that $L\{t^{-1/2}\} = \left(\dfrac{\pi}{s}\right)^{1/2}$. Hence

$$\Gamma(\tfrac{1}{2}) = \sqrt{\pi}. \tag{7}$$

60. Periodic functions

Suppose the function $F(t)$ is periodic with period ω:

$$F(t + \omega) = F(t). \tag{1}$$

The function is completely determined by (1) once the nature of $F(t)$ throughout one period, $0 \leq t < \omega$, is given. If $F(t)$ has a transform,

$$L\{F(t)\} = \int_0^\infty e^{-st} F(t) \, dt, \tag{2}$$

the integral can be written as a sum of integrals,

$$L\{F(t)\} = \sum_{n=0}^\infty \int_{n\omega}^{(n+1)\omega} e^{-st} F(t) \, dt. \tag{3}$$

Let us put $t = n\omega + \beta$. Then (3) becomes

$$L\{F(t)\} = \sum_{n=0}^\infty \int_0^\omega \exp(-sn\omega - s\beta) F(\beta + n\omega) \, d\beta.$$

But $F(\beta + n\omega) = F(\beta)$, by iteration of (1). Hence

$$L\{F(t)\} = \sum_{n=0}^\infty \exp(-sn\omega) \int_0^\omega \exp(-s\beta) F(\beta) \, d\beta. \tag{4}$$

The integral on the right in (4) is independent of n and we can sum the series on the right;

$$\sum_{n=0}^\infty \exp(-sn\omega) = \sum_{n=0}^\infty [\exp(-s\omega)]^n = \frac{1}{1 - e^{-s\omega}}.$$

THEOREM 16: *If $F(t)$ has a Laplace transform and if $F(t + \omega) = F(t)$,*

$$L\{F(t)\} = \frac{\int_0^\omega e^{-s\beta}F(\beta)\,d\beta}{1 - e^{-s\omega}}. \tag{5}$$

Next suppose that a function $H(t)$ has a period $2c$ and that we demand that $H(t)$ be zero throughout the right half of each period. That is,

$$H(t + 2c) = H(t), \tag{6}$$

$$H(t) = g(t), \qquad 0 \leq t < c, \tag{7}$$

$$= 0, \qquad c \leq t < 2c.$$

Then we say that $H(t)$ is a half-wave rectification of $g(t)$. Using (5) we may conclude that for the $H(t)$ defined by (6) and (7),

$$L\{H(t)\} = \frac{\int_0^c \exp{(-s\beta)}g(\beta)\,d\beta}{1 - \exp{(-2cs)}}. \tag{8}$$

EXAMPLE (a): Find the transform of the function $\psi(t, c)$ shown in Figure 16 and defined by

$$\psi(t, c) = 1, \qquad 0 < t < c, \tag{9}$$

$$= 0, \qquad c < t < 2c;$$

$$\psi(t + 2c, c) = \psi(t, c). \tag{10}$$

FIGURE 16

We may use equation (8) and the fact that

$$\int_0^c \exp{(-s\beta)}\,d\beta = \frac{1 - \exp{(-sc)}}{s}$$

to conclude that

$$L\{\psi(t, c)\} = \frac{1}{s} \cdot \frac{1 - \exp{(-sc)}}{1 - \exp{(-2sc)}} = \frac{1}{s} \cdot \frac{1}{1 + \exp{(-sc)}}. \tag{11}$$

EXAMPLE (b): Find the transform of the square-wave function $Q(t, c)$ shown in Figure 17 and defined by

$$Q(t, c) = 1, \qquad 0 < t < c, \tag{12}$$
$$= -1, \qquad c < t < 2c;$$
$$Q(t + 2c, c) = Q(t, c). \tag{13}$$

FIGURE 17

This transform can be obtained by using Theorem 16, but also

$$Q(t, c) = 2\psi(t, c) - 1; \tag{14}$$

hence, from (11),

$$L\{Q(t, c)\} = \frac{1}{s} \left[\frac{2}{1 + \exp{(-sc)}} - 1 \right] = \frac{1}{s} \cdot \frac{1 - \exp{(-sc)}}{1 + \exp{(-sc)}}. \tag{15}$$

By multiplying numerator and denominator of the last fraction above by $\exp{(\frac{1}{2}sc)}$, we may put (15) in the form

$$L\{Q(t, c)\} = \frac{1}{s} \tanh \frac{cs}{2}. \tag{16}$$

Exercises

1. Show that $L\{t^{1/2}\} = \frac{1}{2s} \left(\frac{\pi}{s} \right)^{1/2}, \quad s > 0.$

2. Show that $L\{t^{5/2}\} = \dfrac{15}{8s^3}\left(\dfrac{\pi}{s}\right)^{1/2}$, $s > 0$.

3. Use equation (4), page 165, to derive $L\{\sin kt\}$.

4. Use equation (4), page 165, to derive $L\{\cos kt\}$.

5. Check the known transforms of $\sin kt$ and $\cos kt$ against one another by using Theorem 9, page 164.

6. If n is a positive integer, obtain $L\{t^n e^{kt}\}$ from the known $L\{e^{kt}\}$ by using Theorem 13, page 167.

ANS. $\dfrac{n!}{(s-k)^{n+1}}$, $s > k$.

7. Find $L\{t^2 \sin kt\}$.

ANS. $\dfrac{2k(3s^2 - k^2)}{(s^2 + k^2)^3}$, $s > 0$.

8. Find $L\{t^2 \cos kt\}$.

ANS. $\dfrac{2s(s^2 - 3k^2)}{(s^2 + k^2)^3}$, $s > 0$.

9. For the function

$$F(t) = t + 1, \qquad 0 \leq t \leq 2,$$
$$= 3, \qquad\qquad t > 2,$$

graph $F(t)$ and $F'(t)$. Find $L\{F(t)\}$. Find $L\{F'(t)\}$ in two ways.

ANS. $L\{F'(t)\} = s^{-1}(1 - e^{-2s})$, $s > 0$.

10. For the function

$$H(t) = t + 1, \qquad 0 \leq t \leq 2,$$
$$= 6, \qquad\qquad t > 2,$$

parallel Ex. 9 above.

11. Define a triangular-wave function $T(t, c)$ by

$$T(t, c) = t, \qquad 0 \leq t \leq c,$$
$$= 2c - t, \qquad c < t < 2c;$$
$$T(t + 2c, c) = T(t, c).$$

Sketch $T(t, c)$ and find its Laplace transform.   ANS. $\dfrac{1}{s^2} \tanh \dfrac{cs}{2}$.

12. Show that the derivative of the function $T(t, c)$ of Ex. 11 is, except at certain points, the function $Q(t, c)$ of Example (b), Section 60. Obtain $L\{T(t, c)\}$ from $L\{Q(t, c)\}$.

13. Find $L\{|\sin kt|\}$.

ANS. $\dfrac{k}{s^2 + k^2} \cdot \coth \dfrac{s}{2k}$.

14. Find $L\{|\cos kt|\}$.

15. Define the function $G(t)$ by

$$G(t) = e^t, \qquad 0 \leq t < c,$$
$$G(t + c) = G(t), \qquad t \geq 0.$$

Sketch the graph of $G(t)$ and find its Laplace transform.

ANS. $\dfrac{-1}{s-1} \cdot \dfrac{1 - \exp c(1 - s)}{1 - \exp(-cs)}$, $s > 1$.

16. Define the function $S(t)$ by

$$S(t) = 1 - t, \qquad 0 \leq t < 1,$$
$$S(t + 1) = S(t), \qquad t \geq 0.$$

Sketch the graph of $S(t)$ and find its Laplace transform.

17. Sketch a half-wave rectification of the function $\sin \omega t$, as described below, and find its transform.

$$F(t) = \sin \omega t, \qquad 0 \leq t \leq \frac{\pi}{\omega},$$

$$= 0, \qquad \frac{\pi}{\omega} < t < \frac{2\pi}{\omega};$$

$$F\left(t + \frac{2\pi}{\omega}\right) = F(t).$$

ANS. $\dfrac{\omega}{s^2 + \omega^2} \cdot \dfrac{1}{1 - \exp\left(-\dfrac{s\pi}{\omega}\right)}.$

18. Find $L\{F(t)\}$ where $F(t) = t$ for $0 < t < \omega$ and $F(t + \omega) = F(t)$.

ANS. $\dfrac{1}{s^2} - \dfrac{\omega}{s} \dfrac{\exp(-s\omega)}{1 - \exp(-s\omega)} = \dfrac{1}{s^2} + \dfrac{\omega}{2s}\left(1 - \coth\dfrac{\omega s}{2}\right).$

19. Prove that if $L\{F(t)\} = f(s)$ and if $\dfrac{F(t)}{t}$ is of class A,

$$L\left\{\frac{F(t)}{t}\right\} = \int_s^\infty f(\beta)\, d\beta.$$

Hint: Use Theorem 12, page 166.

CHAPTER 11

Inverse Transforms

61. Definition of an inverse transform

Suppose the function $F(t)$ is to be determined from a differential equation with initial conditions. The Laplace operator L is used to transform the original problem into a new problem from which the transform $f(s)$ is to be found. If the Laplace transformation is to be effective, the new problem must be simpler than the original problem. We first find $f(s)$ and then must obtain $F(t)$ from $f(s)$. It is therefore desirable to develop methods for finding the object function $F(t)$ when its transform $f(s)$ is known.

If

$$L\{F(t)\} = f(s), \tag{1}$$

we say that $F(t)$ is an *inverse Laplace transform*, or an inverse transform, of $f(s)$ and we write

$$F(t) = L^{-1}\{f(s)\}. \tag{2}$$

Since (1) means that

$$\int_0^\infty e^{-st} F(t)\, dt = f(s), \tag{3}$$

it follows at once that an inverse transform is not unique. For example, if $F_1(t)$ and $F_2(t)$ are identical except at a discrete set of points and differ at these points, the value of the integral in (3) is the same for the two functions; their transforms are identical.

Let us employ the term *null function* for any function $N(t)$ for which

$$\int_0^{t_0} N(t)\, dt = 0 \tag{4}$$

for every positive t_0. Lerch's theorem (not proved here) states that if $L\{F_1(t)\} = L\{F_2(t)\}$, then $F_1(t) - F_2(t) = N(t)$. That is, an inverse Laplace transform is unique except for the addition of an arbitrary null function.

The only continuous null function is zero. If an $f(s)$ has a continuous inverse $F(t)$, then $F(t)$ is the only continuous inverse of $f(s)$. If $f(s)$ has an inverse $F_1(t)$ continuous over a specified closed interval, every inverse that is also continuous over that interval is identical with $F_1(t)$ on that interval. Essentially, inverses of the same $f(s)$ differ at most at their points of discontinuity.

In applications, failure of uniqueness caused by addition of a null function is not vital, because the effect of that null function on physical properties of the solution is null. In the problems we treat, the inverse $F(t)$ is required either to be continuous for $t \geqq 0$ or to be sectionally continuous with the values of $F(t)$ at the points of discontinuity specified by each problem. The $F(t)$ is then unique.

A crude, but sometimes effective, method for finding inverse Laplace transforms is to construct a table of transforms (page 199) and then to use it in reverse to find inverse transforms.

We know from Ex. 1, page 153, that

$$L\{\cos kt\} = \frac{s}{s^2 + k^2}. \tag{5}$$

Therefore

$$L^{-1}\left\{\frac{s}{s^2 + k^2}\right\} = \cos kt. \tag{6}$$

We shall refine the above method, and actually make it quite powerful, by developing theorems by which a given $f(s)$ may be expanded into component parts whose inverses are known (found in the table). Other theorems will permit us to write $f(s)$ in alternate forms which yield the desired inverse. The most fundamental of such theorems is one that states that the inverse transformation is a linear operation.

THEOREM 17: *If c_1 and c_2 are constants,*

$$L^{-1}\{c_1 f_1(s) + c_2 f_2(s)\} = c_1 L^{-1}\{f_1(s)\} + c_2 L^{-1}\{f_2(s)\}.$$

Next let us prove a simple, but extremely useful, theorem on the manipulation of inverse transforms. From

$$f(s) = \int_0^\infty e^{-st} F(t)\, dt, \tag{7}$$

we obtain

$$f(s - a) = \int_0^\infty e^{-(s-a)t} F(t)\, dt$$

$$= \int_0^\infty e^{-st} [e^{at} F(t)]\, dt.$$

Thus, from $L^{-1}\{f(s)\} = F(t)$ it follows that

$$L^{-1}\{f(s - a)\} = e^{at} F(t),$$

or

$$L^{-1}\{f(s - a)\} = e^{at} L^{-1}\{f(s)\}. \tag{8}$$

Equation (8) may be rewritten with the exponential transferred to the other side of the equation. We thus obtain the following result.

THEOREM 18: $L^{-1}\{f(s)\} = e^{-at} L^{-1}\{f(s - a)\}.$

EXAMPLE (a):   Find $L^{-1}\left\{\dfrac{15}{s^2 + 4s + 13}\right\}.$

First complete the square in the denominator.

$$L^{-1}\left\{\frac{15}{s^2 + 4s + 13}\right\} = L^{-1}\left\{\frac{15}{(s + 2)^2 + 9}\right\}.$$

Since we know that $L^{-1}\left\{\dfrac{k}{s^2 + k^2}\right\} = \sin kt$, we proceed as follows:

$$L^{-1}\left\{\frac{15}{s^2 + 4s + 13}\right\} = 5L^{-1}\left\{\frac{3}{(s + 2)^2 + 9}\right\} = 5e^{-2t} L^{-1}\left\{\frac{3}{s^2 + 9}\right\} = 5e^{-2t} \sin 3t,$$

in which we have used Theorem 18.

EXAMPLE (b):   Evaluate $L^{-1}\left\{\dfrac{s+1}{s^2+6s+25}\right\}$.

We write

$$L^{-1}\left\{\frac{s+1}{s^2+6s+25}\right\} = L^{-1}\left\{\frac{s+1}{(s+3)^2+16}\right\}.$$

Then

$$L^{-1}\left\{\frac{s+1}{s^2+6s+25}\right\} = e^{-3t}L^{-1}\left\{\frac{s-2}{s^2+16}\right\}$$

$$= e^{-3t}\left[L^{-1}\left\{\frac{s}{s^2+16}\right\} - \tfrac{1}{2}L^{-1}\left\{\frac{4}{s^2+16}\right\}\right]$$

$$= e^{-3t}(\cos 4t - \tfrac{1}{2}\sin 4t).$$

Exercises

In Exs. 1–10, obtain $L^{-1}\{f(s)\}$ from the given $f(s)$.

1. $\dfrac{1}{s^2+2s+5}$.   ANS. $\tfrac{1}{2}e^{-t}\sin 2t$.

2. $\dfrac{1}{s^2-6s+10}$.   ANS. $e^{3t}\sin t$.

3. $\dfrac{s}{s^2+2s+5}$.   ANS. $e^{-t}(\cos 2t - \tfrac{1}{2}\sin 2t)$.

4. $\dfrac{s}{s^2-6s+13}$.   ANS. $e^{3t}(\cos 2t + \tfrac{3}{2}\sin 2t)$.

5. $\dfrac{1}{s^2+8s+16}$.   ANS. te^{-4t}.

6. $\dfrac{s}{s^2+8s+16}$.   ANS. $e^{-4t}(1-4t)$.

7. $\dfrac{s-5}{s^2+6s+13}$.   ANS. $e^{-3t}(\cos 2t - 4\sin 2t)$.

8. $\dfrac{2s-1}{s^2+4s+29}$.   ANS. $e^{-2t}(2\cos 5t - \sin 5t)$.

9. $\dfrac{3s+1}{(s+1)^4}$.   ANS. $e^{-t}\left(\dfrac{3}{2}t^2 - \dfrac{1}{3}t^3\right)$.

10. $\dfrac{s^2}{(s+2)^3}$.   ANS. $e^{-2t}(1-4t+2t^2)$.

11. Show that for n a non-negative integer

$$L^{-1}\left\{\frac{1}{(s+a)^{n+1}}\right\} = \frac{t^n e^{-at}}{n!}.$$

12. Show that for $m > -1$,

$$L^{-1}\left\{\frac{1}{(s+a)^{m+1}}\right\} = \frac{t^m e^{-at}}{\Gamma(m+1)}.$$

13. Show that

$$L^{-1}\left\{\frac{1}{(s+a)^2+b^2}\right\} = \frac{1}{b} e^{-at} \sin bt.$$

14. Show that

$$L^{-1}\left\{\frac{s}{(s+a)^2+b^2}\right\} = \frac{1}{b} e^{-at} (b \cos bt - a \sin bt).$$

15. For $a > 0$, show that from $L^{-1}\{f(s)\} = F(t)$ it follows that

$$L^{-1}\{f(as)\} = \frac{1}{a} F\left(\frac{t}{a}\right).$$

16. For $a > 0$, show that from $L^{-1}\{f(s)\} = F(t)$ it follows that

$$L^{-1}\{f(as+b)\} = \frac{1}{a} \exp\left(-\frac{bt}{a}\right) F\left(\frac{t}{a}\right).$$

62. A step function

Applications frequently deal with situations that change abruptly at specified times. We need a notation for a function that will suppress a given term up to a certain value of t and insert the term for all larger t. The function we are about to introduce leads us to a powerful tool for the constructing of inverse transforms.

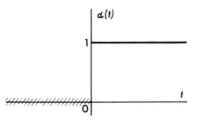

FIGURE 18

Let us define function $\alpha(t)$ by

$$\alpha(t) = 0, \qquad t < 0, \tag{1}$$
$$= 1, \qquad t \geq 0.$$

The graph of $\alpha(t)$ is shown in Figure 18.

The definition (1) says that $\alpha(t)$ is zero when the argument is negative and $\alpha(t)$ is unity when the argument is positive or is zero. It follows that

$$\alpha(t - c) = 0, \qquad t < c, \tag{2}$$
$$= 1, \qquad t \geq c.$$

The α function permits easy designation of the result of translating the graph of $F(t)$. If the graph of

$$y = F(t), \qquad t \geq 0, \tag{3}$$

is as shown in Figure 19, the graph of

$$y = \alpha(t - c)F(t - c), \qquad t \geq c, \tag{4}$$

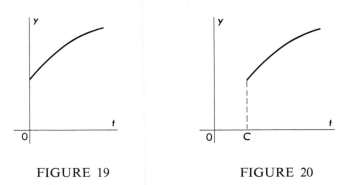

FIGURE 19   FIGURE 20

is that shown in Figure 20. Furthermore, if $F(x)$ is defined for $-c \leq x < 0$, $F(t - c)$ is defined for $0 \leq t < c$ and the y of (4) is zero for $0 \leq t < c$ because of the negative argument in $\alpha(t - c)$. Notice that the values of $F(x)$ for negative x have no bearing on this result because each value is multiplied by zero (from the α); only the existence of F for negative arguments is needed.

The Laplace transform of $\alpha(t - c)F(t - c)$ is related to that of $F(t)$. Consider

$$L\{\alpha(t - c)F(t - c)\} = \int_0^\infty e^{-st}\alpha(t - c)F(t - c)\,dt.$$

Since $\alpha(t - c) = 0$ for $0 \leq t < c$ and $\alpha(t - c) = 1$ for $t \geq c$, we get

$$L\{\alpha(t - c)F(t - c)\} = \int_c^\infty e^{-st}F(t - c)\, dt.$$

Now put $t - c = v$ in the integral to obtain

$$L\{\alpha(t - c)F(t - c)\} = \int_0^\infty e^{-s(c+v)}F(v)\, dv$$

$$= e^{-cs}\int_0^\infty e^{-sv}F(v)\, dv.$$

Since a definite integral is independent of the variable of integration,

$$\int_0^\infty e^{-sv}F(v)\, dv = \int_0^\infty e^{-st}F(t)\, dt = L\{F(t)\} = f(s).$$

Therefore we have shown that

$$L\{\alpha(t - c)F(t - c)\} = e^{-cs}L\{F(t)\} = e^{-cs}f(s). \tag{5}$$

THEOREM 19:   *If* $L^{-1}\{f(s)\} = F(t)$, *if* $c \geq 0$, *and if* $F(t)$ *be assigned values* (*no matter what ones*) *for* $-c \leq t < 0$,

$$L^{-1}\{e^{-cs}f(s)\} = F(t - c)\alpha(t - c). \tag{6}$$

EXAMPLE (a):   Find $L\{y(t)\}$ where (Figure 21)

$$y(t) = t^2,\qquad 0 < t < 2,$$
$$= 6,\qquad t > 2.$$

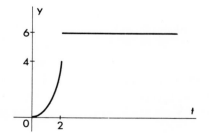

FIGURE 21

Here, direct use of the definition of a transform yields

$$L\{y(t)\} = \int_0^2 t^2 e^{-st} \, dt + \int_2^\infty 6e^{-st} \, dt.$$

Although the above integrations are not difficult, we prefer to use the α function.

Since $\alpha(t - 2) = 0$ for $t < 2$ and $\alpha(t - 2) = 1$ for $t \geq 2$, we build the $y(t)$ in the following way. The crude trial

$$y_1 = t^2$$

works for $0 < t < 2$, but we wish to knock out the t^2 when $t > 2$. Hence we write

$$y_2 = t^2 - t^2 \alpha(t - 2).$$

This gives t^2 for $t < 2$ and zero for $t > 2$. Then we add the term $6\alpha(t - 2)$ and finally arrive at

$$y(t) = t^2 - t^2 \alpha(t - 2) + 6\alpha(t - 2). \tag{7}$$

The y of (7) is the y of our example and, of course, it can be written at once after a little practice with the α function.

Unfortunately, the y of (7) is not yet in the best form for our purpose. The theorem we wish to use gives us

$$L\{F(t - c)\alpha(t - c)\} = e^{-cs} f(s).$$

Therefore we must have the coefficient of $\alpha(t - 2)$ expressed as a function of $(t - 2)$. Since

$$-t^2 + 6 = -(t^2 - 4t + 4) - 4(t - 2) + 2,$$

$$y(t) = t^2 - (t - 2)^2 \alpha(t - 2) - 4(t - 2)\alpha(t - 2) + 2\alpha(t - 2), \tag{8}$$

from which it follows at once that

$$L\{y(t)\} = \frac{2}{s^3} - \frac{2e^{-2s}}{s^3} - \frac{4e^{-2s}}{s^2} + \frac{2e^{-2s}}{s}.$$

EXAMPLE (b):   Find and sketch a function $g(t)$ for which

$$g(t) = L^{-1}\left\{\frac{3}{s} - \frac{4e^{-s}}{s^2} + \frac{4e^{-3s}}{s^2}\right\}.$$

We know that $L^{-1}\left\{\dfrac{4}{s^2}\right\} = 4t$. By Theorem 19 we then get

$$L^{-1}\left\{\frac{4e^{-s}}{s^2}\right\} = 4(t - 1)\alpha(t - 1)$$

and

$$L^{-1}\left\{\frac{4e^{-3s}}{s^2}\right\} = 4(t-3)\alpha(t-3).$$

We may therefore write

$$g(t) = 3 - 4(t-1)\alpha(t-1) + 4(t-3)\alpha(t-3). \tag{9}$$

To write $g(t)$ without the α function, consider first the interval

$$0 \leq t < 1$$

in which $\alpha(t-1) = 0$ and $\alpha(t-3) = 0$. We find

$$g(t) = 3, \qquad 0 \leq t < 1. \tag{10}$$

For $1 \leq t < 3$, $\alpha(t-1) = 1$, and $\alpha(t-3) = 0$. Hence

$$g(t) = 3 - 4(t-1) = 7 - 4t, \qquad 1 \leq t < 3. \tag{11}$$

For $t \geq 3$, $\alpha(t-1) = 1$ and $\alpha(t-3) = 1$, so

$$g(t) = 3 - 4(t-1) + 4(t-3) = -5, \qquad t \geq 3. \tag{12}$$

Equations (10), (11), and (12) are equivalent to equation (9). The graph of $g(t)$ is shown in Figure 22.

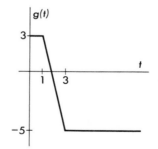

FIGURE 22

Exercises

In Exs. 1–7 sketch the graph of the given function for $t \geq 0$.

1. $\alpha(t - c)$.
2. $\alpha(t - 1) + 3\alpha(t - 3) - 6\alpha(t - 4)$.

3. $(t-2)\alpha(t-2)$.
4. $\sin(t-\pi)\cdot\alpha(t-\pi)$.
5. $(t-\pi)^2\alpha(t-\pi)$.
6. $t^2-(t-2)^2\alpha(t-2)$.
7. $t^2-t^2\alpha(t-2)$.

In Exs. 8–15, express $F(t)$ in terms of the α function and find $L\{F(t)\}$.

8. $F(t)=2,$ $0<t<1,$
       $=t,$ $t>1.$ ANS. $\dfrac{2}{s}+e^{-s}\left(\dfrac{1}{s^2}-\dfrac{1}{s}\right).$

9. $F(t)=6,$ $0<t<4,$
       $=2t+1,$ $t>4.$ ANS. $\dfrac{6}{s}+e^{-4s}\left(\dfrac{2}{s^2}+\dfrac{3}{s}\right).$

10. $F(t)=t^2,$ $0<t<1,$
      $=4,$ $t>1.$ ANS. $\dfrac{2}{s^3}+e^{-s}\left(\dfrac{3}{s}-\dfrac{2}{s^2}-\dfrac{2}{s^3}\right).$

11. $F(t)=t^2,$ $0<t<2,$
      $=4,$ $2\le t\le4,$
      $=0,$ $t>4.$ ANS. $\dfrac{2}{s^3}-e^{-2s}\left(\dfrac{4}{s^2}+\dfrac{2}{s^3}\right)-\dfrac{4}{s}e^{-4s}.$

12. $F(t)=t^2,$ $0<t<2,$
      $=t-1,$ $2<t<3,$
      $=7,$ $t>3.$ ANS. $\dfrac{2}{s^3}-e^{-2s}\left(\dfrac{3}{s}+\dfrac{3}{s^2}+\dfrac{2}{s^3}\right)+e^{-3s}\left(\dfrac{5}{s}-\dfrac{1}{s^2}\right).$

13. $F(t)=e^{-t},$ $0<t<2,$
      $=0,$ $t>2.$ ANS. $\dfrac{1-\exp(-2s-2)}{s+1}.$

14. $F(t)=\sin 3t,$ $0<t<\tfrac12\pi,$
      $=0,$ $t>\tfrac12\pi.$ ANS. $\dfrac{3+s\exp(-\tfrac12\pi s)}{s^2+9}.$

15. $F(t)=\sin 3t,$ $0<t<\pi,$
      $=0,$ $t>\pi.$ ANS. $\dfrac{3(1+e^{-\pi s})}{s^2+9}.$

16. Find and sketch an inverse Laplace transform of

$$\frac{5e^{-3s}}{s}-\frac{e^{-s}}{s}.$$

         ANS. $F(t)=5\alpha(t-3)-\alpha(t-1).$

17. Evaluate $L^{-1}\left\{\dfrac{e^{-4s}}{(s+2)^3}\right\}.$ ANS. $\tfrac12(t-4)^2\exp[-2(t-4)]\,\alpha(t-4).$

18. If $F(t)$ is to be continuous for $t\ge0$ and

$$F(t)=L^{-1}\left\{\frac{e^{-3s}}{(s+1)^3}\right\},$$

evaluate $F(2), F(5), F(7).$ ANS. $F(2)=0,\ F(5)=2e^{-2},\ F(7)=8e^{-4}.$

19. If $F(t)$ is to be continuous for $t\ge0$ and

$$F(t)=L^{-1}\left\{\frac{(1-e^{-2s})(1-3e^{-2s})}{s^2}\right\},$$

evaluate $F(1), F(3), F(5).$ ANS. $F(1)=1,\ F(3)=-1,\ F(5)=-4.$

20. Prove that $\psi(t,c)=\displaystyle\sum_{n=0}^{\infty}(-1)^n\alpha(t-nc)$ is the same function as was used in Example (a), Section 60. Note that for any specific t, the series is finite; no question of convergence is involved.

21. Obtain the transform of the half-wave rectification $F(t)$ of $\sin t$ by writing

$$F(t) = \sin t \; \psi(t, \pi)$$

in terms of the ψ of Ex. 20 above. Use the fact that

$$(-1)^n \sin t = \sin (t - n\pi).$$

Check your result with that in Ex. 17, page 173.

63. A convolution theorem

We now seek a formula for the inverse transform of a product of transforms. Given

$$L^{-1}\{f(s)\} = F(t), \qquad L^{-1}\{g(s)\} = G(t), \tag{1}$$

in which $F(t)$ and $G(t)$ are assumed to be functions of class A, we shall obtain a formula for

$$L^{-1}\{f(s)g(s)\}. \tag{2}$$

Since $f(s)$ is the transform of $F(t)$, we may write

$$f(s) = \int_0^\infty e^{-st}F(t) \, dt. \tag{3}$$

Since $g(s)$ is the transform of $G(t)$,

$$g(s) = \int_0^\infty e^{-s\beta}G(\beta) \, d\beta, \tag{4}$$

in which, to avoid confusion, we have used β (rather than t) as the variable of integration in the definite integral.

By equation (4), we have

$$f(s)g(s) = \int_0^\infty e^{-s\beta}f(s)G(\beta) \, d\beta. \tag{5}$$

On the right in (5) we encounter the product $e^{-s\beta}f(s)$. By Theorem 19, page 180, we know that from

$$L^{-1}\{f(s)\} = F(t) \tag{6}$$

it follows that

$$L^{-1}\{e^{-s\beta}f(s)\} = F(t - \beta)\alpha(t - \beta), \tag{7}$$

in which α is the step function discussed in Section 62. Equation (7) means that

$$e^{-s\beta}f(s) = \int_0^\infty e^{-st}F(t - \beta)\alpha(t - \beta) \, dt. \tag{8}$$

With the aid of (8) we may put equation (5) in the form

$$f(s)g(s) = \int_0^\infty \int_0^\infty e^{-st} G(\beta) F(t-\beta)\alpha(t-\beta)\,dt\,d\beta. \tag{9}$$

Since $\alpha(t-\beta) = 0$ for $0 < t < \beta$ and $\alpha(t-\beta) = 1$ for $t \geq \beta$, equation (9) may be rewritten as

$$f(s)g(s) = \int_0^\infty \int_\beta^\infty e^{-st} G(\beta) F(t-\beta)\,dt\,d\beta. \tag{10}$$

In (10), the integration in the $t\beta$-plane covers the shaded region shown in Figure 23. The elements are summed from $t = \beta$ to $t = \infty$ and then from $\beta = 0$ to $\beta = \infty$.

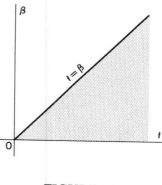

FIGURE 23

By the methods of advanced calculus it can be shown that, because $F(t)$ and $G(t)$ are functions of class A, it is legitimate to interchange the order of integration on the right in equation (10). From Figure 23 we see that in the new order of integration, the elements are to be summed from $\beta = 0$ to $\beta = t$ and then from $t = 0$ to $t = \infty$. We thus obtain

$$f(s)g(s) = \int_0^\infty \int_0^t e^{-st} G(\beta) F(t-\beta)\,d\beta\,dt,$$

or

$$f(s)g(s) = \int_0^\infty e^{-st} \left[\int_0^t G(\beta) F(t-\beta)\,d\beta \right] dt. \tag{11}$$

Since the right member of (11) is precisely the Laplace transform of

$$\int_0^t G(\beta)F(t-\beta)\,d\beta,$$

we have arrived at the desired result, which is called the convolution theorem for the Laplace transform.

THEOREM 20: *If $L^{-1}\{f(s)\} = F(t)$, if $L^{-1}\{g(s)\} = G(t)$, and if $F(t)$ and $G(t)$ are functions of class A, page 161, then*

$$L^{-1}\{f(s)g(s)\} = \int_0^t G(\beta)F(t-\beta)\,d\beta.$$

It is easy to show that the right member of equation (12) is also a function of class A.

Of course F and G are interchangeable in (12), since f and g enter (12) symmetrically. We may replace (12) by

$$L^{-1}\{f(s)g(s)\} = \int_0^t F(\beta)G(t-\beta)\,d\beta, \tag{13}$$

a result which also follows from (12) by a change of variable of integration.

EXAMPLE   Evaluate $L^{-1}\left\{\dfrac{f(s)}{s}\right\}$.

Let $L^{-1}\{f(s)\} = F(t)$. Since

$$L^{-1}\left\{\frac{1}{s}\right\} = 1,$$

we use Theorem 20 to conclude that

$$L^{-1}\left\{\frac{f(s)}{s}\right\} = \int_0^t F(\beta)\,d\beta.$$

Exercises

In Exs. 1–3 find the Laplace transform of the given convolution integral.

1. $\displaystyle\int_0^t (t-\beta)\sin 2\beta\,d\beta$.   ANS. $\dfrac{2}{s(s^2+4)}$.

2. $\displaystyle\int_0^t e^{-(t-\beta)}\cos \beta\,d\beta$.   ANS. $\dfrac{s}{(s+1)(s^2+1)}$.

3. $\displaystyle\int_0^t (t-\beta)^2 e^{\beta}\,d\beta$.   ANS. $\dfrac{2}{s^3(s-1)}$.

In Exs. 4–6, find an inverse transform of the given $f(s)$ using the convolution theorem.

4. $\dfrac{k}{s(s^2+k^2)}$.   ANS. $\dfrac{1}{k}(1-\cos kt)$.

5. $\dfrac{1}{s^2(s-1)}$.

ANS. $e^t - t - 1$.

6. $\dfrac{1}{(s^2+1)^2}$.

ANS. $\frac{1}{2}(\sin t - t \cos t)$.

64. Simple initial value problems

As we have seen in Section 53, the Laplace operator will transform a differential equation with constant coefficients into an algebraic equation in the transformed function. Several additional examples will now be treated in detail so that we can get some feeling for the advantages and disadvantages of the transform method. One fact is apparent from the start: this method is at its best when the boundary conditions are actually initial conditions, those giving the value of the function and its derivatives at time zero.

EXAMPLE (a):   Solve the problem

$$y''(t) + \beta^2 y(t) = A \sin \omega t; \qquad y(0) = 1, \ y'(0) = 0. \tag{1}$$

Here A, β, ω are constants. Since $\beta = 0$ would make the problem one of elementary calculus and since a change in sign of β or ω would not alter the character of the problem, we may assume that β and ω are positive.

Let $L\{y(t)\} = u(s)$.

Then $L\{y'(t)\} = su(s) - 1$,

$$L\{y''(t)\} = s^2 u(s) - s \cdot 1 - 0,$$

and application of the operator L transforms the problem (1) into

$$s^2 u(s) - s + \beta^2 u(s) = \frac{A\omega}{s^2 + \omega^2},$$

from which

$$u(s) = \frac{s}{s^2 + \beta^2} + \frac{A\omega}{(s^2 + \beta^2)(s^2 + \omega^2)}. \tag{2}$$

We need the inverse transform of the right member of (2). The form of that inverse depends upon whether β and ω are equal or unequal.
If $\omega \neq \beta$,

$$u(s) = \frac{s}{s^2 + \beta^2} + \frac{A\omega}{\beta^2 - \omega^2}\left(\frac{1}{s^2 + \omega^2} - \frac{1}{s^2 + \beta^2}\right)$$

$$= \frac{s}{s^2 + \beta^2} + \frac{A}{\beta(\beta^2 - \omega^2)}\left(\frac{\omega\beta}{s^2 + \omega^2} - \frac{\omega\beta}{s^2 + \beta^2}\right).$$

Now $y(t) = L^{-1}\{u(s)\}$ so, for $\omega \neq \beta$,

$$y(t) = \cos \beta t + \frac{A}{\beta(\beta^2 - \omega^2)} (\beta \sin \omega t - \omega \sin \beta t). \tag{3}$$

If $\omega = \beta$, the transform (2) becomes

$$u(s) = \frac{s}{s^2 + \beta^2} + \frac{A\beta}{(s^2 + \beta^2)^2}. \tag{4}$$

We know from equation (8) of Section 58 that

$$L^{-1}\left\{\frac{1}{(s^2 + \beta^2)^2}\right\} = \frac{1}{2\beta^3} (\sin \beta t - \beta t \cos \beta t).$$

Hence, for $\omega = \beta$,

$$y(t) = \cos \beta t + \frac{A}{2\beta^2} (\sin \beta t - \beta t \cos \beta t). \tag{5}$$

It is a simple matter to show that this function is indeed the solution of the given initial value problem.

Note that the initial conditions were satisfied automatically by this method when Theorem 10 was applied. We get, not the general solution with arbitrary constants still to be determined, but that particular solution which satisfies the desired initial conditions. The transform method also gives us some insight into the reason that the solution takes different forms according to whether ω and β are equal or unequal.

EXAMPLE (b):   Solve the problem

$$x''(t) + 2x'(t) + x(t) = 3te^{-t}; \qquad x(0) = 4, \quad x'(0) = 2. \tag{6}$$

Let $L\{x(t)\} = y(s)$. Then the operator L converts (6) into

$$s^2 y(s) - 4s - 2 + 2[sy(s) - 4] + y(s) = \frac{3}{(s + 1)^2},$$

or

$$y(s) = \frac{4s + 10}{(s + 1)^2} + \frac{3}{(s + 1)^4}. \tag{7}$$

We may write

$$y(s) = \frac{4(s + 1) + 6}{(s + 1)^2} + \frac{3}{(s + 1)^4}$$

or
$$y(s) = \frac{4}{s+1} + \frac{6}{(s+1)^2} + \frac{3}{(s+1)^4}.$$

Employing the inverse transform, we obtain

$$x(t) = (4 + 6t + \tfrac{1}{2}t^3)e^{-t}. \tag{8}$$

Again the knowledge of initial conditions contributed to the efficiency of our method. In obtaining and in using equation (7), those terms that came from the initial values $x(0)$ and $x'(0)$ were not combined with the term that came from the transform of the right member of the differential equation. To combine such terms rarely simplifies and frequently complicates the task of obtaining the inverse transform.

From the solution

$$x(t) = (4 + 6t + \tfrac{1}{2}t^3)e^{-t} \tag{8}$$

the student should obtain the derivatives

$$x'(t) = (2 - 6t + \tfrac{3}{2}t^2 - \tfrac{1}{2}t^3)e^{-t},$$
$$x''(t) = (-8 + 9t - 3t^2 + \tfrac{1}{2}t^3)e^{-t},$$

and thus verify that the x of (8) satisfies both the differential equation and the initial conditions of the problem (6). Such verification not only checks our work but also removes any need to justify temporary assumptions about the right to use the Laplace transform theorems on the function $x(t)$ during the time that the function is still unknown.

EXAMPLE (c): Solve the problem

$$x''(t) + 4x(t) = \psi(t); \qquad x(0) = 1, \qquad x'(0) = 0, \tag{9}$$

in which $\psi(t)$ is defined by

$$\psi(t) = 4t, \qquad 0 \leqq t \leqq 1, \tag{10}$$
$$= 4, \qquad t > 1.$$

We seek, of course, a solution valid in the range $t \geqq 0$ in which the right member $\psi(t)$ is defined.

In this problem another phase of the power of the Laplace transform method begins to emerge. The fact that the function $\psi(t)$ in the differential equation has discontinuous derivatives makes the use of the classical method of undetermined coefficients somewhat awkward, but such discontinuities do not interfere at all with the simplicity of the Laplace transform method.

In attacking this problem, let us put $L\{x(t)\} = h(s)$. We need to obtain $L\{\psi(t)\}$. In terms of the α function we may write, from (10),

$$\psi(t) = 4t - 4(t-1)\alpha(t-1), \qquad t \geqq 0. \tag{11}$$

From (11) it follows that

$$L\{\psi(t)\} = \frac{4}{s^2} - \frac{4e^{-s}}{s^2}.$$

Therefore the application of the operator L transforms problem (9) into

$$s^2 h(s) - s - 0 + 4h(s) = \frac{4}{s^2} - \frac{4e^{-s}}{s^2},$$

from which

$$h(s) = \frac{s}{s^2+4} + \frac{4}{s^2(s^2+4)} - \frac{4e^{-s}}{s^2(s^2+4)}.$$

Now

$$\frac{4}{s^2(s^2+4)} = \frac{1}{s^2} - \frac{1}{s^2+4},$$

so (12) becomes

$$h(s) = \frac{s}{s^2+4} + \frac{1}{s^2} - \frac{1}{s^2+4} - \left(\frac{1}{s^2} - \frac{1}{s^2+4}\right)e^{-s}. \tag{13}$$

Since $x(t)) = L^{-1}\{h(s)\}$, we obtain the desired solution

$$x(t) = \cos 2t + t - \tfrac{1}{2}\sin 2t - [(t-1) - \tfrac{1}{2}\sin 2(t-1)]\,\alpha(t-1). \tag{14}$$

It is easy to verify our solution. From (14) it follows that

$$x'(t) = -2\sin 2t + 1 - \cos 2t - [1 - \cos 2(t-1)]\,\alpha(t-1), \tag{15}$$

$$x''(t) = -4\cos 2t + 2\sin 2t - 2\sin 2(t-1)\,\alpha(t-1). \tag{16}$$

Therefore $x(0) = 1$ and $x'(0) = 0$, as desired. Also, from (14) and (16), we get

$$x''(t) + 4x(t) = 4t - 4(t-1)\,\alpha(t-1) = \psi(t), \qquad t \geq 0.$$

EXAMPLE (d): Solve the problem

$$x''(t) + k^2 x(t) = F(t); \qquad x(0) = A, \qquad x'(0) = B. \tag{17}$$

Here k, A, B are constants and $F(t)$ is a known but unstipulated function. For the time being, think of $F(t)$ as a function whose Laplace transform exists. Let

$$L\{x(t)\} = u(s), \qquad L\{F(t)\} = f(s).$$

Then the Laplace operator transforms problem (17) into

$$s^2 u(s) - As - B + k^2 u(s) = f(s),$$

$$u(s) = \frac{As + B}{s^2 + k^2} + \frac{f(s)}{s^2 + k^2}. \tag{18}$$

To get the inverse transform of the last term in (18), we use the convolution theorem. Thus we arrive at

$$x(t) = A \cos kt + \frac{B}{k} \sin kt + \frac{1}{k} \int_0^t F(t - \beta) \sin k\beta \, d\beta,$$

or

$$x(t) = A \cos kt + \frac{B}{k} \sin kt + \frac{1}{k} \int_0^t F(\beta) \sin k(t - \beta) \, d\beta. \tag{19}$$

Verification of the solution (19) is simple. Once that check has been performed, the need for the assumption that $F(t)$ has a Laplace transform is removed. It does not matter what method we use to get a solution (with certain exceptions naturally imposed during college examinations) if the validity of the result can be verified from the result itself.

EXAMPLE (e):   Solve the problem

$$w''(x) + 2w'(x) + w(x) = x; \qquad w(0) = -3, \qquad w(1) = -1. \tag{20}$$

In this example the boundary conditions are not both of the initial condition type. Using x, rather than t, as independent variable, let

$$L\{w(x)\} = g(s). \tag{21}$$

We know $w(0) = -3$, but we also need $w'(0)$ in order to write the transform of $w''(x)$. Hence we put

$$w'(0) = B \tag{22}$$

and hope to determine B later by using the condition that $w(1) = -1$.

The transformed problem is

$$s^2 g(s) - s(-3) - B + 2[sg(s) - (-3)] + g(s) = \frac{1}{s^2}$$

from which

$$g(s) = \frac{-3(s + 1) + B - 3}{(s + 1)^2} + \frac{1}{s^2(s + 1)^2}. \tag{23}$$

But, by the usual partial fractions expansion,

$$\frac{1}{s^2(s + 1)^2} = -\frac{2}{s} + \frac{1}{s^2} + \frac{2}{s + 1} + \frac{1}{(s + 1)^2},$$

so

$$g(s) = \frac{1}{s^2} - \frac{2}{s} - \frac{1}{s + 1} + \frac{B - 2}{(s + 1)^2}, \tag{24}$$

from which we obtain

$$w(x) = x - 2 - e^{-x} + (B - 2)xe^{-x}. \tag{25}$$

We have yet to impose the condition that $w(1) = -1$. From (25) with $x = 1$, we get

$$-1 = 1 - 2 - e^{-1} + (B - 2)e^{-1},$$

so $B = 3$.

Thus our final result is

$$w(x) = x - 2 - e^{-x} + xe^{-x}. \tag{26}$$

The problem in Example (e) may be solved efficiently by the methods of Chapter 7. See also Exs. 23–44 below.

Exercises

In Exs. 1–14, solve the problem by the Laplace transform method. Verify that your solution satisfies the differential equation and the initial conditions.

1. $x''(t) + 4x'(t) + 4x(t) = 4e^{-2t}$; $x(0) = -1$, $x'(0) = 4$.
     ANS. $x(t) = e^{-2t}(2t^2 + 2t - 1)$.

2. $x''(t) + x(t) = 6 \cos 2t$; $x(0) = 3$, $x'(0) = 1$.
     ANS. $x(t) = 5 \cos t + \sin t - 2 \cos 2t$.

3. $y''(t) - y(t) = 5 \sin 2t$; $y(0) = 0$, $y'(0) = 1$.   ANS. $y(t) = 3 \sinh t - \sin 2t$.

4. $y''(t) + 6y'(t) + 9y(t) = 6t^2 e^{-3t}$; $y(0) = 0$, $y'(0) = 0$.   ANS. $y(t) = \frac{1}{2}t^4 e^{-3t}$.

5. $x''(t) + 4x(t) = 2t - 8$; $x(0) = 1$, $x'(0) = 0$.
     ANS. $x(t) = 3 \cos 2t - \frac{1}{4} \sin 2t + \frac{1}{2}t - 2$.

6. $x''(t) + 2x'(t) = 8t$; $x(0) = 0$, $x'(0) = 0$.   ANS. $x(t) = 2t^2 - 2t + 1 - e^{-2t}$.

7. $u''(t) + 4u(t) = 15e^t$; $u(0) = 1$, $u'(0) = 3$.   ANS. $u(t) = 3e^t - 2 \cos 2t$.

8. $u''(t) + 4u'(t) + 3u(t) = 12$; $u(0) = 7$, $u'(0) = 1$.
     ANS. $u(t) = 4 + 5e^{-t} - 2e^{-3t}$.

9. $y''(x) + 9y(x) = 40e^x$; $y(0) = 5$, $y'(0) = -2$.
     ANS. $y(x) = 4e^x + \cos 3x - 2 \sin 3x$.

10. $y''(x) + y(x) = 4e^x$; $y(0) = 0$, $y'(0) = 0$.   ANS. $y(x) = 2(e^x - \cos x - \sin x)$.

11. $x''(t) + 3x'(t) + 2x(t) = 4t^2$; $x(0) = 0$, $x'(0) = 0$.
     ANS. $x(t) = 2t^2 - 6t + 7 - 8e^{-t} + e^{-2t}$.

12. $x''(t) - 4x'(t) + 4x(t) = 4 \cos 2t$; $x(0) = 2$, $x'(0) = 5$.
     ANS. $x(t) = 2e^{2t}(1 + t) - \frac{1}{2} \sin 2t$.

13. $x''(t) + x(t) = F(t)$; $x(0) = 0$, $x'(0) = 0$, in which

$$F(t) = 4, \quad 0 \le t \le 2,$$
$$= t + 2, \quad t > 2.$$

     ANS. $x(t) = 4 - 4 \cos t + [(t - 2) - \sin (t - 2)]\alpha(t - 2)$.

14. $x''(t) + x(t) = H(t)$; $x(0) = 1$, $x'(0) = 0$, in which

$$H(t) = 3, \quad 0 \le t \le 4,$$
$$= 2t - 5, \quad t > 4.$$

     ANS. $x(t) = 3 - 2 \cos t + 2[t - 4 - \sin (t - 4)]\alpha(t - 4)$.

15. $x''(t) + x(t) = G(t)$; $x(0) = 0$, $x'(0) = 1$, in which

$$G(t) = 1, \quad 0 \le t < \pi/2,$$
$$= 0, \quad t \ge \pi/2.$$

ANS. $x(t) = 1 - \cos t + \sin t - \alpha(t - \pi/2)(1 - \sin t).$

16. $x''(t) + 4x(t) = M(t);\ x(0) = x'(0) = 0,$ in which

$$M(t) = \sin t - \alpha(t - 2\pi) \sin (t - 2\pi).$$

ANS. $x(t) = \frac{1}{6}[1 - \alpha(t - 2\pi)](2 \sin t - \sin 2t).$

17. Compute $y(\frac{1}{2}\pi)$ and $y(2 + \frac{1}{2}\pi)$ for the function $y(x)$ that satisfies the initial value problem

$$y''(x) + y(x) = (x - 2)\alpha(x - 2);\ y(0) = 0,\ y'(0) = 0.$$

ANS. $y(\frac{1}{2}\pi) = 0,\ y(2 + \frac{1}{2}\pi) = \frac{1}{2}\pi - 1.$

18. Compute $x(1)$ and $x(4)$ for the function $x(t)$ that satisfies the initial value problem

$$x''(t) + 2x'(t) + x(t) = 2 + (t - 3)\alpha(t - 3);\ x(0) = 2,\ x'(0) = 1.$$

ANS. $x(1) = 2 + e^{-1},\ x(4) = 1 + 3e^{-1} + 4e^{-4}.$

19. Solve the problem

$$x''(t) + 2x'(t) + x(t) = F(t);\ x(0) = 0,\ x'(0) = 0.$$

ANS. $x(t) = \displaystyle\int_0^t \beta e^{-\beta} F(t - \beta)\, d\beta.$

20. Solve the problem

$$y''(t) - k^2 y(t) = H(t);\ y(0) = 0,\ y'(0) = 0.$$

ANS. $y(t) = \dfrac{1}{k} \displaystyle\int_0^t H(t - \beta) \sinh k\beta\, d\beta.$

21. Solve the problem

$$y''(t) + 4y'(t) + 13y(t) = F(t);\ y(0) = 0,\ y'(0) = 0.$$

22. Solve the problem

$$x''(t) + 6x'(t) + 9x(t) = F(t);\ x(0) = A,\ x'(0) = B.$$

ANS. $x(t) = e^{-3t}[A + (B + 3A)t] + \displaystyle\int_0^t \beta e^{-3\beta} F(t - \beta)\, d\beta.$

In Exs. 23–42, use the Laplace transform method with the realization that these exercises were not constructed with the Laplace transform technique in mind. Compare your work with that done in solving the same problems by the methods of Chapter 7. See pages 119–120.

23. Ex. 1.	**24.** Ex. 2.
25. Ex. 3.	**26.** Ex. 11.
27. Ex. 14.	**28.** Ex. 20.
29. Ex. 21.	**30.** Ex. 22.
31. Ex. 23.	**32.** Ex. 36.
33. Ex. 37.	**34.** Ex. 38.
35. Ex. 39.	**36.** Ex. 40.
37. Ex. 41.	**38.** Ex. 42.

39. Ex. 43.   **40.** Ex. 44.
41. Ex. 45.   **42.** Ex. 46.
43. Solve the problem

$$x''(t) - 4x'(t) + 4x(t) = e^{2t}; \; x'(0) = 0, \, x(1) = 0.$$

ANS. $x(t) = \frac{1}{2}(1 - t)^2 e^{2t}.$

44. Solve the problem

$$x''(t) + 4x(t) = -8t^2; \; x(0) = 3, \, x(\frac{1}{4}\pi) = 0.$$

ANS. $x(t) = 2 \cos 2t + (\frac{1}{8}\pi^2 - 1) \sin 2t + 1 - 2t^2.$

65. Special integral equations

A differential equation may be loosely described as one that contains a derivative of a dependent variable; the equation contains a dependent variable under a derivative sign. An equation that contains a dependent variable under an integral sign is called an integral equation.

Because of the convolution theorem, the Laplace transform is an excellent tool for solving a very special class of integral equations. We know from Theorem 20 that if

$$L\{F(t)\} = f(s)$$

and

$$L\{G(t)\} = g(s),$$

then

$$L\left\{ \int_0^t F(\beta)G(t - \beta) \, d\beta \right\} = f(s)g(s).$$

The relation (1) suggests the use of the Laplace transform in solving equations that contain convolution integrals.

EXAMPLE (a):   Find $F(t)$ from the integral equation

$$F(t) = 4t - 3 \int_0^t F(\beta) \sin (t - \beta) \, d\beta. \tag{2}$$

The integral in (2) is in precisely the right form to permit the use of the convolution theorem. Let

$$L\{F(t)\} = f(s).$$

Then, since

$$L\{\sin t\} = \frac{1}{s^2 + 1},$$

application of Theorem 20 yields

$$L\left\{\int_0^t F(\beta) \sin(t - \beta)\, d\beta\right\} = \frac{f(s)}{s^2 + 1}.$$

Therefore, the Laplace operator converts equation (2) into

$$f(s) = \frac{4}{s^2} - \frac{3f(s)}{s^2 + 1}. \tag{3}$$

We need to obtain $f(s)$ from (3) and then $F(t)$ from $f(s)$. From (3) we get

$$\left(1 + \frac{3}{s^2 + 1}\right) f(s) = \frac{4}{s^2},$$

or

$$f(s) = \frac{4(s^2 + 1)}{s^2(s^2 + 4)} = \frac{1}{s^2} + \frac{3}{s^2 + 4}.$$

Therefore

$$F(t) = L^{-1}\left\{\frac{1}{s^2} + \frac{3}{s^2 + 4}\right\},$$

or

$$F(t) = t + \tfrac{3}{2} \sin 2t. \tag{4}$$

That the $F(t)$ of (4) is a solution of equation (2) may be verified directly. Such a check is frequently tedious. We shall show that for the F of (4), the right-hand side of equation (2) reduces to the left-hand side of (2). Since

$$RHS = 4t - 3 \int_0^t (\beta + \tfrac{3}{2} \sin 2\beta) \sin(t - \beta)\, d\beta,$$

we integrate by parts with the choice shown in the table.

$(\beta + \tfrac{3}{2} \sin 2\beta)$	$\sin(t - \beta)\, d\beta$
$(1 + 3 \cos 2\beta)\, d\beta$	$\cos(t - \beta)$

It thus follows that

$$RHS = 4t - 3\left[(\beta + \tfrac{3}{2} \sin 2\beta) \cos(t - \beta)\right]_0^t$$
$$+ 3 \int_0^t (1 + 3 \cos 2\beta) \cos(t - \beta)\, d\beta,$$

from which

$$RHS = 4t - 3(t + \tfrac{3}{2} \sin 2t) + 3 \int_0^t \cos(t - \beta)\, d\beta$$
$$+ 9 \int_0^t \cos 2\beta \cos(t - \beta)\, d\beta,$$

or

$$RHS = t - \tfrac{9}{2} \sin 2t - 3\Big[\sin (t - \beta)\Big]_0^t + \tfrac{9}{2} \int_0^t \Big[\cos (t + \beta) + \cos (t - 3\beta)\Big] d\beta.$$

This leads us to the result

$$RHS = t - \tfrac{9}{2} \sin 2t + 3 \sin t + \tfrac{9}{2}\Big[\sin (t + \beta) - \tfrac{1}{3} \sin (t - 3\beta)\Big]_0^t$$

$$= t - \tfrac{9}{2} \sin 2t + 3 \sin t + \tfrac{9}{2} \sin 2t + \tfrac{3}{2} \sin 2t - \tfrac{9}{2} \sin t + \tfrac{3}{2} \sin t,$$

or

$$RHS = t + \tfrac{3}{2} \sin 2t = F(t) = LHS,$$

as desired.

It is important to realize that the original equation

$$F(t) = 4t - 3 \int_0^t F(\beta) \sin (t - \beta) \, d\beta \qquad (2)$$

could equally well have been encountered in the equivalent form

$$F(t) = 4t - 3 \int_0^t F(t - \beta) \sin \beta \, d\beta.$$

An essential ingredient for the success of the method being used is that the integral involved be in exactly the convolution integral form. We must have zero to the independent variable as limits of integration, and an integrand that is the product of a function of the variable of integration by a function of the difference between the independent variable and the variable of integration. The fact that integrals of that form appear with significant frequency in physical problems keeps the topic of this section from being relegated to the role of a mathematical parlor game.

EXAMPLE (b):   Solve the equation

$$g(x) = \tfrac{1}{2}x^2 - \int_0^x (x - y)g(y) \, dy. \qquad (5)$$

Again the integral involved is one of the convolution type with x playing the role of the independent variable. Let the Laplace transform of $g(x)$ be some as yet unknown function $h(z)$:

$$L\{g(x)\} = h(z). \qquad (6)$$

Since $L\{\tfrac{1}{2}x^2\} = \dfrac{1}{z^3}$ and $L\{x\} = \dfrac{1}{z^2}$, we may apply the operator L throughout (5) and obtain

$$h(z) = \frac{1}{z^3} - \frac{h(z)}{z^2},$$

from which

$$\left(1 + \frac{1}{z^2}\right)h(z) = \frac{1}{z^3},$$

or

$$h(z) = \frac{1}{z(z^2+1)} = \frac{z^2+1-z^2}{z(z^2+1)} = \frac{1}{z} - \frac{z}{z^2+1}.$$

Then

$$g(x) = L^{-1}\left\{\frac{1}{z} - \frac{z}{z^2+1}\right\}$$

or

$$g(x) = 1 - \cos x. \qquad (7)$$

Verification of (7) is simple. For the right member of (5) we get

$$RHS = \tfrac{1}{2}x^2 - \int_0^x (x - y)(1 - \cos y)\, dy$$

$$= \tfrac{1}{2}x^2 - \Big[(x - y)(y - \sin y)\Big]_0^x - \int_0^x (y - \sin y)\, dy$$

$$= \tfrac{1}{2}x^2 - 0 - \Big[\tfrac{1}{2}y^2 + \cos y\Big]_0^x$$

$$= \tfrac{1}{2}x^2 - \tfrac{1}{2}x^2 - \cos x + 1 = 1 - \cos x = LHS.$$

Exercises

In Exs. 1–4, solve the given equation and verify your solution.

1. $F(t) = 1 + 2\displaystyle\int_0^t F(t - \beta)e^{-2\beta}\, d\beta.$ ANS. $F(t) = 1 + 2t.$

2. $F(t) = 1 + \displaystyle\int_0^t F(\beta)\sin(t - \beta)\, d\beta.$ ANS. $F(t) = 1 + \tfrac{1}{2}t^2.$

3. $F(t) = t + \displaystyle\int_0^t F(t - \beta)e^{-\beta}\, d\beta.$ ANS. $F(t) = t + \tfrac{1}{2}t^2.$

4. $F(t) = 4t^2 - \displaystyle\int_0^t F(t - \beta)e^{-\beta}\, d\beta.$ ANS. $F(t) = -1 + 2t + 2t^2 + e^{-2t}.$

In Exs. 5–8, solve the given equation. If sufficient time is available, verify your solution.

5. $F(t) = t^3 + \displaystyle\int_0^t F(\beta)\sin(t - \beta)\, d\beta.$ ANS. $F(t) = t^3 + \tfrac{1}{20}t^5.$

6. $F(t) = 8t^2 - 3\displaystyle\int_0^t F(\beta)\sin(t - \beta)\, d\beta.$

7. $F(t) = t^2 - 2 \int_0^t F(t - \beta) \sinh 2\beta \, d\beta.$ ANS. $F(t) = t^2 - \frac{1}{3} t^4.$

8. $F(t) = 1 + 2 \int_0^t F(t - \beta) \cos \beta \, d\beta.$ ANS. $F(t) = 1 + 2te^t.$

In Exs. 9–12, solve the given equation.

9. $H(t) = 9e^{2t} - 2 \int_0^t H(t - \beta) \cos \beta \, d\beta.$

10. $H(y) = y^2 + \int_0^y H(x) \sin (y - x) \, dx.$ ANS. $H(y) = y^2 + \frac{1}{12} y^4.$

11. $g(x) = e^{-x} - 2 \int_0^x g(\beta) \cos (x - \beta) \, d\beta.$ ANS. $g(x) = e^{-x}(1 - x)^2.$

12. $y(t) = 6t + 4 \int_0^t (\beta - t)^2 y(\beta) \, d\beta.$

                          ANS. $y(t) = e^{2t} - e^{-t}(\cos \sqrt{3} t - \sqrt{3} \sin \sqrt{3} t).$

13. Solve the following equation for $F(t)$ with the condition that $F(0) = 4$:

$$F'(t) = t + \int_0^t F(t - \beta) \cos \beta \, d\beta. \qquad \text{ANS.} \quad F(t) = 4 + \tfrac{5}{2} t^2 + \tfrac{1}{24} t^4.$$

14. Solve the following equation for $F(t)$ with the condition that $F(0) = 0$:

$$F'(t) = \sin t + \int_0^t F(t - \beta) \cos \beta \, d\beta. \qquad \text{ANS.} \quad F(t) = \tfrac{1}{2} t^2.$$

15. Show that the equation of Ex. 3 above can be put in the form

$$e^t F(t) = te^t + \int_0^t e^\beta F(\beta) \, d\beta. \tag{A}$$

Differentiate each member of (A) with respect to t and thus replace the integral equation with a differential equation. Note that $F(0) = 0$. Find $F(t)$ by this method.

16. Solve the equation

$$\int_0^t F(t - \beta) e^{-\beta} \, d\beta = t$$

by two methods; use the convolution theorem and the basic idea introduced in Ex. 15. Note that no differential equation need be solved in this instance.

TABLE OF TRANSFORMS

Whenever n is used, it denotes a non-negative integer.

The range of validity may be determined from the appropriate text material. Many other transforms will be found in the examples and exercises.

$f(s) = L\{F(t)\}$	$F(t)$
$f(s-a)$	$e^{at}F(t)$
$f(as+b)$	$\dfrac{1}{a}\exp\left(-\dfrac{bt}{a}\right)F\left(\dfrac{t}{a}\right)$
$\dfrac{1}{s}e^{-cs}, \quad c>0$	$\alpha(t-c)=0, \quad 0\leq t<c,$ $=1, \quad t\geq c$
$e^{-cs}f(s), \quad c>0$	$F(t-c)\alpha(t-c)$
$f_1(s)f_2(s)$	$\displaystyle\int_0^t F_1(\beta)F_2(t-\beta)\,d\beta$
$\dfrac{1}{s}$	1
$\dfrac{1}{s^{n+1}}$	$\dfrac{t^n}{n!}$
$\dfrac{1}{s^{x+1}}, \quad x>-1$	$\dfrac{t^x}{\Gamma(x+1)}$
$s^{-1/2}$	$(\pi t)^{-1/2}$
$\dfrac{1}{s+a}$	e^{-at}
$\dfrac{1}{(s+a)^{n+1}}$	$\dfrac{t^n e^{-at}}{n!}$
$\dfrac{k}{s^2+k^2}$	$\sin kt$
$\dfrac{s}{s^2+k^2}$	$\cos kt$
$\dfrac{k}{s^2-k^2}$	$\sinh kt$
$\dfrac{s}{s^2-k^2}$	$\cosh kt$
$\dfrac{2k^3}{(s^2+k^2)^2}$	$\sin kt - kt\cos kt$
$\dfrac{2ks}{(s^2+k^2)^2}$	$t\sin kt$
$\ln\left(1+\dfrac{1}{s}\right)$	$\dfrac{1-e^{-t}}{t}$

$f(s) = F\{L(t)\}$	$F(t)$
$\ln \dfrac{s+k}{s-k}$	$\dfrac{2\sinh kt}{t}$
$\ln\left(1 - \dfrac{k^2}{s^2}\right)$	$\dfrac{2}{t}(1 - \cosh kt)$
$\ln\left(1 + \dfrac{k^2}{s^2}\right)$	$\dfrac{2}{t}(1 - \cos kt)$
$\operatorname{Arctan}\dfrac{k}{s}$	$\dfrac{\sin kt}{t}$

CHAPTER 12

Applications

66. Vibration of a spring

Consider a steel spring attached to a support and hanging downward. Within certain elastic limits the spring will obey Hooke's law: if the spring is stretched or compressed, its change in length will be proportional to the force exerted upon the spring and, when that force is removed, the spring will return to its original position with its length and other physical properties unchanged. There is, therefore, associated with each spring a numerical constant, the ratio of the force exerted to the displacement produced by that force. If a force of magnitude Q pounds stretches the spring c feet, the relation

$$Q = kc \tag{1}$$

defines the spring constant k in units of pounds per foot.

Let a body B weighing w pounds be attached to the lower end of a spring (Figure 24) and brought to the point of equilibrium where it can remain at

FIGURE 24   FIGURE 25

rest. Once the weight B is moved from the point of equilibrium E in Figure 25, the motion of B will be determined by a differential equation and associated initial conditions.

Let t be time measured in seconds after some initial moment when the motion begins. Let x, in feet, be distance measured positive downward (negative upward) from the point of equilibrium, as in Figure 25. We assume that the motion of B takes place entirely in a vertical line, so the velocity and acceleration are given by the first and second derivatives of x with respect to t.

In addition to the force proportional to displacement (Hooke's law), there will in general be a retarding force caused by resistance of the medium in which the motion takes place or by friction. We are interested here in only such retarding forces as can be well approximated by a term proportional to the velocity because we restrict our study to problems involving linear differential equations. Such a retarding force will contribute to the total force acting on B a term $bx'(t)$, in which b is a constant to be determined experimentally for the medium in which the motion takes place. Some common retarding forces, such as one proportional to the cube of the velocity, lead to nonlinear differential equations which are not amenable to treatment by the Laplace transform.

The weight of the spring is usually negligible compared to the weight B, so we use for the mass of our system the weight of B divided by g, the constant acceleration of gravity. If no forces other than those described above act upon the weight, the displacement x must satisfy the equation

$$\frac{w}{g} x''(t) + bx'(t) + kx(t) = 0. \tag{2}$$

Suppose an additional vertical force, due to the motion of the support or to presence of a magnetic field, etc., is imposed upon the system. The new, impressed force, will depend upon time and we may use $F(t)$ to denote the acceleration which it alone would impart to the weight B. Then the impressed force is $\dfrac{w}{g} F(t)$ and equation (2) is replaced by

$$\frac{w}{g} x''(t) + bx'(t) + kx(t) = \frac{w}{g} F(t). \tag{3}$$

At time zero, let the weight be displaced by an amount x_0 from the equilibrium point and let the weight be given an initial velocity v_0. Either or both of x_0 and v_0 may be zero in specific instances. The problem of determining the position of the weight at any time t becomes that of solving the initial value problem consisting of the differential equation

$$\frac{w}{g} x''(t) + bx'(t) + kx(t) = \frac{w}{g} F(t), \qquad \text{for} \quad t > 0, \tag{4}$$

and the initial conditions

$$x(0) = x_0, \qquad x'(0) = v_0. \tag{5}$$

It is convenient to rewrite equation (4) in the form

$$x''(t) + 2\gamma x'(t) + \beta^2 x(t) = F(t), \tag{6}$$

in which we have put

$$\frac{bg}{w} = 2\gamma, \qquad \frac{kg}{w} = \beta^2.$$

We may choose $\beta > 0$ and we know $\gamma \geqq 0$. Note that $\gamma = 0$ corresponds to a negligible retarding force.

Impressed forces so ill-behaved that their Laplace transforms do not exist are hardly worth considering. We therefore let

$$L\{x(t)\} = u(s), \quad L\{F(t)\} = f(s), \tag{7}$$

and obtain from the problem (5) and (6) the transformed problem

$$s^2 u(s) - sx_0 - v_0 + 2\gamma[su(s) - x_0] + \beta^2 u(s) = f(s),$$

$$u(s) = \frac{sx_0 + v_0 + 2\gamma x_0}{s^2 + 2\gamma s + \beta^2} + \frac{f(s)}{s^2 + 2\gamma s + \beta^2},$$

which we write as

$$u(s) = \frac{x_0(s + \gamma) + v_0 + \gamma x_0}{(s + \gamma)^2 + \beta^2 - \gamma^2} + \frac{f(s)}{(s + \gamma)^2 + \beta^2 - \gamma^2}. \tag{8}$$

The desired $x(t)$ is the inverse transform of $u(s)$.

Here we begin to reap benefits from our use of the Laplace transform. Even before we get $x(t)$ we can see that its form will depend upon whether the denominator in (8) has distinct real linear factors, or equal factors, or is the sum of two squares. That is, the form of $x(t)$ will depend upon whether $\beta < \gamma$, $\beta = \gamma$, or $\beta > \gamma$. Furthermore, if $\gamma \neq 0$, we can predict the presence of a damping factor $e^{-\gamma t}$ in $x(t)$.

The inverse of the $u(s)$ of equation (8) can be obtained with our standard methods, including the convolution theorem. When the $F(t)$ is reasonably simple, one of the types which occur frequently in practice, the convolution theorem leads to forms less desirable than those obtained by the other methods in Chapter 11.

We shall now consider separately the various situations that arise according to the choice of parameters β and γ and the forcing function $F(t)$ in this problem of the vibrating spring.

In treating spring problems we are particularly interested in impressed forces that lead to $F(t)$ of forms such as those listed:

(a) No impressed force: $F(t) = 0$;

(b) Simple harmonic forcing function:

$$F(t) = A_1 \sin \omega t + A_2 \cos \omega t;$$

(c) Temporary constant force:

$$F(t) = A, \quad 0 < t < t_0,$$
$$= 0, \quad\quad\; t > t_0;$$

(d) A delayed form of (c):

$$F(t) = 0, \quad\;\; 0 < t < t_0,$$
$$= A, \quad t_0 < t < t_1,$$
$$= 0, \quad\quad\;\; t > t_1;$$

(e) $F(t) = $ the half-wave rectification of a sine curve.

It will become apparent when we study electric circuits in Chapter 14 that all of our present work carries over to simple circuit problems with new meanings attached to the parameters and functions involved. In circuit theory we shall add to the forms of $F(t)$ listed above both $F(t)$ equal to a constant and $F(t)$ equal to the square-wave function that appeared in Section 60.

67. Undamped vibrations

If $\gamma = 0$ in the problem of Section 66, the transform becomes

$$u(s) = \frac{x_0 s + v_0}{s^2 + \beta^2} + \frac{f(s)}{s^2 + \beta^2}. \tag{1}$$

The inverse transform of the first term on the right in (1) is

$$x_0 \cos \beta t + \frac{v_0}{\beta} \sin \beta t,$$

which contributes to $x(t)$ a simple harmonic motion, called the *natural component* of the motion, natural because it is independent of the forcing function $F(t)$. From the last term in (1) we obtain the forced component, the form of which is dependent upon $F(t)$.

Instead of jumping from (1) to the general solution

$$x(t) = x_0 \cos \beta t + v_0 \beta^{-1} \sin \beta t + \beta^{-1} \int_0^t F(t - v) \sin \beta v \, dv, \tag{2}$$

we prefer to obtain $x(t)$ without a convolution integral for the specific types of $F(t)$ which occur often. Equation (2) was easily obtained but it leaves all the labor of simplification to the unfortunate user who has a particular $F(t)$ with which to deal.

EXAMPLE (a):   Solve the spring problem with no damping but with a forcing function $F(t) = A \sin \omega t$.

The differential equation of motion is

$$\frac{w}{g} x''(t) + kx(t) = \frac{w}{g} A \sin \omega t$$

and is readily put into the form

$$x''(t) + \beta^2 x(t) = A \sin \omega t \tag{3}$$

with the introduction of $\beta^2 = kg/w$. We shall assume initial conditions

$$x(0) = x_0, \qquad x'(0) = v_0.$$

Let $L\{x(t)\} = u(s)$. Then (3) and (4) yield

$$s^2 u(s) - sx_0 - v_0 + \beta^2 u(s) = \frac{A\omega}{s^2 + \omega^2},$$

or

$$u(s) = \frac{sx_0 + v_0}{s^2 + \beta^2} + \frac{A\omega}{(s^2 + \beta^2)(s^2 + \omega^2)}. \tag{5}$$

The last term in (5) will lead to different inverse transforms according to whether $\omega = \beta$ or $\omega \neq \beta$. The case $\omega = \beta$ leads to resonance, which will be discusssed in the next section.

If $\omega \neq \beta$, equation (5) yields

$$u(s) = \frac{sx_0 + v_0}{s^2 + \beta^2} + \frac{A\omega}{\omega^2 - \beta^2}\left(\frac{1}{s^2 + \beta^2} - \frac{1}{s^2 + \omega^2}\right). \tag{6}$$

From (6) it follows at once that

$$x(t) = x_0 \cos \beta t + v_0 \beta^{-1} \sin \beta t + \frac{A\omega}{\beta(\omega^2 - \beta^2)} \sin \beta t - \frac{A}{\omega^2 - \beta^2} \sin \omega t. \tag{7}$$

That the x of (7) is a solution of the problem (3) and (4) is easily verified. A study of (7) is simple and leads at once to conclusions such as that $x(t)$ is bounded, etc. The first two terms on the right in (7) yield the natural harmonic component of the motion, the last two terms form the forced component.

EXAMPLE (b): A spring is such that it would be stretched 6 inches by a 12-pound weight. Let the weight be attached to the spring and pulled down 4 inches below the equilibrium point. If the weight is started with an upward velocity of 2 feet per second, describe the motion. No damping or impressed force is present.

We know that the acceleration of gravity enters our work in the expression for the mass. We wish to use the value $g = 32$ ft. per sec. per sec. and we must use consistent units, so we put all lengths into feet.

First we determine the spring constant k from the fact that the 12-pound weight stretches the spring 6 inches, $\frac{1}{2}$ ft. Thus $12 = \frac{1}{2}k$ so that $k = 24$ lb. per ft.

The differential equation of the motion is therefore

$$\tfrac{12}{32}x''(t) + 24x(t) = 0. \tag{8}$$

At time zero the weight is 4 inches ($\frac{1}{3}$ ft.) below the equilibrium point, so $x(0) = \frac{1}{3}$. The initial velocity is negative (upward), so $x'(0) = -2$. Thus our problem is that of solving

$$x''(t) + 64x(t) = 0; \qquad x(0) = \tfrac{1}{3}, \qquad x'(0) = -2. \tag{9}$$

We let $L\{x(t)\} = u(s)$ and conclude at once that

$$s^2 u(s) - \tfrac{1}{3}s + 2 + 64u(s) = 0,$$

from which

$$u(s) = \frac{\frac{1}{3}s - 2}{s^2 + 64}.$$

Then

$$x(t) = \tfrac{1}{3} \cos 8t - \tfrac{1}{4} \sin 8t. \tag{10}$$

A detailed study of the motion is straightforward once (10) has been obtained. The amplitude of the motion is

$$\sqrt{(\tfrac{1}{3})^2 + (\tfrac{1}{4})^2} = \tfrac{5}{12};$$

that is, the weight oscillates between points 5 inches above and below E. The period is $\tfrac{1}{4}\pi$ sec.

EXAMPLE (c): A spring, with spring constant 0.75 lb. per ft., lies on a long smooth (frictionless) table. A 6-lb. weight is attached to the spring and is at rest (velocity zero) at the equilibrium position. A 1.5-lb. force is applied to the support along the line of action of the spring for 4 seconds and is then removed. Discuss the motion.

We must solve the problem

$$\tfrac{6}{32}x''(t) + \tfrac{3}{4}x(t) = H(t); \qquad x(0) = 0, \qquad x'(0) = 0, \tag{11}$$

in which

$$H(t) = 1.5, \qquad 0 < t < 4,$$
$$= 0, \qquad\qquad t > 4.$$

Now $H(t) = 1.5[1 - \alpha(t - 4)]$ in terms of the α function of Section 62. Therefore we rewrite our problem (11) in the form

$$x''(t) + 4x(t) = 8[1 - \alpha(t - 4)]; \quad x(0) = 0, \quad x'(0) = 0. \tag{12}$$

Let $L\{x(t)\} = u(s)$. Then (12) yields

$$s^2u(s) + 4u(s) = \frac{8}{s}(1 - e^{-4s}),$$

or

$$u(s) = \frac{8(1 - e^{-4s})}{s(s^2 + 4)}$$

$$= 2\left(\frac{1}{s} - \frac{s}{s^2 + 4}\right)(1 - e^{-4s}).$$

The desired solution is

$$x(t) = 2(1 - \cos 2t) - 2[1 - \cos 2(t - 4)]\alpha(t - 4). \tag{13}$$

Of course, the solution (13) can be broken down into the two relations

$$\text{For } 0 \le t \le 4, \qquad x(t) = 2(1 - \cos 2t), \tag{14}$$

$$\text{For } t > 4, \qquad x(t) = 2[\cos 2(t - 4) - \cos 2t], \tag{15}$$

if those forms seem simpler to use.

Verification of the solution (13), or (14) and (15), is direct. The student should show that

$$\operatorname*{Lim}_{t \to 4^-} x(t) = \operatorname*{Lim}_{t \to 4^+} x(t) = 2(1 - \cos 8) = 2.29$$

and

$$\operatorname*{Lim}_{t \to 4^-} x'(t) = \operatorname*{Lim}_{t \to 4^+} x'(t) = 4 \sin 8 = 3.96.$$

From (13) or (14) we see that in the range $0 < t < 4$, the maximum deviation of the weight from the starting point is $x = 4$ ft. and occurs at $t = \frac{1}{2}\pi = 1.57$ sec. At $t = 4$, $x = 2.29$ ft. as shown above. For $t > 4$, equation (15) takes over and thereafter the motion is simple harmonic with a maximum x of 3.03 ft. Indeed, for $t > 4$,

$$\max |x(t)| = 2\sqrt{(1 - \cos 8)^2 + \sin^2 8}$$

$$= 2\sqrt{2}\sqrt{1 - \cos 8}$$

$$= 2\sqrt{2.2910} = 3.03.$$

Example (c) is one type of problem for which the Laplace transform technique is particularly useful. Such problems can be solved by the older classical methods, but with much less simplicity and dispatch.

68. Resonance

In the problem of undamped vibrations of a spring, one of the examples we encountered was

$$x''(t) + \beta^2 x(t) = A \sin \omega t; \qquad x(0) = x_0, \qquad x'(0) = v_0. \tag{1}$$

The solution of (1) was obtained by putting $L\{x(t)\} = u(s)$ and getting

$$u(s) = \frac{sx_0 + v_0}{s^2 + \beta^2} + \frac{A\omega}{(s^2 + \beta^2)(s^2 + \omega^2)}. \tag{2}$$

From (2) we see that the inverse transform differs according to whether $\omega = \beta$ or $\omega \ne \beta$. The latter has been studied. Let us now assume $\omega = \beta$.

Our problem is to solve

$$x''(t) + \beta^2 x(t) = A \sin \beta t; \qquad x(0) = x_0, \quad x'(0) = v_0, \tag{3}$$

with the aid of

$$u(s) = \frac{sx_0 + v_0}{s^2 + \beta^2} + \frac{A\beta}{(s^2 + \beta^2)^2}. \tag{4}$$

We already know, from page 167, that

$$L^{-1}\left\{\frac{1}{(s^2 + \beta^2)^2}\right\} = \frac{1}{2\beta^3}(\sin \beta t - \beta t \cos \beta t).$$

Therefore (4) leads us to the solution

$$x(t) = x_0 \cos \beta t + \frac{v_0}{\beta} \sin \beta t + \frac{A}{2\beta^2}(\sin \beta t - \beta t \cos \beta t). \tag{5}$$

That (5) satisfies all the conditions of (3) is readily verified.

In the solution (5) the terms proportional to $\cos \beta t$ and $\sin \beta t$ are bounded, but the term with $\beta t \cos \beta t$ can be made as large as we wish by proper choice of t. This building up of large amplitudes in the vibration when $\omega = \beta$ in (1) is called *resonance*.

Exercises

1. A spring is such that a 5-pound weight stretches it 6 inches. The 5-pound weight is attached, the spring reaches equilibrium, then the weight is pulled down 3 inches below the equilibrium point and started off with an upward velocity of 6 ft. per sec. Find an equation giving the position of the weight at all subsequent times.
   ANS. $x = \frac{1}{4}(\cos 8t - 3 \sin 8t)$.

2. A spring is stretched 1.5 inches by a 2-pound weight. Let the weight be pushed up 3 inches above E and then released. Describe the motion.
   ANS. $x = -\frac{1}{4} \cos 16t$.

3. For the spring and weight of Ex. 2, let the weight be pulled down 4 inches below E and given a downward initial velocity of 8 ft. per sec. Describe the motion.
   ANS. $x = \frac{1}{3} \cos 16t + \frac{1}{2} \sin 16t$.

4. Show that the answer to Ex. 3 can be written $x = 0.60 \sin (16t + \phi)$ where $\phi = \text{Arctan } \frac{2}{3}$.

5. A spring is such that a 4-pound weight stretches it 6 inches. An impressed force $\frac{1}{2} \cos 8t$ is acting on the spring. If the 4-pound weight is started from the equilibrium point with an imparted upward velocity of 4 ft. per sec., determine the position of the weight as a function of time.
   ANS. $x = \frac{1}{4}(t - 2) \sin 8t$.

6. A spring is such that it is stretched 6 inches by a 12-pound weight. The 12-pound weight is pulled down 3 inches below the equilibrium point and then released. If there is an impressed force of magnitude $9 \sin 4t$ pounds, describe the motion. Assume that the impressed force acts downward for very small t.
   ANS. $x = \frac{1}{4} \cos 8t - \frac{1}{4} \sin 8t + \frac{1}{2} \sin 4t$.

7. Show that the answer to Ex. 6 can be written

$$x = \frac{1}{4}\sqrt{2} \cos (8t + \pi/4) + \frac{1}{2} \sin 4t.$$

8. A spring is such that a 2-pound weight stretches it $\frac{1}{2}$ ft. An impressed force $\frac{1}{4}\sin 8t$ is acting upon the spring. If the 2-pound weight is released from a point 3 inches below the equilibrium point, determine the equation of motion.

ANS. $x = \frac{1}{4}(1-t)\cos 8t + \frac{1}{32}\sin 8t$ (ft.).

9. For the motion of Ex. 8, find the first four times at which stops occur and find the position at each stop. ANS. $t = \pi/8, \pi/4, 1, 3\pi/8$ (sec.) and $x = -0.15, +0.05, +0.03, +0.04$ (ft.), respectively.

10. Determine the position to be expected, if nothing such as breakage interferes, at the time of the 65th stop, when $t = 8\pi$ (sec.), in Ex. 8.

ANS. $x = -6.0$ (ft.).

11. A spring is such that a 16-pound weight stretches it 1.5 inches. The weight is pulled down to a point 4 inches below the equilibrium point and given an initial downward velocity of 4 ft. per sec. An impressed force of $360\cos 4t$ pounds is applied. Find the position and velocity of the weight at time $t = \pi/8$ seconds. ANS. At $t = \pi/8$(sec.), $x = -\frac{8}{3}$ (ft.), $v = -8$ (ft./sec.).

12. A spring is stretched 3 inches by a 5-pound weight. Let the weight be started from E with an upward velocity of 12 ft. per sec. Describe the motion.

ANS. $x = -1.06\sin 11.3t$.

13. For the spring and weight of Ex. 12, let the weight be pulled down 4 inches below E and then given an upward velocity of 8 ft. per sec. Describe the motion. ANS. $x = 0.33\cos 11.3t - 0.71\sin 11.3t$.

14. Find the amplitude of the motion in Ex. 13. ANS. 0.78 ft.

15. A 20-pound weight stretches a certain spring 10 inches. Let the spring first be compressed 4 inches, and then the 20-pound weight attached and given an initial downward velocity of 8 ft. per sec. Find how far the weight would drop.

ANS. 35 in.

16. A spring is such that an 8-pound weight would stretch it 6 inches. Let a 4-pound weight be attached to the spring, pushed up 2 inches above its equilibrium point and then released. Describe the motion. ANS. $x = -\frac{1}{6}\cos 11.3t$.

17. If the 4-pound weight of Ex. 16 starts at the same point, 2 inches above E, but with an upward velocity of 15 ft. per sec., when will the weight reach its lowest point? ANS. At $t =$ approximately 0.4 sec.

18. A spring is such that it is stretched 4 inches by a 10-pound weight. Suppose the 10-pound weight to be pulled down 5 inches below E and then given a downward velocity of 15 ft. per sec. Describe the motion.

ANS. $x = 0.42\cos 9.8t + 1.53\sin 9.8t$
$= 1.59\cos(9.8t - \phi)$, where $\phi =$ Arctan 3.64.

19. A spring is such that it is stretched 4 inches by an 8-pound weight. Suppose the weight to be pulled down 6 inches below E and then given an upward velocity of 8 ft. per sec. Describe the motion.

ANS. $x = 0.50\cos 9.8t - 0.82\sin 9.8t$.

20. Show that the answer to Ex. 19 can be written $x = 0.96\cos(9.8t + \phi)$ where $\phi =$ Arctan 1.64.

21. A spring is such that a 4-pound weight stretches it 6 inches. The 4-pound weight is attached to the vertical spring and reaches its equilibrium point. The weight is then ($t = 0$) drawn downward 3 inches and released. There is a simple harmonic exterior force equal to $\sin 8t$ impressed upon the whole system. Find

the time for each of the first four stops following $t = 0$. Put the stops in chrono-
logical order.   ANS. $t = \pi/8, \frac{1}{2}, \pi/4, 3\pi/8$ (sec.).

22. A spring is stretched 1.5 inches by a 4-pound weight. Let the weight be pulled
down 3 inches below equilibrium and released. If there is an impressed force
$8 \sin 16t$ acting upon the spring, describe the motion.
                    ANS. $x = \frac{1}{4}(1 - 8t) \cos 16t + \frac{1}{8} \sin 16t$.

23. For the motion of Ex. 22, find the first four times at which stops occur and find
the position at each stop.   ANS. $t = \frac{1}{8}, \pi/16, \pi/8, 3\pi/16$ (sec.) and
$x = +0.11, +0.14, -0.54, +0.93$ (ft.), respectively.

69. Damped vibrations

In the general linear spring problem of Section 66, we were confronted
with

$$x''(t) + 2\gamma x'(t) + \beta^2 x(t) = F(t); \qquad x(0) = x_0, \qquad x'(0) = v_0, \qquad (1)$$

in which $\gamma = \dfrac{bg}{w}$ and $\beta^2 = \dfrac{kg}{w}$, $\beta > 0$. We let

$$L\{x(t)\} = u(s), \qquad L\{F(t)\} = f(s)$$

and obtained

$$u(s) = \frac{x_0(s + \gamma) + v_0 + \gamma x_0}{(s + \gamma)^2 + \beta^2 - \gamma^2} + \frac{f(s)}{(s + \gamma)^2 + \beta^2 - \gamma^2}. \qquad (2)$$

We are now concerned with $\gamma > 0$; a non-negligible retarding force is present.
We know that the form of the inverse transform of $u(s)$ depends upon whether
$\beta > \gamma$, $\beta = \gamma$, or $\beta < \gamma$.

If $\beta > \gamma$, $\beta^2 - \gamma^2 > 0$, so let us put

$$\beta^2 - \gamma^2 = \delta^2. \qquad (3)$$

Then (2) becomes

$$u(s) = \frac{x_0(s + \gamma) + v_0 + \gamma x_0}{(s + \gamma)^2 + \delta^2} + \frac{f(s)}{(s + \gamma)^2 + \delta^2} \qquad (4)$$

and we arrive at

$$x(t) = e^{-\gamma t}[x_0 \cos \delta t + (v_0 + \gamma x_0)\delta^{-1} \sin \delta t] + \psi_1(t) \qquad (5)$$

in which $\psi_1(t)$ is an inverse transform of the last term in (4). The function
$\psi_1(t)$ can always be written in terms of $F(t)$ by the convolution theorem,
but that leads to undesirable complications for the most common choices
of $F(t)$. In the solution (5), the presence of the damping factor $e^{-\gamma t}$ shows
that the natural component of the motion approaches zero as $t \to \infty$.

If in (1) and (2) we have $\beta = \gamma$, the transform

$$u(s) = \frac{x_0(s + \gamma) + v_0 + \gamma x_0}{(s + \gamma)^2} + \frac{f(s)}{(s + \gamma)^2} \tag{6}$$

leads us to the solution

$$x(t) = e^{-\gamma t}[x_0 + (v_0 + \gamma x_0)t] + \psi_2(t), \tag{7}$$

in which $\psi_2(t)$ is an inverse of $(s + \gamma)^{-2}f(s)$ and is easily determined once $F(t)$ is stipulated. Again the natural component has the damping factor $e^{-\gamma t}$ in it.

If in (1) and (2) we have $\beta < \gamma$, $\gamma^2 - \beta^2 > 0$, and we put

$$\gamma^2 - \beta^2 = \sigma^2. \tag{8}$$

Then (2) becomes

$$u(s) = \frac{x_0(s + \gamma) + v_0 + \gamma x_0}{(s + \gamma)^2 - \sigma^2} + \frac{f(s)}{(s + \gamma)^2 - \sigma^2}, \tag{9}$$

which leads to the solution

$$x(t) = e^{-\gamma t}[x_0 \cosh \sigma t + (v_0 + \gamma x_0)\sigma^{-1} \sinh \sigma t] + \psi_3(t), \tag{10}$$

in which $\psi_3(t)$ is an inverse of the last term in (9). By (8) we see that $\gamma > \sigma$, so that once more the natural component of the $x(t)$ in (10) approaches zero as $t \to \infty$.

Suppose for the moment that we have $F(t) \equiv 0$, so the natural component of the motion is all that is under consideration. If $\beta > \gamma$, equation (5) holds and the motion is a *damped oscillatory* one. If $\beta = \gamma$, equation (7) holds and

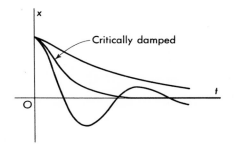

FIGURE 26

the motion is not oscillatory; it is called *critically damped* motion. If $\beta < \gamma$, (10) holds and the motion is said to be *overdamped*; the parameter γ is larger than it needs to be to remove the oscillations. Figure 26 shows a representative graph of each type of motion mentioned in this paragraph, a damped oscillatory motion, a critically damped motion, and an overdamped motion.

EXAMPLE: Solve the problem of Example (b), Section 67, with an added damping force of magnitude $0.6|v|$. Such a damping force can be realized by immersing the weight B in a thick liquid.

The initial value problem to be solved is

$$\tfrac{12}{32}x''(t) + 0.6x'(t) + 24x(t) = 0; \qquad x(0) = \tfrac{1}{3}, \qquad x'(0) = -2. \quad (11)$$

Put $L\{x(t)\} = u(s)$. Then (11) yields

$$(s^2 + 1.6s + 64)u(s) = \tfrac{1}{3}(s - 4.4),$$

from which we obtain

$$x(t) = \tfrac{1}{3}L^{-1}\left\{\frac{s - 4.4}{(s + 0.8)^2 + 63.36}\right\}$$

$$= \tfrac{1}{3}\exp(-0.8t)L^{-1}\left\{\frac{s - 5.2}{s^2 + 63.36}\right\}.$$

Therefore the desired solution is

$$x(t) = \exp(-0.8t)(0.33\cos 8.0t - 0.22\sin 8.0t), \quad (12)$$

a portion of its graph being shown in Figure 27.

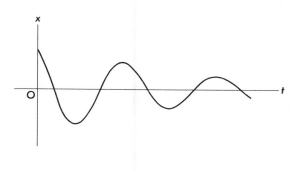

FIGURE 27

Exercises

1. A certain straight-line motion is determined by the differential equation

$$\frac{d^2x}{dt^2} + 2\gamma \frac{dx}{dt} + 169x = 0$$

and the conditions that when $t = 0$, $x = 0$ and $v = 8$ ft. per sec.
    (a) Find the value of γ that leads to critical damping, determine x in terms of t, and draw the graph for $0 \leq t \leq 0.2$.
                           ANS. $\gamma = 13(1/\text{sec.})$, $x = 8te^{-13t}$.
    (b) Use $\gamma = 12$. Find x in terms of t and draw the graph.
                                 ANS. $x = 1.6e^{-12t} \sin 5t$.
    (c) Use $\gamma = 14$. Find x in terms of t and draw the graph.
                           ANS. $x = 0.77(e^{-8.8t} - e^{-19.2t})$.

2. A spring is such that a 2-pound weight stretches it $\frac{1}{2}$ foot. An impressed force $\frac{1}{4} \sin 8t$ and a damping force of magnitude $|v|$ are both acting on the spring. The weight starts $\frac{1}{4}$ foot below the equilibrium point with an imparted upward velocity of 3 ft. per sec. Find a formula for the position of the weight at time t.
                           ANS. $x = \frac{3}{32}e^{-8t}(3 - 8t) - \frac{1}{32} \cos 8t$.

3. A spring is such that a 4-pound weight stretches it 0.64 feet. The 4-pound weight is pushed up $\frac{1}{3}$ foot above the point of equilibrium and then started with a downward velocity of 5 ft. per sec. The motion takes place in a medium which furnishes a damping force of magnitude $\frac{1}{4}|v|$ at all times. Find the equation describing the position of the weight at time t.
                           ANS. $x = \frac{1}{3}e^{-t}(2 \sin 7t - \cos 7t)$.

4. A spring is such that a 4-pound weight stretches it 0.32 feet. The weight is attached to the spring and moves in a medium which furnishes a damping force of magnitude $\frac{3}{2}|v|$. The weight is drawn down $\frac{1}{2}$ foot below the equilibrium point and given an initial upward velocity of 4 ft. per sec. Find the position of the weight thereafter.   ANS. $x = \frac{1}{8}e^{-6t}(4 \cos 8t - \sin 8t)$.

5. A spring is such that a 4-pound weight stretches the spring 0.4 feet. The 4-pound weight is attached to the spring (suspended from a fixed support) and the system is allowed to reach equilibrium. Then the weight is started from equilibrium position with an imparted upward velocity of 2 ft. per sec. Assume that the motion takes place in a medium which furnishes a retarding force of magnitude numerically equal to the speed, in feet per second, of the moving weight. Determine the position of the weight as a function of time.
                           ANS. $x = -\frac{1}{4}e^{-4t} \sin 8t$.

6. A spring is stretched 6 inches by a 3-pound weight. The 3-pound weight is attached to the spring and then started from equilibrium with an imparted upward velocity of 12 ft. per sec. Air resistance furnishes a retarding force equal in magnitude to $0.03|v|$. Find the equation of motion.
                           ANS. $x = -1.5e^{-0.16t} \sin 8t$.

7. A spring is such that a 2-pound weight stretches it 6 inches. There is a damping force present, with magnitude the same as the magnitude of the velocity. An impressed force $(2 \sin 8t)$ is acting on the spring. If, at $t = 0$, the weight is released from a point 3 inches below the equilibrium point, find its position for $t > 0$.   ANS. $x = (\frac{1}{2} + 4t)e^{-8t} - \frac{1}{4} \cos 8t$.

8. A spring is stretched 10 inches by a 4-pound weight. The weight is started 6 inches below the equilibrium point with an upward velocity of 8 ft. per sec. If a resisting medium furnishes a retarding force of magnitude $\frac{1}{4}|v|$, describe the motion.   ANS. $x = e^{-t}[0.50 \cos 6.1t - 1.23 \sin 6.1t]$.

9. For Ex. 8, find the times of the first three stops and the position (to the nearest inch) of the weight at each stop.

ANS. $t_1 = 0.3$ sec., $x_1 = -12$ in.; $t_2 = 0.8$ sec., $x_2 = +6$ in.; $t_3 = 1.3$ sec., $x_3 = -4$ in.

10. A spring is stretched 4 inches by a 2-pound weight. The 2-pound weight is started from the equilibrium point with a downward velocity of 12 ft. per sec. If air resistance furnishes a retarding force of magnitude 0.02 of the velocity, describe the motion.   ANS. $x = 1.22e^{-0.16t} \sin 9.8t$.

11. For Ex. 10, find how long it takes the damping factor to drop to one-tenth its initial value.   ANS.   14.4 sec.

12. For Ex. 10, find the position of the weight at : (a) the first stop; (b) the second stop.   ANS.   (a) $x = 1.2$ ft.; (b) $x = -1.1$ ft.

13. Let the motion of Ex. 8, page 210, be retarded by a damping force of magnitude $0.6|v|$. Find the equation of motion.

ANS. $x = 0.30e^{-4.8t} \cos 6.4t + 0.22e^{-4.8t} \sin 6.4t - 0.05 \cos 8t$ (ft.).

14. Show that whenever $t > 1$ (sec.), the solution of Ex. 13 can be replaced (to the nearest 0.01 ft.) by $x = -0.05 \cos 8t$.

15. Let the motion of Ex. 8, page 210, be retarded by a damping force of magnitude $|v|$. Find the equation of motion and also determine its form (to the nearest 0.01 ft.) for $t > 1$ (sec.).

ANS. $x = \frac{9}{32}(8t + 1)e^{-8t} - \frac{1}{32} \cos 8t$ (ft.); for $t > 1$, $x = -\frac{1}{32} \cos 8t$.

16. Let the motion of Ex. 8, page 210, be retarded by a damping force of magnitude $\frac{5}{3}|v|$. Find the equation of motion.

ANS. $x = 0.30e^{-(8/3)t} - 0.03e^{-24t} - 0.02 \cos 8t$.

17. Alter Ex. 6, page 209, by inserting a damping force of magnitude one-half that of the velocity and then determine x.

ANS. $x = \exp\left(-\frac{2}{3}t\right)(0.30 \cos 8.0t - 0.22 \sin 8.0t) - 0.05 \cos 4t + 0.49 \sin 4t$.

18. A spring is stretched 6 inches by a 4-pound weight. Let the weight be pulled down 6 inches below equilibrium and given an initial upward velocity of 7 ft. per sec. Assuming a damping force twice the magnitude of the velocity, describe the motion and sketch the graph at intervals of 0.05 sec. for $0 \le t \le 0.3$ (sec.).   ANS. $x = \frac{1}{2}e^{-8t}(1 - 6t)$.

19. An object weighing w pounds is dropped from a height h feet above the earth. At time t(sec.) after the object is dropped, let its distance from the starting point be x (ft.), measured positive downward. Assuming air resistance to be negligible, show that x must satisfy the equation

$$\frac{w}{g}\frac{d^2x}{dt^2} = w$$

as long as $x < h$. Find x.   ANS. $x = \frac{1}{2}gt^2$.

20. Let the weight of Ex. 19 be given an initial velocity v_0. Let v be the velocity at time t. Determine v and x.   ANS. $v = gt + v_0$, $x = \frac{1}{2}gt^2 + v_0 t$.

21. From the results in Ex. 20, find a relation that does not contain t explicitly.   ANS. $v^2 = v_0^2 + 2gx$.

22. If air resistance furnishes an additional force proportional to the velocity in the motion studied in Exs. 19 and 20, show that the equation of motion becomes

$$\frac{w}{g}\frac{d^2x}{dt^2} + b\frac{dx}{dt} = w. \tag{A}$$

Solve equation (A) given the conditions

$$\text{when } t = 0, x = 0 \text{ and } v = v_0. \tag{B}$$

Use $a = bg/w$.   ANS. $x = a^{-1}gt + a^{-2}(av_0 - g)(1 - e^{-at})$.

23. To compare the results of Exs. 20 and 22 when $a = bg/w$ is small, use the power series for e^{-at} in the answer for Ex. 22 and discard all terms involving a^n for $n \geq 3$.   ANS. $x = \frac{1}{2}gt^2 + v_0 t - \frac{1}{6}at^2(3v_0 + gt) + \frac{1}{24}a^2t^3(4v_0 + gt)$.

24. The equation of motion of the vertical fall of a man with a parachute may be roughly approximated by equation (A) of Ex. 22. Suppose a 180-pound man drops from a great height and attains a velocity of 20 miles per hour after a long time. Determine the implied coefficient b of equation (A).

ANS.   6.1 (lb.)(sec.) per ft.

25. A particle is moving along the x-axis according to the law

$$\frac{d^2x}{dt^2} + 6\frac{dx}{dt} + 25x = 0.$$

If the particle started at $x = 0$ with an initial velocity of 12 ft. per sec. to the left, determine: (a) x in terms of t; (b) the times at which stops occur; and (c) the ratio between the numerical values of x at successive stops.

ANS.   (a)$x = -3e^{-3t}\sin 4t$,
(b) $t = 0.23 + \frac{1}{4}n\pi$, $n = 0, 1, 2, 3, \ldots$, (c) 0.095.

70. The simple pendulum and the deflection of beams

A rod of length C feet is suspended by one end so it can swing freely in a vertical plane. Let a weight B (the bob) of w pounds be attached to the free end of the rod, and let the weight of the rod be negligible compared to the weight of the bob.

Let θ (radians) be the angular displacement from the vertical, as shown in Figure 28, of the rod at time t (sec.). The tangential component of the force w (lb.) is $w \sin \theta$ and it tends to decrease θ. Then, neglecting the weight of the rod and using $S = C\theta$ as a measure of arc length from the vertical position, we may conclude that

$$\frac{w}{g}\frac{d^2S}{dt^2} = -w \sin \theta. \tag{1}$$

Since $S = C\theta$ and C is constant, (1) becomes

$$\frac{d^2\theta}{dt^2} + \frac{g}{C}\sin \theta = 0. \tag{2}$$

FIGURE 28

The solution of equation (2) is not elementary; it involves an elliptic integral. If θ is small, however, $\sin \theta$ and θ are nearly equal and (2) is closely approximated by the much simpler equation

$$\frac{d^2\theta}{dt^2} + \beta^2\theta = 0; \qquad \beta^2 = \frac{g}{C}. \tag{3}$$

The solution of (3) with pertinent initial conditions gives usable results whenever those conditions are such that θ remains small, say $|\theta| < 0.3$ (radians).

As a further example, we consider a beam of length $2c$, as shown in Figure 29. Denote distance from one end of the beam by x, the deflection of the beam by y. If the beam is subjected to a vertical load $W(x)$, the deflection y must satisfy the equation

$$EI \frac{d^4y}{dx^4} = W(x), \qquad \text{for } 0 < x < 2c, \tag{1}$$

in which E, the modulus of elasticity, and I, a moment of inertia, are known constants associated with the particular beam.

The slope of the curve of deflection is $y'(x)$, the bending moment is $EIy''(x)$, and the shearing force is $EIy'''(x)$. Common boundary conditions are of the following types:

(a) Beam imbedded in a support: $y = 0$ and $y' = 0$ at the point;
(b) Beam simply supported: $y = 0$ and $y'' = 0$ at the point;
(c) Beam free: $y'' = 0$ and $y''' = 0$ at the point.

Problems in the transverse displacement of a beam take the form of the differential equation (1) with boundary conditions at each end of the beam.

Such problems can be solved by integration with the use of a little algebra. There are however two reasons for employing our transform method in such problems. Frequently the load function, or its derivative, is discontinuous. Beam problems also give us a chance to examine a useful device in which a problem over a finite range is solved with the aid of an associated problem over an infinite range.

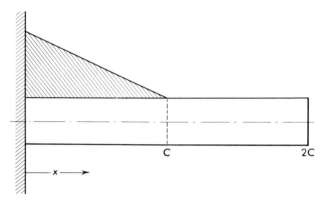

FIGURE 29

EXAMPLE: Find the displacement y throughout the beam of Figure 29, in which the load is assumed to decrease uniformly from w_0 at $x = 0$ to zero at $x = c$ and to remain zero from $x = c$ to $x = 2c$. The weight of the beam is to be negligible. The beam is imbedded at $x = 0$ and free at $x = 2c$.

We are to solve the problem

$$EI \frac{d^4 y}{dx^4} = \frac{w_0}{c} [c - x + (x - c)\alpha(x - c)], \quad \text{for} \quad 0 < x < 2c; \tag{2}$$

$$y(0) = 0, \qquad y'(0) = 0; \tag{3}$$

$$y''(2c) = 0, \qquad y'''(2c) = 0. \tag{4}$$

The student should verify that the right member of (2) is the stipulated load function

$$W(x) = \frac{w_0}{c} (c - x), \qquad \text{for} \quad 0 \leq x \leq c, \tag{5}$$

$$= 0, \qquad \qquad \text{for} \quad c < x \leq 2c.$$

To apply the transform technique, with x playing the role for which we usually employ t, we need first to extend the range of x so it will run from 0 to ∞. That is, instead of the problem (2), (3), (4), we shall solve the problem consisting of

$$EI \frac{d^4 y}{dx^4} = H(x), \quad \text{for} \quad 0 < x < \infty, \tag{6}$$

and the conditions (3) and (4). In (6) the function $H(x)$ is to be chosen by us except that $H(x)$ must agree with $W(x)$ over the range $0 < x < 2c$. The solution of the problem (6), (3), (4) will then be used only in the range $0 \leqq x \leqq 2c$. Of the various choices for $H(x)$, it seems simplest to use

$$H(x) = \frac{w_0}{c} [c - x + (x - c)\alpha(x - c)], \quad \text{for } 0 < x < \infty. \tag{7}$$

That is, in practice we ordinarily retain the equation (2) and merely extend the range from $0 < x < 2c$ to $0 < x < \infty$. The student must, however, keep in mind that we cannot apply the Laplace operator to the function $W(x)$ of (5), since that function is not defined over the entire range $0 < x < \infty$. We shall solve (6) and conclude that the solution is valid for (2) on the range $0 \leqq x \leqq 2c$, over which (2) and (6) are identical.

Let

$$L\{EI y(x)\} = u(s);$$

$$u(s) = EI \int_0^\infty e^{-sx} y(x) \, dx. \tag{8}$$

To transform $EI y^{(4)}(x)$ we need to use the values of $EI y(x)$ and its first three derivatives at $x = 0$. From (3) we know that

$$EI y(0) = 0, \quad EI y'(0) = 0.$$

Put

$$EI y''(0) = A, \quad EI y'''(0) = B. \tag{9}$$

The constants A and B must be determined by using the conditions (4).

By our usual methods we obtain, for the $H(x)$ of (7),

$$L\{H(x)\} = \frac{w_0}{c} L\{c - x + (x - c)\alpha(x - c)\}$$

$$= \frac{w_0}{c} \left(\frac{c}{s} - \frac{1}{s^2} + \frac{e^{-cs}}{s^2} \right).$$

Thus the differential equation (6) is transformed into

$$s^4 u(s) - s^3 \cdot 0 - s^2 \cdot 0 - s \cdot A - B = \frac{w_0}{c} \left(\frac{c}{s} - \frac{1}{s^2} + \frac{e^{-cs}}{s^2} \right),$$

from which we get

$$u(s) = \frac{A}{s^3} + \frac{B}{s^4} + \frac{w_0}{c}\left(\frac{c}{s^5} - \frac{1}{s^6} + \frac{e^{-cs}}{s^6}\right). \tag{10}$$

Now $L^{-1}\{u(s)\} = EIy(x)$. Hence

$$EIy(x) = \tfrac{1}{2}Ax^2 + \tfrac{1}{6}Bx^3 + \frac{w_0}{120c}[5cx^4 - x^5 + (x - c)^5\alpha(x - c)]. \tag{11}$$

From (11) we obtain

$$EIy'(x) = Ax + \tfrac{1}{2}Bx^2 + \frac{w_0}{24c}[4cx^3 - x^4 + (x - 4)^4\alpha(x - c)], \tag{12}$$

$$EIy''(x) = A + Bx + \frac{w_0}{6c}[3cx^2 - x^3 + (x - c)^3\alpha(x - c)], \tag{13}$$

$$EIy'''(x) = B + \frac{w_0}{2c}[2cx - x^2 + (x - c)^2\alpha(x - c)]. \tag{14}$$

By differentiating both members of equation (14), we can see that the y of (11) is a solution of (6) over the infinite range and, more important, a solution of (2) over the range $0 < x < 2c$.

With the aid of equations (11) through (14) we can now determine A and B to make the y satisfy appropriate conditions at $x = 2c$, whether the beam be free, imbedded, or pin-supported there. In our example the beam is to be free at $x = 2c$; the solution is to satisfy the conditions

$$y''(2c) = 0, \qquad y'''(2c) = 0. \tag{4}$$

Using (13) and (14), and a little work, we find that (4) requires $A = \tfrac{1}{6}w_0 c^2$, $B = -\tfrac{1}{2}w_0 c$. We are thus led to the solution

$$EIy(x) = \tfrac{1}{12}w_0 c^2x^2 - \tfrac{1}{12}w_0 cx^3 + \frac{w_0}{120c}[5cx^4 - x^5 + (x - c)^5\alpha(x - c)], \tag{15}$$

for $0 \leqq x \leqq 2c$.

The student should verify by differentiations and appropriate substitutions that the y of (15) satisfies the original differential equation (2) and boundary conditions (3) and (4).

From (15) we can obtain whatever information we wish. For example, at $x = \tfrac{1}{2}c$ the bending moment is

$$EIy''(\tfrac{1}{2}c) = w_0 c^2[\tfrac{1}{6} - \tfrac{1}{4} + \tfrac{1}{6}(-\tfrac{1}{8} + \tfrac{3}{4} + 0)] = \tfrac{1}{48}w_0 c^2.$$

Exercises

1. A clock has a 6-inch pendulum. The clock ticks once for each time that the pendulum completes a swing, returning to its original position. How many times does the clock tick in 30 seconds?   ANS.   38 times.

2. A 6-inch pendulum is released from rest at an angle one-tenth of a radian from the vertical. Using $g = 32$ (ft. per sec. per sec.), describe the motion.

ANS. $\theta = 0.1 \cos 8t$ (radians).

3. For the pendulum of Ex. 2, find the maximum angular speed and its first time of occurrence.   ANS.   0.8 (rad. per sec.) at 0.2 sec.

4. A 6-inch pendulum is started with a velocity of one radian per second, toward the vertical, from a position one-tenth radian from the vertical. Describe the motion.   ANS. $\theta = \frac{1}{10} \cos 8t - \frac{1}{8} \sin 8t$ (radians).

5. For Ex. 4, find to the nearest degree the maximum angular displacement from the vertical.   ANS.   9°.

6. Interpret as a pendulum problem and solve:

$$\frac{d^2\theta}{dt^2} + \beta^2\theta = 0 : \beta^2 = \frac{g}{C},$$ (A)

when $t = 0$, $\theta = \theta_0$ and $\omega = \frac{d\theta}{dt} = \omega_0$.   (B)

ANS. $\theta = \theta_0 \cos \beta t + \beta^{-1}\omega_0 \sin \beta t$ (radians).

7. Find the maximum angular displacement from the vertical for the pendulum of Ex. 6.   ANS. $\theta_{max} = (\theta_0{}^2 + \beta^{-2}\omega_0{}^2)^{1/2}$.

In Exs. 8–11, find the y that satisfies equation (1), page 217, with the given load function $W(x)$ and the given conditions at the ends of the beam. (See (a), (b), (c), page 217.) Verify your solutions.

8. $W(x)$ as in the example introduced on page 218; beam imbedded at both $x = 0$ and $x = 2c$.

ANS. $EIy(x) = \frac{23}{480}w_0 c^2x^2 - \frac{3}{40}w_0 cx^3$

$$+ \frac{w_0}{120c} [5cx^4 - x^5 + (x - c)^5\alpha(x - c)].$$

9. $W(x) = 0$,   for $0 < x < \frac{1}{2}c$,

$\qquad = w_0$,   for $\frac{1}{2}c < x < \frac{3}{2}c$,

$\qquad = 0$,   for $\frac{3}{2}c < x < 2c$;

beam imbedded at $x = 0$, free at $x = 2c$.

ANS. $EIy(x) = \frac{1}{2}w_0 c^2x^2 - \frac{1}{6}w_0 cx^3$

$\qquad\qquad + \frac{1}{24}w_0[(x - \frac{1}{2}c)^4\alpha(x - \frac{1}{2}c) - (x - \frac{3}{2}c)^4\alpha(x - \frac{3}{2}c)]$.

10. $W(x) = w_0[1 - \alpha(x - c)]$ (describe the load); beam to be imbedded at $x = 0$ and pin-supported (simply supported) at $x = 2c$.

ANS. $EIy(x) = \frac{9}{64}w_0 c^2x^2 - \frac{19}{128}w_0 cx^3 + \frac{1}{24}w_0[x^4 - (x - c)^4\alpha(x - c)]$.

11. $W(x) = \frac{w_0}{c}(2c - x)$,   for $0 < x < c$,

$\qquad = w_0$,   for $c < x < 2c$;

beam to be imbedded at $x = 0$ and free at $x = 2c$.

ANS. $EIy(x) = \frac{13}{12}w_0 c^2x^2 - \frac{5}{12}w_0 cx^3 + \frac{1}{24}w_0 x^4$

$$+ \frac{w_0}{120c} [5cx^4 - x^5 + (x - c)^5\alpha(x - c)].$$

CHAPTER 13

Systems of Equations

71. The Laplace transform method

The Laplace operator can be used to transform a system of linear differential equations with constant coefficients into a system of algebraic equations.

EXAMPLE (a):   Solve the system of equations

$$x''(t) - x(t) + 5y'(t) = t,$$ (1)

$$y''(t) - 4y(t) - 2x'(t) = -2,$$ (2)

with the initial conditions

$$x(0) = 0, \qquad x'(0) = 0, \qquad y(0) = 0, \qquad y'(0) = 0.$$ (3)

Let $L\{x(t)\} = u(s)$ and $L\{y(t)\} = v(s)$. Then, application of the Laplace operator transforms the problem into that of solving a pair of simultaneous algebraic equations:

$$(s^2 - 1)u(s) + 5sv(s) = \frac{1}{s^2}, \tag{4}$$

$$-2su(s) + (s^2 - 4)v(s) = -\frac{2}{s}. \tag{5}$$

We solve equations (4) and (5) to obtain

$$u(s) = \frac{11s^2 - 4}{s^2(s^2 + 1)(s^2 + 4)}, \tag{6}$$

$$v(s) = \frac{-2s^2 + 4}{s(s^2 + 1)(s^2 + 4)}. \tag{7}$$

Seeking the inverse transforms of u and v, we first expand the right members of (6) and (7) into partial fractions:

$$u(s) = -\frac{1}{s^2} + \frac{5}{s^2 + 1} - \frac{4}{s^2 + 4}, \tag{8}$$

$$v(s) = \frac{1}{s} - \frac{2s}{s^2 + 1} + \frac{s}{s^2 + 4}. \tag{9}$$

Since $x(t) = L^{-1}\{u(s)\}$ and $y(t) = L^{-1}\{v(s)\}$, we get the desired result

$$x(t) = -t + 5 \sin t - 2 \sin 2t, \tag{10}$$

$$y(t) = 1 - 2 \cos t + \cos 2t, \tag{11}$$

which is easily verified by direct substitution into (1), (2), and (3).

The foregoing procedure is simple in concept, but of course its practical use will depend on our ability to find the inverse transforms of $u(s)$ and $v(s)$. On the other hand, the use of the transform theory can help us gain insight into the general theory of systems of linear differential equations. We illustrate this idea in the following example.

EXAMPLE (b):   Solve the system

$$\frac{dx}{dt} = y + F(t), \tag{12}$$

$$\frac{dy}{dt} = x + G(t). \tag{13}$$

Here we presume that the transforms of the functions $x(t)$, $y(t)$, $F(t)$, and $G(t)$ all exist and are given by $u(s)$, $v(s)$, $f(s)$, and $g(s)$, respectively. We then have

$$su(s) - c_1 = v(s) + f(s), \tag{14}$$

$$sv(s) - c_2 = u(s) + g(s), \tag{15}$$

where c_1 and c_2 represent the initial values of $x(t)$ and $y(t)$. We can rewrite equations (14) and (15) in the form

$$su(s) - v(s) = c_1 + f(s), \tag{16}$$

$$-u(s) + sv(s) = c_2 + g(s). \tag{17}$$

Using Cramer's rule, the solution of the algebraic system (16) and (17) may be written

$$u(s) = \frac{\begin{vmatrix} c_1 + f(s) & -1 \\ c_2 + g(s) & s \end{vmatrix}}{s^2 - 1} = \frac{\begin{vmatrix} c_1 & -1 \\ c_2 & s \end{vmatrix}}{s^2 - 1} + \frac{\begin{vmatrix} f(s) & -1 \\ g(s) & s \end{vmatrix}}{s^2 - 1}, \tag{18}$$

$$v(s) = \frac{\begin{vmatrix} s & c_1 + f(s) \\ -1 & c_2 + g(s) \end{vmatrix}}{s^2 - 1} = \frac{\begin{vmatrix} s & c_1 \\ -1 & c_2 \end{vmatrix}}{s^2 - 1} + \frac{\begin{vmatrix} s & f(s) \\ -1 & g(s) \end{vmatrix}}{s^2 - 1}. \tag{19}$$

A careful examination of equations (18) and (19) reveals several important properties of the pair of functions, $x(t)$ and $y(t)$, we are seeking. First, each of these functions can be considered as the sum of two functions; that is,

$$x(t) = x_c(t) + x_p(t),$$

$$y(t) = y_c(t) + y_p(t).$$

The notation used is intended to remind us of a similar situation we met when we were dealing with a single linear differential equation with one dependent variable. We note that the pair of functions, $x_c(t)$ and $y_c(t)$, is a solution of the system (12) and (13) in the case where $F(t) = G(t) = 0$ (and of course $f(s) = g(s) = 0$). Moreover, each of the functions $x_c(t)$ and $y_c(t)$ involves the constants c_1 and c_2 that are the initial values of $x(t)$ and $y(t)$.

On the other hand, the functions $x_p(t)$ and $y_p(t)$, whereas independent of the initial conditions, are intimately related to the functions $F(t)$ and $G(t)$.

Although it is possible to obtain the functions $x(t)$ and $y(t)$ from (18) and (19) by using convolution integrals (see Ex. 9 below), let us simplify the problem by considering a particular case.

EXAMPLE (c): Solve the system of equations (12) and (13) if $F(t) = 1$ and $G(t) = t$.

Equations (18) and (19) now become

$$u(s) = \frac{\begin{vmatrix} c_1 & -1 \\ c_2 & s \end{vmatrix}}{s^2 - 1} + \frac{\begin{vmatrix} \dfrac{1}{s} & -1 \\ \dfrac{1}{s^2} & s \end{vmatrix}}{s^2 - 1}, \tag{20}$$

$$v(s) = \frac{\begin{vmatrix} s & c_1 \\ -1 & c_2 \end{vmatrix}}{s^2 - 1} + \frac{\begin{vmatrix} s & \frac{1}{s} \\ -1 & \frac{1}{s^2} \end{vmatrix}}{s^2 - 1}. \tag{21}$$

These equations may be written

$$u(s) = \frac{c_1 + c_2}{2(s - 1)} + \frac{c_1 - c_2}{2(s + 1)} - \frac{1}{s^2} + \frac{1}{s - 1} - \frac{1}{s + 1}. \tag{22}$$

$$v(s) = \frac{c_1 + c_2}{2(s - 1)} - \frac{c_1 - c_2}{2(s + 1)} - \frac{2}{s} + \frac{1}{s - 1} + \frac{1}{s + 1}, \tag{23}$$

where we have taken care to keep the two parts of each of these functions separate. The inversion of equations (22) and (23) yields

$$x(t) = \frac{c_1 + c_2}{2} e^t + \frac{c_1 - c_2}{2} e^{-t} - t + e^t - e^{-t}, \tag{24}$$

$$y(t) = \frac{c_1 + c_2}{2} e^t - \frac{c_1 - c_2}{2} e^{-t} - 2 + e^t + e^{-t}. \tag{25}$$

The student should now verify directly that the pair of functions, $x_c(t)$ and $y_c(t)$, which involve the initial values c_1 and c_2, is a solution of the system

$$\frac{dx}{dt} = y \quad \text{and} \quad \frac{dy}{dt} = x.$$

This system results from placing $F(t) = G(t) = 0$ in equations (12) and (13). He should also verify that the remaining part of the solution, $x_p(t)$ and $y_p(t)$, is a particular solution of the system (12) and (13) with $F(t) = 1$ and $G(t) = t$. Finally, it is easy to show that $x(0) = c_1$ and $y(0) = c_2$.

Exercises

In Exs. 1–8, use the Laplace transform method to solve the given system.

1. $x''(t) - 3x'(t) - y'(t) + 2y(t) = 14t + 3$,
$x'(t) - 3x(t) + y'(t) = 1; x(0) = 0, x'(0) = 0, y(0) = 6.5$.

         ANS. $x(t) = 2 - \frac{1}{2}e^t - \frac{1}{2}e^{3t} - e^{-2t}$,
                    $y(t) = 7t + 5 - e^t + \frac{5}{2}e^{-2t}$.

2. $2x'(t) + 2x(t) + y'(t) - y(t) = 3t$,
$x'(t) + x(t) + y'(t) + y(t) = 1; x(0) = 1, y(0) = 3$.

         ANS. $x(t) = t + 3e^{-t} - 2e^{-3t}$,
                    $y(t) = 1 - t + 2e^{-3t}$.

3. $x'(t) - 2x(t) - y'(t) - y(t) = 6e^{3t}$,
$2x'(t) - 3x(t) + y'(t) - 3y(t) = 6e^{3t}$; $x(0) = 3$, $y(0) = 0$.

ANS. $x(t) = (1 + 2t)e^t + 2e^{3t}$,
$y(t) = (1 - t)e^t - e^{3t}$.

4. $x''(t) + 2x(t) - y'(t) = 2t + 5$,
$x'(t) - x(t) + y'(t) + y(t) = -2t - 1$; $x(0) = 3$, $x'(0) = 0$, $y(0) = -3$.

ANS. $x(t) = t + 2 + e^{-2t} + \sin t$,
$y(t) = 1 - t - 3e^{-2t} - \cos t$.

5. The equations of Example (a) of Section 71 with initial conditions $x(0) = 0$, $x'(0) = 0$, $y(0) = 1$, $y'(0) = 0$.

ANS. $x(t) = -t - \frac{5}{3}\sin t + \frac{4}{3}\sin 2t$,
$y(t) = 1 + \frac{2}{3}\cos t - \frac{2}{3}\cos 2t$.

6. The equations of Example (a) of Section 71 with initial conditions $x(0) = 9$, $x'(0) = 2$, $y(0) = 1$, $y'(0) = 0$.

ANS. $x(t) = -t + 15\cos t - 5\sin t - 6\cos 2t + 4\sin 2t$,
$y(t) = 1 + 2\cos t + 6\sin t - 2\cos 2t - 3\sin 2t$.

7. $x''(t) + y'(t) - y(t) = 0$,
$2x'(t) - x(t) + z'(t) - z(t) = 0$,
$x'(t) + 3x(t) + y'(t) - 4y(t) + 3z(t) = 0$;
$x(0) = 0$, $x'(0) = 1$, $y(0) = 0$, $z(0) = 0$.

8. $x''(t) - x(t) + 5y'(t) = \beta(t)$,
$y''(t) - 4y(t) - 2x'(t) = 0$,
in which $\beta(t) = 6t$, $0 \leq t \leq 2$,
$= 12$, $t > 2$;
$x(0) = 0$, $x'(0) = 0$, $y(0) = 0$, $y'(0) = 0$.

ANS. $x(t) = -2(3t - 5\sin t + \sin 2t)$
$+ 2[3(t - 2) - 5\sin (t - 2) + \sin 2(t - 2)]\alpha(t - 2)$,
$y(t) = 3 - 4\cos t + \cos 2t$
$- [3 - 4\cos (t - 2) + \cos 2(t - 2)]\alpha(t - 2)$.

9. Write the solution of the system of Example (b) in Section 71 in terms of convolution integrals.

10. Use the results of Ex. 9 to obtain the solution of Example (c) in Section 71.

In Exs. 11 and 12, write the solution in terms of convolution integrals.

11. $x'(t) - 2y(t) = F(t)$,
$y'(t) + x(t) = G(t)$; $x(0) = 1$, $y(0) = 0$.

12. $2x'(t) + 3y(t) = F(t)$,
$y'(t) + 2x(t) = G(t)$; $x(0) = 2$, $y(0) = 1$.

13. Consider the initial value problem
$x'(t) = ax + by + f(t)$,
$y'(t) = cx + dy + g(t)$; $x(0) = c_1$, $y(0) = c_2$,
where a, b, c, d, and c_1, c_2 are constants. Use an argument similar to that of Example (b) of Section 71 to show that the solution, if it exists, should have the form

$$x(t) = x_c(t) + x_p(t),$$
$$y(t) = y_c(t) + y_p(t),$$

where $x_c(t)$ and $y_c(t)$ depend on c_1 and c_2 whereas $x_p(t)$ and $y_p(t)$ depend on $f(t)$ and $g(t)$.

14. For the initial value problem of Ex. 13, state a reasonable definition for a first-order homogeneous linear system with constant coefficients. Now state a theorem that expresses the results of Ex. 13 for the solution of a nonhomogeneous system.

15. Consider the initial value problem

$$x'(t) + 2y(t) = 0,$$
$$x''(t) + 2y'(t) + 2y(t) = 2e^t;$$
$$x(0) = 1, \ x'(0) = 0, \ y(0) = 0.$$

(a) Show that the Laplace transform method produces

$$x = 3 - 2e^t, \ y = e^t.$$

(b) Verify that these functions satisfy the differential equations but do not satisfy the initial conditions.

(c) By elementary elimination, show that a solution of the system of differential equations has the form

$$x = c_1 - 2e^t, \ y = e^t,$$

and thus the initial conditions given are not compatible with the system of equations.

72. The differential operator method

In solving systems of simultaneous linear equations, the differential operator notation is another convenient tool. Consider the system

$$y'' - y + 5v' = x, \tag{1}$$
$$2y' - v'' + 4v = 2,$$

with independent variable x and dependent variables y and v. It is natural to attack the system (1) by eliminating one dependent variable to obtain a single equation in the other dependent variable. Using $D = d/dx$, write the system (1) in the form

$$(D^2 - 1)y + 5Dv = x, \tag{2}$$
$$2Dy - (D^2 - 4)v = 2.$$

Then, elimination of one dependent variable is straightforward. We may, for instance, operate upon the first equation with $2D$ and upon the second equation with $(D^2 - 1)$, and then subtract one from the other, obtaining

$$[10D^2 + (D^2 - 1)(D^2 - 4)]v = 2Dx - (D^2 - 1)2,$$

or

$$(D^4 + 5D^2 + 4)v = 4. \tag{3}$$

In a similar manner v may be eliminated; the resultant equation for y is

$$[(D^2 - 1)(D^2 - 4) + 10D^2]y = (D^2 - 4)x + 5D(2),$$

or

$$(D^4 + 5D^2 + 4)y = -4x. \tag{4}$$

From equations (3) and (4) it follows at once that

$$v = 1 + a_1 \cos x + a_2 \sin x + a_3 \cos 2x + a_4 \sin 2x \tag{5}$$

and

$$y = -x + b_1 \cos x + b_2 \sin x + b_3 \cos 2x + b_4 \sin 2x. \tag{6}$$

The a's and b's have yet to be chosen to make (5) and (6) satisfy the original equations, rather than just the equations (3) and (4), which resulted from the original ones after certain eliminations were performed.

Combining (by substitution) the v of (5) and the y of (6) with the first equation of the system (2) leads to the identity

$$x - 2b_1 \cos x - 2b_2 \sin x - 5b_3 \cos 2x - 5b_4 \sin 2x \tag{7}$$
$$- 5a_1 \sin x + 5a_2 \cos x - 10a_3 \sin 2x + 10a_4 \cos 2x \equiv x.$$

That (7) be an identity in x demands that

$$\begin{aligned} -2b_1 + 5a_2 &= 0, \\ -2b_2 - 5a_1 &= 0, \\ -5b_3 + 10a_4 &= 0, \\ -5b_4 - 10a_3 &= 0. \end{aligned} \tag{8}$$

Relations between the a's and b's equivalent to the relations (8) follow from substitution of the v of (5) and the y of (6) into the second equation of the system (2).

We conclude that a set of solutions of the system (2) is

$$v = 1 + a_1 \cos x + a_2 \sin x + a_3 \cos 2x + a_4 \sin 2x, \tag{9}$$
$$y = -x + \tfrac{5}{2}a_2 \cos x - \tfrac{5}{2}a_1 \sin x + 2a_4 \cos 2x - 2a_3 \sin 2x,$$

in which a_1, a_2, a_3, a_4 are arbitrary constants.

The equations (3) and (4) for v and y can be written with the aid of determinants. From the system (2) above we may write at once

$$\begin{vmatrix} (D^2 - 1) & 5D \\ 2D & -(D^2 - 4) \end{vmatrix} v = \begin{vmatrix} (D^2 - 1) & x \\ 2D & 2 \end{vmatrix},$$

which reduces to equation (3) above, if care is used in the interpretation of the right-hand member. The determinant on the right is to be interpreted as

$$(D^2 - 1)(2) - 2D(x),$$

not as the differential operator $2(D^2 - 1) - x(2D)$.

Determinants are extremely useful in any treatment of the theory of systems of linear equations. For many simple systems which arise in practice, no such powerful tool is needed.

There are other techniques for treating a system such as (2). For example, we may first obtain (3) and from it v as in equation (5). Next we wish to find an equation giving y in terms of v; that is, we seek to eliminate from the system (2) those terms that involve derivatives of y. From (2) we obtain the two equations

$$(2D^2 - 2)y + 10Dv = 2x, \tag{10}$$

$$2D^2y - (D^3 - 4D)v = 0, \tag{11}$$

the latter by operating with D on each member of the second equation of the system (2). From (10) and (11) it follows at once that

$$2y - D^3v - 6Dv = -2x,$$

or

$$y = -x + \tfrac{1}{2}D^3v + 3Dv. \tag{12}$$

The v of equation (5) may now be used in (12) to compute the y which was given in the solution (9). In this method of solution there is no need to obtain (4), (6), (7), or (8).

Both methods outlined here are available whenever the system is linear with constant coefficients. Such systems appear naturally in the study of electric networks which will be discussed in the next chapter.

Systems of nonlinear equations and systems of linear equations with variable coefficients will not be studied in this book.

Exercises

In Exs. 1–4, use the differential operator method.

1. Ex. 1, Section 71.   **2.** Ex. 2, Section 71.
3. Ex. 3, Section 71.   **4.** Ex. 4, Section 71.

In Exs. 5–17, use either of the two methods of this chapter.

5. $v' - 2v + 2w' = 2 - 4e^{2x},$
   $2v' - 3v + 3w' - w = 0.$

ANS. $v = a_1e^x + a_2 e^{-2x} + 5e^{2x} - 1,$
      $w = \tfrac{1}{2}a_1e^x - a_2 e^{-2x} - e^{2x} + 3.$

6. $(3D + 2)v + (D - 6)w = 5e^x,$
   $(4D + 2)v + (D - 8)w = 5e^x + 2x - 3.$

ANS. $v = a_1 \cos 2x + a_2 \sin 2x + 2e^x - 3x + 5,$
      $w = a_2 \cos 2x - a_1 \sin 2x + e^x - x.$

7. $(D^2 + 6)y + Dv = 0,$
   $(D + 2)y + (D - 2)v = 2.$

ANS. $y = c_1e^{3x} + c_2 \cos 2x + c_3 \sin 2x,$
      $v = -1 - 5c_1e^{3x} + c_3 \cos 2x - c_2 \sin 2x.$

8. $D^2 y - (2D - 1)v = 1,$
$(2D + 1)y + (D^2 - 4)v = 0.$

ANS. $v = 1 + a_1 e^x + a_2 e^{-x} + a_3 \cos x + a_4 \sin x,$
$y = 4 + a_1 e^x - 3a_2 e^{-x} + (a_3 - 2a_4) \cos x + (2a_3 + a_4) \sin x.$

9. $(D^2 - 3D)y - (D - 2)z = 14x + 7,$
$(D - 3)y + Dz = 1.$

ANS. $y = 2 + a_1 e^x + a_2 e^{3x} + a_3 e^{-2x},$
$z = 7 + 7x + 2a_1 e^x - \frac{5}{2}a_3 e^{-2x}.$

10. $(D^3 + D^2 - 1)u + (D^3 + 2D^2 + 3D + 1)v = 3 - x ,$
$(D - 1)u + (D + 1)v = 3 - x.$

ANS. $u = 2x + a_1 + a_2 \cos x + a_3 \sin x,$
$v = x + a_1 - a_3 \cos x + a_2 \sin x.$

11. $(D^2 + 1)y + 4(D - 1)v = 4e^x,$
$(D - 1)y + (D + 9)v = 0;$ when $x = 0, y = 5, y' = 0, v = \frac{1}{2}.$

ANS. $y = 2e^x + 2e^{-x} + e^{-2x} (\cos x + 2 \sin x),$
$v = \frac{1}{2}e^{-x} + e^{-2x} \sin x.$

12. $\dfrac{d^2 x}{dt^2} + x - 2\dfrac{dy}{dt} = 2t,$

$2\dfrac{dx}{dt} - x + \dfrac{dy}{dt} - 2y = 7.$

ANS. $x = 2t - 2 + b_1 e^t + b_2 e^{-t} + b_3 e^{-2t},$
$y = -t - 1 + b_1 e^t - b_2 e^{-t} - \frac{5}{4}b_3 e^{-2t}.$

13. $2(D + 1)y + (D - 1)w = x + 1,$
$(D + 3)y + (D + 1)w = 4x + 14.$

ANS. $y = x + 2 + c_1 e^{-x} \cos 2x + c_2 e^{-x} \sin 2x,$
$w = x + 6 + (c_2 - c_1)e^{-x} \cos 2x - (c_1 + c_2)e^{-x} \sin 2x.$

14. $(D + 1)y + (D - 4)v = 6 \cos x,$
$(D - 1)y + (D^2 + 4)v = -6 \sin x.$

ANS. $y = 3 \cos x + 3 \sin x + a_1 + a_2 \cos 3x + a_3 \sin 3x,$
$v = \frac{1}{4}a_1 - \frac{1}{5}(a_2 - 3a_3) \cos 3x - \frac{1}{5}(3a_2 + a_3) \sin 3x.$

15. $2Du + (D - 1)v + (D + 2)w = 0,$
$(D + 2)u + (2D - 3)v - (D - 6)w = 0,$
$2Du - (D + 3)v - Dw = 0.$

ANS. $u = 3c_1 e^{2x} + 3c_2 e^{-x} + 3c_3 e^{x/2},$
$v = 4c_1 e^{2x} - 5c_2 e^{-x} + c_3 e^{x/2},$
$w = -4c_1 e^{2x} - 4c_2 e^{-x} - c_3 e^{x/2}.$

16. $D^2 y + (D - 1)v = 0,$
$(2D - 1)y + (D - 1)w = 0,$
$(D + 3)y + (D - 4)v + 3w = 0.$

ANS. $y = a_1 + a_2 e^x + 3a_3 e^{4x},$
$v = b_2 e^x - a_2 xe^x - 16a_3 e^{4x},$
$w = -a_1 + (b_2 - a_2)e^x - a_2 xe^x - 7a_3 e^{4x}.$

17. Solve the problem of Section 72 by the method of Section 71.

CHAPTER **14**

Electric Circuits and Networks

73. Circuits

The basic laws governing the flow of electric current in a circuit or a network will be given here without derivation. The notation used is common to most texts in electrical engineering and is:

t (sec.) = time
Q (coulombs) = quantity of electricity; e.g., charge on a capacitor
I (amperes) = current, time rate of flow of electricity
E (volts) = electromotive force or voltage
R (ohms) = resistance
L (henrys) = inductance
C (farads) = capacitance.

By the definition of Q and I it follows that

$$I(t) = Q'(t).$$

The current at each point in a network may be determined by solving the equations that result from applying Kirchhoff's laws:

(a) *The sum of the currents into (or away from) any point is zero,*
and
(b) *Around any closed path the sum of the instantaneous voltage drops in a specified direction is zero.*

A circuit is treated as a network containing only one closed path. Figure 30 exhibits an "*RLC* circuit" with some of the customary conventions for indicating various elements.

FIGURE 30

For a circuit, Kirchhoff's current law (a) indicates merely that the current is the same throughout. That law plays a larger role in networks, as we shall see later.

To apply Kirchhoff's voltage law (b), it is necessary to know the contributions of each of the idealized elements in Figure 30. The voltage drop across the resistance is RI, that across the inductance is $LI'(t)$, and that across the capacitor is $C^{-1}Q(t)$. The impressed electromotive force $E(t)$ is contributing a voltage rise.

Assume that at time $t = 0$ the switch shown in Figure 30 is to be closed. At $t = 0$ there is no current flowing, $I(0) = 0$, and if the capacitor is initially without charge, $Q(0) = 0$. From Kirchhoff's law (b), we get the differential equation

$$LI'(t) + RI(t) + C^{-1}Q(t) = E(t), \tag{1}$$

in which

$$I(t) = Q'(t). \tag{2}$$

Equations (1) and (2), with the initial conditions

$$I(0) = 0, \qquad Q(0) = 0, \tag{3}$$

constitute the problem to be solved.

To retain the conventional symbol L for the number of henrys inductance of the circuit, we shall in this section denote by L_t the Laplace operator for which L is used in all other sections of the book.

Let the transforms of $I(t)$, $Q(t)$, $E(t)$ be denoted by lower case letters:

$$L_t\{I(t)\} = i(s), \qquad L_t\{Q(t)\} = q(s), \qquad L_t\{E(t)\} = e(s). \tag{4}$$

The problem (1), (2), and (3) is then transformed into

$$L\,si(s) + Ri(s) + C^{-1}q(s) = e(s), \tag{5}$$

$$i(s) = sq(s). \tag{6}$$

From (5) and (6) we find either or both of $i(s)$ and $q(s)$,

$$i(s) = \frac{se(s)}{Ls^2 + Rs + C^{-1}}, \tag{7}$$

$$q(s) = \frac{e(s)}{Ls^2 + Rs + C^{-1}}. \tag{8}$$

Then $I(t)$ and $Q(t)$ are obtained as inverse transforms from (7) and (8).

From (7), (8), or the differential equation

$$LQ''(t) + RQ'(t) + C^{-1}Q(t) = E(t), \tag{9}$$

it follows that the circuit problem is equivalent to a problem in damped vibrations of a spring (Section 69). The resistance term $RQ'(t)$ parallels the damping term in vibration problems. The analogies between electrical and mechanical systems are useful in practice.

FIGURE 31

EXAMPLE: In the RL circuit with the schematic diagram shown in Figure 31, let the switch be closed at $t = 0$. At some later time, $t = t_0$, the direct current element, the constant E, is to be removed from the circuit, which remains closed. Find the current for all $t > 0$.

The initial value problem to be solved is

$$LI'(t) + RI(t) = E(t); \qquad I(0) = 0, \tag{10}$$

$$E(t) = E[1 - \alpha(t - t_0)]. \tag{11}$$

Let the transform of $I(t)$ be $i(s)$. We know the transform of $E(t)$. Therefore we obtain the transformed problem

$$sLi(s) + Ri(s) = \frac{E}{s}[1 - \exp(-t_0 s)], \tag{12}$$

from which

$$i(s) = \frac{E[1 - \exp(-t_0 s)]}{s(sL + R)}. \tag{13}$$

Now

$$\frac{1}{s(sL + R)} = \frac{1}{R}\left(\frac{1}{s} - \frac{1}{s + RL^{-1}}\right),$$

so

$$i(s) = \frac{E}{R}\left(\frac{1}{s} - \frac{1}{s + RL^{-1}}\right)[1 - \exp(-t_0 s)].$$

Therefore

$$I(t) = \frac{E}{R}\left[1 - \alpha(t - t_0) - \exp\left(-\frac{R}{L}t\right) + \exp\left\{-\frac{R}{L}(t - t_0)\right\}\alpha(t - t_0)\right]. \tag{14}$$

The student should verify (14) and show that it can be written

$$\text{For } 0 \leq t \leq t_0, \qquad I(t) = \frac{E}{R}\left[1 - \exp\left(-\frac{Rt}{L}\right)\right]; \tag{15}$$

$$\text{For } t > t_0, \qquad I(t) = I(t_0)\exp\left[-\frac{R}{L}(t - t_0)\right]. \tag{16}$$

74. Simple networks

Systems of differential equations occur naturally in the application of Kirchhoff's laws to electric networks. The use of the Laplace operator makes the solution of such systems a straightforward, though often laborious, process. For the general theory of networks the Laplace operator is a tool of great value. We restrict ourselves to extremely simple situations which should be sufficient to indicate the procedure commonly used.

EXAMPLE (a): Determine the character of the current $I_1(t)$ in the network having the schematic diagram in Figure 32, under the assumption that when the switch is closed the currents are each zero.

FIGURE 32

In a network, we apply Kirchhoff's laws, page 232, to obtain a system of equations to determine the currents. Since there are three dependent variables, I_1, I_2, I_3, we need three equations.

From the current law it follows that

$$I_1 = I_2 + I_3. \tag{1}$$

Application of the voltage law to the circuit on the left in Figure 32 yields

$$R_1 I_1 + L_2 I_2' = E. \tag{2}$$

Using the voltage law on the outside circuit, we get

$$R_1 I_1 + R_3 I_3 + L_3 I_3' = E. \tag{3}$$

Still another equation can be obtained from the circuit on the right in Figure 32:

$$R_3 I_3 + L_3 I_3' - L_2 I_2' = 0. \tag{4}$$

Equation (4) also follows at once from equations (2) and (3); it may be used instead of either (2) or (3).

We wish to obtain $I_1(t)$ from the initial value problem consisting of equations (1), (2), (3), and the conditions $I_1(0) = 0$, $I_2(0) = 0$, $I_3(0) = 0$. One of the three initial conditions is redundant because of equation (1).

Let $L\{I_k(t)\} = i_k(s)$ for each of $k = 1, 2, 3$. Then use of the operator L transforms our problem into the algebraic one of solving the equations

$$i_1 - i_2 - i_3 = 0, \tag{5}$$

$$R_1 i_1 + s L_2 i_2 = \frac{E}{s}, \tag{6}$$

$$R_1 i_1 + (R_3 + s L_3) i_3 = \frac{E}{s}. \tag{7}$$

Since we desire only $i_1(s)$, let us use determinants to write the solution

$$i_1(s) = \cfrac{\begin{vmatrix} 0 & -1 & -1 \\ \dfrac{E}{s} & s L_2 & 0 \\ \dfrac{E}{s} & 0 & (R_3 + s L_3) \end{vmatrix}}{\Delta} = \frac{E}{s} \cdot \frac{R_3 + s(L_2 + L_3)}{\Delta}, \tag{8}$$

in which

$$\Delta = \begin{vmatrix} 1 & -1 & -1 \\ R_1 & s L_2 & 0 \\ R_1 & 0 & (R_3 + s L_3) \end{vmatrix} = \begin{vmatrix} 1 & 0 & 0 \\ R_1 & (s L_2 + R_1) & R_1 \\ R_1 & R_1 & (R_1 + R_3 + s L_3) \end{vmatrix}.$$

Then

$$\Delta = L_2 L_3 s^2 + (R_1 L_2 + R_3 L_2 + R_1 L_3)s + R_1 R_3. \tag{9}$$

We are interested in the factors of Δ. Consider the equation

$$\Delta = 0. \tag{10}$$

Equation (10) has no positive roots. Its discriminant

$$(R_1 L_2 + R_3 L_2 + R_1 L_3)^2 - 4 L_2 L_3 R_1 R_3$$

may be written

$$(R_1 L_2)^2 + 2 R_1 L_2 (R_3 L_2 + R_1 L_3) + (R_3 L_2 + R_1 L_3)^2 - 4 L_2 L_3 R_1 R_3,$$

which equals

$$(R_1 L_2)^2 + 2 R_1 L_2 (R_3 L_2 + R_1 L_3) + (R_3 L_2 - R_1 L_3)^2$$

and is therefore positive. Thus we see that equation (10) has two distinct negative roots. Call them $(-a_1)$ and $(-a_2)$. It follows that

$$\Delta = L_2 L_3 (s + a_1)(s + a_2),$$

and we have, from (8),

$$i_1(s) = \frac{E}{s} \frac{R_3 + s(L_2 + L_3)}{L_2 L_3 (s + a_1)(s + a_2)}. \tag{11}$$

The right member of equation (11) has a partial fractions expansion

$$i_1(s) = \frac{A_0}{s} + \frac{A_1}{s + a_1} + \frac{A_2}{s + a_2}, \tag{12}$$

so

$$I_1(t) = A_0 + A_1 \exp(-a_1 t) + A_2 \exp(-a_2 t).$$

EXAMPLE (b):   For the network shown in Figure 33, set up the equations for the determination of the currents I_1, I_2, I_3, and the charge Q_3. Assume that when the switch is closed all currents and charges are zero. Obtain the transformed problem.

FIGURE 33

Using Kirchhoff's laws we write the equations

$$I_1 = I_2 + I_3, \tag{13}$$

$$R_1 I_1 + L_2 \frac{dI_2}{dt} = E \sin \omega t, \tag{14}$$

$$R_1 I_1 + R_3 I_3 + \frac{1}{C_3} Q_3 = E \sin \omega t; \tag{15}$$

and the definition of current as time rate of change of charge yields

$$I_3 = \frac{dQ_3}{dt}. \tag{16}$$

Our problem consists of the four equations (13) through (16) with the initial conditions that

$$I_2(0) = 0, \qquad I_3(0) = 0, \qquad Q_3(0) = 0. \tag{17}$$

Let $L\{I_k(t)\} = i_k(s)$, $k = 1, 2, 3$, and $L\{Q_3(t)\} = q_3(s)$. Then the transformed problem is the problem of solving the algebraic system

$$i_1 - i_2 - i_3 = 0, \tag{18}$$

$$R_1 i_1 + sL_2 i_2 = \frac{E\omega}{s^2 + \omega^2}, \tag{19}$$

$$R_1 i_1 + R_3 i_3 + \frac{1}{C_3} q_3 = \frac{E\omega}{s^2 + \omega^2}, \tag{20}$$

$$i_3 = sq_3. \tag{21}$$

Exercises

1. For the RL circuit of Figure 31, page 233, find the current I if the direct current element E is not removed from the circuit.
    ANS. $I = ER^{-1}[1 - \exp(-RtL^{-1})]$.
2. Solve Ex. 1 if the direct-current element is replaced by an alternating-current element $E \cos \omega t$. For convenience, use the notation

$$Z^2 = R^2 + \omega^2 L^2,$$

in which Z is called the steady-state impedance of this circuit.
    ANS. $I = EZ^{-2}[\omega L \sin \omega t + R \cos \omega t - R \exp(-RtL^{-1})]$.
3. Solve Ex. 2, replacing $E \cos \omega t$ with $E \sin \omega t$.
4. Figure 34 shows an RC circuit with an alternating-current element inserted. Assume that the switch is closed at $t = 0$ at which time $Q = 0$ and $I = 0$. Use the notation

$$Z^2 = R^2 + (\omega C)^{-2},$$

where Z is the steady-state impedance of this circuit. Find I for $t > 0$.
    ANS. $I = EZ^{-2}[R \sin \omega t + (\omega C)^{-1} \cos \omega t - (\omega C)^{-1} \exp(-tR^{-1}C^{-1})]$.

FIGURE 34

5. In Figure 34, replace the alternating-current element with a direct-current element $E = 50$ volts and use $R = 10$ ohms, $C = 4(10)^{-4}$ farad. Assume that when the switch is closed (at $t = 0$) the charge on the capacitor is 0.015 coulomb. Find the initial current in the circuit and the current for $t > 0$.

      ANS. $I(0) = 1.25(\text{amp})$, $I(t) = 1.25 \exp(-250t)(\text{amp.})$.

6. In Figure 30, page 232, find $I(t)$ if $E(t) = 60$ volts, $R = 40$ ohms, $C = 5(10)^{-5}$ farad, $L = 0.02$ henry. Assume $I(0) = 0$, $Q(0) = 0$.

      ANS. $I = 3000t \exp(-1000t)(\text{amp.})$.

7. In Ex. 6, find the maximum current.   ANS. $I_{max} = 3e^{-1}$ (amp.).

In Exs. 8–11, use Figure 30, page 232, with $E(t) = E \sin \omega t$ and with the following notations used to simplify the appearance of the formulas:

$$a = \frac{R}{2L}, \quad b^2 = a^2 - \frac{1}{LC}, \quad \beta^2 = \frac{1}{LC} - a^2,$$

$$\gamma = \omega L - \frac{1}{\omega C}, \quad Z^2 = R^2 + \gamma^2.$$

The quantity Z is the steady-state impedance for an RLC circuit. In each of Exs. 8–11, find $I(t)$ assuming that $I(0) = 0$ and $Q(0) = 0$.

8. Assume that $4L < R^2C$.

    ANS. $I = EZ^{-2}(R \sin \omega t - \gamma \cos \omega t) + \frac{1}{2}Eb^{-1}Z^{-2}[\{\gamma(a + b)$
                 $- \omega R\} \exp\{-(a - b)t\} + \{\omega R - \gamma(a - b)\} \exp\{-(a + b)t\}]$.

9. Assume that $R^2C < 4L$.

    ANS. $I = EZ^{-2}(R \sin \omega t - \gamma \cos \omega t)$
                 $+ E\beta^{-1}Z^{-2}e^{-at}[\beta\gamma \cos \beta t - a(\gamma + 2\omega^{-1}C^{-1}) \sin \beta t]$.

10. Assume that $R^2C = 4L$.

    ANS. $I = EZ^{-2}(R \sin \omega t - \gamma \cos \omega t) + E\omega^{-1}Z^{-2}e^{-at}[\gamma\omega - a(\gamma\omega + aR)t]$.

11. Show that the answer to Ex. 10 can be put in the form

$$I = EZ^{-2}(R \sin \omega t - \gamma \cos \omega t) + EZ^{-2}e^{-at}[\gamma + (a\gamma - R\omega)t].$$

12. In Ex. 4, replace the alternating current element $E \sin \omega t$ with

$$E[\alpha(t - t_0) - \alpha(t - t_1)], \quad t_1 > t_0 > 0.$$

Graph the new emf. Determine the current in the circuit.

    ANS. $I(t) = \dfrac{E}{R}\left[\exp\left(-\dfrac{t - t_0}{RC}\right)\alpha(t - t_0) - \exp\left(-\dfrac{t - t_1}{RC}\right)\alpha(t - t_1)\right]$.

13. In Figure 35, let $E = 60$ volts, $R_1 = 10$ ohms, $R_3 = 20$ ohms, and $C_2 = 5(10)^{-4}$ farad. Determine the currents if when the switch is closed the capacitor carries a charge of 0.03 coulomb.

      ANS. $I_1 = 2(1 - e^{-300t})$, $I_2 = -3e^{-300t}$, $I_3 = 2 + e^{-300t}$.

14. In Ex. 13, let the initial charge on the capacitor be 0.01 coulomb, but leave the rest of the problem unchanged.

      ANS. $I_1 = 2(1 + e^{-300t})$, $I_2 = 3e^{-300t}$, $I_3 = 2 - e^{-300t}$.

FIGURE 35

FIGURE 36

15. For the network in Figure 36, set up the equations for the determination of the charge Q_3 and the currents I_1, I_2, I_3. Assume all four of those quantities to be zero at time zero. Transform the problem into algebraic form.

FIGURE 37

16. For the network in Figure 37 set up the equations for the determination of the currents. Assume all currents to be zero at time zero. Find $i_1(s) = L\{I_1(t)\}$ and discuss the character of $I_1(t)$ without explicitly finding the function.

CHAPTER **15**

The Existence and Uniqueness
of Solutions

75. Preliminary remarks

The methods of Chapter 2 are strictly dependent on certain special properties (variables separable, exactness, etc.), that may or may not be possessed by an individual equation. It is intuitively plausible that no collection of methods can be found that would permit the explicit solution, in the sense of Chapter 2, of all first-order differential equations. We may seek solutions in other forms, employing infinite series or other limiting processes; we may resort to numerical approximations.

Confronted with this situation, a mathematician reacts by searching for what is known as an existence theorem. He seeks to determine conditions sufficient to insure the existence of a solution that has certain properties. In Chapter 2 we stated such a theorem that we now wish to examine more closely.

76. An existence and uniqueness theorem

Consider the equation of order one

$$\frac{dy}{dx} = f(x, y). \tag{1}$$

Let T denote the rectangular region defined by

$$|x - x_0| \leqq a \qquad \text{and} \qquad |y - y_0| \leqq b,$$

a region with the point (x_0, y_0) at its center. Let the function f in equation (1) and the function $\partial f/\partial y$ be continuous at each point in T. Then there exists an interval, $|x - x_0| \leqq h$, and a function $\phi(x)$ that has the following properties:

(a) $y = \phi(x)$ is a solution of equation (1) on the interval $|x - x_0| \leqq h$;
(b) On the interval $|x - x_0| \leqq h$, $\phi(x)$ satisfies the inequality $|\phi(x) - y_0| \leqq b$;
(c) $\phi(x_0) = y_0$;
(d) $\phi(x)$ is unique on the interval $|x - x_0| \leqq h$ in the sense that it is the only function that has all of the properties (a), (b), and (c).

The interval $|x - x_0| \leqq h$ may or may not need to be smaller than the interval $|x - x_0| \leqq b$ over which conditions were imposed on f and $\partial f/\partial y$.

In rough language, the theorem states that if $f(x, y)$ is sufficiently well behaved near the point (x_0, y_0), the differential equation (1) has a solution that passes through the point (x_0, y_0), and that solution is unique near (x_0, y_0).

A proof of this fundamental theorem is presented in the next three sections. In essence the proof involves showing that a certain sequence of functions has a limit and that the limiting function is the desired solution. The sequence considered will be defined as follows:

$$y_0(x) = y_0,$$

$$y_1(x) = y_0 + \int_{x_0}^{x} f(t, y_0(t)) \, dt,$$

$$y_2(x) = y_0 + \int_{x_0}^{x} f(t, y_1(t)) \, dt,$$

$$\vdots \tag{2}$$

$$y_n(x) = y_0 + \int_{x_0}^{x} f(t, y_{n-1}(t)) \, dt.$$

So that the proof may appear more reasonable, we first consider some examples of the proof for special differential equations.

EXAMPLE (a):   Show that the sequence of functions defined in equations (2) converges to a solution for the initial value problem

$$\frac{dy}{dx} = y; \quad x_0 = 0, \quad y_0 = 1. \tag{3}$$

We find that

$$y_0(x) = 1,$$

$$y_1(x) = 1 + \int_0^x dt = 1 + x,$$

$$y_2(x) = 1 + \int_0^x (1 + t)\, dt = 1 + x + \frac{x^2}{2},$$

$$y_3(x) = 1 + \int_0^x \left(1 + t + \frac{t^2}{2}\right) dt = 1 + x + \frac{x^2}{2} + \frac{x^3}{3!}.$$

From the pattern that is developing, it is easy to conjecture that

$$y_n(x) = \sum_{k=0}^n \frac{x^k}{k!}.$$

Indeed, this is easy to prove by induction. Moreover, the limit of this sequence exists for every real number x because the limit is nothing more than the Maclaurin series expansion for e^x, which converges for every x. That is,

$$\phi(x) = \lim_{n \to \infty} y_n(x) = \sum_{k=0}^\infty \frac{x^k}{k!} = e^x.$$

It is a simple matter to verify that e^x is a solution to the initial value problem (3).

EXAMPLE (b):   Find a solution of the initial value problem

$$\frac{dy}{dx} = x^2; \quad x_0 = 2, \quad y_0 = 1. \tag{4}$$

The sequence defined in (2) above now becomes

$$y_0(x) = 1,$$

$$y_1(x) = 1 + \int_2^x t^2\, dt = \frac{x^3}{3} - \frac{5}{3},$$

$$y_2(x) = 1 + \int_2^x t^2\, dt = \frac{x^3}{3} - \frac{5}{3},$$

$$\vdots$$

$$y_n(x) = 1 + \int_2^x t^2\, dt = \frac{x^3}{3} - \frac{5}{3}.$$

Clearly the limit of this sequence is $\dfrac{x^3}{3} - \dfrac{5}{3}$, and this function is a solution of (4).

Exercises

In each of the following exercises, determine the limit of the sequence defined in (2) above. Verify that the function you obtain is a solution of the initial value problem.

1. $y' = x$; $x_0 = 2$, $y_0 = 1$.
2. $y' = y$; $x_0 = 0$, $y_0 = 2$.
3. $y' = 2y$; $x_0 = 0$, $y_0 = 1$.
4. $y' = x + y$; $x_0 = 0$, $y_0 = 1$.

77. A Lipschitz condition

We have assumed in the hypothesis of the foregoing existence theorem that the function f and its derivative $\partial f/\partial y$ are continuous in the rectangle T. Thus if (x, y_1) and (x, y_2) are points in T, the mean value theorem applies to f as a function of y. Hence, there exists a number y^* between y_1 and y_2 such that

$$f(x, y_1) - f(x, y_2) = \frac{\partial f}{\partial y}(x, y^*)(y_1 - y_2).$$

The assumption that $\partial f/\partial y$ is continuous in T allows us to assert that $\partial f/\partial y$ is bounded there. That is, there exists a number $K > 0$ such that

$$\left|\frac{\partial f}{\partial y}\right| \le K,$$

for every point in T. Since (x, y^*) is in T, it follows that

$$|f(x, y_1) - f(x, y_2)| = \left|\frac{\partial f}{\partial y}(x, y^*)\right| \cdot |y_1 - y_2|,$$

and

$$|f(x, y_1) - f(x, y_2)| \le K|y_1 - y_2|, \tag{1}$$

for every pair of points (x, y_1) and (x, y_2) in T.

The inequality (1) is called a " Lipschitz condition " for the function f. We have shown that under the hypotheses of our existence theorem, the Lipschitz condition (1) holds for every pair of points (x, y_1) and (x, y_2) in T.

In the proof in Section 78 we shall actually use the Lipschitz condition rather than the hypothesized continuity of $\partial f/\partial y$. Thus we could restate the existence theorem in terms of condition (1) instead of assuming $\partial f/\partial y$ is continuous in T.

78. A proof of the existence theorem

One hypothesis of the existence theorem of Section 76 is that f is continuous in the rectangle T. It follows that f must be bounded in T. Let $M > 0$ be a number such that $|f(x, y)| \leq M$ for every point in T. We now take h to be the smaller of the two numbers a and b/M, and define the rectangle R to be the set of points (x, y) for which

$$|x - x_0| \leq h \qquad \text{and} \qquad |y - y_0| \leq b.$$

Clearly R is a subset of T.

As indicated in Section 76, we now consider the sequence of functions

$$y_n(x) = y_0 + \int_{x_0}^{x} f(t, y_{n-1}(t))\, dt \qquad (1)$$

and prove the following lemma:

LEMMA 1:   *If $|x - x_0| \leq h$ then*

$$|y_n(x) - y_0| \leq b,$$

for $n = 1, 2, 3, \ldots$.

The proof of this lemma will be accomplished by induction. First of all, if $|x - x_0| \leq h$ we have

$$
\begin{aligned}
|y_1(x) - y_0| &= \left| \int_{x_0}^{x} f(t, y_0)\, dt \right| \\
&\leq M \left| \int_{x_0}^{x} dt \right| \\
&\leq M |x - x_0| \\
&\leq Mh \\
&\leq b.
\end{aligned}
$$

If we now assume that for $|x - x_0| \leq h$, $|y_k(x) - y_0| \leq b$, it follows that the point $[x, y_k(x)]$ is in R so that $|f(x, y_k(x))| \leq M$. Thus

$$
\begin{aligned}
|y_{k+1}(x) - y_0| &\leq \left| \int_{x_0}^{x} f(t, y_k(t))\, dt \right| \\
&\leq M \left| \int_{x_0}^{x} dt \right| \\
&\leq Mh \\
&\leq b.
\end{aligned}
$$

By induction we can now assert the validity of the lemma.

Lemma 1 may be stated in a slightly different way: if $|x - x_0| \leq h$, then the points $[x, y_n(x)]$, $n = 0, 1, 2, \ldots$, are in R. The Lipschitz condition of Section 77 may now be used to deduce the following lemma.

LEMMA 2:   *If* $|x - x_0| \leq h$ *then*

$$|f(x, y_n(x)) - f(x, y_{n-1}(x))| \leq K|y_n(x) - y_{n-1}(x)|,$$

for $n = 1, 2, 3, \ldots$.

We are now in a position to give an inductive proof of still another lemma.

LEMMA 3:   *If* $|x - x_0| \leq h$, *then*

$$|y_n(x) - y_{n-1}(x)| \leq \frac{MK^{n-1}|x - x_0|^n}{n!} \leq \frac{MK^{n-1}h^n}{n!},$$

for $n = 1, 2, 3, \ldots$.

For the case $n = 1$, we have from the proof of Lemma 1,

$$|y_1(x) - y_0| \leq M|x - x_0|.$$

Assuming that

$$|y_{n-1}(x) - y_{n-2}(x)| \leq \frac{MK^{n-2}|x - x_0|^{n-1}}{(n - 1)!}, \tag{2}$$

we now must show that

$$|y_n(x) - y_{n-1}(x)| \leq \frac{MK^{n-1}|x - x_0|^n}{n!}.$$

We will prove this for the case $x_0 \leq x \leq x_0 + h$. From Lemma 2 we have

$$|y_n(x) - y_{n-1}(x)| = \left| \int_{x_0}^x [f(t, y_{n-1}(t)) - f(t, y_{n-2}(t))] \, dt \right|$$

$$\leq \int_{x_0}^x |f(t, y_{n-1}(t)) - f(t, y_{n-2}(t))| \, dt$$

$$\leq K \int_{x_0}^x |y_{n-1}(t) - y_{n-2}(t)| \, dt.$$

Using the hypothesis (2) we conclude that

$$|y_n(x) - y_{n-1}(x)| \leq \frac{MK^{n-1}}{(n-1)!} \int_{x_0}^x (t - x_0)^{n-1} \, dt,$$

or

$$|y_n(x) - y_{n-1}(x)| \leq \frac{MK^{n-1}}{n!} |x - x_0|^n. \tag{3}$$

For the case $x_0 - h \leqq x \leqq x_0$, the same type of argument will yield the same result. The proof of Lemma 3 is thus complete.

To utilize the results of Lemma 3 we now compare the two infinite series

$$\sum_{n=1}^{\infty} [y_n(x) - y_{n-1}(x)] \quad \text{and} \quad \sum_{n=1}^{\infty} \frac{MK^{n-1}h^n}{n!}.$$

The second of these series is an absolutely convergent series. Moreover, by Lemma 3, the second series dominates the first series. Hence, by the Weierstrass M test the series

$$\sum_{n=1}^{\infty} [y_n(x) - y_{n-1}(x)] \tag{4}$$

converges absolutely and uniformly on the interval $|x - x_0| \leqq h$. If we consider the kth partial sum of the series (4)

$$\sum_{n=1}^{k} [y_n(x) - y_{n-1}(x)] = [y_1(x) - y_0(x)] + [y_2(x) - y_1(x)] + \cdots$$
$$+ [y_k(x) - y_{k-1}(x)],$$

we see that

$$\sum_{n=1}^{k} [y_n(x) - y_{n-1}(x)] = y_k(x).$$

That is, the statement that the series (4) converges absolutely and uniformly is equivalent to the statement that the sequence $y_n(x)$ converges uniformly on the interval

$$|x - x_0| \leqq h.$$

If we now define

$$\phi(x) = \lim_{n \to \infty} y_n(x)$$

and recall from the definition of the sequence $y_n(x)$ that each $y_n(x)$ is continuous on $|x - x_0| \leqq h$, it follows (since the convergence is uniform) that $\phi(x)$ is also continuous and

$$\phi(x) = \lim_{n \to \infty} y_n(x) = y_0 + \lim_{n \to \infty} \int_{x_0}^{x} f(t, y_{n-1}(t)) \, dt.$$

Because of the continuity of f and the uniform convergence of the sequence $y_n(x)$, we may interchange the order of the two limiting processes to show that $\phi(x)$ is a solution of the integral equation

$$\phi(x) = y_0 + \int_{x_0}^{x} f(t, \phi(t)) \, dt. \tag{5}$$

It follows immediately upon differentiation of equation (5) that $\phi(x)$ is a solution of the differential equation $dy/dx = f(x, y)$ on the interval $|x - x_0| \leqq h$. Furthermore, it is clear from equation (5) that $\phi(x_0) = y_0$.

Finally, since we have shown in Lemma 1 that $|y_n(x) - y_0| \leq b$ for each n and for $|x - x_0| \leq h$, it follows that the same inequality must hold for $\phi(x) = \lim_{n \to \infty} y_n(x)$. That is, if $|x - x_0| \leq h$, then $|\phi(x) - y_0| \leq b$.

Thus we have completed the proof of parts (a), (b), and (c) of the existence theorem of Section 76.

79. A proof of the uniqueness theorem

We must now show that the function $\phi(x)$ obtained in Section 78 is unique. Suppose there is another function $Y(x)$, such that $dY/dx = f[x, Y(x)]$, $Y(x_0) = y_0$, and $|Y(x) - y_0| \leq b$ for $|x - x_0| \leq h$. Then we may write

$$Y(x) = y_0 + \int_{x_0}^{x} f(t, Y(t)) \, dt.$$

If we compare $Y(x)$ to the functions of the sequence $y_n(x)$ of Section 78 we see that

$$|Y(x) - y_n(x)| \leq \left| \int_{x_0}^{x} [f(t, Y(t)) - f(t, y_{n-1}(t))] \, dt \right|. \tag{1}$$

We shall now show that as $n \to \infty$ the integral on the right side of (1) approaches zero for $|x - x_0| \leq h$. It will then follow that $Y(x) = \lim_{n \to \infty} y_n(x)$, so that finally $Y(x) \equiv \phi(x)$ on the interval $|x - x_0| \leq h$.

For any x on the interval $|x - x_0| \leq h$ it is true that $[x, Y(x)]$ and $[x, y_{n-1}(x)]$ are in the rectangle R, hence the Lipschitz condition of Section 77 will allow us to change (1) into

$$|Y(x) - y_n(x)| \leq K \int_{x_0}^{x} |Y(t) - y_{n-1}(t)| \, dt. \tag{2}$$

We now proceed by an inductive proof and limit our attention to values of x greater than x_0. (A similar argument obtains the same result for $x_0 - h \leq x \leq x_0$.) For $n = 1$, we have

$$|Y(x) - y_1(x)| \leq K \int_{x_0}^{x} |Y(t) - y_0| \, dt$$

$$\leq Kb(x - x_0).$$

We wish also to show that the assumption

$$|Y(x) - y_{n-1}(x)| \leq \frac{K^{n-1} b(x - x_0)^{n-1}}{(n-1)!}$$

leads to the conclusion

$$|Y(x) - y_n(x)| \leq \frac{K^n b(x - x_0)^n}{n!}.$$ (3)

This will complete an inductive argument for the relation (3). We have for $x_0 \leq x \leq x_0 + h$,

$$|Y(x) - y_n(x)| \leq \int_{x_0}^{x} |f(t, Y(t)) - f(t, y_{n-1}(t))| \, dt$$

$$\leq K \int_{x_0}^{x} |Y(t) - y_{n-1}(t)| \, dt$$

$$\leq \frac{K^n b}{(n-1)!} \int_{x_0}^{x} (t - x_0)^{n-1} \, dt$$

$$\leq \frac{K^n b}{n!} (x - x_0)^n,$$

thus completing the proof of relation (3).

For $|x - x_0| \leq h$ we have from the inequality (3),

$$|Y(x) - y_n(x)| \leq \frac{K^n b h^n}{n!}.$$ (4)

As $n \to \infty$ the expression on the right side of relation (4) approaches zero. Hence it follows that for $|x - x_0| \leq h$, $y_n(x) \to Y(x)$. Thus $Y(x)$ must be the same function $\phi(x)$ we obtained in Section 78. That is, the solution $\phi(x)$ is unique.

80. Other existence theorems

The existence theorem we have proved in the preceding sections for a first-order equation can be extended to equations of higher order. The simplest such extension is to equations of second order that can be written in the form

$$y'' = f(x, y, y').$$ (1)

It is natural to expect the theorem to involve continuity requirements on the function f and its partial derivatives. The theorem may be stated as follows:

THEOREM: *If the function f of equation (1) and its partial derivatives with respect to y and y' are continuous functions in a region T defined by*

$$|x - x_0| \leq a, \qquad |y - y_0| \leq b, \qquad |y' - y_0'| \leq c,$$

then there exists an interval $|x - x_0| \leq h$ and a unique function $\phi(x)$ such that $\phi(x)$ is a solution of (1) for all x in the interval $|x - x_0| \leq h$, $\phi(x_0) = y_0$, and $\phi'(x_0) = y_0'$.

A proof of this theorem that is quite similar to the proof given in Sections 78 and 79 can be found in Ince.* The generalization of the theorem to equations of higher order is direct.

* E. L. Ince, *Ordinary Differential Equations* (London: Longmans, Green and Co., 1927), Chapter 3.

CHAPTER 16

Nonlinear Equations

81. Preliminary remarks

The existence and uniqueness theorem of Chapter 15 made no distinction between linear and nonlinear differential equations. We know from our study in the earlier chapters of this book, however, that the methods we have found for actually determining solutions of a given equation often depend on the equation being a linear one. For example, in Chapter 2 we found that certain particular kinds of first-order nonlinear equations can be solved; that is, if the equation is exact, separable, homogeneous, and so on. On the other hand, if a first-order equation is linear, we have a method which can produce all possible solutions of the differential equation.

The fact is, there is no general method for solving first-order nonlinear differential equations, even if the existence of such solutions can be shown by the theorems of Chapter 15. Indeed, the determination of such solutions is often difficult if not impossible.

In this chapter we shall briefly discuss a few of the special difficulties that arise with nonlinear equations and a few techniques that will find solutions for certain particular types of equations.

82. Factoring the left member

To give illustration to the kind of complexity that may arise in nonlinear situations, we consider first a relatively simple complication. For an equation of the form

$$f(x, y, y') = 0, \tag{1}$$

it may be possible to factor the left member. The problem of solving (1) is then replaced by two or more problems of simpler type. The latter may be capable of solution by the methods of Chapters 2 and 4.

Since y' will be raised to powers in the example and exercises, let us simplify the printing and writing by a common device, using p for y':

$$p = \frac{dy}{dx}.$$

EXAMPLE: Solve the differential equation

$$xyp^2 + (x + y)p + 1 = 0. \tag{2}$$

The left member of equation (2) is readily factored. Thus (2) leads to

$$(xp + 1)(yp + 1) = 0,$$

from which it follows that either

$$yp + 1 = 0 \tag{3}$$

or

$$xp + 1 = 0. \tag{4}$$

From equation (3) in the form

$$y\,dy + dx = 0$$

it follows that

$$y^2 = -2(x - c_1). \tag{5}$$

Equation (4) may be written

$$x\,dy + dx = 0$$

from which, for $x \neq 0$,

$$dy + \frac{dx}{x} = 0,$$

so

$$y = -\ln|c_2 x|. \qquad (6)$$

We say, and it is very rough language, that the solutions of (2) are (5) and (6). Particular solutions may be made up from these solutions; they may be drawn from (5) alone, from (6) alone, or conceivably pieced together by using (5) in some intervals and (6) in others. At a point where a solution from (5) is to be joined with a solution from (6), the slope must remain continuous (see Ex. 21 below), so the piecing together must take place along the line $y = x$. Note (see Ex. 24) that the second derivative, which does not enter the differential equation, need not be continuous.

The existence of these three sets of particular solutions of (2), that is, solutions from (5), from (6), or from (5) and (6), leads to an interesting phenomenon in initial value problems. Consider the problem of finding a solution of (2) such that the solution passes through the point $(-\frac{1}{2}, 2)$. If the result is to be valid for the interval $-1 < x < -\frac{1}{4}$, there are two answers, which will be found in Ex. 25, following. If the result is to be valid for $-1 < x < \frac{1}{2}$, there is only one answer (Ex. 26), one of the two answers to Ex. 25. If the result is to be valid in $-1 < x < 2$, there is only one answer (Ex. 27).

Exercises

In Exs. 1–18, find the solutions in the sense of (5) and (6) above.

1. $x^2 p^2 - y^2 = 0$.
ANS. $y = c_1 x,\ xy = c_2$.

2. $xp^2 - (2x + 3y)p + 6y = 0$.
ANS. $y = c_1 x^3,\ y = 2x + c_2$.

3. $x^2 p^2 - 5xyp + 6y^2 = 0$.
ANS. $y = c_1 x^2,\ y = c_2 x^3$.

4. $x^2 p^2 + xp - y^2 - y = 0$.
ANS. $y = c_1 x,\ x(y + 1) = c_2$.

5. $xp^2 + (1 - x^2 y)p - xy = 0$.
ANS. $y = c_1 \exp(\tfrac{1}{2}x^2),\ y = -\ln|c_2 x|$.

6. $p^2 - (x^2 y + 3)p + 3x^2 y = 0$.
ANS. $y = 3x + c_1,\ x^3 = 3\ln|c_2 y|$.

7. $xp^2 - (1 + xy)p + y = 0$.
ANS. $y = \ln|c_1 x|,\ x = \ln|c_2 y|$.

8. $p^2 - x^2 y^2 = 0$.
ANS. $x^2 = 2\ln|c_1 y|,\ x^2 = -2\ln|c_2 y|$.

9. $(x + y)^2 p^2 = y^2$.
ANS. $x = y\ln|c_1 y|,\ y(2x + y) = c_2$.

10. $yp^2 + (x - y^2)p - xy = 0$.
ANS. $x^2 + y^2 = c_1{}^2,\ y = c_2 e^x$.

11. $p^2 - xy(x + y)p + x^3 y^3 = 0$.
ANS. $y(x^2 + c_1) = -2,\ x^3 = 3\ln|c_2 y|$.

12. $(4x - y)p^2 + 6(x - y)p + 2x - 5y = 0$.
ANS. $x + y = c_1,\ (2x + y)^2 = c_2(y - x)$.

13. $(x - y)^2 p^2 = y^2$.
ANS. $x = -y\ln|c_1 y|,\ y(2x - y) = c_2$.

14. $xyp^2 + (xy^2 - 1)p - y = 0$.
ANS. $y^2 = 2\ln|c_1 x|,\ x = -\ln|c_2 y|$.

15. $(x^2 + y^2)^2 p^2 = 4x^2 y^2$.
ANS. $y^2 - x^2 = c_1 y,\ y(3x^2 + y^2) = c_2$.

16. $(y + x)^2 p^2 + (2y^2 + xy - x^2)p + y(y - x) = 0$.
ANS. $y^2 + 2xy = c_1,\ y^2 + 2xy - x^2 = c_2$.

17. $xy(x^2 + y^2)(p^2 - 1) = p(x^4 + x^2 y^2 + y^4)$.
ANS. $y^2(y^2 + 2x^2) = c_1,\ y^2 = 2x^2\ln|c_2 x|$.

18. $xp^3 - (x^2 + x + y)p^2 + (x^2 + xy + y)p - xy = 0.$

ANS. $y = c_1 x,\ y = x + c_2,\ x^2 = 2(y - c_3).$

Exs. 19–27 refer to the example of this section. There the differential equation

$$xyp^2 + (x + y)p + 1 = 0 \tag{2}$$

was shown to have the solutions

$$y^2 = -2(x - c_1) \tag{5}$$

and

$$y = -\ln|c_2 x|. \tag{6}$$

19. Show that of the family (5) above, the only curve that passes through the point $(1, 1)$ is $y = (3 - 2x)^{1/2}$ and that this solution is valid for $x < \frac{3}{2}$.

20. Show that of the family (6) above, the only curve that passes through the point $(1, 1)$ is $y = 1 - \ln x$ and that this solution is valid for $0 < x$.

21. Show that the function defined by

$$y = (2 - x)^{1/2} \quad \text{for } x \le 1,$$

$$y = -\ln x \qquad \text{for } x \ge 1,$$

is a solution of equation (2) for all $x \ne 1$, but fails to have a derivative at $x = 1$ and is therefore not a solution there.

22. Show that if a solution of (2) is to be pieced together from (5) and (6), then the slopes of the curves must be equal where the pieces join. Show that the pieces must therefore be joined at a point on the line $y = x$.

23. Show that the function determined by

$$y = (3 - 2x)^{1/2} \quad \text{for } x \le 1,$$

$$y = 1 - \ln x \qquad \text{for } 1 \le x$$

is a solution of equation (2) and is valid for all x. The interesting portion of this curve is shown in Figure 38.

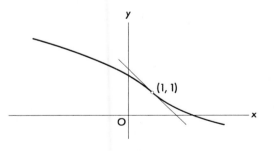

FIGURE 38

24. Show for the solution given in Ex. 23 that y'' is not continuous at $x = 1$. Show that as $x \to 1^-$, $y'' \to -1$, and as $x \to 1^+$, $y'' \to +1$.

25. Find those solutions of (2) which are valid in $-1 < x < -\frac{1}{4}$ and each of which has its graph passing through the point $(-\frac{1}{2}, 2)$.
ANS. $y = (3 - 2x)^{1/2}$; and $y = 2 - \ln 2 - \ln(-x)$.

26. Find that solution of (2) which is valid for $-1 < x < \frac{1}{2}$ and has its graph passing through the point $(-\frac{1}{2}, 2)$. ANS. $y = (3 - 2x)^{1/2}$.

27. Find that solution of (2) which is valid for $-1 < x < 2$ and has its graph passing through the point $(-\frac{1}{2}, 2)$. ANS. $y = (3 - 2x)^{1/2}$ for $x \le 1$,
$y = 1 - \ln x$ for $1 \le x$.

83. Singular solutions

Let us solve the differential equation

$$y^2 p^2 - a^2 + y^2 = 0. \tag{1}$$

Here

$$yp = \pm\sqrt{a^2 - y^2},$$

so we may write

$$\frac{y\,dy}{\sqrt{a^2 - y^2}} = dx, \tag{2}$$

or

$$-\frac{y\,dy}{\sqrt{a^2 - y^2}} = dx, \tag{3}$$

or (if the division by $\sqrt{a^2 - y^2}$ cannot be effected)

$$a^2 - y^2 = 0. \tag{4}$$

From (2) it follows that

$$x = c_1 - \sqrt{a^2 - y^2}, \tag{5}$$

while from (3) that

$$x = c_2 + \sqrt{a^2 - y^2}, \tag{6}$$

and from (4) that

$$y = a \quad \text{or} \quad y = -a. \tag{7}$$

Graphically, the solutions (5) are left-hand semicircles with radius a and centered on the x-axis; the solutions (6) are right-hand semicircles of radius a, centered on the x-axis. We may combine (5) and (6) into

$$(x - c)^2 + y^2 = a^2, \tag{8}$$

which we might be tempted to call the "general" solution of (1). However, from either of equations (7) we get $p = 0$, so that $y = a$ and $y = -a$ are both solutions of equation (1), but neither of these functions is a special case of (8).

We therefore see that the use of the term "general" solution for the functions defined implicitly by (8) is not consistent with the usage of the term as applied to linear differential equations. For linear equations any solution was a particular case of the general solution. It is perhaps unfortunate that the words "general solution" are used for the one-parameter family of solutions defined by (8). The particular solutions $y = a$ and $y = -a$ are called singular solutions. (It should be clear that linear equations cannot have singular solutions.)

A *singular solution* of a nonlinear first-order differential equation is any solution that

(a) is not a special case of the general solution, and

(b) is, at each of its points, tangent to some element of the one-parameter family that is the general solution.

Figure 39 shows several elements of the family of circles given by equation

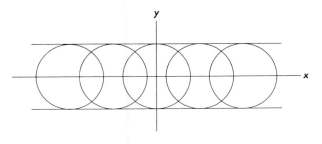

FIGURE 39

(8) and also shows the two lines representing $y = a$ and $y = -a$. At each point of either line, the line is tangent to an element of the family of circles. A curve which at each of its points is tangent to an element of a one-parameter family of curves is called an *envelope* of that family.

84. The c-discriminant equation

Consider the differential equation of first order,

$$f(x, y, p) = 0; \qquad p = \frac{dy}{dx}, \tag{1}$$

in which the left member is a polynomial in x, y, and p. It may not be possible to factor the left member into factors which are themselves polynomials in x, y, and p. Then the equation is said to be irreducible.

The general solution of (1) will be a one-parameter family,

$$\phi(x, y, c) = 0. \tag{2}$$

A singular solution, if it exists, for equation (1) must be an envelope of the family (2). Each point on the envelope is a point of tangency of the envelope with some element of the family (2) and is determined by the value of c that identifies that element of the family. Then the envelope has parametric equations, $x = x(c)$ and $y = y(c)$, with the c of equation (2) as the parameter. The functions $x(c)$ and $y(c)$ are as yet unknown to us. But the x and y of the point of contact must also satisfy equation (2), from which we get, by differentiation with respect to c, the equation

$$\frac{\partial\phi}{\partial x}\frac{dx}{dc} + \frac{\partial\phi}{\partial y}\frac{dy}{dc} + \frac{\partial\phi}{\partial c} = 0. \tag{3}$$

The slope of the envelope and the slope of the family element concerned must be equal at the point of contact. That slope can be determined by differentiating equation (2) with respect to x, keeping c constant. Thus it follows that

$$\frac{\partial\phi}{\partial x} + \frac{\partial\phi}{\partial y}\frac{dy}{dx} = 0. \tag{4}$$

Equations (3) and (4) both hold at the point of contact and from them it follows that

$$\frac{\partial\phi}{\partial c} = 0. \tag{5}$$

We now have two equations, $\phi = 0$ and $\partial\phi/\partial c = 0$, which must be satisfied by x, y, and c. These two equations may be taken as the desired parametric equations. They contain any envelope which may exist for the original family of curves, $\phi = 0$. Fortunately, there is no need for us to put these equations into the form $x = x(c)$, $y = y(c)$.

The equation that results from the elimination of c from the equations $\phi = 0$ and $\partial\phi/\partial c = 0$ is called the *c-discriminant equation** of the family $\phi = 0$. It is a necessary and sufficient condition that the equation

$$\phi(x, y, c) = 0, \tag{2}$$

considered as an equation in c, have at least two of its roots equal.

---

* The c-discriminant equation may contain a locus of cusps of the elements of the general solution and a locus of nodes of those elements, as well as the envelope which aroused our interest in it.

There is nothing in our work to guarantee that the *c*-discriminant equation, or any part of it, will be a solution of the differential equation. To get the *c*-discriminant equation we need the general solution. During the process of obtaining the general solution, we find also the singular solution, if there is one.

85. The *p*-discriminant equation

Suppose that in the irreducible differential equation

$$f(x, y, p) = 0 \tag{1}$$

the polynomial *f* is of degree *n* in *p*. There will be *n* roots of equation (1), each yielding a result of the form

$$p = g(x, y). \tag{2}$$

If at a point (x_0, y_0) the equation (1) has, as an equation in *p*, all its roots distinct, then near (x_0, y_0) there will be *n* distinct equations of the type of equation (2). Near (x_0, y_0) the right members of these *n* equations will be single-valued and may satisfy the conditions of the existence theorem described in Chapter 15. But if at (x_0, y_0) equation (1) has at least two of its roots equal, then at least two of the *n* equations like (2) will have right members assuming the same value at (x_0, y_0). For such equations there is no region, no matter how small, surrounding (x_0, y_0) in which the right member is single-valued. Hence the existence theorem of Chapter 15 cannot be applied when equation (1) has two or more equal roots as an equation in *p*. Therefore we must give separate consideration to the locus of points (x, y) for which (1) has at least two of its roots equal.

The condition that equation (1) have at least two equal roots as an equation in *p* is that both $f = 0$ and $\partial f/\partial p = 0$. These two equations in the three variables *x*, *y*, and *p* are parametric equations of a curve in the *xy*-plane with *p* playing the role of parameter. The equation that results when *p* is eliminated from the parametric equations $f = 0$ and $\partial f/\partial p = 0$ is called the *p-discriminant equation*.

If an envelope of the general solution of $f = 0$ exists, it will be contained in the *p*-discriminant equation. No proof is included here.* For us the *p*-discriminant equation is useful in two ways. When a singular solution is obtained in the natural course of solving an equation, the *p*-discriminant

---

* For more detail on singular solutions and the discriminants see E. L. Ince, *Ordinary Differential Equations* (London: Longmans, Green and Co., 1927), pp. 82–92.

equation furnishes us with a check. If none of our methods of attack leads to a general solution, then the p-discriminant equation offers functions which may be particular (including singular) solutions of the differential equation. Then the p-discriminant equation should be tested for possible solutions of the differential equation. Such particular solutions make, of course, no contribution toward finding the general solution.

The p-discriminant equation may contain singular solutions, solutions that are not singular, and functions that are not solutions at all.

Exercises

1. For the quadratic equation

$$f = Ap^2 + Bp + C = 0,$$

with A, B, C functions of x and y, show that the p-discriminant obtained by eliminating p from $f = 0$ and $\partial f / \partial p = 0$ is the familiar equation

$$B^2 - 4AC = 0.$$

2. For the cubic $p^3 + Ap + B = 0$, show that the p-discriminant equation is $4A^3 + 27B^2 = 0$.

3. For the cubic $p^3 + Ap^2 + B = 0$, show that the p-discriminant equation is $B(4A^3 + 27B) = 0$.

4. Set up the condition that the equation $x^3p^2 + x^2yp + 4 = 0$ have equal roots as a quadratic in p. Compare with the singular solution $xy^2 = 16$.

5. Show that the condition that the equation $xyp^2 + (x + y)p + 1 = 0$ of the example of Section 82 have equal roots in p is $(x - y)^2 = 0$ and that the latter equation does not yield a solution of the differential equation. Was there a singular solution?

6. For the equation $y^2p^2 - a^2 + y^2 = 0$ of Section 83, find the condition for equal roots in p and compare with the singular solution.

7. For the differential equation of Ex. 6 show that the function defined by

$$y = [a^2 - (x + 2a)^2]^{1/2} \quad \text{for } -3a < x \leqq -2a,$$
$$y = a \quad \text{for } -2a \leqq x \leqq 2a,$$
$$y = [a^2 - (x - 2a)^2]^{1/2} \quad \text{for } 2a \leqq x < 3a,$$

is a solution. Sketch the graph and show how it was pieced together from the general solution and the singular solution given in equations (5), (6), and (7) of Section 83.

In Exs. 8–16, obtain (a) the p-discriminant equation and (b) those solutions of the differential equation that are contained in the p-discriminant.

8. $xp^2 - 2yp + 4x = 0$.   ANS. (a) $y^2 - 4x^2 = 0$; (b) $y = 2x$, $y = -2x$.

9. $3x^4p^2 - xp - y = 0$.   ANS. (a) $x^2(1 + 12x^2y) = 0$; (b) $x = 0$, $12x^2y = -1$.

10. $p^2 - xp - y = 0$.   ANS. (a) $x^2 + 4y = 0$; (b) None.

11. $p^2 - xp + y = 0$.   ANS. (a) $x^2 - 4y = 0$; (b) $x^2 - 4y = 0$.

12. $p^2 + 4x^5p - 12x^4y = 0$.   ANS.   (a) $x^4(x^6 + 3y) = 0$; (b) $3y = -x^6$.

13. $4y^3p^2 - 4xp + y = 0$.   ANS.   (a) $(y^2 - x)(y^2 + x) = 0$; (b) Same as (a).

14. $4y^3p^2 + 4xp + y = 0$. See also Ex. 13.   ANS.   (a) $(y^2 - x)(y^2 + x) = 0$;
                                               (b) None.

15. $p^3 + xp^2 - y = 0$.   ANS.   (a) $y(4x^3 - 27y) = 0$; (b) $y = 0$.

16. $y^4p^3 - 6xp + 2y = 0$.   ANS.   (a) $y^8(y^2 - 2x)(y^4 + 2xy^2 + 4x^2) = 0$;
                                               (b) $y = 0$, $y^2 = 2x$.

17. For the differential equation of Ex. 4 above, the general solution will be found to be $cxy + 4x + c^2 = 0$. Find the condition that this quadratic equation in c have equal roots. Compare that condition with the singular solution.

86. Eliminating the dependent variable

Suppose the equation

$$f(x, y, p) = 0; \qquad p = \frac{dy}{dx}, \tag{1}$$

is of a form such that we can readily solve it for the dependent variable y and write

$$y = g(x, p). \tag{2}$$

We can differentiate equation (2) with respect to x and, since $dy/dx = p$, get an equation

$$h\left(x, p, \frac{dp}{dx}\right) = 0 \tag{3}$$

involving only x and p. If we can solve equation (3), we will have two equations relating x, y, and p, namely, equation (2) and the solution of (3). These together form parametric equations of the solution of (1) with p now considered a parameter. Or, if p be eliminated between (2) and the solution of (3), then a solution in the nonparametric form is obtained.

EXAMPLE: Solve the differential equation

$$xp^2 - 3yp + 9x^2 = 0, \quad \text{for } x > 0. \tag{4}$$

Rewrite (4) as

$$3y = xp + 9x^2/p. \tag{5}$$

Then differentiate both members of (5) with respect to x, using the fact that $dy/dx = p$, thus getting

$$3p = p + \frac{18x}{p} + \left(x - \frac{9x^2}{p^2}\right)\frac{dp}{dx},$$

or

$$2p\left(1 - \frac{9x}{p^2}\right) = x\left(1 - \frac{9x}{p^2}\right)\frac{dp}{dx}. \tag{6}$$

From (6) it follows that either

$$1 - \frac{9x}{p^2} = 0 \tag{7}$$

or

$$2p = x\frac{dp}{dx}. \tag{8}$$

First consider (8), which leads to

$$2\frac{dx}{x} = \frac{dp}{p}$$

so

$$p = cx^2. \tag{9}$$

Therefore equations (4) and (9), with p as a parameter, constitute a solution of (4) looked upon as a differential equation with $p = dy/dx$.

In this example it is easy to eliminate p from equations (4) and (9), so we perform that elimination. The result is

$$x \cdot c^2 x^4 - 3y \cdot cx^2 + 9x^2 = 0.$$

Since $x > 0$, we have

$$c^2 x^3 - 3cy + 9 = 0,$$

or

$$3cy = c^2 x^3 + 9.$$

Now put $c = 3k$ to get

$$ky = k^2 x^3 + 1. \tag{10}$$

Equation (10) with k as an arbitrary constant is called the general solution of the differential equation (4).

We have yet to deal with equation (7). Note that (7) is an algebraic relation between x and p in contrast to the differential relation (8) which we have already used. We reason that the elimination of p from (7) and (4) may lead to a solution of the differential equation (4) and that the solution will not involve an arbitrary constant. From (7) it is seen that $p = 3x^{1/2}$ or $p = -3x^{1/2}$. Either of these expressions for p may be substituted into (4) and will lead to

$$y^2 = 4x^3. \tag{11}$$

It is not difficult to show that equation (11) defines two solutions of the differential equation. These solutions are not special cases of the general solution (10). They are singular solutions. Equation (11) has for its graph the envelope of the family of curves given by equation (10). The solutions defined by (11) are also easily obtained from the p-discriminant equation.

87. Clairaut's equation

Any differential equation of the form

$$y = px + f(p), \tag{1}$$

where $f(p)$ contains neither x nor y explicitly, can be solved at once by the method of Section 86. Equation (1) is called *Clairaut's equation*.

Let us differentiate both members of (1) with respect to x, thus getting

$$p = p + [x + f'(p)]p',$$

$$[x + f'(p)]\frac{dp}{dx} = 0. \tag{2}$$

Then either

$$\frac{dp}{dx} = 0 \tag{3}$$

or

$$x + f'(p) = 0. \tag{4}$$

The solution of the differential equation (3) is, of course, $p = c$, where c is an arbitrary constant. Returning to the differential equation (1), we can now write its general solution as

$$y = cx + f(c), \tag{5}$$

a result easily verified by direct substitution into the differential equation (1). Note that (5) is the equation of a family of straight lines.

Now consider equation (4). Since $f(p)$ and $f'(p)$ are known functions of p, equations (4) and (1) together constitute a set of parametric equations giving x and y in terms of the parameter p. Indeed, from equation (4) it follows that

$$x = -f'(p), \tag{6}$$

which, combined with equation (1), yields

$$y = f(p) - pf'(p). \tag{7}$$

If $f(p)$ is not a linear function of p and not a constant, it can be shown (Exs. 1 and 2 below) that (6) and (7) are parametric equations of a nonlinear solution of the differential equation (1). Since the general solution (5) represents a straight line for each value of c, the solution (6) and (7) cannot be a special case of (5); it is a singular solution.

EXAMPLE (a): Solve the differential equation

$$y = px + p^3.$$ (8)

Since (8) is a Clairaut equation, we can write its general solution

$$y = cx + c^3$$

at once.

Then using (6) and (7) we obtain the parametric equations

$$x = -3p^2, \quad y = -2p^3,$$ (9)

of the singular solutions. The parameter p may be eliminated from equations (9), yielding the form

$$27y^2 = -4x^3$$ (10)

for the singular solutions. See Figure 40.

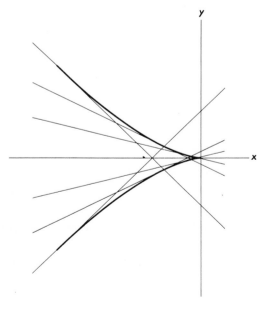

FIGURE 40

EXAMPLE (b): Solve the differential equation

$$(x^2 - 1)p^2 - 2xyp + y^2 - 1 = 0. \tag{11}$$

Rewrite (11) as

$$x^2 p^2 - 2xyp + y^2 - 1 - p^2 = 0.$$

Then it is clear that the equation is of the form

$$(y - xp)^2 - 1 - p^2 = 0 \tag{12}$$

and so could be broken up into two equations, each of Clairaut's form. Then the general solution of (11) is obtained by replacing p everywhere in it by an arbitrary constant c. That is,

$$(x^2 - 1)c^2 - 2xyc + y^2 - 1 = 0 \tag{13}$$

is the general solution of (11). The solution (13) is composed of two families of straight lines,

$$y = c_1 x + \sqrt{1 + c_1^2} \tag{14}$$

and

$$y = c_2 x - \sqrt{1 + c_2^2}. \tag{15}$$

From the p-discriminant equation for (11) we obtain at once the singular solutions defined by

$$x^2 + y^2 = 1. \tag{16}$$

Exercises

1. Let α be a parameter and prove that if $f''(\alpha)$ exists, then

$$x = -f'(\alpha), \quad y = f(\alpha) - \alpha f'(\alpha) \tag{17}$$

is a solution of the differential equation $y = px + f(p)$. *Hint:* use dx and dy to get p in terms of α and then show that $y - px - f(p)$ vanishes identically.
2. Prove that if $f''(\alpha) \neq 0$, then (17) above is not a special case of the general solution $y = cx + f(c)$. *Hint:* show that the slope of the graph of one solution depends upon x whereas the slope of the graph of the other does not depend upon x.

In Exs. 3–30, find the general solution and also the singular solution, if it exists.

3. $p^2 + x^3 p - 2x^2 y = 0.$ ANS. $c^2 + cx^2 = 2y$; sing. sol., $8y = -x^4$.
4. $p^2 + 4x^5 p - 12x^4 y = 0.$ ANS. $12y = c(c + 4x^3)$; sing. sol., $3y = -x^6$.
5. $2xp^3 - 6yp^2 + x^4 = 0.$ ANS. $2c^3 x^3 = 1 - 6c^2 y$; sing. sol., $2y = x^2$.
6. $p^2 - xp + y = 0.$ ANS. $y = cx - c^2$; sing. sol., $x^2 = 4y$.

7. $y = px + kp^2$.   ANS. $y = cx + kc^2$; sing. sol., $x^2 = -4ky$.

8. $x^8p^2 + 3xp + 9y = 0$.   ANS. $x^3(y + c^2) + c = 0$; sing. sol., $4x^6y = 1$.

9. $x^4p^2 + 2x^3yp - 4 = 0$.   ANS. $x^2(1 + cy) = c^2$.

10. $xp^2 - 2yp + 4x = 0$.   ANS. $x^2 = c(y - c)$; sing. sol., $y = 2x$ and $y = -2x$.

11. $3x^4p^2 - xp - y = 0$.   ANS. $xy = c(3cx - 1)$; sing. sol., $12x^2y = -1$.

12. $xp^2 + (x - y)p + 1 - y = 0$.

     ANS. $xc^2 + (x - y)c + 1 - y = 0$; sing. sol., $(x + y)^2 = 4x$.

13. $p(xp - y + k) + a = 0$.

     ANS. $c(xc - y + k) + a = 0$; sing. sol., $(y - k)^2 = 4ax$.

14. $x^6p^3 \rightarrow 3xp - 3y = 0$.   ANS. $3xy = c(xc^2 - 3)$; sing. sol., $9x^3y^2 = 4$.

15. $y = x^8p^3 - xp$.   ANS. $xy = c(c^2x - 1)$; sing. sol., $27x^3y^2 = 4$.

16. $xp^4 - 2yp^3 + 12x^3 = 0$.   ANS. $2c^3y = c^4x^2 + 12$; sing. sol., $3y^2 = \pm 8x^3$.

17. $xp^3 - yp^2 + 1 = 0$.   ANS. $xc^3 - yc^2 + 1 = 0$; sing. sol., $4y^3 = 27x^2$.

18. $y = px + p^n$, for $n \neq 0$, $n \neq 1$.

     ANS. $y = cx + c^n$; sing. sol., $\left(\dfrac{x}{n}\right)^n = -\left(\dfrac{y}{n-1}\right)^{n-1}$.

19. $p^2 - xp - y = 0$.   ANS. $3x = 2p + cp^{-1/2}$ and $3y = p^2 - cp^{1/2}$.

20. $2p^3 + xp - 2y = 0$.   ANS. $x = 2p(3p + c)$ and $y = p^2(4p + c)$.

21. $2p^2 + xp - 2y = 0$.   ANS. $x = 4p \ln|pc|$ and $y = p^2[1 + 2 \ln|pc|]$.

22. $p^3 + 2xp - y = 0$.   ANS. $4x = -3p^2 + cp^{-2}$ and $2y = -p^3 + cp^{-1}$.

23. $4xp^2 - 3yp + 3 = 0$.   ANS. $2x = 3p^{-2} + cp^{-4}$ and $3y = 9p^{-1} + 2cp^{-3}$.

24. $p^3 - xp + 2y = 0$.   ANS. $x = p(c - 3p)$ and $2y = p^2(c - 4p)$.

25. $5p^2 + 6xp - 2y = 0$.   ANS. $p^3(x + p)^2 = c$ and $2y = 6xp + 5p^2$.

26. $2xp^2 + (2x - y)p + 1 - y = 0$.   ANS. $p^2x = (1 + p)^{-1} + \ln|c(1 + p)|$ and $py = 1 + (1 + p)^{-1} + 2 \ln|c(1 + p)|$.

27. $5p^2 + 3xp - y = 0$.   ANS. $p^3(x + 2p)^2 = c$ and $y = 3xp + 5p^2$.

28. $p^2 + 3xp - y = 0$.   ANS. $p^3(5x + 2p)^2 = c$ and $y = 3xp + p^2$.

29. $y = xp + x^3p^2$.   ANS. $x^2 = cp^{-4/3} - 2p^{-1}$ and $y = xp + x^3p^2$.

30. $8y = 3x^2 + p^2$.   ANS. $(p - 3x)^3 = c(p - x)$ and $8y = 3x^2 + p^2$.

88. Dependent variable missing

Consider a second-order equation,

$$f(x, y', y'') = 0, \tag{1}$$

which does not contain the dependent variable y explicitly. Let us put

$$y' = p.$$

Then

$$y'' = \frac{dp}{dx}$$

and equation (1) may be replaced by

$$f\left(x, p, \frac{dp}{dx}\right) = 0, \tag{2}$$

an equation of order one in p. If we can find p from equation (2), then y can be obtained from $y' = p$ by an integration.

EXAMPLE: Solve the equation

$$xy'' - (y')^3 - y' = 0 \tag{3}$$

of Example (b), page 12.

Since y does not appear explicitly in the differential equation (3), put $y' = p$. Then

$$y'' = \frac{dp}{dx},$$

so equation (3) becomes

$$x \frac{dp}{dx} - p^3 - p = 0.$$

Separation of variables leads to

$$\frac{dp}{p(p^2 + 1)} = \frac{dx}{x}$$

or

$$\frac{dp}{p} - \frac{p \, dp}{p^2 + 1} = \frac{dx}{x},$$

from which

$$\ln |p| - \tfrac{1}{2} \ln (p^2 + 1) + \ln |c_1| = \ln |x| \tag{4}$$

follows.

Equation (4) yields

$$c_1 p(p^2 + 1)^{-1/2} = x, \tag{5}$$

which we wish to solve for p. From (5) we conclude that

$$c_1^2 p^2 = x^2(1 + p^2),$$

$$p^2 = \frac{x^2}{c_1^2 - x^2}.$$

But $p = y'$, so we have

$$dy = \pm \frac{x \, dx}{\sqrt{c_1^2 - x^2}}. \tag{6}$$

The solutions of (6) are

$$y - c_2 = \mp(c_1{}^2 - x^2)^{1/2},$$

or

$$x^2 + (y - c_2)^2 = c_1{}^2. \tag{7}$$

Equation (7) is the desired general solution of the differential equation (3). Note that in dividing by p early in the work we might have discarded the solutions $y = k(p = 0)$, where k is constant. But (7) can be put in the form

$$c_3(x^2 + y^2) + c_4 y + 1 = 0, \tag{8}$$

with new arbitrary constants c_3 and c_4. Then the choice $c_3 = 0$, $c_4 = -1/k$ yields the solution $y = k$.

89. Independent variable missing

A second-order equation

$$f(y, y', y'') = 0 \tag{1}$$

in which the independent variable x does not appear explicitly can be reduced to a first-order equation in y and y'. Put

$$y' = p,$$

then

$$y'' = \frac{dp}{dx} = \frac{dy}{dx}\frac{dp}{dy} = p\frac{dp}{dy},$$

so equation (1) becomes

$$f\left(y, p, p\frac{dp}{dy}\right) = 0. \tag{2}$$

We try to determine p in terms of y from equation (2) and then substitute the result into $y' = p$.

EXAMPLE: Solve the equation

$$yy'' + (y')^2 + 1 = 0 \tag{3}$$

of Ex. 8, page 14.

Since the independent variable does not appear explicitly in equation (3), we put $y' = p$ and obtain

$$y'' = p\frac{dp}{dy}$$

as before. Then equation (3) becomes

$$yp\frac{dp}{dy} + p^2 + 1 = 0, \tag{4}$$

in which the variables p and y are easily separated.
From (4) it follows that

$$\frac{p\,dp}{p^2 + 1} + \frac{dy}{y} = 0,$$

from which

$$\tfrac{1}{2}\ln(p^2 + 1) + \ln|y| = \ln|c_1|,$$

so

$$p^2 + 1 = c_1{}^2 y^{-2}. \tag{5}$$

We solve equation (5) for p and find that

$$p = \pm\frac{(c_1{}^2 - y^2)^{1/2}}{y}.$$

Therefore

$$\frac{dy}{dx} = \pm\frac{(c_1{}^2 - y^2)^{1/2}}{y}$$

or

$$\pm y(c_1{}^2 - y^2)^{-1/2}\,dy = dx.$$

Then

$$\mp(c_1{}^2 - y^2)^{1/2} = x - c_2.$$

from which we obtain the final result

$$(x - c_2)^2 + y^2 = c_1{}^2.$$

Exercises

1. $y'' = x(y')^3$.   ANS. $x = c_1 \sin(y + c_2)$.
2. $x^2 y'' + (y')^2 - 2xy' = 0$; when $x = 2$, $y = 5$ and $y' = -4$.
                                               ANS. $y = \tfrac{1}{2}x^2 + 3x - 3 + 9\ln(3 - x)$.
3. $x^2 y'' + (y')^2 - 2xy' = 0$; when $x = 2$, $y = 5$ and $y' = 2$.
                                               ANS. $x^2 = 2(y - 3)$.
4. $yy'' + (y')^2 = 0$.   ANS.   See Ex. 20, page 14.
5. $y^2 y'' + (y')^3 = 0$.   ANS. $x = c_1 y - \ln|c_2 y|$.
6. $(y + 1)y'' = (y')^2$.   ANS. $y + 1 = c_2 e^{c_1 x}$.
7. $2ay'' + (y')^3 = 0$.   ANS. $(y - c_2)^2 = 4a(x - c_1)$.
8. Do Ex. 7 by another method.
9. $xy'' = y' + x^5$; when $x = 1$, $y = \tfrac{1}{2}$ and $y' = 1$.   ANS. $24y = x^6 + 9x^2 + 2$.

10. $xy'' + y' + x = 0$; when $x = 2$, $y = -1$ and $y' = -\frac{1}{2}$.

        ANS. $y = -\frac{1}{4}x^2 + \ln(\frac{1}{2}x)$.

11. $y'' = 2y(y')^3$.   ANS. $y^3 = 3(c_2 - x - c_1 y)$.

12. $yy'' + (y')^3 - (y')^2 = 0$.   ANS. $x = y - c_1 \ln |c_2 y|$.

13. $y'' + \beta^2 y = 0$. Check your result by solving the equation in two ways.

14. $yy'' + (y')^3 = 0$.   ANS. $x = c_1 + y \ln |c_2 y|$.

15. $y'' \cos x = y'$.   ANS. $y = c_2 + c_1 \ln(1 - \sin x)$.

16. $y'' = x(y')^2$; when $x = 2$, $y = \frac{1}{4}\pi$ and $y' = -\frac{1}{4}$.   ANS. $x = 2 \cot y$.

17. $y'' = x(y')^2$; when $x = 0$, $y = 1$ and $y' = \frac{1}{2}$.   ANS. $y = 1 + \frac{1}{2} \ln \dfrac{2 + x}{2 - x}$.

18. $y'' = -e^{-2y}$; when $x = 3$, $y = 0$ and $y' = 1$.   ANS. $y = \ln(x - 2)$.

19. $y'' = -e^{-2y}$; when $x = 3$, $y = 0$ and $y' = -1$.   ANS. $y = \ln(4 - x)$.

20. $2y'' = \sin 2y$; when $x = 0$, $y = \pi/2$ and $y' = 1$.

        ANS. $x = -\ln(\csc y + \cot y)$.

21. $2y'' = \sin 2y$; when $x = 0$, $y = -\pi/2$ and $y' = 1$.

        ANS. $x = \ln(-\csc y - \cot y)$.

22. Show that if you can perform the integrations encountered, then you can solve any equation of the form $y'' = f(y)$.

23. $x^3 y'' - x^2 y' = 3 - x^2$.   ANS. $y = x^{-1} + x + c_1 x^2 + c_2$.

24. $y'' = (y')^2$.   ANS. $y = -\ln |c_2(c_1 - x)|$; or $x = c_1 + c_3 e^{-y}$.

25. $y'' = e^x (y')^2$.   ANS. $c_1 y + c_2 = -\ln |c_1 e^{-x} - 1|$.

26. $2y'' = (y')^3 \sin 2x$; when $x = 0$, $y = 1$ and $y' = 1$.

        ANS. $y = 1 + \ln(\sec x + \tan x)$.

27. $x^2 y'' + (y')^2 = 0$.   ANS. $c_1{}^2 y = c_1 x + \ln |c_2(c_1 x - 1)|$.

28. $y'' = 1 + (y')^2$.   ANS. $e^y \cos(x + c_1) = c_2$.

29. Do Ex. 28 by another method.

30. $y'' = [1 + (y')^2]^{3/2}$. Solve in three ways, by considering the geometric significance of the equation, and by the methods of this chapter.

31. $yy'' = (y')^2[1 - y' \sin y - yy' \cos y]$.   ANS. $x = c_1 \ln |c_2 y| - \cos y$.

32. $(1 + y^2)y'' + (y')^3 + y' = 0$.   ANS. $x = c_2 + c_1 y - (1 + c_1{}^2) \ln |y + c_1|$.

33. $[yy'' + 1 + (y')^2]^2 = [1 + (y')^2]^3$.   ANS. $(y - c_1)^2 + (x - c_2)^2 = c_1{}^2$.

34. $x^2 y'' = y'(2x - y')$; when $x = -1$, $y = 5$ and $y' = 1$.

        ANS. $2y - 1 = (x - 2)^2 + 8 \ln(x + 2)$.

35. $x^2 y'' = y'(3x - 2y')$.   ANS. $2y = x^2 + c_2 - c_1 \ln |x^2 + c_1|$.

36. $xy'' = y'(2 - 3xy')$.   ANS. $3y = c_2 + \ln |x^3 + c_1|$.

37. $x^4 y'' = y'(y' + x^3)$; when $x = 1$, $y = 2$ and $y' = 1$.

        ANS. $y = 1 + x^2 - \ln\left(\dfrac{1 + x^2}{2}\right)$.

38. $y'' = 2x + (x^2 - y')^2$.   ANS. $3y = x^3 + c_2 - 3 \ln |x + c_1|$.

39. $(y'')^2 - 2y'' + (y')^2 - 2xy' + x^2 = 0$; when $x = 0$, $y = \frac{1}{2}$ and $y' = 1$.

        ANS. $2y = 1 + x^2 + 2 \sin x$.

40. $(y'')^2 - xy'' + y' = 0$.   ANS.   General solution: $2y = c_1 x^2 - 2c_1{}^2 x + c_2$; family of singular solutions: $12y = x^3 + k$.

41. $(y'')^3 = 12y'(xy'' - 2y')$.   ANS.   General solution: $y = c_1(x - c_1)^3 + c_2$; family of singular solutions: $9y = x^4 + k$.

42. $3yy'y'' = (y')^3 - 1$.   ANS. $27c_1(y + c_1)^2 = 8(x + c_2)^3$.

43. $4y(y')^2 y'' = (y')^4 + 3$.   ANS. $256c_1(y - c_1)^3 = 243(x - c_2)^4$.

90. The catenary

Let a cable of uniformly distributed weight w (lb. per ft.) be suspended between two supports at points A and B as indicated in Figure 41. The cable

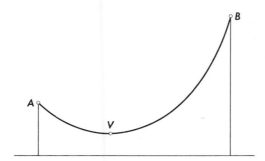

FIGURE 41

will sag and there will be a lowest point V as indicated in the figure. We wish to determine the curve formed by the suspended cable. That curve is called the *catenary*.

Choose coordinate axes as shown in Figure 42, the y-axis vertical through the point V and the x-axis horizontal and passing at a distance y_0 (to be chosen later) below V. Let s represent length (ft.) of the cable measured from V to the variable point P with coordinates (x, y). Then the portion of the cable from V to P is subject to the three forces shown in Figure 42. Those

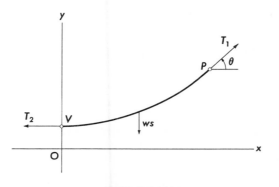

FIGURE 42

forces are: (a) the gravitational force ws (lb.) acting downward through the center of gravity of the portion of the cable from V to P, (b) the tension T_1 (lb.) acting tangentially at P, and (c) the tension T_2 (lb.) acting horizontally (again tangentially) at V. The tension T_1 is a variable; the tension T_2 is constant.

Since equilibrium is assumed, the algebraic sum of the vertical components of these forces is zero and the algebraic sum of the horizontal components of these forces is also zero. Therefore, if θ is the angle of inclination, from the horizontal, of the tangent to the curve at the point (x, y), we have

$$T_1 \sin \theta - ws = 0 \tag{1}$$

and

$$T_1 \cos \theta - T_2 = 0. \tag{2}$$

But $\tan \theta$ is the slope of the curve of the cable, so

$$\tan \theta = \frac{dy}{dx}. \tag{3}$$

We may eliminate the variable tension T_1 from equations (1) and (2) and obtain

$$\tan \theta = \frac{ws}{T_2}. \tag{4}$$

The constant T_2/w has the dimension of a length. Put $T_2/w = a$ (ft.). Then equation (4) becomes

$$\tan \theta = \frac{s}{a}. \tag{5}$$

From equations (3) and (5) we see that

$$\frac{s}{a} = \frac{dy}{dx}. \tag{6}$$

Now we know from calculus that since s is the length of arc of the curve, then

$$\frac{ds}{dx} = \sqrt{1 + \left(\frac{dy}{dx}\right)^2}. \tag{7}$$

From (6) we get $\dfrac{1}{a}\dfrac{ds}{dx} = \dfrac{d^2y}{dx^2}$, so the elimination of s yields the differential equation

$$\frac{d^2y}{dx^2} = \frac{1}{a}\sqrt{1 + \left(\frac{dy}{dx}\right)^2}. \tag{8}$$

The desired equation of the curve assumed by the suspended cable is that solution of the differential equation (8) which also satisfies the initial conditions

$$\text{when } x = 0, \quad y = y_0 \quad \text{and} \quad \frac{dy}{dx} = 0. \tag{9}$$

Equation (8) fits into either of the types studied in this chapter. It is left as an exercise for the student to solve the differential equation (8) with the conditions (9) and arrive at the result

$$y = a \cosh \frac{x}{a} + y_0 - a. \tag{10}$$

Then, of course, the sensible choice $y_0 = a$ is made, so the equation of the desired curve (the catenary) is

$$y = a \cosh \frac{x}{a}.$$

Miscellaneous exercises

1. $x^3 p^2 + x^2 yp + 4 = 0.$ ANS. $cxy + 4x + c^2 = 0$; sing. sol., $xy^2 = 16.$

2. $6xp^2 - (3x + 2y)p + y = 0.$ ANS. $y^3 = c_1 x, \, 2y = x + c_2.$

3. $9p^2 + 3xy^4 p + y^5 = 0.$ ANS. $cy^3(x - c) = 1$; sing. sol., $x^2 y^3 = 4.$

4. $4y^3 p^2 - 4xp + y = 0.$ ANS. $y^4 = 4c(x - c)$; sing. sol., $y^2 = x.$

5. $x^6 p^2 - 2xp - 4y = 0.$ ANS. $x^2(y - c^2) = c$; sing. sol., $4x^4 y = -1.$

6. $5p^2 + 6xp - 2y = 0.$ ANS. $x = cp^{-3/2} - p$ and $2y = 6cp^{-1/2} - p^2.$

7. Do Ex. 6 by another method.

8. $y^2 p^2 - y(x + 1)p + x = 0.$ ANS. $x^2 - y^2 = c_1, \, y^2 = 2(x - c_2).$

9. $4x^5 p^2 + 12x^4 yp + 9 = 0.$ ANS. $x^3(2cy - 1) = c^2$; sing. sol., $x^3 y^2 = 1.$

10. $4y^2 p^3 - 2xp + y = 0.$ ANS. $y^2 = 2c(x - 2c^2)$; sing. sol., $8x^3 = 27y^4.$

11. $p^4 + xp - 3y = 0.$ ANS. $5x = 4p^3 + cp^{1/2}$ and $15y = 9p^4 + cp^{3/2}.$

12. Do Ex. 11 by another method.

13. $xp^2 + (k - x - y)p + y = 0$, the equation of Ex. 5, page 14.

    ANS. $xc^2 + (k - x - y)c + y = 0$;

    sing. sol., $(x - y)^2 - 2k(x + y) + k^2 = 0.$

14. $x^2 p^3 - 2xyp^2 + y^2 p + 1 = 0.$

    ANS. $x^2 c^3 - 2xyc^2 + y^2 c + 1 = 0$; sing. sol., $27x = -4y^3.$

15. $16xp^2 + 8yp + y^6 = 0.$ ANS. $y^2(c^2 x + 1) = 2c$; sing. sol., $xy^4 = 1.$

16. $xp^2 - (x^2 + 1)p + x = 0.$ ANS. $x^2 = 2(y - c_1), \, y = \ln|c_2 x|.$

17. $p^3 - 2xp - y = 0.$ ANS. $8x = 3p^2 + cp^{-2/3}$ and $4y = p^3 - cp^{1/3}.$

18. Do Ex. 17 by another method.

19. $9xy^4 p^2 - 3y^5 p - 1 = 0.$ ANS. $cy^3 = c^2 x - 1$; sing. sol., $y^6 = -4x.$

20. $x^2 p^2 - (2xy + 1)p + y^2 + 1 = 0.$

    ANS. $x^2 c^2 - (2xy + 1)c + y^2 + 1 = 0$; sing. sol., $4x^2 - 4xy - 1 = 0.$

21. $x^6 p^2 = 8(2y + xp).$ ANS. $c^2 x^2 = 8(2x^2 y - c)$; sing. sol., $x^4 y = -1.$

22. $x^2 p^2 = (x - y)^2.$ ANS. $x(x - 2y) = c_1, \, y = -x \ln|c_2 x|.$

23. $xp^3 - 2yp^2 + 4x^2 = 0.$ See Ex. 10 above.

         ANS. $x^2 = 4c(y - 8c^2)$; sing. sol., $8y^3 = 27x^4.$

24. $(p + 1)^2(y - px) = 1.$

         ANS. $(c + 1)^2(y - cx) = 1$; sing. sol., $4(x + y)^3 = 27x^2.$

25. $p^3 - p^2 + xp - y = 0.$

         ANS. $y = cx + c^3 - c^2$; sing. sol. with parametric equations,

$$x = 2\alpha - 3\alpha^2 \text{ and } y = \alpha^2 - 2\alpha^3.$$

26. $xp^2 + y(1 - x)p - y^2 = 0.$ ANS. $xy = c_1, x = \ln|c_2 y|.$

27. $yp^2 - (x + y)p + y = 0.$

         ANS. $py = c \exp(p^{-1})$ and $px = y(p^2 - p + 1)$; sing. sol., $y = x.$

CHAPTER 17

The Power Series Method

91. Linear equations and power series

The solution of linear equations with constant coefficients can be accomplished by the methods developed earlier in the book. The general linear equation of the first order yields to an integrating factor as was seen in Chapter 2. For linear ordinary differential equations with variable coefficients and of order greater than one, probably the most generally effective method of attack is that based upon the use of power series.

To simplify the work and the statement of theorems, the equations treated here will be restricted to those with polynomial coefficients. The difficulties to be encountered, the methods of attack, and the results accomplished all remain essentially unchanged when the coefficients are permitted to be functions that have power series expansions valid about some point. (Such functions are called *analytic functions.*)

Consider the homogeneous linear equation of the second order,

$$b_0(x)y'' + b_1(x)y' + b_2(x)y = 0, \tag{1}$$

with polynomial coefficients. If $b_0(x)$ does not vanish at $x = 0$, then in some interval about $x = 0$, staying away from the nearest point where $b_0(x)$ does vanish, it is safe to divide throughout by $b_0(x)$. Thus we replace equation (1) by

$$y'' + p(x)y' + q(x)y = 0, \tag{2}$$

in which the coefficients $p(x)$, $q(x)$ are rational functions of x with denominators that do not vanish at $x = 0$.

We shall now show that it is reasonable to expect* a solution of (2) that is a power series in x and that contains two arbitrary constants. Let $y = y(x)$ be a solution of equation (2). We assign arbitrarily the values of y and y' at $x = 0$; $y(0) = A$, $y'(0) = B$.

Equation (2) yields

$$y''(x) = -p(x)y'(x) - q(x)y(x), \tag{3}$$

so $y''(0)$ may be computed directly, because $p(x)$ and $q(x)$ are well behaved at $x = 0$. From equation (3) we get

$$y'''(x) = -p(x)y''(x) - p'(x)y'(x) - q(x)y'(x) - q'(x)y(x), \tag{4}$$

so $y'''(0)$ can be computed once $y''(0)$ is known.

The above process can be continued as long as we wish, and therefore we can determine successively $y^{(n)}(0)$ for as many integral values of n as may be desired. Now, by Maclaurin's formula in calculus,

$$y(x) = y(0) + \sum_{n=1}^{\infty} y^{(n)}(0) \frac{x^n}{n!} ; \tag{5}$$

that is, the right member of (5) will converge to the value $y(x)$ throughout some interval about $x = 0$ if $y(x)$ is sufficiently well behaved at and near $x = 0$. Thus we can determine the function $y(x)$ and are led to a solution in power series form.

For actually obtaining the solutions for specific equations, we shall study another method, to be illustrated in examples, a technique far superior to the brute-force method used above. What we have gained from the present discussion is the knowledge that it is reasonable to seek a power series solution. Once we know that, it remains only to develop good methods for finding the solution and theorems regarding the validity of the results so found.

---

* This is no proof. For proof see, for instance, E. D. Rainville, *Intermediate Differential Equations*, 2nd ed. (New York: The Macmillan Co., 1964), pp. 67–71.

92. Convergence of power series

From calculus we know that the power series

$$\sum_{n=0}^{\infty} a_n x^n$$

converges either at $x = 0$ only, or for all finite x, or the series converges in an interval $-R < x < R$ and diverges outside that interval. Unless the series converges at only one point, it represents, where it does converge, a function $f(x)$ in the sense that the series has at each value x the sum $f(x)$.

If

$$f(x) = \sum_{n=0}^{\infty} a_n x^n, \qquad -R < x < R,$$

then also

$$f'(x) = \sum_{n=0}^{\infty} n a_n x^{n-1}, \qquad -R < x < R,$$

and

$$\int_0^x f(y)\, dy = \sum_{n=0}^{\infty} \frac{a_n x^{n+1}}{n+1}, \qquad -R < x < R.$$

That is, the series is termwise differentiable and integrable in the sense that the series of the derivatives of the separate terms converges to the derivative of the sum of the original series and similarly for integration. It is important that the interval of convergence remains unchanged. We are not concerned here with convergence behavior at the endpoints of that interval.

Let us look more closely into the reason that a series has a particular interval of convergence rather than some other one. An elementary example from calculus is

$$\frac{1}{1-x} = \sum_{n=0}^{\infty} x^n, \qquad -1 < x < 1. \tag{1}$$

It is reasonable to suspect that the misbehavior of the function $1/(1-x)$ at $x = 1$ is what lies behind the fact that the interval of convergence terminates at $x = 1$. That it must extend that far is not so evident. The point $x = -1$ has no bearing in this instance; the interval is terminated at that end by the requirement that it be symmetric about $x = 0$.

Now let us replace x in (1) by $(-x^2)$ to get

$$\frac{1}{1+x^2} = \sum_{n=0}^{\infty} (-1)^n x^{2n}, \qquad -1 < x < 1. \tag{2}$$

Again the interval of convergence is $-1 < x < 1$, but the function $f(x) = 1/(1+x^2)$ is well behaved for all real x. What stopped the interval of convergence at $x = 1$ is not so clear. The fact is that we need to consider x as a complex variable to understand what is going on here.

We use the ordinary Argand diagram for complex numbers. Let $x = a + ib$, a and b real, with $i = \sqrt{-1}$, and associate with the point (a, b) in the plane the number $a + ib$. Now mark on the diagram those points (values of x) for which the function $1/(1+x^2)$ does not exist. The points are $x = i$, $x = -i$, where the denominator $(1 + x^2)$ vanishes. In books on functions of a complex variable it is shown that the series in (2) converges for all values of x inside the circle shown in Figure 43. The interval of convergence given in (2) is merely a cross-section of the region of convergence in the complex plane.

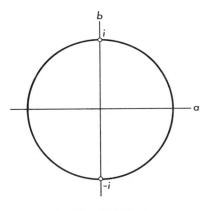

FIGURE 43

A power series in a complex variable x always has as its region of convergence the interior of a circle, if we are willing to admit the extreme cases in which the circle degenerates into a single point or expands over the whole complex plane.

Points at which the denominator of a rational function vanishes are the most elementary examples of singularities of an analytic function. The circle of convergence of a power series cannot have inside it a singularity of the function represented by the series. The circle of convergence has its center at the origin and passes through the singularity nearest the origin.

The function

$$\frac{x - 2}{(x - 3)(x - 4)(x^2 + 25)}$$

has a denominator which vanishes at $x = 3, 4, 5i, -5i$. The function then has a power series expansion valid inside a circle (Figure 44) with center at $x = 0$ and extending as far as the nearest $(x = 3)$ of the points where the function misbehaves. For real x, the interval of convergence is $-3 < x < 3$.

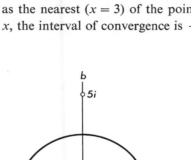

FIGURE 44

93. Ordinary points and singular points

For a linear differential equation

$$b_0(x)y^{(n)} + b_1(x)y^{(n-1)} + \cdots + b_n(x)y = R(x) \tag{1}$$

with polynomial coefficients, the point $x = x_0$ is called an *ordinary point* of the equation if $b_0(x_0) \neq 0$. A *singular point* of the linear equation (1) is any point $x = x_1$ for which $b_0(x_1) = 0$. In this chapter we shall obtain power series solutions valid near an ordinary point of a linear equation. In the next chapter we shall get power series solutions valid near a certain kind of singular point of the equation.

A knowledge of the location of the singular points of a differential equation will be useful to us later. Any point that is not a singular point is an ordinary point, so we list only the former.

We have left undiscussed the matter of a "point at infinity" in the complex plane, a concept of great utility. It is not necessary for this elementary discussion. As a result of this omission, however, it is necessary for us to attach the words "in the finite plane" to any statement purporting to list all singular points of a differential equation. The concept of a point at infinity will be introduced in Section 104.

The differential equation

$$(1 - x^2)y'' - 6xy' - 4y = 0 \tag{2}$$

has $x = 1$ and $x = -1$ as its only singular points in the finite complex plane. The equation

$$y'' + 2xy' + y = 0$$

has no singular points in the finite plane. The equation

$$xy'' + y' + xy = 0$$

has the origin, $x = 0$, as the only singular point in the finite plane.

Exercises

For each equation, list all of the singular points in the finite plane.

1. $(x^2 + 4)y'' - 6xy' + 3y = 0.$ ANS. $x = 2i, -2i.$
2. $x(3 - x)y'' - (3 - x)y' + 4xy = 0.$ ANS. $x = 0, 3.$
3. $4y'' + 3xy' + 2y = 0.$ ANS.   None.
4. $x(x - 1)^2y'' + 3xy' + (x - 1)y = 0.$ ANS. $x = 0, 1.$
5. $x^2y'' + xy' + (1 - x^2)y = 0.$
6. $x^4y'' + y = 0.$
7. $(1 + x^2)y'' - 2xy' + 6y = 0.$
8. $(x^2 - 4x + 3)y'' + x^2y' - 4y = 0.$
9. $x^2(1 - x)^3y'' + (1 + 2x)y = 0.$
10. $6xy'' + (1 - x^2)y' + 2y = 0.$
11. $4xy'' + y = 0.$
12. $4y'' + y = 0.$
13. $x^2(x^2 - 9)y'' + 3xy' - y = 0.$
14. $x^2(1 + 4x^2)y'' - 4xy' + y = 0.$
15. $(2x + 1)(x - 3)y'' - y' + (2x + 1)y = 0.$
16. $x^3(x^2 - 4)^2y'' + 2(x^2 - 4)y' - xy = 0.$
17. $x(x^2 + 1)^2y'' - y = 0.$
18. $(x^2 + 6x + 8)y'' + 3y = 0.$
19. $(4x + 1)y'' + 3xy' + y = 0.$

94. Validity of the solutions near an ordinary point

Suppose $x = 0$ is an ordinary point of the linear equation

$$b_0(x)y'' + b_1(x)y' + b_2(x)y = 0. \tag{1}$$

It is proved in more advanced books that there is a solution

$$y = \sum_{n=0}^{\infty} a_n x^n \tag{2}$$

which contains two arbitrary constants, namely, a_0 and a_1, and which converges inside a circle with center at $x = 0$ and extending out to the singular
point (or points) nearest $x = 0$. If the differential equation has no singular
points in the finite plane, then the solution (2) is valid for all finite x. There
remains, of course, the job of finding a_n for $n \geq 2$. That is a major part of
our work in solving a particular equation.

It is necessary to realize that the theorem quoted states that the series
involved converges inside a certain circle. It does not state that the series
diverges outside that circle. In a particular instance it may be that the circle
of convergence happens to extend farther than the minimum given by the
theorem. In any case, the circle of convergence passes through a singular
point of the equation—it may not be the nearest singular point.

95. Solutions near an ordinary point

In solving numerical equations, the technique employed in the following
examples will be found useful.

EXAMPLE (a):   Solve the equation

$$y'' + 4y = 0 \tag{1}$$

near the ordinary point $x = 0$.

The equation we are considering has no singular points in the finite plane.
Hence we may expect to find a solution

$$y = \sum_{n=0}^{\infty} a_n x^n \tag{2}$$

valid for all real x and with a_0 and a_1 arbitrary. Substituting the series into (1)
gives us

$$\sum_{n=0}^{\infty} n(n-1)a_n x^{n-2} + 4\sum_{n=0}^{\infty} a_n x^n = 0. \tag{3}$$

We now change the indexing of the terms in the second sum in (3), so that the series will involve x^{n-2} in its general term. Thus (3) becomes

$$\sum_{n=0}^{\infty} n(n-1)a_n x^{n-2} + 4\sum_{n=2}^{\infty} a_{n-2} x^{n-2} = 0. \tag{4}$$

We can now add the two series to obtain

$$\sum_{n=2}^{\infty} [n(n-1)a_n + 4a_{n-2}]x^{n-2} = 0, \tag{5}$$

because the first two terms of the first sum in (4) are zero.

We now use the fact that for a power series to vanish identically over any interval, each coefficient in the series must be zero. Thus for (5) to be valid in some interval it must be true that

$$n(n-1)a_n + 4a_{n-2} = 0, \qquad \text{for} \quad n \geq 2.$$

This relation may be written (since $n \geq 2$)

$$a_n = \frac{-4a_{n-2}}{n(n-1)}. \tag{6}$$

Relation (6) may be used to obtain a_n for $n \geq 2$ in terms of a_0 and a_1 which are left arbitrary. We have

$$a_2 = \frac{-4a_0}{2 \cdot 1} \qquad\qquad a_3 = \frac{-4a_1}{3 \cdot 2}$$

$$a_4 = \frac{-4a_2}{4 \cdot 3} \qquad\qquad a_5 = \frac{-4a_3}{5 \cdot 4}$$

$$\vdots \qquad\qquad\qquad \vdots$$

$$a_{2k} = \frac{-4a_{2k-2}}{2k(2k-1)} \qquad a_{2k+1} = \frac{-4a_{2k-1}}{(2k+1)(2k)}.$$

In writing out these particular cases of equation (6) we have taken pains to keep the a's with even or odd subscripts in separate columns. If we now multiply the corresponding members of the equations of the first column, we obtain

$$a_2 a_4 \cdots a_{2k} = \frac{(-1)^k 4^k}{(2k)!} a_0 a_2 \cdots a_{2k-2},$$

which simplifies to

$$a_{2k} = \frac{(-1)^k 4^k}{(2k)!} a_0, \qquad \text{for} \quad k \geq 1. \tag{7}$$

A similar argument applied to the right column in the foregoing array gives us

$$a_{2k+1} = \frac{(-1)^k 4^k a_1}{(2k+1)!}, \qquad \text{for } k \geq 1. \tag{8}$$

We now wish to substitute the expressions for the a's back into the assumed series for y,

$$y = \sum_{n=0}^{\infty} a_n x^n. \tag{2}$$

Since we have different forms for a_{2k} and a_{2k+1} we first rewrite (2) in the form

$$y = a_0 + \sum_{k=1}^{\infty} a_{2k} x^{2k} + a_1 x + \sum_{k=1}^{\infty} a_{2k+1} x^{2k+1},$$

and then we use (7) and (8) to obtain

$$y = a_0 \left[1 + \sum_{k=1}^{\infty} \frac{(-1)^k 4^k x^{2k}}{(2k)!} \right] + a_1 \left[x + \sum_{k=1}^{\infty} \frac{(-1)^k 4^k x^{2k+1}}{(2k+1)!} \right]. \tag{9}$$

It is possible to rewrite equation (9) in the form

$$y = a_0 \left[1 + \sum_{k=1}^{\infty} \frac{(-1)^k (2x)^{2k}}{(2k)!} \right] + \tfrac{1}{2} a_1 \left[2x + \sum_{k=1}^{\infty} \frac{(-1)^k (2x)^{2k+1}}{(2k+1)!} \right]. \tag{10}$$

The two series in (10) are the Maclaurin series for the functions $\cos 2x$ and $\sin 2x$, so that finally we may write

$$y = a_0 \cos 2x + \tfrac{1}{2} a_1 \sin 2x.$$

Thus we have shown that the solution of equation (1) is a linear combination of $\cos 2x$ and $\sin 2x$, a fact that could have been obtained immediately by the methods of Chapter 6.

EXAMPLE (b):   Solve the equation

$$(1 - x^2) y'' - 6xy' - 4y = 0 \tag{11}$$

near the ordinary point $x = 0$.

The only singular points that this equation has in the finite plane are $x = 1$ and $x = -1$. Hence we know in advance that there is a solution

$$y = \sum_{n=0}^{\infty} a_n x^n \tag{12}$$

valid in $|x| < 1$ and with a_0 and a_1 arbitrary.

To determine the a_n, $n > 1$, we substitute the y of equation (12) into the left member of (11). We get

$$\sum_{n=0}^{\infty} n(n-1)a_n x^{n-2} - \sum_{n=0}^{\infty} n(n-1)a_n x^n - \sum_{n=0}^{\infty} 6na_n x^n - \sum_{n=0}^{\infty} 4a_n x^n = 0,$$

or

$$\sum_{n=0}^{\infty} n(n-1)a_n x^{n-2} - \sum_{n=0}^{\infty} (n^2 + 5n + 4)a_n x^n = 0, \qquad (13)$$

in which we have combined series that contained the same powers of x.

Next let us factor the coefficient in the second series in equation (13), writing

$$\sum_{n=0}^{\infty} n(n-1)a_n x^{n-2} - \sum_{n=0}^{\infty} (n+1)(n+4)a_n x^n = 0. \qquad (14)$$

Relations for the determination of the a_n will be obtained by using the fact that for a power series to vanish identically over any interval, each coefficient in the series must be zero. Therefore we wish next to write the two series in equation (14) in a form in which the exponents on x will be the same so we can easily pick off the coefficient of each power of x.

Let us shift the index in the second series, replacing n everywhere by $(n - 2)$. Then the summation which started with the old $n = 0$ will now start with $n - 2 = 0$, or the new $n = 2$. Thus we obtain

$$\sum_{n=0}^{\infty} n(n-1)a_n x^{n-2} - \sum_{n=2}^{\infty} (n-1)(n+2)a_{n-2} x^{n-2} = 0. \qquad (15)$$

In equation (15) the coefficient of each separate power of x must be zero. For $n = 0$ and $n = 1$, the second series has not yet started, so we get contributions from the first series only. In detail, we have

$$n = 0: \quad 0 \cdot a_0 = 0,$$
$$n = 1: \quad 0 \cdot a_1 = 0,$$
$$n \geq 2: \quad n(n-1)a_n - (n-1)(n+2)a_{n-2} = 0.$$

As was expected, a_0 and a_1 are arbitrary. The relation for $n \geq 2$ can be used to determine the other a's in terms of a_0 and a_1. Since

$$n(n-1) \neq 0$$

for $n \geq 2$, we can write

$$n \geq 2: \quad a_n = \frac{n+2}{n} a_{n-2}. \qquad (16)$$

Equation (16) is called a *recurrence relation*. It gives a_n in terms of preceding a's. In this particular case, each a is determined by the a with subscript two lower than its own and consequently, eventually, by either a_0 or a_1, according to whether the original a had an even or an odd subscript.

A recurrence relation is a special kind of *difference equation*. In difference equations the arguments of the unknown function (the subscripts in our relations) need not differ by integers. There are books and courses on difference equations and the calculus of finite differences paralleling the books and courses on differential equations and calculus.

It is convenient to arrange the iterated instances of the relation (16) in two vertical columns [two columns because the subscripts in (16) differ by two], thus using successively $n = 2, 4, 6, \ldots$, and $n = 3, 5, 7, \ldots$, to obtain

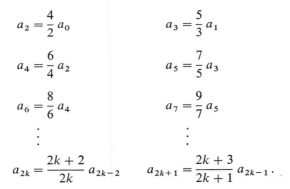

$$a_2 = \frac{4}{2} a_0 \qquad\qquad a_3 = \frac{5}{3} a_1$$

$$a_4 = \frac{6}{4} a_2 \qquad\qquad a_5 = \frac{7}{5} a_3$$

$$a_6 = \frac{8}{6} a_4 \qquad\qquad a_7 = \frac{9}{7} a_5$$

$$\vdots \qquad\qquad\qquad \vdots$$

$$a_{2k} = \frac{2k + 2}{2k} a_{2k-2} \qquad a_{2k+1} = \frac{2k + 3}{2k + 1} a_{2k-1}.$$

Next, obtain the product of corresponding members of the equations in the first column. The result,

$$k \geq 1: \quad a_2 a_4 a_6 \cdots a_{2k} = \frac{4 \cdot 6 \cdot 8 \cdots (2k + 2)}{2 \cdot 4 \cdot 6 \cdots (2k)} a_0 a_2 a_4 \cdots a_{2k-2},$$

simplifies at once to

$$k \geq 1: \quad a_{2k} = (k + 1)a_0,$$

thus giving us each a with an even subscript in terms of a_0.

Similarly, from the right column in the array above we get

$$k \geq 1: \quad a_{2k+1} = \frac{5 \cdot 7 \cdot 9 \cdots (2k + 3)}{3 \cdot 5 \cdot 7 \cdots (2k + 1)} a_1,$$

or

$$k \geq 1: \quad a_{2k+1} = \frac{2k + 3}{3} a_1,$$

thus giving us each a with an odd subscript in terms of a_1.

We need next to substitute the expressions we have obtained for the a's into the assumed series for y,

$$y = \sum_{n=0}^{\infty} a_n x^n. \tag{12}$$

The nature of our expressions for the a's, depending on whether the subscript is odd or even, dictates that we should first split the series in (12) into two series, one containing all the terms with even subscripts, and the other containing all the terms with odd subscripts. We write

$$y = \left[a_0 + \sum_{k=1}^{\infty} a_{2k} x^{2k} \right] + \left[a_1 x + \sum_{k=1}^{\infty} a_{2k+1} x^{2k+1} \right],$$

and then use our known results for a_{2k} and a_{2k+1} to obtain the general solution in the form

$$y = a_0 \left[1 + \sum_{k=1}^{\infty} (k+1)x^{2k} \right] + a_1 \left[x + \sum_{k=1}^{\infty} \frac{2k+3}{3} x^{2k+1} \right]. \tag{17}$$

These series converge at least for $|x| < 1$, as we know from the theory. That they converge there and only there can be verified by applying elementary convergence tests.

It happens in this example that the solution (17) may be written more simply as

$$y = a_0 \sum_{k=0}^{\infty} (k+1)x^{2k} + a_1 \sum_{k=0}^{\infty} \frac{2k+3}{3} x^{2k+1}. \tag{18}$$

Indeed, the series can be summed in terms of elementary functions,

$$y = \frac{a_0}{(1-x^2)^2} + \frac{a_1(3x - x^3)}{3(1-x^2)^2}.$$

Such simplifications may be important when they can be accomplished in a particular problem, but it must be realized that our goal was to obtain equation (17) and to know where it is a valid solution. Additional steps taken after that goal is reached are frequently irrelevant to the essential desire to find a computable solution of the differential equation.

The length of the work in solving this partiuclar equation is largely due to detailed steps, many of which will be taken mentally as we acquire more experience.

EXAMPLE (c):   Solve the equation

$$y'' + (x-1)^2 y' - 4(x-1)y = 0 \tag{19}$$

about the ordinary point $x = 1$.

To solve an equation "about the point $x = x_0$" means to obtain solutions valid in a region surrounding the point, solutions expressed in powers of $(x - x_0)$.

We first translate the axes, putting $x - 1 = v$. Then equation (19) becomes

$$\frac{d^2y}{dv^2} + v^2 \frac{dy}{dv} - 4vy = 0. \tag{20}$$

Always in a pure translation, $x - x_0 = v$, we have $dy/dx = dy/dv$, etc.

As usual we put

$$y = \sum_{n=0}^{\infty} a_n v^n \tag{21}$$

and from (20) obtain

$$\sum_{n=0}^{\infty} n(n - 1)a_n v^{n-2} + \sum_{n=0}^{\infty} na_n v^{n+1} - \sum_{n=0}^{\infty} 4a_n v^{n+1} = 0. \tag{22}$$

Collecting like terms in (22) yields

$$\sum_{n=0}^{\infty} n(n - 1)a_n v^{n-2} + \sum_{n=0}^{\infty} (n - 4)a_n v^{n+1} = 0,$$

which, with a shift of index from n to $(n - 3)$ in the second series, gives

$$\sum_{n=0}^{\infty} n(n - 1)a_n v^{n-2} + \sum_{n=3}^{\infty} (n - 7)a_{n-3} v^{n-2} = 0. \tag{23}$$

Therefore a_0 and a_1 are arbitrary and for the remainder we have

$$n = 2: \quad 2a_2 = 0,$$

$$n \geqq 3: \quad n(n - 1)a_n + (n - 7)a_{n-3} = 0,$$

$$a_n = -\frac{n - 7}{n(n - 1)} a_{n-3}.$$

This time the a's fall into three groups, those that come from a_0, from a_1, and from a_2. We use three columns:

a_0 arb.	a_1 arb.	$a_2 = 0$
$a_3 = -\dfrac{-4}{3 \cdot 2} a_0$	$a_4 = -\dfrac{-3}{4 \cdot 3} a_1$	$a_5 = -\dfrac{-2}{5 \cdot 4} a_2 = 0$
$a_6 = -\dfrac{-1}{6 \cdot 5} a_3$	$a_7 = -\dfrac{0}{7 \cdot 6} a_4 = 0$	$a_8 = (\ )a_5 = 0$
$a_9 = -\dfrac{2}{9 \cdot 8} a_6$	$a_{10} = -\dfrac{3}{10 \cdot 9} a_7 = 0$	$a_{11} = 0$
$\vdots$	$\vdots$	$\vdots$
$a_{3k} = -\dfrac{3k - 7}{3k(3k - 1)} a_{3k-3}$	$a_{3k+1} = 0, k \geqq 2$	$a_{3k+2} = 0, k \geqq 1.$

With the usual multiplication scheme, the first column yields

$$k \geq 1: \quad a_{3k} = \frac{(-1)^k[(-4)(-1) \cdot 2 \cdots (3k-7)]a_0}{[3 \cdot 6 \cdot 9 \cdots (3k)][2 \cdot 5 \cdot 8 \cdots (3k-1)]}.$$

For the a's which are determined by a_1, we see that $a_4 = \frac{1}{4}a_1$ but that each of the others is zero. Since $a_2 = 0$, all the a's proportional to it, a_5, a_8, etc., are also zero.

For y we now have

$$y = a_0\left[1 + \sum_{k=1}^{\infty} \frac{(-1)^k[(-4)(-1) \cdot 2 \cdots (3k-7)]v^{3k}}{[3 \cdot 6 \cdot 9 \cdots (3k)][2 \cdot 5 \cdot 8 \cdots (3k-1)]}\right] + a_1(v + \tfrac{1}{4}v^4).$$

Since $v = x - 1$, the solution appears as

$$y = a_0\left[1 + \sum_{k=1}^{\infty} \frac{(-1)^k[(-4)(-1) \cdot 2 \cdots (3k-7)](x-1)^{3k}}{[3 \cdot 6 \cdot 9 \cdots (3k)][2 \cdot 5 \cdot 8 \cdots (3k-1)]}\right]$$

$$+ a_1[(x-1) + \tfrac{1}{4}(x-1)^4]. \qquad (24)$$

The original differential equation has no singular point in the finite plane, so the series in (24) is convergent for all finite x. In computations, of course, it is most useful in the neighborhood of the point $x = 1$.

The coefficient of $(x-1)^{3k}$ is sufficiently complicated to warrant attempts to simplify it. In the product $3 \cdot 6 \cdot 9 \cdots (3k)$ there are k factors, each a multiple of 3. Thus we arrive at

$$3 \cdot 6 \cdot 9 \cdots (3k) = 3^k(1 \cdot 2 \cdot 3 \cdots k) = 3^k k!.$$

Furthermore, all but the first two factors inside the square bracket in the numerator also appear in the denominator. With a little more argument, testing the terms $k = 0, 1, 2$, since the factors to be cancelled do not appear until $k > 2$, it can be shown that

$$y = a_0 \sum_{k=0}^{\infty} \frac{4(-1)^k(x-1)^{3k}}{3^k(3k-1)(3k-4)k!} + a_1[(x-1) + \tfrac{1}{4}(x-1)^4]. \qquad (25)$$

In the exercises below, the equations are mostly homogeneous and of second order. Raising the order of the equation introduces nothing except additional labor, as can be seen by doing Ex. 18. A nonhomogeneous equation with right member having a power series expansion is theoretically no worse to handle than a homogeneous one; it is merely a matter of equating coefficients in two power series.

The treatment of equations leading to recurrence relations involving more than two different a's is left for Chapter 18.

Exercises

Unless it is otherwise requested, find the general solution valid near the origin. Always state the region of validity of the solution.

1. Solve the equation $y'' + y = 0$ both by series and by elementary methods and compare your answers.

2. Solve the equation $y'' - 4y = 0$ by series and by elementary methods.

3. $y'' + 3xy' + 3y = 0$.

ANS. $y = a_0\left[1 + \sum_{k=1}^{\infty} \frac{(-3)^k x^{2k}}{2^k k!}\right] + a_1\left[x + \sum_{k=1}^{\infty} \frac{(-3)^k x^{2k+1}}{3 \cdot 5 \cdot 7 \cdots (2k+1)}\right];$

valid for all finite x.

4. $(1 + 4x^2)y'' - 8y = 0$.

ANS. $y = a_0(1 + 4x^2) + a_1 \sum_{k=0}^{\infty} \frac{(-1)^{k+1} 2^{2k} x^{2k+1}}{4k^2 - 1}$; valid for $|x| < \frac{1}{2}$.

5. $(1 + x^2)y'' - 4xy' + 6y = 0$.

ANS. $y = a_0(1 - 3x^2) + a_1(x - \frac{1}{3}x^3)$; valid for all finite x.

6. $(1 + x^2)y'' + 10xy' + 20y = 0$.

ANS. $y = \dfrac{a_0}{3} \sum_{k=0}^{\infty} (-1)^k(k+1)(2k+1)(2k+3)x^{2k}$

$+ \dfrac{a_1}{6} \sum_{k=0}^{\infty} (-1)^k(k+1)(k+2)(2k+3)x^{2k+1}$;

valid for $|x| < 1$.

7. $(x^2 + 4)y'' + 2xy' - 12y = 0$.   ANS. $y = a_0\left[1 + \sum_{k=1}^{\infty} \frac{3(-1)^k(k+1)x^{2k}}{2^{2k}(2k-1)(2k-3)}\right]$

$+ a_1(x + \frac{5}{12}x^3)$; valid for $|x| < 2$.

8. $(x^2 - 9)y'' + 3xy' - 3y = 0$.

ANS. $y = a_0\left[1 - \sum_{k=1}^{\infty} \frac{[3 \cdot 5 \cdot 7 \cdots (2k+1)]x^{2k}}{(18)^k(2k-1)k!}\right] + a_1 x$; valid for $|x| < 3$.

9. $y'' + 2xy' + 5y = 0$.   ANS. $y = a_0\left[1 + \sum_{k=1}^{\infty} \frac{(-1)^k[5 \cdot 9 \cdot 13 \cdots (4k+1)]x^{2k}}{(2k)!}\right]$

$+ a_1\left[x + \sum_{k=1}^{\infty} \frac{(-1)^k[7 \cdot 11 \cdot 15 \cdots (4k+3)]x^{2k+1}}{(2k+1)!}\right];$

valid for all finite x.

10. $(x^2 + 4)y'' + 6xy' + 4y = 0$.

ANS. $y = a_0\left[1 + \sum_{k=1}^{\infty} \frac{(-1)^k(k+1)x^{2k}}{2^{2k}}\right] + a_1\left[x + \sum_{k=1}^{\infty} \frac{(-1)^k(2k+3)x^{2k+1}}{3 \cdot 2^{2k}}\right];$

valid for $|x| < 2$.

11. $2y'' + xy' - 4y = 0$.

ANS. $y = a_0(1 + x^2 + \frac{1}{12}x^4) + a_1 \sum_{k=0}^{\infty} \frac{3(-1)^k x^{2k+1}}{2^{2k}k!(2k-3)(2k-1)(2k+1)}$;

valid for all finite x.

12. $(1 + 2x^2)y'' - 5xy' + 3y = 0$.

ANS. $y = a_0\left[1 + \sum_{k=1}^{\infty} \dfrac{3(-1)^k[(-1) \cdot 3 \cdot 7 \cdots (4k-5)]x^{2k}}{2^k k!(2k-3)(2k-1)}\right] + a_1(x + \tfrac{1}{3}x^3)$;

valid for $|x| < 1/\sqrt{2}$.

13. $y'' + x^2 y = 0$.

ANS. $y = a_0\left[1 + \sum_{k=1}^{\infty} \dfrac{(-1)^k x^{4k}}{2^{2k}k! \cdot 3 \cdot 7 \cdot 11 \cdots (4k-1)}\right]$

$+ a_1\left[x + \sum_{k=1}^{\infty} \dfrac{(-1)^k x^{4k+1}}{2^{2k}k! \cdot 5 \cdot 9 \cdot 13 \cdots (4k+1)}\right]$;

valid for all finite x.

14. $y'' - 2(x+3)y' - 3y = 0$. Solve about $x = -3$.

ANS. $y = a_0\left[1 + \sum_{k=1}^{\infty} \dfrac{3 \cdot 7 \cdot 11 \cdots (4k-1)(x+3)^{2k}}{(2k)!}\right]$

$+ a_1\left[(x+3) + \sum_{k=1}^{\infty} \dfrac{5 \cdot 9 \cdot 13 \cdots (4k+1)(x+3)^{2k+1}}{(2k+1)!}\right]$;

valid for all finite x.

15. $y'' + (x-2)y = 0$. Solve about $x = 2$.

ANS. $y = a_0\left[1 + \sum_{k=1}^{\infty} \dfrac{(-1)^k(x-2)^{3k}}{3^k k! [2 \cdot 5 \cdot 8 \cdots (3k-1)]}\right]$

$+ a_1\left[(x-2) + \sum_{k=1}^{\infty} \dfrac{(-1)^k(x-2)^{3k+1}}{3^k k! [4 \cdot 7 \cdot 10 \cdots (3k+1)]}\right]$;

valid for all finite x.

16. $(1 - 4x^2)y'' + 6xy' - 4y = 0$.

ANS. $y = a_0(1 + 2x^2) + a_1\left[x - \sum_{k=1}^{\infty} \dfrac{1 \cdot 5 \cdot 9 \cdots (4k-3)x^{2k+1}}{k!(4k^2-1)}\right]$;

valid for $|x| < \tfrac{1}{2}$.

17. $(1 + 2x^2)y'' + 3xy' - 3y = 0$.

ANS. $y = a_1 x + a_0\left[1 + \sum_{k=1}^{\infty} \dfrac{(-1)^{k+1} 3 \cdot 7 \cdot 11 \cdots (4k-1)x^{2k}}{2^k(2k-1)k!}\right]$;

valid for $|x| < 1/\sqrt{2}$.

18. $y''' + x^2 y'' + 5xy' + 3y = 0$.

ANS. $y = a_0\left[1 + \sum_{k=1}^{\infty} \dfrac{(-1)^k x^{3k}}{2 \cdot 5 \cdot 8 \cdots (3k-1)}\right] + a_1\left[x + \sum_{k=1}^{\infty} \dfrac{(-1)^k x^{3k+1}}{3^k k!}\right]$

$+ a_2\left[x^2 + \sum_{k=1}^{\infty} \dfrac{(-1)^k x^{3k+2}}{4 \cdot 7 \cdot 10 \cdots (3k+1)}\right]$; valid for all finite x.

19. $y'' + xy' + 3y = x^2$.

ANS. $y = -\tfrac{2}{15} + \tfrac{1}{5}x^2 + a_0 \sum_{k=0}^{\infty} \dfrac{(-1)^k(2k+1)x^{2k}}{2^k k!}$

$+ a_1 \sum_{k=0}^{\infty} \dfrac{(-1)^k(k+1)x^{2k+1}}{1 \cdot 3 \cdot 5 \cdots (2k+1)}$;

valid for all finite x.

20. $y'' + 2xy' + 2y = 0$.

21. $y'' + 3xy' + 7y = 0$.

22. $2y'' + 9xy' - 36y = 0.$

23. $(x^2 + 4)y'' + xy' - 9y = 0.$

24. $(x^2 + 4)y'' + 3xy' - 8y = 0.$

25. $(1 + 9x^2)y'' - 18y = 0.$

26. $(x^2 - 2x + 2)y'' - 4(x - 1)y' + 6y = 0$; solve about $x = 1.$

27. $(1 + 3x^2)y'' + 13xy' + 7y = 0.$

28. $(1 + 2x^2)y'' + 11xy' + 9y = 0.$

CHAPTER 18

Solutions Near Regular
Singular Points

96. Regular singular points

Suppose that the point $x = x_0$ is a singular point of the equation

$$b_0(x)y'' + b_1(x)y' + b_2(x)y = 0 \qquad (1)$$

with polynomial coefficients. Then $b_0(x_0) = 0$, so $b_0(x)$ has a factor $(x - x_0)$ to some power.

Let us put equation (1) into the form

$$y'' + p(x)y' + q(x)y = 0. \qquad (2)$$

Since $x = x_0$ is a singular point, and since $p(x)$ and $q(x)$ are rational functions of x, at least one (maybe both) of $p(x)$ and $q(x)$ has a denominator that contains the factor $(x - x_0)$.

In what follows we assume that both $p(x)$ and $q(x)$ have been reduced so that in each case the numerator and denominator contain no common factors.

If $x = x_0$ is a singular point of equation (2), and if the denominator of $p(x)$ does not contain the factor $(x - x_0)$ to a power higher than one, and if the denominator of $q(x)$ does not contain the factor $(x - x_0)$ to a power higher than two, then $x = x_0$ is called a *regular singular point* of equation (2).

If $x = x_0$ is a singular point but is not a regular singular point, then it is called an *irregular singular point*.

EXAMPLE (a): Classify the singular points, in the finite plane, of the equation

$$x(x - 1)^2(x + 2)y'' + x^2y' - (x^3 + 2x - 1)y = 0. \tag{3}$$

For this equation

$$p(x) = \frac{x}{(x - 1)^2(x + 2)}$$

and

$$q(x) = \frac{-(x^3 + 2x - 1)}{x(x - 1)^2(x + 2)}.$$

The singular points in the finite plane are $x = 0, 1, -2$. Consider $x = 0$. The factor x is absent from the denominator of $p(x)$ and it appears to the first power in the denominator of $q(x)$. Hence $x = 0$ is a regular singular point of equation (3).

Now consider $x = 1$. The factor $(x - 1)$ appears to the second power in the denominator of $p(x)$. That is a higher power than is permitted in the definition of a regular singular point. Hence it does not matter how $(x - 1)$ appears in $q(x)$; the point $x = 1$ is an irregular singular point.

The factor $(x + 2)$ appears to the first power in the denominator of $p(x)$, just as high as is permitted, and to the first power also in the denominator of $q(x)$, so $x = -2$ is a regular singular point.

In summary, equation (3) has in the finite plane the following singular points: regular singular points at $x = 0$, $x = -2$; irregular singular point at $x = 1$. The methods of Section 104 will show that (3) has also an irregular singular point "at infinity."

EXAMPLE (b): Classify the singular points in the finite plane for the equation

$$x^4(x^2 + 1)(x - 1)^2y'' + 4x^3(x - 1)y' + (x + 1)y = 0.$$

Here

$$p(x) = \frac{4}{x(x^2 + 1)(x - 1)} = \frac{4}{x(x - i)(x + i)(x - 1)}$$

and

$$q(x) = \frac{x + 1}{x^4(x + i)(x - i)(x - 1)^2}.$$

Therefore the desired classification is:

R.S.P. at $x = i, -i, 1$;   I.S.P. at $x = 0$.

Singular points of a linear equation of higher order are classified in much the same way. For instance, the singular point $x = x_0$ of the equation

$$y''' + p_1(x)y'' + p_2(x)y' + p_3(x)y = 0$$

is called regular if the factor $(x - x_0)$ does not appear in the denominator of $p_1(x)$ to a power higher than one, of $p_2(x)$ to a power higher than two, of $p_3(x)$ to a power higher than three. If it is not regular, a singular point is irregular.

This chapter is devoted to the solution of linear equations near regular singular points. Solutions near irregular singular points present a great deal more difficulty and are not studied in this book.

Exercises

For each equation, locate and classify all its singular points in the finite plane. (See Section 104 for the concept of a singular point "at infinity.")

1. $x^3(x - 1)y'' + (x - 1)y' + 4xy = 0$.   ANS. R.S.P. at $x = 1$; I.S.P. at $x = 0$.
2. $x^2(x^2 - 4)y'' + 2x^3y' + 3y = 0$.   ANS. R.S.P. at $x = 0, 2, -2$; no I.S.P.
3. $y'' + xy = 0$.   ANS. No S.P. (in the finite plane).
4. $x^2y'' + y = 0$.   ANS. R.S.P. at $x = 0$; no I.S.P.
5. $x^4y'' + y = 0$.   ANS. No R.S.P.; I.S.P. at $x = 0$.
6. $(x^2 + 1)(x - 4)^3y'' + (x - 4)^2y' + y = 0$.
          ANS. R.S.P. at $x = i, -i$; I.S.P. at $x = 4$.
7. $x^2(x - 2)y'' + 3(x - 2)y' + y = 0$.   ANS. R.S.P. at $x = 2$; I.S.P. at $x = 0$.
8. $x^2(x - 4)^2y'' + 3xy' - (x - 4)y = 0$.   ANS. R.S.P. at $x = 0$; I.S.P. at $x = 4$.
9. $x^2(x + 2)y'' + (x + 2)y' + 4y = 0$.
10. $x(x + 3)y'' + y' - y = 0$.
11. $x^3y'' + 4y = 0$.
12. $(x - 1)(x + 2)y'' + 5(x + 2)y' + x^2y = 0$.
13. $(1 + 4x^2)y'' + 6xy' - 9y = 0$.
14. $(1 + 4x^2)^2y'' + 6x(1 + 4x^2)y' - 9y = 0$.
15. $(1 + 4x^2)^2y'' + 6xy' - 9y = 0$.
16. $(x - 1)^2(x + 4)^2y'' + (x + 4)y' + 7y = 0$.
17. $(2x + 1)^4y'' + (2x + 1)y' - 8y = 0$.
18. $x^4y'' + 2x^3y' + 4y = 0$.

97. The indicial equation

As in Chapter 17, whenever we wish to obtain solutions about a point other than $x = 0$, we first translate the origin to that point and then proceed with the usual technique. Hence we concentrate our attention on solutions valid about $x = 0$.

Let $x = 0$ be a regular singular point of the equation

$$y'' + p(x)y' + q(x)y = 0 \tag{1}$$

where p and q are rational functions of x. Then $p(x)$ cannot have in its denominator the factor x to a power higher than one. Therefore

$$p(x) = \frac{r(x)}{x}$$

where $r(x)$ is a rational function of x and $r(x)$ exists at $x = 0$. We know that such a rational function, this $r(x)$, has a power series expansion about $x = 0$. Then there exists the expansion

$$p(x) = \frac{p_0}{x} + p_1 + p_2 x + p_3 x^2 + \cdots, \tag{2}$$

valid in some region surrounding $x = 0$.

By a similar argument we find that there exists an expansion

$$q(x) = \frac{q_0}{x^2} + \frac{q_1}{x} + q_2 + q_3 x + q_4 x^2 + \cdots \tag{3}$$

about $x = 0$.

We shall see in a formal manner that it is reasonable to expect equation (1) to have a solution of the form

$$y = \sum_{n=0}^{\infty} a_n x^{n+c} = a_0 x^c + a_1 x^{1+c} + a_2 x^{2+c} + \cdots \tag{4}$$

for properly chosen c and a_n's. The facts will be stated in the next section.

If we put the series for y, $p(x)$, and $q(x)$ into equation (1) and consider only the first few terms, we get

$$c(c - 1)a_0 x^{c-2} + (1 + c)ca_1 x^{c-1} + (2 + c)(1 + c)a_2 x^c + \cdots$$

$$+ \left[\frac{p_0}{x} + p_1 + p_2 x + \cdots\right][ca_0 x^{c-1} + (1 + c)a_1 x^c + (2 + c)a_2 x^{1+c} + \cdots]$$

$$+ \left[\frac{q_0}{x^2} + \frac{q_1}{x} + q_2 + \cdots\right][a_0 x^c + a_1 x^{1+c} + a_2 x^{2+c} + \cdots] = 0.$$

Performing the indicated multiplications, we find that we have

$$c(c - 1)a_0 x^{c-2} + (1 + c)ca_1 x^{c-1} + (2 + c)(1 + c)a_2 x^c + \cdots$$

$$+ p_0 ca_0 x^{c-2} + [p_0(1 + c)a_1 + p_1 ca_0]x^{c-1} + \cdots + q_0 a_0 x^{c-2}$$

$$+ [q_0 a_1 + q_1 a_0]x^{c-1} + \cdots = 0.$$

From the fact that the coefficient of x^{c-2} must vanish we obtain

$$[c(c - 1) + p_0 c + q_0]a_0 = 0. \tag{5}$$

We may insist that $a_0 \neq 0$ because a_0 is the coefficient of the lowest power of x appearing in the solution (4), no matter what that lowest power is. So from (5) it follows that

$$c^2 + (p_0 - 1)c + q_0 = 0, \tag{6}$$

which is called the *indicial equation* (at $x = 0$). The p_0 and q_0 are known constants; equation (6) is a quadratic equation giving us two roots, $c = c_1$ and $c = c_2$.

To distinguish between the roots of the indicial equation, we shall denote by c_1 the root whose real part is not smaller than the real part of the other root. Thus, if the roots are real, $c_1 \geqq c_2$; if the roots are imaginary, $\text{Re}(c_1) \geqq \text{Re}(c_2)$. For brevity we call c_1 the "larger" root.

Superficially, it appears that there should be two solutions of the form (4), one from each of these values of c. In each solution the a_0 should be arbitrary and the succeeding a's should be determined by equating to zero the coefficients of the higher powers of $x(x^{c-1}, x^c, x^{1+c}$, etc.) in the identity just above equation (5).

This superficial conclusion is correct if the difference of the roots c_1 and c_2 is not integral. If that difference is integral, however, a logarithmic term may enter the solution. The reasons for this strange behavior will be made clear when we develop a method for obtaining the solutions.

98. Form and validity of the solutions near a regular singular point

Let $x = 0$ be a regular singular point of the equation

$$y'' + p(x)y' + q(x)y = 0. \tag{1}$$

It can be proved that equation (1) always has a general solution either of the form

$$y = A \sum_{n=0}^{\infty} a_n x^{n+c_1} + B \sum_{n=0}^{\infty} b_n x^{n+c_2} \tag{2}$$

or of the form

$$y = (A + B \ln x) \sum_{n=0}^{\infty} a_n x^{n+c_1} + B \sum_{n=0}^{\infty} b_n x^{n+c_2} \tag{3}$$

in which A and B are arbitrary constants. Furthermore, it is proved that the infinite series which occur in the above forms of solution converge in at least the annular region bounded by two circles centered at $x = 0$, one of arbitrarily small radius, the other extending to the singular point (of the equation) nearest $x = 0$.

99. Indicial equation with difference of roots nonintegral

The equation

$$2xy'' + (1 + x)y' - 2y = 0 \tag{1}$$

has a regular singular point at $x = 0$ and no other singular points for finite x. Let us assume that there is a solution of the form

$$y = \sum_{n=0}^{\infty} a_n x^{n+c}. \tag{2}$$

Direct substitution of this y into equation (1) yields

$$\sum_{n=0}^{\infty} 2(n + c)(n + c - 1)a_n x^{n+c-1} + \sum_{n=0}^{\infty} (n + c)a_n x^{n+c-1}$$

$$+ \sum_{n=0}^{\infty} (n + c)a_n x^{n+c} - 2 \sum_{n=0}^{\infty} a_n x^{n+c} = 0,$$

or

$$\sum_{n=0}^{\infty} (n + c)(2n + 2c - 1)a_n x^{n+c-1} + \sum_{n=0}^{\infty} (n + c - 2)a_n x^{n+c} = 0. \tag{3}$$

Having collected like terms, we next shift index to bring all the exponents of x down to the smallest one present. This choice is used to get a recurrence relation for a_n rather than one for a_{n+1} or some other a. In equation (3), we replace the index n in the second summation by $(n-1)$, thus getting

$$\sum_{n=0}^{\infty} (n+c)(2n+2c-1)a_n x^{n+c-1} + \sum_{n=1}^{\infty} (n+c-3)a_{n-1} x^{n+c-1} = 0. \quad (4)$$

Once more we reason that the total coefficient of each power of x in the left member of (4) must vanish. The second summation does not start its contribution until $n=1$. Hence the equations for the determination of c and the a's are

$$n = 0: \quad c(2c-1)a_0 = 0,$$
$$n \geqq 1: \quad (n+c)(2n+2c-1)a_n + (n+c-3)a_{n-1} = 0.$$

Since we may without loss of generality assume $a_0 \neq 0$, the indicial equation, that which determines c, is

$$c(2c-1) = 0. \quad (5)$$

The indicial equation always comes from the $n=0$ term when the technique being presented in this book is employed.

From (5) we see that $c_1 = \frac{1}{2}$ and $c_2 = 0$. The difference of the roots is $s = c_1 - c_2 = \frac{1}{2}$, which is nonintegral. When s is not an integer, the method we are using always gives two linearly independent solutions of the form (2), one with each choice of c.

Let us return to the recurrence relation using the value $c = c_1 = \frac{1}{2}$. We have

$$n \geqq 1: \quad (n+\tfrac{1}{2})(2n+1-1)a_n + (n+\tfrac{1}{2}-3)a_{n-1} = 0,$$

$$n \geqq 1: \quad a_n = -\frac{(2n-5)a_{n-1}}{2n(2n+1)}.$$

As usual we use a vertical array and then form the product to get a formula for a_n. We have

$$a_0 \ arb.$$

$$a_1 = -\frac{(-3)a_0}{2 \cdot 3}$$

$$a_2 = -\frac{(-1)a_1}{4 \cdot 5}$$

$$a_3 = -\frac{(1)a_2}{6 \cdot 7}$$

$$\vdots$$

$$a_n = -\frac{(2n-5)a_{n-1}}{2n(2n+1)},$$

so the product yields, for $n \geq 1$,

$$a_n = \frac{(-1)^n[(-3)(-1)(1) \cdots (2n-5)]a_0}{[2 \cdot 4 \cdot 6 \cdots (2n)][3 \cdot 5 \cdot 7 \cdots (2n+1)]}. \tag{6}$$

The formula (6) may be simplified to the form

$$a_n = \frac{(-1)^n \cdot 3a_0}{2^n n!(2n-3)(2n-1)(2n+1)}. \tag{7}$$

Using $a_0 = 1$, the a_n from (7), and the pertinent value of c, $c_1 = \frac{1}{2}$, we may now write a particular solution. It is

$$y_1 = x^{1/2} + \sum_{n=1}^{\infty} \frac{(-1)^n 3x^{n+\frac{1}{2}}}{2^n n!(2n-3)(2n-1)(2n+1)}. \tag{8}$$

The notation y_1 is to emphasize that this particular solution corresponds to the root c_1 of the indicial equation. Our next task will be to get a particular solution y_2 corresponding to the smaller root c_2. Then the general solution, if it is desired, may be written at once as

$$y = Ay_1 + By_2$$

with A and B arbitrary constants.

In returning to the recurrence relation just above the indicial equation (5) with the intention of using $c = c_2 = 0$, it is evident that the a's will be different from those with $c = c_1$. Hence it is wise to change notation. Let us use b's instead of a's. With $c = 0$, the recurrence relation becomes

$$n \geq 1: n(2n-1)b_n + (n-3)b_{n-1} = 0.$$

The corresponding vertical array is:

$$b_0 \text{ arb.}$$

$$b_1 = -\frac{(-2)b_0}{1 \cdot 1}$$

$$b_2 = -\frac{(-1)b_1}{2 \cdot 3}$$

$$b_3 = -\frac{(0)b_2}{3 \cdot 5}$$

$$\vdots$$

$$b_n = -\frac{(n-3)b_{n-1}}{n(2n-1)}.$$

Then $b_n = 0$ for $n \geq 3$ and, using $b_0 = 1$, b_1 and b_2 may be computed and found to have the values $b_1 = 2$ and $b_2 = \frac{1}{6} b_1 = \frac{1}{3}$. Therefore a second solution is

$$y_2 = 1 + 2x + \tfrac{1}{3} x^2. \tag{9}$$

Since the differential equation has no singular point, other than $x = 0$, in the finite plane, we conclude that the linearly independent solutions y_1 of (8) and y_2 of (9) are valid at least for $|x| > 0$. The validity of (9) is evident in this particular example because the series terminates.

The student should associate with each solution the region of validity guaranteed by the general theorem quoted in Section 98, though from now on the printed answers to the exercises will omit statement of the region of validity.

Exercises

For each equation, obtain two linearly independent solutions valid near the origin. Always state the region of validity of each solution that you obtain.

1. $2x(x-1)y'' + 3(x-1)y' - y = 0$.

ANS. $y_1 = 1 - \sum\limits_{n=1}^{\infty} \dfrac{x^n}{4n^2 - 1}$; $y_2 = x^{-1/2} - x^{1/2}$.

2. $4xy'' + 3y' - 3y = 0$.   ANS. $y_1 = x^{1/4} + \sum\limits_{n=1}^{\infty} \dfrac{(-3)^n x^{n+1/4}}{n! \, 5 \cdot 9 \cdot 13 \cdots (4n+1)}$;

$y_2 = 1 + \sum\limits_{n=1}^{\infty} \dfrac{(-3)^n x^n}{n! \, 3 \cdot 7 \cdot 11 \cdots (4n-1)}$.

3. $2x^2(x+1)y'' + x(7x-1)y' + y = 0$.

ANS. $y_1 = x + \tfrac{1}{15} \sum\limits_{n=1}^{\infty} (-1)^n (2n+3)(2n+5)x^{n+1}$;

$y_2 = x^{1/2} + \tfrac{1}{2} \sum\limits_{n=1}^{\infty} (-1)^n (n+1)(n+2)x^{n+1/2}$.

4. $2xy'' + 5(1+2x)y' + 5y = 0$.

ANS. $y_1 = 1 + \sum\limits_{n=1}^{\infty} \dfrac{3(-5)^n x^n}{n! \, (2n+1)(2n+3)}$; $y_2 = x^{-3/2} - 10x^{-1/2}$.

5. $8x^2 y'' + 10xy' - (1+x)y = 0$.

ANS. $y_1 = x^{1/4} + \sum\limits_{n=1}^{\infty} \dfrac{x^{n+1/4}}{2^n n! \, 7 \cdot 11 \cdot 15 \cdots (4n+3)}$;

$y_2 = x^{-1/2} + \sum\limits_{n=1}^{\infty} \dfrac{x^{n-1/2}}{2^n n! \, 1 \cdot 5 \cdot 9 \cdots (4n-3)}$.

6. $3xy'' + (2-x)y' - 2y = 0$.

ANS. $y_1 = \sum\limits_{n=0}^{\infty} \dfrac{(3n+4)x^{n+1/3}}{4 \cdot 3^n n!}$; $y_2 = 1 + \sum\limits_{n=1}^{\infty} \dfrac{(n+1)x^n}{2 \cdot 5 \cdot 8 \cdots (3n-1)}$.

7. $2x(x+3)y'' - 3(x+1)y' + 2y = 0.$

ANS. $y_1 = x^{3/2} + \sum\limits_{n=1}^{\infty} \dfrac{(-1)^{n+1}x^{n+3/2}}{3^{n-1}(2n-1)(2n+1)(2n+3)}$; $y_2 = 1 + \frac{2}{3}x + \frac{1}{9}x^2.$

8. $2x^2y'' - x(2x+1)y' + (1-5x)y = 0.$

ANS. $y_1 = x + \frac{1}{15} \sum\limits_{n=1}^{\infty} \dfrac{(2n+3)(2n+5)x^{n+1}}{n!}$;

$y_2 = x^{1/2} + \sum\limits_{n=1}^{\infty} \dfrac{2^{n-1}(n+1)(n+2)x^{n+1/2}}{1 \cdot 3 \cdot 5 \cdots (2n-1)}.$

9. $9x^2y'' + 3x(x+3)y' - (1+4x)y = 0.$

ANS. $y_1 = x^{1/3} + \frac{1}{5}x^{4/3}$; $y_2 = x^{-1/3} + \sum\limits_{n=1}^{\infty} \dfrac{10(-1)^n x^{n-1/3}}{3^n n! \, (3n-5)(3n-2)}.$

10. $2xy'' + (1-2x^2)y' - 4xy = 0.$

ANS. $y_1 = \sum\limits_{k=0}^{\infty} \dfrac{x^{2k+1/2}}{2^k k!} = x^{1/2}e^{x^2/2}$; $y_2 = 1 + \sum\limits_{k=1}^{\infty} \dfrac{2^k x^{2k}}{3 \cdot 7 \cdot 11 \cdots (4k-1)}.$

11. $x(4-x)y'' + (2-x)y' + 4y = 0.$

ANS. $y_1 = x^{1/2} + \sum\limits_{n=1}^{\infty} \dfrac{(2n+3)[(-3)(-1) \cdot 1 \cdots (2n-5)]x^{n+1/2}}{3 \cdot 2^{3n} n!}$;

$y_2 = 1 - 2x + \frac{1}{2}x^2.$

12. $3x^2y'' + xy' - (1+x)y = 0.$ ANS. $y_1 = x + \sum\limits_{n=1}^{\infty} \dfrac{x^{n+1}}{n! \, 7 \cdot 10 \cdot 13 \cdots (3n+4)}$;

$y_2 = x^{-1/3} + \sum\limits_{n=1}^{\infty} \dfrac{x^{n-1/3}}{n!(-1) \cdot 2 \cdot 5 \cdots (3n-4)}.$

13. $2xy'' + (1+2x)y' + 4y = 0.$

ANS. $y_1 = \sum\limits_{n=0}^{\infty} \dfrac{(-1)^n(2n+3)x^{n+1/2}}{3 \cdot n!}$; $y_2 = 1 + \sum\limits_{n=1}^{\infty} \dfrac{(-1)^n 2^n(n+1)x^n}{1 \cdot 3 \cdot 5 \cdots (2n-1)}.$

14. $2xy'' + (1+2x)y' - 5y = 0.$

ANS. $y_1 = x^{1/2} + \frac{4}{3}x^{3/2} + \frac{4}{15}x^{5/2}$; $y_2 = \sum\limits_{n=0}^{\infty} \dfrac{15(-1)^{n+1}x^n}{n! \, (2n-5)(2n-3)(2n-1)}.$

15. $2x^2y'' - 3x(1-x)y' + 2y = 0.$ ANS. $y_1 = x^2 + \sum\limits_{n=1}^{\infty} \dfrac{(-1)^n 3^n(n+1)x^{n+2}}{5 \cdot 7 \cdot 9 \cdots (2n+3)}$;

$y_2 = x^{1/2} + \sum\limits_{n=1}^{\infty} \dfrac{(-1)^{n+1} 3^n(2n-1)x^{n+1/2}}{2^n n!}.$

16. $2x^2y'' + x(4x-1)y' + 2(3x-1)y = 0.$

ANS. $y_1 = \sum\limits_{n=0}^{\infty} \dfrac{(-1)^n 2^n x^{n+2}}{n!} = x^2 e^{-2x}$;

$y_2 = x^{-1/2} + \sum\limits_{n=1}^{\infty} \dfrac{(-1)^n 4^n x^{n-1/2}}{(-3)(-1) \cdot 1 \cdots (2n-5)}.$

17. $2xy'' - (1+2x^2)y' - xy = 0.$

ANS. $y_1 = x^{3/2} + \sum\limits_{k=1}^{\infty} \dfrac{2^k x^{2k+3/2}}{7 \cdot 11 \cdot 15 \cdots (4k+3)}$; $y_2 = 1 + \sum\limits_{k=1}^{\infty} \dfrac{x^{2k}}{2^k k!} = \exp(\frac{1}{2}x^2).$

18. The equation of Ex. 17 above has a particular solution $y_2 = \exp(\frac{1}{2}x^2)$ obtained by the series method. Make a change of dependent variable in the differential equation, using $y = v \exp(\frac{1}{4}x^2)$ (the device of Section 43), and thus obtain the general solution in "closed form."

$$\text{ANS.} \quad y = c_1 \exp(\tfrac{1}{4}x^2) + c_2 \exp(\tfrac{1}{4}x^2) \int_0^x \beta^{1/2} \exp(-\tfrac{1}{2}\beta^2)\, d\beta.$$

In Exs. 19–22, use the power series method. What is causing the recurrence relations to degenerate into one-term relations?

19. $2x^2y'' + xy' - y = 0.$ ANS. $y_1 = x; y_2 = x^{-1/2}.$
20. $2x^2y'' - 3xy' + 2y = 0.$ ANS. $y_1 = x^2; y_2 = x^{1/2}.$
21. $9x^2y'' + 2y = 0.$ ANS. $y_1 = x^{2/3}; y_2 = x^{1/3}.$
22. $2x^2y'' + 5xy' - 2y = 0.$ ANS. $y_1 = x^{1/2}; y_2 = x^{-2}.$

23. Obtain $\dfrac{dy}{dx}$ and $\dfrac{d^2y}{dx^2}$ in terms of derivatives of y with respect to a new independent variable t related to x by $t = \ln x$.

$$\text{ANS.} \quad \frac{dy}{dx} = e^{-t}\frac{dy}{dt}, \quad \frac{d^2y}{dx^2} = e^{-2t}\left[\frac{d^2y}{dt^2} - \frac{dy}{dt}\right].$$

24. Use the result of Ex. 23 above to show that the change of independent variable from x to t, where $t = \ln x$, transforms the equation*

$$ax^2 \frac{d^2y}{dx^2} + bx \frac{dy}{dx} + cy = 0,$$

a, b, c constants, into a linear equation with constant coefficients.

Solve Exs. 25–34 by the method implied by Ex. 24 above; that is, by changing independent variable to $t = \ln x$.

25. Ex. 19.   26. Ex. 20.
27. Ex. 21.   28. Ex. 22.
29. $x^2y'' + 2xy' - 12y = 0.$ ANS. $y_1 = x^3; y_2 = x^{-4}.$
30. $x^2y'' + xy' - 9y = 0.$ ANS. $y_1 = x^3; y_2 = x^{-3}.$
31. $x^2y'' - 3xy' + 4y = 0.$ ANS. $y = x^2(c_1 + c_2 \ln x).$
32. $x^2y'' - 5xy' + 9y = 0.$ ANS. $y = x^3(c_1 + c_2 \ln x).$
33. $x^2y'' + 5xy' + 5y = 0.$ ANS. $y = x^{-2}[c_1 \cos(\ln x) + c_2 \sin(\ln x)].$
34. $(x^3D^3 + 4x^2D^2 - 8xD + 8)y = 0.$ You will need to extend the result of Ex. 23 to the third derivative, obtaining

$$x^3 \frac{d^3y}{dx^3} = \frac{d^3y}{dt^3} - 3\frac{d^2y}{dt^2} + 2\frac{dy}{dt}.$$

ANS. $y = c_1x + c_2 x^2 + c_3 x^{-4}.$

100. Differentiation of a product of functions

It will soon prove necessary for us to differentiate efficiently a product of a number of functions. Suppose that

$$u = u_1 u_2 u_3 \cdots u_n, \tag{1}$$

* An equation such as the one of this exercise, which contains only terms of the kind cx^kD^ky with c constant and $k = 0, 1, 2, 3, \ldots$, is called an equation of *Cauchy type*, or of *Euler type*.

each of the u's being a function of the parameter c. Let differentiation with respect to c be indicated by primes. Then from

$$\ln u = \ln u_1 + \ln u_2 + \ln u_3 + \cdots + \ln u_n$$

it follows that

$$\frac{u'}{u} = \frac{u'_1}{u_1} + \frac{u'_2}{u_2} + \frac{u'_3}{u_3} + \cdots + \frac{u'_n}{u_n}.$$

Hence

$$u' = u\left(\frac{u'_1}{u_1} + \frac{u'_2}{u_2} + \frac{u'_3}{u_3} + \cdots + \frac{u'_n}{u_n}\right). \tag{2}$$

Thus to differentiate a product we may multiply the original product by a conversion factor (which converts the product into its derivative) consisting of the sum of the derivatives of the logarithms of the separate factors.

When the factors involved are themselves powers of polynomials, there is a convenient way of forming mentally the conversion factor. That factor is the sum of the conversion factors for the individual parts.

The way most of us learned to differentiate a power of a quantity is to multiply the exponent, the derivative of the original quantity, and the quantity with its exponent lowered by one. Thus, if

$$y = (ac + b)^k,$$

then

$$\frac{dy}{dc} = y\left(\frac{ka}{ac + b}\right),$$

the division by $(ac + b)$ converting $(ac + b)^k$ into $(ac + b)^{k-1}$.

EXAMPLE (a):   If

$$u = \frac{c^2(c + 1)}{(4c - 1)^3(7c + 2)^6},$$

then

$$\frac{du}{dc} = u\left(\frac{2}{c} + \frac{1}{c + 1} - \frac{12}{4c - 1} - \frac{42}{7c + 2}\right).$$

Note that the denominator factors in the function u are thought of as numerator factors with negative exponents.

EXAMPLE (b):   If

$$y = \frac{c+n}{c(c+1)(c+2)\cdots(c+n-1)},$$

then

$$\frac{dy}{dc} = y\left\{\frac{1}{c+n} - \frac{1}{c} - \frac{1}{c+1} - \frac{1}{c+2} - \cdots - \frac{1}{c+n-1}\right\}.$$

EXAMPLE (c):   If

$$w = \frac{2^n c^3}{[(c+2)(c+3)\cdots(c+n+1)]^2},$$

then

$$\frac{dw}{dc} = w\left\{\frac{3}{c} - 2\left(\frac{1}{c+2} + \frac{1}{c+3} + \cdots + \frac{1}{c+n+1}\right)\right\}.$$

101. Indicial equation with equal roots

When the indicial equation has equal roots, the method of Section 99 cannot yield two linearly independent solutions. The work with one value of c would be a pure repetition of that with the other value of c. A new attack is needed.

Consider the problem of solving the equation

$$x^2 y'' + 3xy' + (1 - 2x)y = 0 \tag{1}$$

about the regular singular point $x = 0$. It will turn out that the roots of the indicial equation are equal, a fact which can be determined ahead of time by setting up the indicial equation as developed in the theory, page 296. Here

$$p(x) = \frac{3}{x}, \quad q(x) = \frac{1 - 2x}{x^2},$$

so $p_0 = 3$ and $q_0 = 1$. The indicial equation is

$$c^2 + 2c + 1 = 0,$$

with roots $c_1 = c_2 = -1$.

Any attempt to obtain solutions by putting

$$y = \sum_{n=0}^{\infty} a_n x^{n+c} \tag{2}$$

into equation (1) is certain to force us to choose $c = -1$ and thus get only one solution. We know that we must not choose c yet if we are to get two solutions. Hence let us put the y of equation (2) into the left member of equation (1) and try to come as close as we can to making that left member zero without choosing c.

It is convenient to have a notation for the left member of equation (1); let us use

$$L(y) = x^2 y'' + 3xy' + (1 - 2x)y. \tag{3}$$

For the y of equation (2) we find that

$$L(y) = \sum_{n=0}^{\infty} (n + c)(n + c - 1)a_n x^{n+c} + \sum_{n=0}^{\infty} 3(n + c)a_n x^{n+c}$$
$$+ \sum_{n=0}^{\infty} a_n x^{n+c} - \sum_{n=0}^{\infty} 2a_n x^{n+c+1},$$

from which

$$L(y) = \sum_{n=0}^{\infty} [(n + c)^2 + 2(n + c) + 1]a_n x^{n+c} - \sum_{n=0}^{\infty} 2a_n x^{n+c+1}.$$

The usual simplifications lead to

$$L(y) = \sum_{n=0}^{\infty} (n + c + 1)^2 a_n x^{n+c} - \sum_{n=1}^{\infty} 2a_{n-1} x^{n+c}. \tag{4}$$

Recalling that the indicial equation comes from setting the coefficient in the $n = 0$ term equal to zero, we purposely avoid trying to make that term vanish yet. But by choosing the a's and leaving c as a parameter we can make every term but that first one in $L(y)$ vanish. Therefore we set equal to zero each coefficient, except for the $n = 0$ term, of the various powers of x on the right in equation (4); thus

$$n \geqq 1: \quad (n + c + 1)^2 a_n - 2a_{n-1} = 0. \tag{5}$$

The successive application of the recurrence relation (5) will determine each a_n, $n \geqq 1$, in terms of a_0 and c. Indeed, from the array

$$a_1 = \frac{2a_0}{(c + 2)^2}$$

$$a_2 = \frac{2a_1}{(c + 3)^2}$$

$$\vdots$$

$$a_n = \frac{2a_{n-1}}{(c + n + 1)^2},$$

it follows by the usual multiplication device that

$$n \geq 1: \quad a_n = \frac{2^n a_0}{[(c + 2)(c + 3) \cdots (c + n + 1)]^2}.$$

To arrive at a specific solution, let us choose $a_0 = 1$.

Using the a's determined above, we write a y which is dependent upon both x and c, namely,

$$y(x, c) = x^c + \sum_{n=1}^{\infty} a_n(c)x^{n+c}, \tag{6}$$

in which

$$n \geq 1: \quad a_n(c) = \frac{2^n}{[(c + 2)(c + 3) \cdots (c + n + 1)]^2}. \tag{7}$$

The y of equation (6) has been so determined that for that y the right member of equation (4) must reduce to a single term, the $n = 0$ term. That is, for the $y(x, c)$ of equation (6), we have

$$L[y(x, c)] = (c + 1)^2 x^c. \tag{8}$$

A solution of the original differential equation is a function y for which $L(y) = 0$. Now we see why the choice $c = -1$ yields a solution; it makes the right member of equation (8) zero.

But the factor $(c + 1)$ occurs squared in equation (8), an automatic consequence of the equality of the roots of the indicial equation. We know from elementary calculus that if a function contains a power of a certain factor, dependent upon c, then the derivative with respect to c of that function contains the same factor to a power one lower than in the original.

For equation (8), in particular, differentiation of each member with respect to c yields

$$\frac{\partial}{\partial c} L[y(x, c)] = L\left[\frac{\partial y(x, c)}{\partial c}\right] = 2(c + 1)x^c + (c + 1)^2 x^c \ln x, \tag{9}$$

the right member containing the factor $(c + 1)$ to the first power, as we knew it must from the theorem quoted.

In (9), the order of differentiations with respect to x and c was interchanged. It is best to avoid the need for justifying such steps by verifying the solutions, (13) and (14) below, directly. The verification in this instance is straightforward but a bit lengthy and is omitted here.

From equations (8) and (9) it can be seen that two solutions of the equation $L(y) = 0$ are

$$y_1 = [y(x, c)]_{c=-1} = y(x, -1)$$

and

$$y_2 = \left[\frac{\partial y(x, c)}{\partial c}\right]_{c=-1}$$

because $c = -1$ makes the right member of each of equations (8) and (9) vanish. That y_1 and y_2 are linearly independent will be evident later.

We have

$$y(x, c) = x^c + \sum_{n=1}^{\infty} a_n(c)x^{n+c} \tag{6}$$

and we need $\partial y(x, c)/\partial c$. From (6) it follows that

$$\frac{\partial y(x, c)}{\partial c} = x^c \ln x + \sum_{n=1}^{\infty} a_n(c)x^{n+c} \ln x + \sum_{n=1}^{\infty} a_n'(c)x^{n+c},$$

which simplifies at once to the form

$$\frac{\partial y(x, c)}{\partial c} = y(x, c) \ln x + \sum_{n=1}^{\infty} a_n'(c)x^{n+c}. \tag{10}$$

The solutions y_1 and y_2 will be obtained by putting $c = -1$ in equations (6) and (10); that is,

$$y_1 = x^{-1} + \sum_{n=1}^{\infty} a_n(-1)x^{n-1}, \tag{11}$$

$$y_2 = y_1 \ln x + \sum_{n=1}^{\infty} a_n'(-1)x^{n-1}. \tag{12}$$

Therefore we need to evaluate $a_n(c)$ and $a_n'(c)$ at $c = -1$. We know that

$$a_n(c) = \frac{2^n}{[(c + 2)(c + 3) \cdots (c + n + 1)]^2},$$

from which by the method of Section 100 we obtain immediately

$$a_n'(c) = -2a_n(c)\left\{\frac{1}{c + 2} + \frac{1}{c + 3} + \cdots + \frac{1}{c + n + 1}\right\}.$$

We now use $c = -1$ to obtain

$$a_n(-1) = \frac{2^n}{(n!)^2}$$

and

$$a_n'(-1) = -2 \cdot \frac{2^n}{(n!)^2}\left\{1 + \tfrac{1}{2} + \tfrac{1}{3} + \cdots + \tfrac{1}{n}\right\}.$$

A frequently used notation for a partial sum of the harmonic series is useful here. It is

$$H_n = 1 + \frac{1}{2} + \frac{1}{3} + \cdots + \frac{1}{n} = \sum_{k=1}^{n} \frac{1}{k}.$$

We can now write $a_n'(-1)$ more simply as

$$a_n'(-1) = -\frac{2^{n+1}H_n}{(n!)^2}.$$

Finally, the desired solutions can be written in the form

$$y_1 = x^{-1} + \sum_{n=1}^{\infty} \frac{2^n x^{n-1}}{(n!)^2} \tag{13}$$

and

$$y_2 = y_1 \ln x - \sum_{n=1}^{\infty} \frac{2^{n+1}H_n x^{n-1}}{(n!)^2}. \tag{14}$$

The general solution, valid for all finite $x \neq 0$, is

$$y = Ay_1 + By_2,$$

with A and B arbitrary constants. The linear independence of y_1 and y_2 should be evident because of the presence of $\ln x$ in y_2. In detail, xy_1 has a power series expansion about $x = 0$, but xy_2 does not, so they cannot be proportional.

Examination of the procedure used in solving this differential equation shows that the method is in no way dependent upon the specific coefficients except that the indicial equation has equal roots. That is, the success of the method is due to the fact that the $n = 0$ term in $L(y)$ contains a square factor.

When the indicial equation has equal roots, $c_2 = c_1$, then two linearly independent solutions will always appear in the form

$$y_1 = x^{c_1} + \sum_{n=1}^{\infty} a_n x^{n+c_1},$$

$$y_2 = y_1 \ln x + \sum_{n=1}^{\infty} b_n x^{n+c_1},$$

where c_1, a_n, b_n are dependent upon the coefficients in the particular equation being solved.

Exercises

Obtain two linearly independent solutions valid about $x = 0$ unless otherwise instructed.

1. $x^2y'' - x(1+x)y' + y = 0.$

$$\text{ANS.} \quad y_1 = \sum_{n=0}^{\infty} \frac{x^{n+1}}{n!} = xe^x; \quad y_2 = y_1 \ln x - \sum_{n=1}^{\infty} \frac{H_n x^{n+1}}{n!}.$$

2. $4x^2y'' + (1 - 2x)y = 0.$

$$\text{ANS.} \quad y_1 = \sum_{n=0}^{\infty} \frac{x^{n+1/2}}{2^n(n!)^2}; \quad y_2 = y_1 \ln x - \sum_{n=1}^{\infty} \frac{H_n x^{n+1/2}}{2^{n-1}(n!)^2}.$$

3. $x^2y'' + x(x-3)y' + 4y = 0.$

$$\text{ANS.} \quad y_1 = \sum_{n=0}^{\infty} \frac{(-1)^n(n+1)x^{n+2}}{n!};$$

$$y_2 = y_1 \ln x + \sum_{n=1}^{\infty} \frac{(-1)^{n+1}[n+(n+1)H_n]x^{n+2}}{n!}.$$

4. $x^2y'' + 3xy' + (1 + 4x^2)y = 0.$

$$\text{ANS.} \quad y_1 = \sum_{k=0}^{\infty} \frac{(-1)^k x^{2k-1}}{(k!)^2}; \quad y_2 = y_1 \ln x - \sum_{k=1}^{\infty} \frac{(-1)^k H_k x^{2k-1}}{(k!)^2}.$$

5. $x(1+x)y'' + (1+5x)y' + 3y = 0.$

$$\text{ANS.} \quad y_1 = 1 + \tfrac{1}{2}\sum_{n=1}^{\infty} (-1)^n(n+1)(n+2)x^n;$$

$$y_2 = y_1 \ln x - \tfrac{3}{2}(y_1 - 1) + \tfrac{1}{2}\sum_{n=1}^{\infty} (-1)^n(2n+3)x^n.$$

6. $xy'' + y' + xy = 0.$ This is known as Bessel's equation of index zero. It is widely encountered in both pure and applied mathematics. (See also Sections 111 and 112.)

$$\text{ANS.} \quad y_1 = \sum_{k=0}^{\infty} \frac{(-1)^k x^{2k}}{2^{2k}(k!)^2}; \quad y_2 = y_1 \ln x - \sum_{k=1}^{\infty} \frac{(-1)^k H_k x^{2k}}{2^{2k}(k!)^2}.$$

7. $x^2y'' - x(1 + 3x)y' + (1 - 6x)y = 0.$

$$\text{ANS.} \quad y_1 = \sum_{n=0}^{\infty} \frac{3^n(n+1)(n+2)x^{n+1}}{2 \cdot n!};$$

$$y_2 = y_1 \ln x + \sum_{n=1}^{\infty} \frac{3^n(n+1)(n+2)(H_{n+2} - 2H_n - \tfrac{3}{2})x^{n+1}}{2 \cdot n!}.$$

8. $x^2y'' + x(x-1)y' + (1 - x)y = 0.$

$$\text{ANS.} \quad y_1 = x; \quad y_2 = y_1 \ln x + \sum_{n=1}^{\infty} \frac{(-1)^n x^{n+1}}{n \cdot n!}.$$

9. $x(x-2)y'' + 2(x-1)y' - 2y = 0.$

$$\text{ANS.} \quad y_1 = 1 - x; \quad y_2 = y_1 \ln x + \tfrac{5}{2}x - \sum_{n=2}^{\infty} \frac{(n+1)x^n}{2^n n(n-1)}.$$

10. Solve the equation of Ex. 9 about the point $x = 2.$

$$\text{ANS.} \quad y_1 = 1 + (x - 2);$$

$$y_2 = y_1 \ln(x-2) - \tfrac{5}{2}(x-2) - \sum_{n=2}^{\infty} \frac{(-1)^n(n+1)(x-2)^n}{2^n n(n-1)}.$$

11. Solve about $x = 4$: $4(x-4)^2y'' + (x-4)(x-8)y' + xy = 0.$

$$\text{ANS.} \quad y_1 = \sum_{n=0}^{\infty} \frac{(-1)^n(n+1)(x-4)^{n+1}}{2^{2n}n!};$$

$$y_2 = y_1 \ln(x-4) + \sum_{n=1}^{\infty} \frac{(-1)^n(n+1)(H_{n+1} - 2H_n - 1)(x-4)^{n+1}}{2^{2n}n!}.$$

12. $xy'' + (1 - x^2)y' - xy = 0.$ ANS. $y_1 = 1 + \sum\limits_{k=1}^{\infty} \dfrac{1 \cdot 3 \cdot 5 \cdots (2k-1)x^{2k}}{2^{2k}(k!)^2}$;

$$y_2 = y_1 \ln x + \sum_{k=1}^{\infty} \dfrac{1 \cdot 3 \cdot 5 \cdots (2k-1)\left\{1 + \frac{1}{3} + \cdots + \dfrac{1}{2k-1} - H_k\right\}x^{2k}}{2^{2k}(k!)^2}.$$

13. Show that

$$1 + \tfrac{1}{3} + \tfrac{1}{5} + \cdots + \dfrac{1}{2k-1} = H_{2k} - \tfrac{1}{2}H_k$$

and apply the result to simplification of the formula for y_2 in the answer to Ex. 12.

14. $x^2y'' + x(3 + 2x)y' + (1 + 3x)y = 0.$ In simplifying y_2, use the formula given in Ex. 13.

     ANS. $y_1 = x^{-1} + \sum\limits_{n=1}^{\infty} \dfrac{(-1)^n 1 \cdot 3 \cdot 5 \cdots (2n-1)x^{n-1}}{(n!)^2}$;

$$y_2 = y_1 \ln x + \sum_{n=1}^{\infty} \dfrac{(-1)^n 1 \cdot 3 \cdot 5 \cdots (2n-1)(2H_{2n} - 3H_n)x^{n-1}}{(n!)^2}.$$

15. $4x^2y'' + 8x(x+1)y' + y = 0.$

     ANS. $y_1 = x^{-1/2} + \sum\limits_{n=1}^{\infty} \dfrac{(-1)^n[(-1) \cdot 1 \cdot 3 \cdot 5 \cdots (2n-3)]x^{n-1/2}}{(n!)^2}$;

$$y_2 = y_1 \ln x$$
$$+ \sum_{n=1}^{\infty} \dfrac{(-1)^n[(-1) \cdot 1 \cdot 3 \cdots (2n-3)](2H_{2n-2} - H_{n-1} - 2H_n - 2)x^{n-1/2}}{(n!)^2}.$$

16. $x^2y'' + 3x(1+x)y' + (1 - 3x)y = 0.$

     ANS. $y_1 = x^{-1} + 6 + \tfrac{9}{2}x$; $y_2 = y_1 \ln x - 15 - \tfrac{81}{4}x + \sum\limits_{n=3}^{\infty} \dfrac{2(-3)^n x^{n-1}}{n! \, n(n-1)(n-2)}.$

17. $xy'' + (1 - x)y' - y = 0.$

     ANS. $y_1 = 1 + \sum\limits_{n=1}^{\infty} \dfrac{x^n}{n!} = e^x$; $y_2 = y_1 \ln x - \sum\limits_{n=1}^{\infty} \dfrac{H_n x^n}{n!}.$

18. Refer to Ex. 17 above. There one solution was found to be $y_1 = e^x$. Use the change of dependent variable, $y = ve^x$, to obtain the general solution of the differential equation in the form

$$y = k_1 e^x \int_{k_2}^{x} \beta^{-1} e^{-\beta} \, d\beta.$$

102. Indicial equation with difference of roots a positive integer, nonlogarithmic case

Consider the equation

$$xy'' - (4 + x)y' + 2y = 0. \tag{1}$$

As usual, let $L(y)$ stand for the left member of (1) and put

$$y = \sum_{n=0}^{\infty} a_n x^{n+c}. \tag{2}$$

At once we find that for the y of equation (2), the left member of equation (1) takes the form

$$L(y) = \sum_{n=0}^{\infty} [(n + c)(n + c - 1) - 4(n + c)]a_n x^{n+c-1} - \sum_{n=0}^{\infty} (n + c - 2)a_n x^{n+c}$$

or

$$L(y) = \sum_{n=0}^{\infty} (n + c)(n + c - 5)a_n x^{n+c-1} - \sum_{n=1}^{\infty} (n + c - 3)a_{n-1} x^{n+c-1}.$$

The indicial equation is $c(c - 5) = 0$, so

$$c_1 = 5, \quad c_2 = 0, \quad s = c_1 - c_2 = 5.$$

We reason that we may hope for two power series solutions, one starting with an x^0 term, one with an x^5 term. If we use the large root $c = 5$ and try a series

$$\sum_{n=0}^{\infty} a_n x^{n+5},$$

it is evident that we can get at most one solution; the x^0 term would never enter.

On the other hand, if we use the smaller root $c = 0$, then a trial solution of the form

$$\sum_{n=0}^{\infty} a_n x^{n+0}$$

has a chance of picking up both solutions because the $n = 5$ $(n = s)$ term does contain x^5.

If s is a positive integer, we try a series of the form (2) using the smaller root c_2. If a_0 and a_s both turn out to be arbitrary, we obtain the general solution by this method. Otherwise the relation that should determine a_s will be impossible (with our usual assumption that $a_0 \neq 0$) and the general solution will involve a logarithm as it did in the case of equal roots. That logarithmic case will be treated in the next section.

Let us return to the numerical problem. Using the smaller root $c = 0$, we now know that for

$$y = \sum_{n=0}^{\infty} a_n x^n \tag{3}$$

we get

$$L(y) = \sum_{n=0}^{\infty} n(n-5)a_n x^{n-1} - \sum_{n=1}^{\infty} (n-3)a_{n-1}x^{n-1}.$$

Therefore, to make $L(y) = 0$, we must have

$$n = 0: \quad 0 \cdot a_0 = 0, \ (a_0 \text{ arbitrary}),$$
$$n \geq 1: \quad n(n-5)a_n - (n-3)a_{n-1} = 0.$$

Since division by $(n-5)$ cannot be accomplished until $n > 5$, it is best to write out the separate relations through the critical one for a_5. We thus obtain

$$n = 1: \quad -4a_1 + 2a_0 = 0,$$
$$n = 2: \quad -6a_2 + a_1 = 0,$$
$$n = 3: \quad -6a_3 + 0 \cdot a_2 = 0,$$
$$n = 4: \quad -4a_4 - a_3 = 0,$$
$$n = 5: \quad 0 \cdot a_5 - 2a_4 = 0,$$
$$n \geq 6: \quad a_n = \frac{(n-3)a_{n-1}}{n(n-5)}.$$

It follows from these relations that

$$a_1 = \tfrac{1}{2}a_0,$$
$$a_2 = \tfrac{1}{6}a_1 = \tfrac{1}{12}a_0,$$
$$a_3 = 0,$$
$$a_4 = 0,$$
$$0 \cdot a_5 = 0,$$

so a_5 is arbitrary. Each a_n, $n > 5$, will be obtained from a_5. In the usual way it is found that

$$a_6 = \frac{3a_5}{6 \cdot 1},$$
$$a_7 = \frac{4a_6}{7 \cdot 2},$$
$$\vdots$$
$$a_n = \frac{(n-3)a_{n-1}}{n(n-5)},$$

from which

$$a_n = \frac{3 \cdot 4 \cdot 5 \cdots (n-3)a_5}{[6 \cdot 7 \cdot 8 \cdots n](n-5)!} = \frac{3 \cdot 4 \cdot 5a_5}{(n-2)(n-1)n(n-5)!}.$$

Therefore, with a_0 and a_5 arbitrary, the general solution may be written

$$y = a_0(1 + \tfrac{1}{2}x + \tfrac{1}{12}x^2) + a_5\left[x^5 + \sum_{n=6}^{\infty} \frac{60x^n}{(n-5)!\,n(n-1)(n-2)}\right].$$

The coefficient of a_5 may also be written, with a shift of index, in the form shown below:

$$\sum_{n=0}^{\infty} \frac{60x^{n+5}}{n!(n+5)(n+4)(n+3)}.$$

Before proceeding to the exercises, let us examine an equation for which the fortunate circumstance a_0 and a_s both arbitrary does not occur. For the equation

$$x^2y'' + x(1-x)y' - (1+3x)y = 0 \tag{4}$$

the trial

$$y = \sum_{n=0}^{\infty} a_n x^{n+c}$$

leads to

$$L(y) = \sum_{n=0}^{\infty} (n+c+1)(n+c-1)a_n x^{n+c} - \sum_{n=1}^{\infty} (n+c+2)a_{n-1}x^{n+c}.$$

Since $c_1 = 1$ and $c_2 = -1$, we use $c = -1$ and find the relations

$$n \geq 1: \quad n(n-2)a_n - (n+1)a_{n-1} = 0,$$

with a_0 arbitrary. Let us write down the separate relations out to the critical one,

$$n = 1: \quad -a_1 - 2a_0 = 0,$$
$$n = 2: \quad 0 \cdot a_2 - 3a_1 = 0,$$
$$n \geq 3: \quad a_n = \frac{(n+1)a_{n-1}}{n(n-2)}.$$

It follows that

$$a_1 = -2a_0,$$
$$0 \cdot a_2 = 3a_1 = -6a_0.$$

These relations cannot be satisfied except by choosing $a_0 = 0$. But if that is done, a_2 will be the only arbitrary constant and the only solution coming out of the work will be that corresponding to the large value of c, $c = 1$. This is an instance where a logarithmic solution is indicated and the equation will be solved in the next section.

A good way to waste time is to use $a_0 = 0$, $a_1 = 0$, a_2 arbitrary, and to determine a_n, $n \geq 3$, from the above recurrence relation. In that way extra work can be done to get a solution which will be reobtained automatically when solving the equation by the method of the next section.

Exercises

Obtain the general solution near $x = 0$ except when instructed otherwise. State the region of validity of each solution.

1. $x^2 y'' + 2x(x - 2)y' + 2(2 - 3x)y = 0.$

ANS. $y = a_0(x - 2x^2 + 2x^3) + a_3 \left[x^4 + \sum\limits_{n=4}^{\infty} \dfrac{6(-2)^{n-3} x^{n+1}}{n!} \right].$

2. $x^2(1 + 2x)y'' + 2x(1 + 6x)y' - 2y = 0.$

ANS. $y = a_0(x^{-2} - 6x^{-1} + 24) + a_3 \left[x + \tfrac{1}{20} \sum\limits_{n=4}^{\infty} (-2)^{n-3}(n + 2)(n + 1)x^{n-2} \right].$

3. $x^2 y'' + x(2 + 3x)y' - 2y = 0.$

ANS. $y = a_0(x^{-2} - 3x^{-1} + \tfrac{9}{2}) + a_3 \left[x + \sum\limits_{n=4}^{\infty} \dfrac{2(-1)^{n-3} 3^{n-2} x^{n-2}}{n!} \right].$

4. $xy'' - (3 + x)y' + 2y = 0.$

ANS. $y = a_0(1 + \tfrac{2}{3}x + \tfrac{1}{6}x^2) + a_4 \sum\limits_{n=4}^{\infty} \dfrac{24(n - 3)x^n}{n!}.$

5. $x(1 + x)y'' + (x + 5)y' - 4y = 0.$

ANS. $y = a_0(x^{-4} + 4x^{-3} + 5x^{-2}) + a_4(1 + \tfrac{4}{5}x + \tfrac{1}{5}x^2).$

6. Solve the equation of Ex. 5 about the point $x = -1.$

ANS. $y = a_0[1 + (x + 1) + \tfrac{1}{4}(x + 1)^2] + \dfrac{a_5}{12} \sum\limits_{n=5}^{\infty} (n - 4)(n - 3)(n + 1)(x + 1)^n.$

7. $x^2 y'' + x^2 y' - 2y = 0.$

ANS. $y = a_0(x^{-1} - \tfrac{1}{2}) + 6a_3 \sum\limits_{n=3}^{\infty} \dfrac{(-1)^{n+1}(n - 2)x^{n-1}}{n!}.$

8. $x(1 - x)y'' - 3y' + 2y = 0.$ ANS. $y = a_0(1 + \tfrac{2}{3}x + \tfrac{1}{3}x^2) + a_4 \sum\limits_{n=4}^{\infty} (n - 3)x^n.$

9. Solve the equation of Ex. 8 about the point $x = 1.$

ANS. $y = a_0[(x - 1)^{-2} + 4(x - 1)^{-1}] + a_2[1 + \tfrac{2}{3}(x - 1) + \tfrac{1}{6}(x - 1)^2].$

10. $xy'' + (4 + 3x)y' + 3y = 0.$

ANS. $y = a_0(x^{-3} - 3x^{-2} + \tfrac{9}{2}x^{-1}) + 6a_3 \sum\limits_{n=3}^{\infty} \dfrac{(-3)^{n-3} x^{n-3}}{n!}.$

11. $xy'' - 2(x + 2)y' + 4y = 0.$

ANS. $y = a_0(1 + x + \tfrac{1}{3}x^2) + a_5 \sum\limits_{n=5}^{\infty} \dfrac{60 \cdot 2^{n-5} x^n}{(n - 5)!\, n(n - 1)(n - 2)}.$

12. $xy'' + (3 + 2x)y' + 4y = 0.$

ANS. $y = a_0 x^{-2} + a_2 \sum_{n=2}^{\infty} \dfrac{(-1)^n 2^{n-1} x^{n-2}}{n \cdot (n-2)!}.$

13. $x(x + 3)y'' - 9y' - 6y = 0.$

ANS. $y = a_0(1 - \tfrac{2}{3}x + \tfrac{1}{3}x^2 - \tfrac{4}{27}x^3) + a_4\left[x^4 + \sum_{n=5}^{\infty} \dfrac{(-1)^n(n+1)x^n}{5 \cdot 3^{n-4}}\right].$

14. $x(1 - 2x)y'' - 2(2 + x)y' + 8y = 0.$

ANS. $y = a_0(1 + 2x + 2x^2) + \tfrac{1}{3}a_5 \sum_{n=5}^{\infty} 2^{n-7}(n-4)(n-3)(n+1)x^n.$

15. $xy'' + (x^3 - 1)y' + x^2 y = 0.$

ANS. $y = a_0 \sum_{k=0}^{\infty} \dfrac{(-1)^k x^{3k}}{3^k k!} + a_2\left[x^2 + \sum_{k=1}^{\infty} \dfrac{(-1)^k x^{3k+2}}{5 \cdot 8 \cdot 11 \cdots (3k+2)}\right].$

16. $x^2(4x - 1)y'' + x(5x + 1)y' + 3y = 0.$

ANS. $y = a_0(x^{-1} - 1) + a_4\left[x^3 + 12 \sum_{n=5}^{\infty} \dfrac{13 \cdot 17 \cdot 21 \cdots (4n-7)x^{n-1}}{(n-4)! \cdot n(n-1)}\right].$

103. Indicial equation with difference of roots a positive integer, logarithmic case

In the preceding section we examined the equation

$$x^2 y'' + x(1 - x)y' - (1 + 3x)y = 0 \qquad (1)$$

and found that its indicial equation has roots $c_1 = 1$, $c_2 = -1$. Since there is no power series solution starting with x^{c_2}, we suspect the presence of a logarithmic term and start to treat the equation in the manner of the previous logarithmic case, that of equal roots.

From the assumed form

$$y = \sum_{n=0}^{\infty} a_n x^{n+c}$$

we easily determine the left member of equation (1) to be

$$L(y) = \sum_{n=0}^{\infty} (n + c + 1)(n + c - 1)a_n x^{n+c} - \sum_{n=0}^{\infty} (n + c + 3)a_n x^{n+c+1}$$

$$= \sum_{n=0}^{\infty} (n + c + 1)(n + c - 1)a_n x^{n+c} - \sum_{n=1}^{\infty} (n + c + 2)a_{n-1} x^{n+c}.$$

As usual, each term after the first one in the series for $L(y)$ can be made zero by choosing the a_n, $n \geq 1$, without choosing c. Let us put

$$n \geqq 1: \quad a_n = \dfrac{(n + c + 2)a_{n-1}}{(n + c + 1)(n + c - 1)},$$

from which it follows at once that

$$n \geq 1: \quad a_n = \frac{(c+3)(c+4)\cdots(c+n+2)a_0}{[(c+2)(c+3)\cdots(c+n+1)][c(c+1)\cdots(c+n-1)]},$$

or

$$n \geq 1: \quad a_n = \frac{(c+n+2)a_0}{(c+2)[c(c+1)\cdots(c+n-1)]}.$$

From the a_n obtained above, all terms after the first one in the power series for $L(y)$ have been made to vanish, so with

$$y = a_0 x^c + \sum_{n=1}^{\infty} \frac{(c+n+2)a_0 x^{n+c}}{(c+2)[c(c+1)\cdots(c+n-1)]} \tag{2}$$

it must follow that

$$L(y) = (c+1)(c-1)a_0 x^c. \tag{3}$$

From the larger root, $c = 1$, only one solution can be obtained. From the smaller root, $c = -1$, two solutions would be available following the technique of using $y(x, c)$ and $\partial y(x, c)/\partial c$ as in the case of equal roots if the right member of (3) contained the factor $(c+1)^2$ instead of just $(c+1)$ to the first power. But a_0 is still arbitrary, so we take

$$a_0 = (c+1)$$

to get the desired square factor on the right in equation (3).

Another way of seeing that it is desirable to choose $a_0 = (c+1)$ is as follows. We know that eventually it is going to be necessary to use $c = -1$ in equation (2). But within the series, the denominator contains the factor $(c+1)$ for all terms after the $n = 1$ term. As equation (2) stands now, the terms $n \geq 2$ would not exist with $c = -1$. Therefore we remove the troublesome factor $(c+1)$ from the denominator by choosing $a_0 = (c+1)$.

With $a_0 = (c+1)$ we have

$$y(x, c) = (c+1)x^c + \sum_{n=1}^{\infty} \frac{(c+1)(c+n+2)x^{n+c}}{(c+2)[c(c+1)\cdots(c+n-1)]} \tag{4}$$

for which

$$L[y(x, c)] = (c+1)^2(c-1)x^c. \tag{5}$$

The same argument as the one used when the indicial equation had equal roots shows that the two linearly independent solutions being sought may be obtained as

$$y_1 = y(x, -1), \tag{6}$$

and

$$y_2 = \left(\frac{\partial y(x, c)}{\partial c}\right)_{c=-1}. \tag{7}$$

Naturally, it is wise to cancel the factor $(c + 1)$ from the numerator and denominator in the terms of the series in (4). But the factor $(c + 1)$ does not enter the denominator until the term $n = 2$. Therefore it seems best to write out the terms that far separately. We rewrite equation (4) as

$$y(x, c) = (c + 1)x^c + \frac{(c + 1)(c + 3)x^{1+c}}{(c + 2)c} + \frac{(c + 4)x^{2+c}}{(c + 2)c}$$

$$+ \sum_{n=3}^{\infty} \frac{(c + n + 2)x^{n+c}}{(c + 2)c[(c + 2)(c + 3) \cdots (c + n - 1)]}. \tag{8}$$

Differentiation with respect to c of the members of equation (8) yields

$$\frac{\partial y(x, c)}{\partial c} = y(x, c) \ln x + x^c$$

$$+ \frac{(c + 1)(c + 3)x^{1+c}}{(c + 2)c} \left\{ \frac{1}{c + 1} + \frac{1}{c + 3} - \frac{1}{c + 2} - \frac{1}{c} \right\}$$

$$+ \frac{(c + 4)x^{2+c}}{(c + 2)c} \left\{ \frac{1}{c + 4} - \frac{1}{c + 2} - \frac{1}{c} \right\} \tag{9}$$

$$+ \sum_{n=3}^{\infty} \frac{(c + n + 2)x^{n+c} \left\{ \frac{1}{c + n + 2} - \frac{1}{c + 2} - \frac{1}{c} - \left(\frac{1}{c + 2} + \frac{1}{c + 3} + \cdots + \frac{1}{c + n - 1} \right) \right\}}{(c + 2)c[(c + 2)(c + 3) \cdots (c + n - 1)]}.$$

All that remains to be done is to get y_1 and y_2 by using $c = -1$ in the expressions above for $y(x, c)$ and $\partial y(x, c)/\partial c$. In the third term on the right in equation (9), we first (mentally) insert the factor $(c + 1)$ throughout the quantity in the curly brackets.

The desired solutions are thus found to be

$$y_1 = 0 \cdot x^{-1} + 0 \cdot x^0 - 3x + \sum_{n=3}^{\infty} \frac{(n + 1)x^{n-1}}{(-1)[1 \cdot 2 \cdots (n - 2)]}$$

and

$$y_2 = y_1 \ln x + x^{-1} - 2x^0 - 3x\{\tfrac{1}{3} - 1 + 1\}$$

$$+ \sum_{n=3}^{\infty} \frac{(n + 1)x^{n-1} \left\{ \frac{1}{n + 1} - 1 + 1 - \left(1 + \tfrac{1}{2} + \cdots + \frac{1}{n - 2} \right) \right\}}{(-1)[1 \cdot 2 \cdots (n - 2)]}.$$

These results can be written more compactly as

$$y_1 = -3x - \sum_{n=3}^{\infty} \frac{(n+1)x^{n-1}}{(n-2)!} \tag{10}$$

and

$$y_2 = y_1 \ln x + x^{-1} - 2 - x - \sum_{n=3}^{\infty} \frac{[1-(n+1)H_{n-2}]x^{n-1}}{(n-2)!}. \tag{11}$$

It is also possible to absorb one more term into the summation and to improve the appearance of these results. The student can show that

$$y_1 = -\sum_{n=0}^{\infty} \frac{(n+3)x^{n+1}}{n!}$$

and

$$y_2 = y_1 \ln x + x^{-1} - 2 - \sum_{n=0}^{\infty} \frac{[1-(n+3)H_n]x^{n+1}}{n!}$$

as long as the common conventions (definitions) $H_0 = 0$ and $0! = 1$ are used.

The general solution of the original differential equation is

$$y = Ay_1 + By_2,$$

and it is valid for all finite $x \neq 0$, since the differential equation has no other singular points in the finite plane.

The step taken in passing from equation (4) to equation (8) should be used regularly in this type of solution. Without its use indeterminate forms which may cause confusion will be encountered.

An essential point in this method is the choice $a_0 = (c - c_2)$ where c_2 is the smaller root of the indicial equation.

Exercises

Find two linearly independent solutions valid about $x = 0$, unless otherwise instructed.

1. $xy'' + y = 0$.

ANS. $y_1 = \sum_{n=1}^{\infty} \frac{(-1)^n x^n}{n!(n-1)!}$;

$$y_2 = y_1 \ln x + 1 + x - \sum_{n=2}^{\infty} \frac{(-1)^n (H_n + H_{n-1})x^n}{n!(n-1)!}.$$

2. $x^2 y'' - 3xy' + (3+4x)y = 0$.

ANS. $y_1 = \sum_{n=2}^{\infty} \frac{(-1)^{n+1} 4^n x^{n+1}}{n!(n-2)!}$;

$$y_2 = y_1 \ln x + y_1 + x + 4x^2 + \sum_{n=2}^{\infty} \frac{(-4)^n (H_n + H_{n-2})x^{n+1}}{n!(n-2)!}.$$

3. $2xy'' + 6y' + y = 0$.

ANS. $y_1 = \sum\limits_{n=2}^{\infty} \dfrac{(-1)^{n+1}x^{n-2}}{2^n n!(n-2)!}$;

$$y_2 = y_1 \ln x + y_1 + x^{-2} + \tfrac{1}{2}x^{-1} + \sum\limits_{n=2}^{\infty} \dfrac{(-1)^n(H_n + H_{n-2})x^{n-2}}{2^n n!(n-2)!}.$$

4. $4x^2y'' + 2x(2-x)y' - (1+3x)y = 0$.

ANS. $y_1 = \sum\limits_{n=1}^{\infty} \dfrac{x^{n-1/2}}{2^{n-1}(n-1)!}$;

$$y_2 = y_1 \ln x + 2x^{-1/2} - \sum\limits_{n=2}^{\infty} \dfrac{H_{n-1}x^{n-1/2}}{2^{n-1}(n-1)!}.$$

5. $x^2y'' - x(6+x)y' + 10y = 0$.

ANS. $y_1 = \sum\limits_{n=3}^{\infty} \dfrac{(n+1)x^{n+2}}{2(n-3)!}$;

$$y_2 = y_1 \ln x + \tfrac{1}{2}y_1 + x^2 - x^3 + \tfrac{3}{4}x^4 + \sum\limits_{n=3}^{\infty} \dfrac{[1-(n+1)H_{n-3}]x^{n+2}}{2(n-3)!}.$$

6. $x^2y'' + xy' + (x^2-1)y = 0$. This is Bessel's equation of index one. See also Sections 111 and 112.

ANS. $y_1 = \sum\limits_{k=1}^{\infty} \dfrac{(-1)^k x^{2k-1}}{2^{2k-1}k!(k-1)!}$;

$$y_2 = y_1 \ln x + x^{-1} - \sum\limits_{k=1}^{\infty} \dfrac{(-1)^k(H_k + H_{k-1})x^{2k-1}}{2^{2k}k!(k-1)!}.$$

7. $xy'' + (3+2x)y' + 8y = 0$.

ANS. $y_1 = \sum\limits_{n=2}^{\infty} \dfrac{(-1)^{n+1}2^n(n+1)x^{n-2}}{(n-2)!}$;

$$y_2 = y_1 \ln x + x^{-2} + 4x^{-1} + \sum\limits_{n=2}^{\infty} \dfrac{(-2)^n[(n+1)H_{n-2}-1]x^{n-2}}{(n-2)!}.$$

8. $x(1-x)y'' + 2(1-x)y' + 2y = 0$.

ANS. $y_1 = -2 + 2x$;

$$y_2 = y_1 \ln x + x^{-1} + 1 - 5x + \sum\limits_{n=3}^{\infty} \dfrac{2x^{n-1}}{(n-1)(n-2)}.$$

9. Show that the answers to Ex. 8 may be replaced by

$$y_3 = 1 - x; \quad y_4 = y_3 \ln x - \tfrac{1}{2}x^{-1} + 2x - \sum\limits_{n=3}^{\infty} \dfrac{x^{n-1}}{(n-1)(n-2)}.$$

10. Solve the equation of Ex. 8 near the point $x = 1$.

ANS. $y_1 = 2(x-1)$;

$$y_2 = y_1 \ln (x-1) + 1 - 3(x-1) + \sum\limits_{n=2}^{\infty} \dfrac{(-1)^{n+1}(n+1)(x-1)^n}{n-1}.$$

11. $x^2y'' - 5xy' + (8+5x)y = 0$.

ANS. $y_1 = \sum\limits_{n=2}^{\infty} \dfrac{(-1)^{n+1}5^n x^{n+2}}{n!(n-2)!}$;

$$y_2 = y_1 \ln x + y_1 + x^2 + 5x^3 + \sum\limits_{n=2}^{\infty} \dfrac{(-5)^n(H_n + H_{n-2})x^{n+2}}{n!(n-2)!}.$$

12. $xy'' + (3-x)y' - 5y = 0$.

ANS. $y_1 = -\sum\limits_{n=2}^{\infty} \dfrac{(n+1)(n+2)x^{n-2}}{2(n-3)!}$;

$$y_2 = y_1 \ln x - \tfrac{1}{2}y_1 + x^{-2} - 3x^{-1}$$
$$- \sum\limits_{n=2}^{\infty} \dfrac{(n+1)(n+2)(H_{n+2} - H_n - H_{n-2})x^{n-2}}{2(n-2)!}.$$

13. $9x^2y'' - 15xy' + 7(1 + x)y = 0.$ ANS. $y_1 = \sum\limits_{n=2}^{\infty} \dfrac{(-1)^{n+1}7^n x^{n+1/3}}{3^{2n-1}n!(n-2)!}$;

$$y_2 = y_1 \ln x + 3x^{1/3} + \tfrac{7}{3}x^{4/3} + \sum_{n=2}^{\infty} \frac{(-7)^n(H_n + H_{n-2} - 1)x^{n+1/3}}{3^{2n-1}n!(n-2)!}.$$

14. $x^2y'' + x(1 - 2x)y' - (x + 1)y = 0.$

ANS. $y_1 = \sum\limits_{n=2}^{\infty} \dfrac{1 \cdot 3 \cdot 5 \cdots (2n-3)x^{n-1}}{n!(n-2)!}$;

$$y_2 = y_1 \ln x + x^{-1} + 1 - y_1$$

$$+ \sum_{n=2}^{\infty} \frac{[1 \cdot 3 \cdot 5 \cdots (2n-3)](2H_{2n-2} - H_n - H_{n-1} - H_{n-2})x^{n-1}}{n!(n-2)!}.$$

104. Solution for large x

The power series solutions that have been studied up to this stage converge in regions surrounding some point $x = x_0$, usually the origin. Such solutions, although they may converge for large values of x, are apt to do so with discouraging slowness. For this reason, and for others of a more theoretical nature, we shall investigate the problem of obtaining solutions particularly useful for large x.

Consider the equation

$$b_0(x)y'' + b_1(x)y' + b_2(x)y = 0 \tag{1}$$

with polynomial coefficients. Let us put

$$w = \frac{1}{x}. \tag{2}$$

Then

$$\frac{dy}{dx} = \frac{dw}{dx}\frac{dy}{dw} = -\frac{1}{x^2}\frac{dy}{dw} = -w^2\frac{dy}{dw}$$

and

$$\frac{d^2y}{dx^2} = \frac{dw}{dx}\frac{d}{dw}\left(-w^2\frac{dy}{dw}\right) = -w^2\left(-w^2\frac{d^2y}{dw^2} - 2w\frac{dy}{dw}\right) = w^4\frac{d^2y}{dw^2} + 2w^3\frac{dy}{dw}.$$

Thus equation (1) is transformed into the following equation in y and w:

$$b_0\left(\frac{1}{w}\right)w^4\frac{d^2y}{dw^2} + \left[2w^3b_0\left(\frac{1}{w}\right) - w^2b_1\left(\frac{1}{w}\right)\right]\frac{dy}{dw} + b_2\left(\frac{1}{w}\right)y = 0. \tag{3}$$

Since b_0, b_1, and b_2 are polynomials, equation (3) is readily converted into an equation with polynomial coefficients.

If the point $w = 0$ is an ordinary point or a regular singular point of equation (3), then our previous methods of attack will yield solutions valid for small w. But $w = 1/x$, so small w means large x.

As a matter of terminology, whatever is true about equation (3) at $w = 0$ is said to be true about equation (1) "at the point at infinity." For instance, if the transformed equation has $w = 0$ as an ordinary point, then we say that equation (1) has an ordinary point at infinity. (See Exs. 1–6, page 323.)

EXAMPLE: Obtain solutions valid for large x for the equation

$$x^2y'' + (3x - 1)y' + y = 0. \tag{4}$$

This equation has an irregular singular point at the origin and has no other singular points in the finite plane. To investigate the nature of equation (4) for large x, put $x = 1/w$. We have already found that

$$\frac{dy}{dx} = -w^2 \frac{dy}{dw} \tag{5}$$

and

$$\frac{d^2y}{dx^2} = w^4 \frac{d^2y}{dw^2} + 2w^3 \frac{dy}{dw}. \tag{6}$$

With the aid of (5) and (6) we see that equation (4) becomes

$$\frac{1}{w^2}\left(w^4 \frac{d^2y}{dw^2} + 2w^3 \frac{dy}{dw}\right) + \left(\frac{3}{w} - 1\right)\left(-w^2 \frac{dy}{dw}\right) + y = 0,$$

or

$$w^2 \frac{d^2y}{dw^2} - w(1 - w)\frac{dy}{dw} + y = 0, \tag{7}$$

an equation which we wish to solve about $w = 0$.

Since $w = 0$ is a regular singular point of equation (7), the point at infinity is a regular singular point of equation (4).

From the assumed form

$$y = \sum_{n=0}^{\infty} a_n w^{n+c},$$

it follows from equation (7) by our usual methods that

$$L(y) = \sum_{n=0}^{\infty}(n + c - 1)^2 a_n w^{n+c} + \sum_{n=1}^{\infty}(n + c - 1)a_{n-1}w^{n+c},$$

in which $L(y)$ now represents the left member of equation (7). The indicial equation has equal roots, $c = 1, 1$. Let us set up $y(w, c)$ as usual. From the recurrence relation

$$n \geq 1: \quad a_n = -\frac{a_{n-1}}{n+c-1},$$

it follows that

$$a_n = \frac{(-1)^n a_0}{c(c+1) \cdots (c+n-1)}.$$

Hence we choose

$$y(w, c) = w^c + \sum_{n=1}^{\infty} \frac{(-1)^n w^{n+c}}{c(c+1) \cdots (c+n-1)},$$

and then find that

$$\frac{\partial y(w, c)}{\partial c} = y(w, c) \ln w - \sum_{n=1}^{\infty} \frac{(-1)^n w^{n+c} \left(\dfrac{1}{c} + \dfrac{1}{c+1} + \cdots + \dfrac{1}{c+n-1} \right)}{c(c+1) \cdots (c+n-1)}.$$

Employing the root $c = 1$, we arrive at the solutions

$$y_1 = w + \sum_{n=1}^{\infty} \frac{(-1)^n w^{n+1}}{n!}$$

and

$$y_2 = y_1 \ln w - \sum_{n=1}^{\infty} \frac{(-1)^n H_n w^{n+1}}{n!}.$$

Therefore the original differential equation has the two linearly independent solutions

$$y_1 = \sum_{n=0}^{\infty} \frac{(-1)^n x^{-n-1}}{n!} = x^{-1} e^{-1/x} \tag{8}$$

and

$$y_2 = y_1 \ln (1/x) - \sum_{n=1}^{\infty} \frac{(-1)^n H_n x^{-n-1}}{n!}. \tag{9}$$

These solutions are valid outside a circle centered at the origin and of arbitrarily small radius.

Exercises

In Exs. 1–6, the singular points in the finite plane have already been located and classified. For each equation, determine whether the point at infinity is an ordinary point, a regular singular point, or an irregular singular point. Do not solve the equations.

1. $x^3(x-1)y'' + (x-1)y' + 4xy = 0$. (Ex. 1, p. 294.)   ANS.   Reg. Sing. Pt.
2. $x^2(x^2-4)y'' + 2x^3y' + 3y = 0$. (Ex. 2, p. 294.)   ANS.   Ord. Pt.
3. $y'' + xy = 0$. (Ex. 3, p. 294.)   ANS.   Irreg. Sing. Pt.
4. $x^2y'' + y = 0$. (Ex. 4, p. 294.)   ANS.   Reg. Sing. Pt.
5. $x^4y'' + y = 0$. (Ex. 5, p. 294.)   ANS.   Reg. Sing. Pt.
6. $x^4y'' + 2x^3y' + 4y = 0$. (Ex. 18, p. 294.)   ANS.   Ord. Pt.

In Exs. 7–19, find solutions valid for large x unless otherwise instructed.

7. $x^4y'' + x(1 + 2x^2)y' + 5y = 0$.

$$\text{ANS.} \quad y = a_0 \sum_{k=0}^{\infty} \frac{-15x^{-2k}}{2^k k!(2k-1)(2k-3)(2k-5)} + a_1[x^{-1} - \tfrac{2}{3}x^{-3} + \tfrac{1}{15}x^{-5}].$$

8. $2x^3y'' - x(2 - 5x)y' + y = 0$.

$$\text{ANS.} \quad y_1 = x^{-3/2} + \sum_{n=1}^{\infty} \frac{(-2)^n(n+1)x^{-n-3/2}}{5 \cdot 7 \cdot 9 \cdots (2n+3)}; \quad y_2 = \sum_{n=0}^{\infty} \frac{(-1)^{n+1}(2n-1)x^{-n}}{n!}.$$

9. $x(1-x)y'' - 3y' + 2y = 0$, the equation of Ex. 8, page 314.

$$\text{ANS.} \quad y = a_0(x^2 + 2x + 3) + \tfrac{1}{4}a_3 \sum_{n=0}^{\infty} (n+4)x^{-n-1}.$$

10. $x^3y'' + x(2 - 3x)y' - (5 - 4x)y = 0$. See Ex. 13, page 310.

$$\text{ANS.} \quad y_1 = x^2 + \sum_{n=1}^{\infty} \frac{1 \cdot 3 \cdot 5 \cdots (2n-1)x^{-n+2}}{(n!)^2};$$

$$y_2 = y_1 \ln(1/x) + \sum_{n=1}^{\infty} \frac{1 \cdot 3 \cdot 5 \cdots (2n-1)(2H_{2n} - 3H_n)x^{-n+2}}{(n!)^2}.$$

11. $2x^2(x-1)y'' + x(5x-3)y' + (x+1)y = 0$.

$$\text{ANS.} \quad y_1 = x^{-1}; \quad y_2 = -\sum_{n=0}^{\infty} \frac{x^{-n-1/2}}{2n-1}.$$

12. Solve the equation of Ex. 11 about the point $x = 0$.

$$\text{ANS.} \quad y_3 = \sum_{n=0}^{\infty} \frac{3x^{n+1/2}}{2n+3}; \quad y_4 = x^{-1}.$$

13. $2x^2(1-x)y'' - 5x(1+x)y' + (5-x)y = 0$.

$$\text{ANS.} \quad y_1 = \tfrac{1}{15} \sum_{n=0}^{\infty} (n+1)(2n+3)(2n+5)x^{-n-1};$$

$$y_2 = \tfrac{1}{2} \sum_{n=0}^{\infty} (n+1)(n+2)(2n+1)x^{-n-1/2}.$$

14. Solve the equation of Ex. 13 about the point $x = 0$.

$$\text{ANS.} \quad y_3 = \tfrac{1}{10} \sum_{n=0}^{\infty} (n+1)(n+2)(2n+5)x^{n+5/2};$$

$$y_4 = -\sum_{n=0}^{\infty} (n+1)(2n-1)(2n+1)x^{n+1}.$$

15. $x(1 + x)y'' + (1 + 5x)y' + 3y = 0$, the equation of Ex. 5, page 309.

ANS. $y_1 = \sum_{n=2}^{\infty} (-1)^{n+1}n(n-1)x^{-n-1}$;

$$y_2 = y_1 \ln (1/x) + x^{-1} + x^{-2} + \sum_{n=2}^{\infty} (-1)^{n+1}(n^2 + n - 1)x^{-n-1}.$$

16. $x^2(4 + x^2)y'' + 2x(4 + x^2)y' + y = 0$.

ANS. $y_1 = 1 + \sum_{k=1}^{\infty} \dfrac{(-1)^k[(-1) \cdot 3 \cdot 7 \cdots (4k-5)]^2 x^{-2k}}{(2k)!}$;

$$y_2 = x^{-1} + \sum_{k=1}^{\infty} \frac{(-1)^k[1 \cdot 5 \cdot 9 \cdots (4k-3)]^2 x^{-2k-1}}{(2k+1)!}.$$

17. $x(1 - x)y'' + (1 - 4x)y' - 2y = 0$, the equation of Ex. 18, page 330.

ANS. $y_1 = \sum_{n=1}^{\infty} nx^{-n-1}$; $y_2 = y_1 \ln (1/x) + \sum_{n=0}^{\infty} x^{-n-1}$.

18. $x(1 + 4x)y'' + (1 + 8x)y' + y = 0$, the equation of Ex. 49, page 331.

ANS. $y_1 = x^{-1/2} + \sum_{n=1}^{\infty} \dfrac{(-1)^n[1 \cdot 3 \cdot 5 \cdots (2n-1)]^2 x^{-n-1/2}}{2^{4n}(n!)^2}$;

$$y_2 = y_1 \ln (1/x) + \sum_{n=1}^{\infty} \frac{(-1)^n[1 \cdot 3 \cdot 5 \cdots (2n-1)]^2 (H_{2n} - H_n)x^{-n-1/2}}{2^{4n-2}(n!)^2}.$$

19. The equation of Ex. 6 above

ANS. $y_1 = \cos (2x^{-1})$; $y_2 = \sin (2x^{-1})$.

105. Many-term recurrence relations

In solving an equation near a regular singular point it will sometimes happen that a many-term recurrence relation is encountered. In nonlogarithmic cases, the methods developed in Chapter 18 are easily applied and no complications result except that usually no explicit formula will be obtained for the coefficients.

In logarithmic cases, the methods introduced in Chapter 18, constructing $y(x, c)$ and $\partial y(x, c)/\partial c$, can become awkward when a many-term recurrence relation is present. There is another attack which has its good points.

Consider the problem of solving the equation

$$L(y) = x^2 y'' + x(3 + x)y' + (1 + x + x^2)y = 0 \tag{1}$$

near the origin. From

$$y = \sum_{n=0}^{\infty} a_n x^{n+c} \tag{2}$$

it is easily shown that

$$L(y) = \sum_{n=0}^{\infty} (n + c + 1)^2 a_n x^{n+c} + \sum_{n=1}^{\infty} (n + c)a_{n-1}x^{n+c} + \sum_{n=2}^{\infty} a_{n-2}x^{n+c}. \quad (3)$$

Therefore the indicial equation is $(c + 1)^2 = 0$.

Since the roots of the indicial equation are equal, $c = -1, -1$, it follows that there exist the solutions

$$y_1 = \sum_{n=0}^{\infty} a_n x^{n-1}, \quad (4)$$

$$y_2 = y_1 \ln x + \sum_{n=1}^{\infty} b_n x^{n-1}, \quad (5)$$

valid for all finite $x \neq 0$. The region of validity is obtained from the differential equation; the form of the solutions can be seen by the reasoning in Section 101.

We shall determine the a_n, $n > 0$, by requiring that $L(y_1) = 0$. Then the b_n, $n \geq 1$, will be determined in terms of the a_n by requiring that $L(y_2) = 0$.

From $L(y_1) = 0$ it follows that

$$\sum_{n=0}^{\infty} n^2 a_n x^{n-1} + \sum_{n=1}^{\infty} (n - 1)a_{n-1}x^{n-1} + \sum_{n=2}^{\infty} a_{n-2}x^{n-1} = 0.$$

Let us choose $a_0 = 1$. Then the rest of the a's are determined by

$$n = 1: \quad a_1 + 0 \cdot a_0 = 0,$$
$$n \geq 2: \quad n^2 a_n + (n - 1)a_{n-1} + a_{n-2} = 0.$$

Therefore one solution of the differential equation (1) is

$$y_1 = \sum_{n=0}^{\infty} a_n x^{n-1}, \quad (6)$$

in which $a_0 = 1$, $a_1 = 0$,

$$n \geq 2: \quad a_n = -\frac{(n - 1)a_{n-1} + a_{n-2}}{n^2}.$$

Next we wish to require that $L(y_2) = 0$. From

$$y_2 = y_1 \ln x + \sum_{n=1}^{\infty} b_n x^{n-1} \quad (5)$$

it follows that

$$y_2' = y_1' \ln x + x^{-1}y_1 + \sum_{n=1}^{\infty} (n - 1)b_n x^{n-2}$$

and

$$y_2'' = y_1'' \ln x + 2x^{-1}y_1' - x^{-2}y_1 + \sum_{n=1}^{\infty} (n - 1)(n - 2)b_n x^{n-3}.$$

Now direct computation of $L(y_2)$ yields

$$L(y_2) = L(y_1) \ln x + 2xy_1' - y_1 + xy_1 + 3y_1 + \sum_{n=1}^{\infty} n^2 b_n x^{n-1}$$

$$+ \sum_{n=2}^{\infty} (n-1)b_{n-1} x^{n-1} + \sum_{n=3}^{\infty} b_{n-2} x^{n-1}.$$

Since $L(y_1) = 0$, the requirement $L(y_2) = 0$ leads to the equation

$$\sum_{n=1}^{\infty} n^2 b_n x^{n-1} + \sum_{n=2}^{\infty} (n-1)b_{n-1} x^{n-1} + \sum_{n=3}^{\infty} b_{n-2} x^{n-1}$$

$$= -2xy_1' - 2y_1 - xy_1$$

$$= -\sum_{n=1}^{\infty} 2na_n x^{n-1} - \sum_{n=1}^{\infty} a_{n-1} x^{n-1}, \quad (7)$$

in which the right member has been simplified by using equation (6). From the identity (7), relations for the determination of the b_n from the a_n follow. They are

$$n = 1: \qquad\qquad\qquad b_1 = -2a_1 - a_0,$$
$$n = 2: \qquad\qquad\qquad 4b_2 + b_1 = -4a_2 - a_1,$$
$$n \geq 3: \quad n^2 b_n + (n-1)b_{n-1} + b_{n-2} = -2na_n - a_{n-1}.$$

Therefore the original differential equation has the two linearly independent solutions given by the y_1 of equation (6) and by

$$y_2 = y_1 \ln x + \sum_{n=1}^{\infty} b_n x^{n-1}, \qquad\qquad (8)$$

in which $b_1 = -1$, $b_2 = \frac{1}{2}$,

$$n \geq 3: \quad b_n = -\frac{(n-1)b_{n-1} + b_{n-2}}{n^2} - \frac{2a_n}{n} - \frac{a_{n-1}}{n^2}.$$

If the indicial equation has roots that differ by a positive integer and if a logarithmic solution exists, then the two solutions will have the form

$$y_1 = \sum_{n=0}^{\infty} a_n x^{n+c_1},$$

$$y_2 = y_1 \ln x + \sum_{n=0}^{\infty} b_n x^{n+c_2},$$

where c_1 is the larger and c_2 the smaller root of the indicial equation. The a_n and b_n can still be determined by the procedure used in this section.

Exercises

Solve each equation about $x = 0$ unless otherwise instructed.

1. $x^2 y'' + 3xy' + (1 + x + x^3)y = 0$.

ANS. $y_1 = \sum\limits_{n=0}^{\infty} a_n x^{n-1}$ in which $a_0 = 1$, $a_1 = -1$, $a_2 = \frac{1}{4}$,

$$n \geq 3: a_n = -\frac{a_{n-1} + a_{n-3}}{n^2};$$

$y_2 = y_1 \ln x + \sum\limits_{n=1}^{\infty} b_n x^{n-1}$, in which $b_1 = 2$, $b_2 = -\frac{3}{4}$, $b_3 = \frac{19}{108}$,

$$n \geq 4: b_n = -\frac{b_{n-1} + b_{n-3}}{n^2} - \frac{2a_n}{n}.$$

2. $2x(1 - x)y'' + (1 - 2x)y' + (2 + x)y = 0$.

ANS. $y_1 = \sum\limits_{n=0}^{\infty} a_n x^{n+1/2}$, in which $a_0 = 1$, $a_1 = -\frac{1}{2}$,

$$n \geq 2: a_n = \frac{(2n+1)(2n-3)a_{n-1} - 2a_{n-2}}{2n(2n+1)};$$

$y_2 = \sum\limits_{n=0}^{\infty} b_n x^n$, in which $b_0 = 1$, $b_1 = -2$,

$$n \geq 2: b_n = \frac{2n(n-2)b_{n-1} - b_{n-2}}{n(2n-1)}.$$

3. $xy'' + y' + x(1 + x)y = 0$.

ANS. $y_1 = \sum\limits_{n=0}^{\infty} a_n x^n$, in which $a_0 = 1$, $a_1 = 0$, $a_2 = -\frac{1}{4}$,

$$n \geq 3: a_n = -\frac{a_{n-2} + a_{n-3}}{n^2};$$

$y_2 = y_1 \ln x + \sum\limits_{n=1}^{\infty} b_n x^n$, in which $b_1 = 0$, $b_2 = \frac{1}{4}$, $b_3 = \frac{2}{27}$,

$$n \geq 4: b_n = -\frac{b_{n-2} + b_{n-3}}{n^2} - \frac{2a_n}{n}.$$

4. $x^2 y'' + x(1 + x)y' - (1 - 3x + 6x^2)y = 0$.

ANS. $y = \sum\limits_{n=0}^{\infty} a_n x^{n-1}$, in which a_0 is arbitrary, $a_1 = 2a_0$, a_2 is arbitrary,

$$n \geq 3: a_n = -\frac{(n+1)a_{n-1} - 6a_{n-2}}{n(n-2)}.$$

5. Show that the series in the answer to Ex. 4 start out as follows:

$$y = a_0(x^{-1} + 2 + 4x^2 - \tfrac{5}{2}x^3 + \tfrac{13}{5}x^4 - \tfrac{83}{60}x^5 + \cdots)$$
$$+ a_2(x - \tfrac{4}{3}x^2 + \tfrac{19}{12}x^3 - \tfrac{7}{6}x^4 + \tfrac{53}{72}x^5 + \cdots).$$

6. $xy'' + xy' + (1 + x^4)y = 0$. Here the indicial equation has roots $c = 0$, $c = 1$, and an attempt to get a complete solution without $\ln x$ fails. Then we put

$$y_1 = \sum\limits_{n=0}^{\infty} a_n x^{n+1},$$

$$y_2 = y_1 \ln x + \sum\limits_{n=0}^{\infty} b_n x^n.$$

The coefficient $b_1(s = 1)$ turns out to be arbitrary and we choose it to be zero. Show that the indicated y_1 and y_2 are solutions if $a_0 = 1$,

$$a_1 = -1, a_2 = \tfrac{1}{2}, a_3 = -\tfrac{1}{6}, a_4 = \tfrac{1}{24},$$

$$n \geq 5: a_n = -\frac{(n+1)a_{n-1} + a_{n-5}}{n(n+1)},$$

and if the b's are given by

$$b_0 = -1, b_1 = 0 \text{ (so chosen)}, b_2 = 1, b_3 = -\tfrac{3}{4}, b_4 = \tfrac{11}{36},$$

$$n \geq 5: b_n = -\frac{nb_{n-1} + b_{n-5}}{n(n-1)} - \frac{(2n-1)a_{n-1} + a_{n-2}}{n(n-1)}.$$

7. For the y_1 in Ex. 6, prove that the a_n alternate in sign. Also compute the terms of y_1 out to the x^7 term.

ANS. $y_1 = x - x^2 + \tfrac{1}{3}x^3 - \tfrac{1}{6}x^4 + \tfrac{1}{24}x^5 - \tfrac{1}{24}x^6 + \tfrac{31}{1008}x^7 + \cdots.$

8. $x(x-2)^2 y'' - 2(x-2)y' + 2y = 0.$ ANS. $y_1 = 1 - \tfrac{1}{2}x;$

$$y_2 = y_1 \ln x + \sum_{n=1}^{\infty} b_n x^n, \text{ in which } b_1 = \tfrac{1}{2}, b_2 = -\tfrac{1}{8}, b_3 = -\tfrac{1}{48},$$

$$n \geq 4: b_n = \frac{n-2}{4n^2} [2(2n-1)b_{n-1} - (n-3)b_{n-2}].$$

9. Solve the equation of Ex. 8 about the point $x = 2$.   ANS. $y_1 = (x-2);$

$$y_2 = y_1 \ln (x-2) + \sum_{n=1}^{\infty} \frac{(-1)^n (x-2)^{n+1}}{2^n n}.$$

10. $2xy'' + (1-x)y' - (1+x)y = 0.$

ANS. $y_1 = \sum_{n=0}^{\infty} a_n x^{n+1/2} \text{ in which } a_0 = 1, a_1 = \tfrac{1}{2},$

$$n \geq 2: a_n = \frac{(2n+1)a_{n-1} + 2a_{n-2}}{2n(2n+1)};$$

$$y_2 = \sum_{n=0}^{\infty} b_n x^n \text{ in which } b_0 = 1, b_1 = 1,$$

$$n \geq 2: b_n = \frac{nb_{n-1} + b_{n-2}}{n(2n-1)}.$$

11. Show that the answers to Ex. 10 are also given by

$$y_2 = e^x, y_1 = e^x \int_0^{\sqrt{x}} \exp \left(-\tfrac{2}{3}\beta^2\right) d\beta.$$

106. Summary

Confronted by a linear equation

$$L(y) = 0, \tag{1}$$

we first determine the location and nature of the singular points of the equation. In practice, the use to which the results will be put will dictate that solutions are desired near a certain point or points. In seeking solutions valid about the point $x = x_0$, always first translate the origin, putting $x - x_0 = v$.

Solutions valid near an ordinary point $x = 0$ of equation (1) take the form

$$y = \sum_{n=0}^{\infty} a_n x^n \tag{2}$$

with a_0 and a_1 arbitrary, if equation (1) is of second order.

If $x = 0$ is a regular singular point of equation (1) and we wish to get solutions valid near $x = 0$, we first put

$$y = \sum_{n=0}^{\infty} a_n x^{n+c}. \tag{3}$$

For the y of (3) we obtain by substitution the series for $L(y)$. From the $n = 0$ term of that series the indicial equation may be written. When the difference of the roots of the indicial equation is not an integer, or if the roots are equal, the technique is straightforward following the method of Section 99 or of Section 101.

When the roots differ by a nonzero integer, then the solution may, or may not, involve $\ln x$. The recurrence relation for $n = s$, where s is the difference of the roots, is the critical one. We must then determine whether the relations for $n = 1, 2, \ldots, s$ leave a_0 and a_s both arbitrary. If they do, two power series of the form (3) will be solutions of the differential equation. If a_0 and a_s are not both arbitrary, the case is a logarithmic one. Then the device of Section 103 may be used.

The technique can be varied, if desired, by always choosing the a_n in terms of c so the series for $L(y)$ reduces to a single term. Thus a series of the form

$$y(x, c) = a_0 \left[x^c + \sum_{n=1}^{\infty} f_n(c) x^{n+c} \right] \tag{4}$$

will be determined for which

$$L[y(x, c)] = a_0(c - c_1)(c - c_2) x^{c-k}, \tag{5}$$

where k is zero or one for the equations being treated here and c_1 and c_2 are the roots of the indicial equation. Then it can be determined from the actual coefficients in (4) whether the use of $c = c_1$ and $c = c_2$ will result in two solutions of the differential equation. If $c_1 = c_2$, the results would be identical and the use of $\partial y(x, c)/\partial c$ is indicated. The other logarithmic case will be identified by the fact that some one or more of the coefficients $f_n(c)$ will not exist when $c = c_2$, the smaller root. Then again the differentiation process is needed, after the introduction of $a_0 = c - c_2$.

The method sketched above has a disadvantage in that it seems to tempt the user into automatic application of rules, always a dangerous procedure in mathematics. When a student thoroughly understands what is happening in each of the four possible cases, this method may safely be used and it saves some labor.

Extension of the methods of this and the preceding chapter to linear equations of higher order is direct. As an example, a fourth-order equation whose indicial equation has roots $c = 2, 2, 2, \frac{1}{2}$ would be treated as follows. A series would be determined for $y(x, c)$,

$$y(x, c) = a_0 \left[x^c + \sum_{n=1}^{\infty} f_n(c) x^{n+c} \right]$$

for which the left member of the original equation reduces to one term, such as

$$L[y(x, c)] = (c - 2)^3 (2c - 1) a_0 x^c.$$

Then four linearly independent solutions could be obtained:

$$y_1 = y(x, 2), \quad y_2 = \left[\frac{\partial y(x, c)}{\partial c} \right]_{c=2}, \quad y_3 = \left[\frac{\partial^2 y(x, c)}{\partial c^2} \right]_{c=2}, \quad y_4 = y(x, \tfrac{1}{2}).$$

Miscellaneous exercises

In each exercise, obtain solutions valid near $x = 0$.

1. $xy'' - (2 + x)y' - y = 0.$
2. $x^2 y'' + 2x^2 y' - 2y = 0.$
3. $x^2(1 + x^2)y'' + 2x(3 + x^2)y' + 6y = 0.$
4. $2xy'' + (1 + 2x)y' - 3y = 0.$
5. $x(1 - x^2)y'' - (7 + x^2)y' + 4xy = 0.$
6. $4x^2 y'' - 2x(2 + x)y' + (3 + x)y = 0.$
7. $2xy'' + y' + y = 0.$
8. $4x^2 y'' - x^2 y' + y = 0.$
9. $2x^2 y'' - x(1 + 2x)y' + (1 + 3x)y = 0.$
10. $4x^2 y'' + 3x^2 y' + (1 + 3x)y = 0.$
11. $4x^2 y'' + 2x^2 y' - (x + 3)y = 0.$
12. $x^2 y'' + x(3 + x)y' + (1 + 2x)y = 0.$
13. $x(1 - 2x)y'' - 2(2 + x)y' + 18y = 0.$
14. $x^2 y'' - 3xy' + 4(1 + x)y = 0.$
15. $4x^2 y'' + 2x(x - 4)y' + (5 - 3x)y = 0.$
16. $x(1 - x)y'' - (4 + x)y' + 4y = 0.$

ANS. $y = a_0(1 + x + \tfrac{1}{2}x^2) + \dfrac{a_5}{12} \displaystyle\sum_{n=5}^{\infty} (n - 4)(n - 3)(n + 1)x^n.$

17. Solve the equation of Ex. 16 about the point $x = 1$.

ANS. $y = a_0[(x - 1)^{-4} + 4(x - 1)^{-3} + 5(x - 1)^{-2}]$
$+ a_4[1 + \tfrac{4}{5}(x - 1) + \tfrac{1}{5}(x - 1)^2].$

18. $x(1 - x)y'' + (1 - 4x)y' - 2y = 0.$

19. Show that the solutions of Ex. 18 may be written in the form

$$y_1 = (1-x)^{-2},$$
$$y_2 = (1-x)^{-2}(\ln x - x).$$

20. $xy'' + (1-x)y' + 3y = 0.$ ANS. $y_1 = 1 - 3x + \tfrac{3}{2}x^2 - \tfrac{1}{6}x^3;$

$$y_2 = y_1 \ln x + 7x - \tfrac{23}{4}x^2 + \tfrac{11}{12}x^3 - 6 \sum_{n=4}^{\infty} \frac{x^n}{n!\,n(n-1)(n-2)(n-3)}.$$

21. $xy'' - (2+x)y' - 2y = 0.$

22. $2x^2y'' - x(2x+7)y' + 2(x+5)y = 0.$

23. $(1-x^2)y'' - 10xy' - 18y = 0.$

24. $y'' + 2xy' - 8y = 0.$

25. $2x(1-x)y'' + (1-2x)y' + 8y = 0.$

26. $2x^2y'' - x(1+2x)y' + (1+4x)y = 0.$

27. $x^2y'' - x(1+x^2)y' + (1-x^2)y = 0.$

28. $x^2y'' + x(x^2-3)y' + 4y = 0.$

29. $(1+x^2)y'' - 2y = 0.$

30. $x^2y'' - 3x(1+x)y' + 4(1-x)y = 0.$

31. $y''' + xy = 0.$

32. $xy'' + (1-x^2)y' + 2xy = 0.$

33. $x(1-x^2)y'' + 5(1-x^2)y' - 4xy = 0.$

34. $x^2y'' + xy' - (x^2+4)y = 0.$

35. $2xy'' + (3-x)y' - 3y = 0.$

36. $xy'' + (2-x)y' - y = 0.$

37. $y'' - 2xy' + 6y = 0.$

38. $x^2y'' - x(3+2x)y' + (3-x)y = 0.$

39. $4x^2y'' + 2x(x+2)y' + (5x-1)y = 0.$

40. $xy'' + 3y' - y = 0.$

41. $4x^2y'' + (3x+1)y = 0.$

42. $x^2y'' + x(3x-1)y' + (3x+1)y = 0.$

43. $x^2y'' + x(4x-3)y' + (8x+3)y = 0.$

44. $2(1+x^2)y'' + 7xy' + 2y = 0.$

45. $3xy'' + 2(1-x)y' - 2y = 0.$

46. $xy'' - (1+3x)y' - 4y = 0.$

47. $x^2y'' - x(3+2x)y' + (4-x)y = 0.$

48. $2x(1-x)y'' + y' + 4y = 0.$

49. $x(1+4x)y'' + (1+8x)y' + y = 0.$

50. $xy'' + (3-2x)y' + 4y = 0.$

51. $x^2y'' + x(2x-3)y' + (4x+3)y = 0.$

52. $(1-x^2)y'' - 2xy' + 12y = 0.$

53. $x^2(1+x)y'' + x(3+5x)y' + (1+4x)y = 0.$

54. $x^2y'' + x^2y' + (3x-2)y = 0.$

55. $2x^2y'' + 3xy' - (1+x)y = 0.$

CHAPTER **19**

Equations of Hypergeometric Type

107. Equations to be treated in this chapter

With the methods studied in Chapters 17 and 18, we are able to solve many equations which appear frequently in modern physics and engineering as well as in pure mathematics. We shall consider briefly the hypergeometric equation, Bessel's equation, and the equations that lead to the study of Laguerre, Legendre, and Hermite polynomials. There are, in mathematical literature, thousands of research papers devoted entirely or in part to the study of the functions that are solutions of the equations to be studied in this chapter. Here we do no more than call to the attention of the student the existence of these special functions which are of such great value to theoretical physicists, engineers, and many mathematicians. An introduction to the properties of these and other special functions can be found in Rainville's *Special Functions*, New York, The Macmillan Co., 1960.

108. The factorial function

It will be convenient for us to employ a notation which is widely encountered in advanced mathematics. We define the factorial function $(a)_n$ for n equal to zero or a positive integer by

$$(a)_n = a(a + 1)(a + 2) \cdots (a + n - 1), \qquad \text{for } n \geq 1; \tag{1}$$

$$(a)_0 = 1 \text{ for } a \neq 0.$$

Thus the symbol $(a)_n$ denotes a product of n factors starting with the factor a, each factor being one larger than the factor before it. For instance,

$$(7)_4 = 7 \cdot 8 \cdot 9 \cdot 10,$$

$$(-5)_3 = (-5)(-4)(-3),$$

$$(-\tfrac{1}{2})_3 = (-\tfrac{1}{2})(\tfrac{1}{2})(\tfrac{3}{2}).$$

The factorial function is a generalization of the ordinary factorial. Indeed,

$$(1)_n = 1 \cdot 2 \cdot 3 \cdots n = n!. \tag{2}$$

In our study of the Gamma function in Section 59, we derived the functional relation

$$\Gamma(x + 1) = x\Gamma(x), \qquad \text{for } x > 0. \tag{3}$$

By repeated use of the relation (3), we find that if n is an integer,

$$\begin{aligned}
\Gamma(a + n) &= (a + n - 1)\Gamma(a + n - 1) \\
&= (a + n - 1)(a + n - 2)\Gamma(a + n - 2) \\
&= \cdots \\
&= (a + n - 1)(a + n - 2) \cdots (a)\Gamma(a) \\
&= (a)_n \Gamma(a).
\end{aligned}$$

Therefore the factorial function and the Gamma function are related by

$$(a)_n = \frac{\Gamma(a + n)}{\Gamma(a)}, \quad n \text{ integer}, n > 0, \quad \text{and } a > 0. \tag{4}$$

Actually (4) can be shown to be valid for any complex a except zero or a negative integer.

109. The hypergeometric equation

Let us now consider any second-order linear differential equation that has only three singular points (one could be at infinity). Suppose that each of these singularities is regular. It can be shown* that such an equation can be transformed by change of variables into the hypergeometric equation

$$x(1 - x)y'' + [c - (a + b + 1)x]y' - aby = 0, \tag{1}$$

in which a, b, c are fixed parameters.

Let us solve equation (1) about the regular singular point $x = 0$. For the moment let c be not an integer. For (1), the indicial equation has roots zero and $(1 - c)$. We put

$$y = \sum_{n=0}^{\infty} e_n x^n$$

in equation (1) and thus arrive, after the usual simplifications, at

$$\sum_{n=0}^{\infty} n(n + c - 1)e_n x^{n-1} - \sum_{n=0}^{\infty} (n + a)(n + b)e_n x^n = 0. \tag{2}$$

Shift index in (2) to get

$$\sum_{n=0}^{\infty} n(n + c - 1)e_n x^{n-1} - \sum_{n=1}^{\infty} (n + a - 1)(n + b - 1)e_{n-1} x^{n-1} = 0. \tag{3}$$

We thus find that e_0 is arbitrary and, for $n \geq 1$,

$$e_n = \frac{(n + a - 1)(n + b - 1)}{n(n + c - 1)} e_{n-1}. \tag{4}$$

The recurrence relation (4) may be solved by our customary device. The result is, for $n \geq 1$,

$$e_n = \frac{a(a + 1)(a + 2) \cdots (a + n - 1) \cdot b(b + 1)(b + 2) \cdots (b + n - 1)e_0}{n!\, c(c + 1)(c + 2) \cdots (c + n - 1)}. \tag{5}$$

But (5) is greatly simplified by use of the factorial function. We rewrite (5) as

$$e_n = \frac{(a)_n(b)_n}{n!\,(c)_n} \cdot e_0. \tag{6}$$

Let us choose $e_0 = 1$ and write our first solution of the hypergeometric equation as

$$y_1 = 1 + \sum_{n=1}^{\infty} \frac{(a)_n(b)_n x^n}{(c)_n n!}. \tag{7}$$

---

* See, for instance, E. D. Rainville, *Intermediate Differential Equations*, 2nd ed. (New York: The Macmillan Co., 1964), Chapter 6.

The particular solution y_1 in (7) is called the hypergeometric function and for it a common symbol is $F(a, b; c; x)$. That is,

$$F(a, b; c; x) = 1 + \sum_{n=1}^{\infty} \frac{(a)_n (b)_n x^n}{(c)_n n!},$$

and $y_1 = F(a, b; c; x)$ is a solution of equation (1).

The other root of the indicial equation is $(1 - c)$. We may put

$$y = \sum_{n=0}^{\infty} f_n x^{n+1-c}$$

into equation (1), determine f_n in the usual manner, and arrive at a second solution

$$y_2 = x^{1-c} + \sum_{n=1}^{\infty} \frac{(a + 1 - c)_n (b + 1 - c)_n x^{n+1-c}}{(2 - c)_n n!}. \tag{8}$$

In the hypergeometric notation this second solution (8) may be written

$$y_2 = x^{1-c} F(a + 1 - c, b + 1 - c; 2 - c; x),$$

which means exactly the same as (8). The solutions (7) and (8) are valid in $0 < |x| < 1$, a region extending to the nearest other singular point of the differential equation (1).

If c is an integer, one of the solutions (7) or (8) is correct, but the other involves a zero denominator. For example, if $c = 5$, then in (8), $(2 - c)_n = (-3)_n$ and as soon as $n \geq 4$, $(-3)_n = 0$. For,

$$(-3)_4 = (-3)(-2)(-1)(0) = 0.$$

If c is an integer, but a and b are nonintegral, one of the solutions about $x = 0$ of the hypergeometric equation is of logarithmic type. If c and one or both of a and b are integers, the solution may or may not involve a logarithm. To save space we omit logarithmic solutions of the hypergeometric equation.

110. Laguerre polynomials

The equation

$$xy'' + (1 - x)y' + ny = 0 \tag{1}$$

is called Laguerre's equation. If n is a non-negative integer, one solution of equation (1) is a polynomial.

Consider the solution of (1) about the regular singular point $x = 0$. The indicial equation has equal roots $c = 0, 0$. Hence one solution will involve a logarithm. We seek the nonlogarithmic solution.

Let us put

$$y = \sum_{k=0}^{\infty} a_k x^k$$

into (1) and obtain, in the usual way,

$$\sum_{k=0}^{\infty} k^2 a_k x^{k-1} - \sum_{k=1}^{\infty} (k - 1 - n)a_{k-1}x^{k-1} = 0. \tag{2}$$

From (2) we find that

$$k \geq 1: \quad a_k = \frac{(k - 1 - n)a_{k-1}}{k^2}$$

$$= \frac{(-n)(-n + 1) \cdots (-n + k - 1)a_0}{(k!)^2} = \frac{(-n)_k}{(k!)^2} a_0.$$

If n is a non-negative integer, $(-n)_k = 0$ for $k > n$. Therefore, with a_0 chosen equal to unity, one solution of equation (1) is

$$y_1 = \sum_{k=0}^{n} \frac{(-n)_k x^k}{(k!)^2}. \tag{3}$$

The right member of (3) is called the Laguerre polynomial and is usually denoted by $L_n(x)$:

$$L_n(x) = \sum_{k=0}^{n} \frac{(-n)_k x^k}{(k!)^2} = \sum_{k=0}^{n} \frac{(-1)^k n! x^k}{(k!)^2(n - k)!}. \tag{4}$$

The student should prove the equivalence of the two summations in (4) by showing that

$$(-n)_k = \frac{(-1)^k n!}{(n - k)!}.$$

One solution of (1) is $y_1 = L_n(x)$. The associated logarithmic solution may, after considerable simplification, be put in the form

$$y_2 = L_n(x) \ln x + \sum_{k=1}^{n} \frac{(-n)_k (H_{n-k} - H_n - 2H_k)x^k}{(k!)^2} \tag{5}$$

$$+ \sum_{k=1}^{\infty} \frac{(-1)^n n!(k - 1)! x^{k+n}}{[(k + n)!]^2}.$$

The solution (3) is valid for all finite x; the solution (5) is valid for $0 < |x| < \infty$.

111. Bessel's equation with index not an integer

The equation

$$x^2 y'' + xy' + (x^2 - n^2)y = 0 \tag{1}$$

is called Bessel's equation of index n. Equation (1) has a regular singular

point at $x = 0$, but no other singular points in the finite plane. At $x = 0$ the
roots of the indicial equation are $c_1 = n$, $c_2 = -n$. In this section we assume
that n is not an integer.

It is a simple exercise in the methods of Chapter 18 to show that if n is not an
integer, then two linearly independent solutions of (1) are

$$y_1 = \sum_{k=0}^{\infty} \frac{(-1)^k x^{2k+n}}{2^{2k} k! (1+n)_k}, \tag{2}$$

$$y_2 = \sum_{k=0}^{\infty} \frac{(-1)^k x^{2k-n}}{2^{2k} k! (1-n)_k}, \tag{3}$$

valid in $0 < |x| < \infty$.
The function

$$y_3 = \frac{1}{2^n \Gamma(1+n)} y_1 = \sum_{k=0}^{\infty} \frac{(-1)^k x^{2k+n}}{2^{2k+n} k! \Gamma(k+n+1)},$$

also a solution of equation (1), is called $J_n(x)$, the Bessel function of the first
kind and of index n. Thus

$$y_3 = J_n(x) = \sum_{k=0}^{\infty} \frac{(-1)^k x^{2k+n}}{2^{2k+n} k! \Gamma(k+n+1)} \tag{4}$$

is a solution of (1) and the general solution of (1) may be written

$$y = A J_n(x) + B J_{-n}(x), \quad n \neq \text{an integer}. \tag{5}$$

That $J_{-n}(x)$ is a solution of the differential equation (1) should be evident
from the fact that the parameter n enters (1) only in the term n^2. It is also
true that

$$J_{-n}(x) = \frac{1}{2^{-n} \Gamma(1-n)} y_2.$$

112. Bessel's equation with index an integer

In Bessel's equation

$$x^2 y'' + xy' + (x^2 - n^2)y = 0, \tag{1}$$

let n now be zero or a positive integer. Then

$$y_1 = J_n(x) = \sum_{k=0}^{\infty} \frac{(-1)^k x^{2k+n}}{2^{2k+n} k! \Gamma(k+n+1)} \tag{2}$$

is one solution of equation (1). Any solution linearly independent of (2)
must contain $\ln x$. We have already solved (1) for $n = 0$ in Ex. 6, page 309,
and for $n = 1$ in Ex. 6, page 319.

For n and integer ≥ 2, put

$$y = \sum_{j=0}^{\infty} a_j x^{j+c},$$

proceed with the technique of Section 103, determine $y(x, c)$ and $\dfrac{\partial}{\partial c} y(x, c)$, and then use $c = -n$ to obtain two solutions:

$$y_2 = \sum_{k=n}^{\infty} \frac{(-1)^k x^{2k-n}}{2^{2k-1}(1-n)_{n-1}(k-n)!\, k!} \tag{3}$$

and

$$y_3 = y_2 \ln x + x^{-n} + \sum_{k=1}^{n-1} \frac{(-1)^k x^{2k-n}}{2^{2k}(1-n)_k k!}$$

$$+ \sum_{k=n}^{\infty} \frac{(-1)^{k+1}(H_{k-n} + H_k - H_{n-1})x^{2k-n}}{2^{2k-1}(1-n)_{n-1}(k-n)!\, k!}. \tag{4}$$

A shift of index in (3) from k to $(k+n)$ yields

$$y_2 = \sum_{k=0}^{\infty} \frac{(-1)^{k+n} x^{2k+n}}{2^{2k+2n-1}(1-n)_{n-1}k!(k+n)!}.$$

But for $n \geq 2$, $(1-n)_{n-1} = (-1)^{n-1}(n-1)!$, so

$$y_2 = \frac{-1}{2^{n-1}(n-1)!} J_n(x).$$

We can therefore replace solution (3) with

$$y_1 = J_n(x). \tag{5}$$

By similar manipulations, we replace solution (4) with

$$y_4 = J_n(x) \ln x + \sum_{k=0}^{n-1} \frac{(-1)^{k+1}(n-1)!\, x^{2k-n}}{2^{2k+1-n}k!(1-n)_k}$$

$$+ \frac{1}{2}\sum_{k=0}^{\infty} \frac{(-1)^{k+1}(H_k + H_{k+n})x^{2k+n}}{2^{2k+n}k!(k+n)!}. \tag{6}$$

For n an integer > 1, equations (5) and (6) can be used as the fundamental pair of linearly independent solutions of Bessel's equation (1).

113. Hermite polynomials

The equation

$$y'' - 2xy' + 2ny = 0 \tag{1}$$

is called Hermite's equation. Since equation (1) has no singular points in the finite plane, $x = 0$ is an ordinary point of the equation. We put

$$y = \sum_{j=0}^{\infty} a_j x^j$$

and employ the methods of Chapter 17 to obtain the general solution

$$y = a_0 \left[1 + \sum_{k=1}^{\infty} \frac{2^k(-n)(-n+2) \cdots (-n+2k-2)x^{2k}}{(2k)!} \right]$$

$$+ a_1 \left[x + \sum_{k=1}^{\infty} \frac{2^k(1-n)(1-n+2) \cdots (1-n+2k-2)x^{2k+1}}{(2k+1)!} \right], \qquad (2)$$

valid for all finite x and with a_0 and a_1 arbitrary.

Interest in equation (1) is greatest when n is a positive integer or zero. If n is an even integer, the coefficient of a_0 in (2) terminates, each term for $k \geq \frac{1}{2}(n+2)$ being zero. If n is an odd integer, the coefficient of a_1 in (2) terminates, each term for $k \geq \frac{1}{2}(n+1)$ being zero. Thus Hermite's equation always has a polynomial solution, of degree n, for n zero or a positive integer. It is elementary but tedious to obtain from (2) a single expression for this polynomial solution. The result is

$$H_n(x) = \sum_{k=0}^{[\frac{1}{2}n]} \frac{(-1)^k n! (2x)^{n-2k}}{k!(n-2k)!}, \qquad (3)$$

in which $[\frac{1}{2}n]$ stands for the greatest integer $\leq \frac{1}{2}n$.

The polynomial $H_n(x)$ of (3) is the Hermite polynomial; $y = H_n(x)$ is a solution of equation (1).

114. Legendre polynomials

The equation

$$(1 - x^2)y'' - 2xy' + n(n+1)y = 0 \qquad (1)$$

is called Legendre's equation. Let us solve (1) about the regular singular point $x = 1$. We put $x - 1 = v$ and obtain the transformed equation

$$v(v + 2) \frac{d^2y}{dv^2} + 2(v + 1) \frac{dy}{dv} - n(n+1)y = 0. \qquad (2)$$

At $v = 0$, equation (2) has, as roots of its indicial equation, $c = 0, 0$. Hence one solution is logarithmic. We are interested here only in the non-logarithmic solution.

Following the methods of Chapter 18, put

$$y = \sum_{k=0}^{\infty} a_k v^k$$

into equation (2) and thus arrive at the results: a_0 is arbitrary and

$$k \geqq 1: \quad a_k = \frac{-(k - n - 1)(k + n)a_{k-1}}{2k^2}. \tag{3}$$

Solve the recurrence relation (3) and thus obtain

$$a_k = \frac{(-1)^k(-n)_k(1 + n)_k a_0}{2^k(k!)^2},$$

with the factorial notation of Section 108.

We may now write one solution of equation (1) in the form

$$y_1 = 1 + \sum_{k=1}^{\infty} \frac{(-1)^k(-n)_k(n + 1)_k(x - 1)^k}{2^k(k!)^2}. \tag{4}$$

Since $k! = (1)_k$, we may put (4) into the form

$$y_1 = 1 + \sum_{k=1}^{\infty} \frac{(-n)_k(n + 1)_k}{(1)_k k!} \left(\frac{1 - x}{2}\right)^k. \tag{5}$$

The right member of equation (5) is an example of the hypergeometric function which we met in Section 109. In fact,

$$y_1 = F\left(-n, n + 1; 1; \frac{1 - x}{2}\right). \tag{6}$$

If n is a positive integer or zero, the series in (4), (5), or (6) terminates. It is then called the Legendre polynomial and designated $P_n(x)$. We write our nonlogarithmic solution of Legendre's equation as

$$y_1 = P_n(x) = F\left(-n, n + 1; 1; \frac{1 - x}{2}\right). \tag{7}$$

115. The confluent* hypergeometric equation

The equation

$$xy'' + (c - x)y' - ay = 0 \tag{1}$$

has a regular singular point at $x = 0$ with zero and $(1 - c)$ as roots of the

---

* The concept of confluence of singularities is treated in Chapter 10 of E. D. Rainville's *Intermediate Differential Equations*, 2nd ed. (New York: The Macmillan Co., 1964).

indicial equation there. Equation (1) is called the confluent hypergeometric equation. If c is not an integer, there is no logarithmic solution of (1) about $x = 0$, so we restrict ourselves here to that simple situation.

In the usual manner we put

$$y = \sum_{n=0}^{\infty} b_n x^n$$

into (1) and thus find that b_0 is arbitrary and

$$n \geq 1: \quad b_n = \frac{(n-1+a)b_{n-1}}{n(n-1+c)}.$$

The recurrence relation yields

$$n \geq 1: \quad b_n = \frac{(a)_n b_0}{n!(c)_n}$$

in the notation of the factorial function of Section 108.

Therefore equation (1) has a solution

$$y_1 = 1 + \sum_{n=1}^{\infty} \frac{(a)_n x^n}{(c)_n n!}, \tag{2}$$

valid for all finite x. Note how much the right member of (2) resembles the hypergeometric function

$$F(a, b; c; x) = 1 + \sum_{n=1}^{\infty} \frac{(a)_n (b)_n x^n}{(c)_n n!} \tag{3}$$

of Section 109. In (2), the series has only one numerator parameter, a, and one denominator parameter, c. In (3) there are two numerator parameters, a and b, and one denominator parameter, c. It is therefore customary to use for the right member of (2) a notation like that in (3). We write

$$_1F_1(a; c; x) = 1 + \sum_{n=1}^{\infty} \frac{(a)_n x^n}{(c)_n n!}, \tag{4}$$

with the subscripts before and after the F denoting the number of numerator and denominator parameters, respectively. When it is thought desirable, the function symbol on the left in (3) is similarly written $_2F_1(a, b; c; x)$. Functions of hypergeometric type with any number of numerator and denominator parameters have been studied for many years.

The subscripts on the F play a useful role when the nature of the function, but not its specific parameters, is under discussion. For instance, we say,

"Any $_0F_1$ is essentially a Bessel function of the first kind," and "The Laguerre polynomial is a terminating $_1F_1$." The detailed statements are as follows.

$$J_n(x) = \frac{(x/2)^n}{\Gamma(n+1)} \, _0F_1\left(-; n+1; -\frac{x^2}{4}\right), \tag{5}$$

$$L_n(x) = \, _1F_1(-n; 1; x). \tag{6}$$

We have seen that the differential equation (1) has one solution, as indicated in (2),

$$y_1 = \, _1F_1(a; c; x). \tag{7}$$

The student can show that another solution, linearly independent of (7), is

$$y_2 = x^{1-c} \, _1F_1(a+1-c; 2-c; x), \tag{8}$$

as long as c is not an integer.

Again we omit discussion of the logarithmic solutions which may enter if c is integral.

CHAPTER 20

Numerical Methods

116. General remarks

There is no general method for obtaining an explicit formula for the solution of a differential equation. Specific equations do occur for which no known attack yields a solution or for which the explicit forms of solution are not well adapted to computation. For these reasons, systematic, efficient methods for the numerical approximation to solutions are important. Unfortunately, a clear grasp of good numerical methods requires time-consuming practice and often also the availability of modern computing machines.

This chapter is restricted to a fragmentary discussion of some simple and moderately useful methods. The purpose here is to give the student a concept of the fundamental principles of numerical approximations to solutions. We shall take one problem, which does not yield to the methods developed earlier and apply to it several simple numerical processes.

117. The increment method

We seek to obtain that solution of the differential equation

$$y' = y^2 - x^2 \tag{1}$$

for which $y = 1$ when $x = 0$. We wish to know the solution $y = y(x)$ in the range $0 \leq x \leq \tfrac{1}{2}$.

Equation (1) may be written in differential form as

$$dy = (y^2 - x^2)\, dx. \tag{2}$$

Figure 45 shows the geometrical significance of the differential dy and of

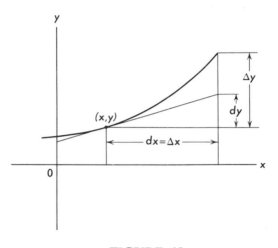

FIGURE 45

Δy, the actual change in y, as induced by an increment dx (or Δx) applied to x. In calculus it is shown that near a point where the derivative exists, dy can be made to approximate Δy as closely as desired by taking Δx sufficiently small.

We know the value of y at $x = 0$; we wish to compute y for $0 \leq x \leq \tfrac{1}{2}$. Suppose we choose $\Delta x = 0.1$; then dy can be computed from

$$dy = (y^2 - x^2)\, \Delta x.$$

Indeed, $dy = (1 - 0)(0.1) = 0.1$. Thus for $x = 0 + 0.1$, the approximate value of y is $1 + 0.1$. Now we have $x = 0.1$, $y = 1.1$. Let us choose $\Delta x = 0.1$ again.

Then

$$dy = [(1.1)^2 - (0.1)^2] \, \Delta x,$$

so $dy = 0.12$. Hence at $x = 0.2$, the approximate value of y is 1.22. The complete computation using $\Delta x = 0.1$ is shown in Table 1.

TABLE 1

$\Delta x = 0.1$

x	y	y^2	x^2	$(y^2 - x^2)$	dy
0.0	1.00	1.00	0.00	1.00	0.10
0.1	1.10	1.21	0.01	1.20	0.12
0.2	1.22	1.49	0.04	1.45	0.14
0.3	1.36	1.85	0.09	1.76	0.18
0.4	1.54	2.37	0.16	2.21	0.22
0.5	1.76				

The increment Δx need not be constant throughout the interval. Where the slope is larger it pays to take the increment smaller. For simplicity in computations, equal increments are used here.

It is helpful to repeat the computation with a smaller increment and to note the changes that result in the approximate values of y. Table 2 shows a computation with $\Delta x = 0.05$ throughout.

TABLE 2

$\Delta x = 0.05$

x	y	y^2	x^2	$(y^2 - x^2)$	dy
0.00	1.000	1.000	0.000	1.000	0.050
0.05	1.050	1.102	0.002	1.100	0.055
0.10	1.105	1.221	0.010	1.211	0.061
0.15	1.166	1.360	0.022	1.338	0.067
0.20	1.233	1.520	0.040	1.480	0.074
0.25	1.307	1.708	0.062	1.646	0.082
0.30	1.389	1.929	0.090	1.839	0.092
0.35	1.481	2.193	0.122	2.071	0.104
0.40	1.585	2.512	0.160	2.352	0.118
0.45	1.703	2.900	0.202	2.698	0.135
0.50	1.838				

In Table 3 the value of y obtained from the computations in Tables 1 and 2 and also the values of y obtained by using $\Delta x = 0.01$ (computation not shown) are exhibited beside the values of y correct to two decimal places. The correct values are obtained by the method of Section 120. Their availability is in a sense accidental. Frequently, we know of no way to obtain the y value correct to a specified degree of accuracy. In such instances it is customary

TABLE 3

	$\Delta x = 0.1$	$\Delta x = 0.05$	$\Delta x = 0.01$	correct
x	y	y	y	y
0.0	1.00	1.00	1.00	1.00
0.1	1.10	1.11	1.11	1.11
0.2	1.22	1.23	1.24	1.25
0.3	1.36	1.39	1.41	1.42
0.4	1.54	1.58	1.62	1.64
0.5	1.76	1.84	1.91	1.93

to resort to decreasing the size of the increment until the y values show changes no larger than the errors we are willing to permit. Then it is *hoped* that the steadying down of the y values is due to our being close to the correct solution rather than (as is quite possible) to the slowness of convergence of the process used.

Exercises

1. Use the increment method with $\Delta x = 0.1$ to compute, in the range $0 \leq x \leq 1$, that solution of the equation

$$y' = x + y$$

   for which $y = 1$ when $x = 0$. Also, solve the initial value problem exactly by elementary methods and compare the y values at intervals of 0.1 in x.
2. Use $\Delta x = 0.05$ in the problem of Ex. 1.
3. Use the method of increments on the initial value problem

$$y' = e^{-xy}; \qquad \text{when } x = 0, \quad y = 0,$$

   first with $\Delta x = 0.2$ and then with $\Delta x = 0.1$, computing y for the interval $0 \leq x \leq 2$.
4. Perform the same computations as in Ex. 3 but for the problem

$$y' = (1 + x^2 + y^2)^{-1}; \qquad \text{when } x = 0, \quad y = 0.$$

118. A method of successive approximation

Next let us attack the same problem as before,

$$y' = y^2 - x^2; \qquad x = 0, \quad y = 1, \tag{1}$$

with y desired in the interval $0 \leq x \leq \frac{1}{2}$, by the method suggested in the discussion of the existence theorem in Chapter 15. Applying the statements made in that discussion, we conclude that the desired solution is $y = y(x)$ where

$$y(x) = \lim_{n \to \infty} y_n(x)$$

and the sequence of approximations $y_n(x)$ is given by $y_0(x) = 1$ and, for $n \geq 1$,

$$y_n(x) = 1 + \int_0^x [y_{n-1}^2(t) - t^2] \, dt. \tag{2}$$

For the problem at hand

$$y_1(x) = 1 + \int_0^x (1 - t^2) \, dt,$$

$$y_1(x) = 1 + x - \tfrac{1}{3}x^3.$$

Next we obtain a second approximation, finding $y_2(x)$ from $y_1(x)$ by means of (2). Thus we find that

$$y_2(x) = 1 + \int_0^x [(1 + t - \tfrac{1}{3}t^3)^2 - t^2] \, dt,$$

$$y_2(x) = 1 + x + x^2 - \tfrac{1}{6}x^4 - \tfrac{2}{15}x^5 + \tfrac{1}{63}x^7.$$

Then $y_3(x)$, $y_4(x)$, ..., can be obtained in a similar manner, each from the preceding element of the sequence $y_n(x)$.

In Table 4 the values taken on by $y_1(x)$, $y_2(x)$, and $y_3(x)$ at intervals of 0.1 in x are shown beside the corresponding values of $y(x)$, correct to two decimal places, as obtained in Section 120.

TABLE 4

x	$y_1(x)$	$y_2(x)$	$y_3(x)$	$y(x)$
0.0	1.00	1.00	1.00	1.00
0.1	1.10	1.11	1.11	1.11
0.2	1.20	1.24	1.25	1.25
0.3	1.29	1.39	1.41	1.42
0.4	1.38	1.56	1.62	1.64
0.5	1.46	1.74	1.87	1.93

It must be realized that the usefulness of this method is not dependent upon our being able to carry out the integrations in a formal sense. It may be best to perform the integrations mechanically with a planimeter, or by some numerical process such as Simpson's rule.

Exercises

1. Apply the method of this section to the problem

$$y' = x + y; \quad \text{when } x = 0, \quad y = 1,$$

of Ex. 1, Section 117. Obtain $y_1(x)$, $y_2(x)$, and $y_3(x)$.

ANS. $y_1(x) = 1 + x + \frac{1}{2}x^2$; $y_2(x) = 1 + x + x^2 + \frac{1}{3}x^3$;
$y_3(x) = 1 + x + x^2 + \frac{1}{3}x^3 + \frac{1}{24}x^4.$

2. Compute a table of values to two decimal places of y_1, y_2, y_3 of Ex. 1 for $x = 0$ to $x = 1$ at intervals of 0.1. Tabulate also the correct values of y obtained from the elementary solution to the problem.

119. An improvement on the preceding method

In the method used in Section 118, each of the $y_n(x)$; $n = 0, 1, 2, \ldots$, yields an approximation to the solution $y = y(x)$. It is plausible that usually the more nearly correct a particular approximation $y_k(x)$, the better will be its successor $y_{k+1}(x)$.

The initial value problem we are treating is

$$y' = y^2 - x^2; \quad x = 0, \quad y = 1$$

and it tells us at once that at $x = 0$, the slope is $y' = 1$. But in Section 118, by blindly following the suggestion in Chapter 15, we started out with $y_0(x) = 1$, a line which does not have the correct slope at $x = 0$.

It is therefore reasonable to alter our initial approximation by choosing $y_0(x)$ to have the correct slope at $x = 0$, still making it also pass through the desired point $x = 0$, $y = 1$. Hence we choose

$$y_0(x) = 1 + x$$

and proceed to compute $y_1(x)$, $y_2(x)$, $\ldots$, as before. The successive stages of approximation to $y(x)$ now become

$$y_1(x) = 1 + \int_0^x [(1 + t)^2 - t^2] \, dt,$$

$$y_1(x) = 1 + x + x^2;$$

and

$$y_2(x) = 1 + \int_0^x [(1 + t + t^2)^2 - t^2] \, dt,$$

$$y_2(x) = 1 + x + x^2 + \frac{2}{3}x^3 + \frac{1}{2}x^4 + \frac{1}{5}x^5;$$

and so on.

In Table 5 the values of y_1, y_2, y_3 obtained by this method are shown beside the correct values of y.

TABLE 5

x	$y_1(x)$	$y_2(x)$	$y_3(x)$	$y(x)$
0.0	1.00	1.00	1.00	1.00
0.1	1.11	1.11	1.11	1.11
0.2	1.24	1.25	1.25	1.25
0.3	1.39	1.41	1.42	1.42
0.4	1.56	1.62	1.64	1.64
0.5	1.75	1.87	1.92	1.93

Exercises

1. Apply the method of this section to obtain approximations y_1, y_2, y_3 for the problem of Ex. 1 of Section 117.

ANS. $y_1(x) = 1 + x + x^2$; $y_2(x) = 1 + x + x^2 + \frac{1}{3}x^3$;

$$y_3(x) = 1 + x + x^2 + \tfrac{1}{3}x^3 + \tfrac{1}{12}x^4.$$

2. Tabulate to two decimal places y_1, y_2, y_3 of Ex. 1 beside the corresponding values of the exact solution $y(x) = 2e^x - 1 - x$.

120. The use of Taylor's theorem

For students familiar with the elementary calculus, the most natural approach to the approximation of solutions is to make use of Taylor's theorem. If we consider the initial value problem

$$y' = F(x, y); \qquad x = x_0, \quad y = y_0, \tag{1}$$

we may be able to compute successive derivatives of the solution $y = y(x)$ at $x = x_0$ by using equation (1). We adopt the notation

$$y_0' = y'(x_0), \quad y_0'' = y''(x_0), \quad \ldots, \quad y_0^{(n)} = y^{(n)}(x_0),$$

and recall that Taylor's theorem suggests the approximation formula

$$y \cong y_0 + y_0'(x - x_0) + \frac{y_0''}{2!}(x - x_0)^2 + \cdots + \frac{y_0^{(n)}}{n!}(x - x_0)^n. \tag{2}$$

One advantage in using the approximation in (2) is that we may be able to estimate the error in our calculation by examining the value of the remainder term in Taylor's theorem. For relation (2) this remainder takes the form

$$\frac{y^{(n+1)}(c)}{(n+1)!}(x - x_0)^{n+1}, \tag{3}$$

where c is some number between x and x_0.

It should be clear that the practicality of this technique for approximating solutions will depend greatly on the difficulty of obtaining values of the derivatives involved. If the function $F(x, y)$ is at all complicated, there may be a great deal of computation necessary to produce a reasonable approximation using Taylor's theorem.

For the example

$$y' = y^2 - x^2; \qquad x_0 = 0, \quad y_0 = 1, \tag{4}$$

it is relatively easy to show that

$$y'' = 2yy' - 2x,$$
$$y''' = 2yy'' + 2(y')^2 - 2,$$
$$y^{iv} = 2yy''' + 6y'y'', \tag{5}$$
$$y^{v} = 2yy^{iv} + 8y'y''' + 6(y'')^2.$$

Thus we can obtain the values

$$y_0 = 1, \quad y_0' = 1, \quad y_0'' = 2, \quad y_0''' = 4, \quad y_0^{iv} = 20, \quad \text{and} \quad y_0^{v} = 96.$$

Equation (2) thus becomes

$$y \cong 1 + x + x^2 + \tfrac{2}{3}x^3 + \tfrac{5}{6}x^4. \tag{6}$$

Some indication of the accuracy of equation (6) is given in Table 6. The values of y obtained from equation (6) for several values of x are exhibited beside the values of y correct to two decimal places.

TABLE 6

x	y	correct y
0.0	1.00	1.00
0.1	1.11	1.11
0.2	1.25	1.25
0.3	1.41	1.42
0.4	1.62	1.64
0.5	1.89	1.93

Another indication of the error in using equation (6) for estimating the value of y for $x = 0.5$ can be obtained by examining the next term in the Taylor's series expansion. That is, we may compute the value of $(96/5!)x^5$ at $x = 0.5$ and find that the error is at least as big as 0.02.

A more careful study of the remainder term given in equation (3) could be used to get a better estimate of the error in our results. In practice, however, it is extremely difficult to make these error estimates because of the complexity of the derivative formulas involved and the fact that the value of c is unknown to us.

Exercises

1. Use Taylor's theorem retaining powers of x^4 to approximate the values of the solution of the problem

$$y' = x + y; \qquad \text{when } x = 0, \quad y = 1.$$

Compute a table of values for $x = 0$ to $x = 1$ at intervals of 0.1. Also solve the initial value problem exactly by elementary methods and compare the estimated values with the correct values.

2. Use the method of Taylor's series to determine to three places the value of the solution of the problem

$$y' = -xy^2; \qquad \text{when } x = 0, \quad y = 1,$$

for $x = 0.1, 0.2$, and 0.3. Compare your results with the values obtained by solving the problem by elementary means.

121. The Runge-Kutta method

From a computational point of view, the major drawback in using Taylor's series to estimate the values of solutions of differential equations is that each coefficient in the series involves a different derivative function. Thus each approximation requires computations of the values of several different functions. We now consider a widely used technique that requires the computation of a single function at several different points rather than the computation of several different functions at a single point.

We consider the initial value problem

$$y' = F(x, y); \qquad \text{when } x = x_n, \quad y = y_n, \tag{1}$$

and for convenience adopt the notation

$$F_n = F(x_n, y_n). \tag{2}$$

Let us begin by considering the tangent line to the solution curve at the point (x_n, y_n). The equation of this line is given by

$$y = y_n + F_n(x - x_n). \tag{3}$$

The value of y for this tangent line at $x = x_n + h$ is thus $y = y_n + hF_n$. If we define $K_1 = F_n$ and compute F at the point $(x_n + h, y_n + hK_1)$ we obtain $K_2 = F(x_n + h, y_n + hK_1)$. Thus K_1 and K_2 represent the values of y' at two points, the two endpoints of a segment of the tangent line. If we consider the arithmetic mean of these values of y', namely $\frac{1}{2}(K_1 + K_2)$, and replace the tangent line with a new line through (x_n, y_n) having this slope, we obtain

$$y = y_n + \tfrac{1}{2}(K_1 + K_2)(x - x_n).$$

For $x = x_n + h$, this line has a point whose y coordinate is

$$y = y_n + \frac{h}{2}(K_1 + K_2), \qquad (4)$$

where

$$K_1 = F_n, \qquad (5)$$

and

$$K_2 = F(x_n + h, y_n + hK_1). \qquad (6)$$

The generalizations of the idea above are the basis for the method of Runge-Kutta. Instead of choosing the tangent line as a means for approximating the value of y at $x = x_n + h$, we choose a line whose slope is an average of the values of y' at several carefully chosen points. When only two points are used, as just shown, the idea can be pictured as in Figure 46.

We now describe the intuitive idea behind the more elaborate scheme. Again we define $K_1 = F_n$ to be the slope at the point P. This time, we define K_2 to be the slope at the midpoint M of the segment of the tangent line PQ.

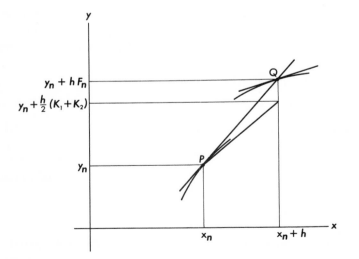

FIGURE 46

From equation (3) we find that M is $(x_n + \frac{1}{2}h, \; y_n + \frac{1}{2}hK_1)$ and thus $K_2 = F(x_n + \frac{1}{2}h, \; y_n + \frac{1}{2}hK_1)$.

The line through P with slope K_2 has equation

$$y = y_n + K_2(x - x_n),$$

and for $x = x_n + \frac{1}{2}h$, we obtain a point on this second line, namely $(x_n + \frac{1}{2}h, \; y_n + \frac{1}{2}hK_2)$. Now, defining $K_3 = F(x_n + \frac{1}{2}h, \; y_n + \frac{1}{2}hK_2)$, we consider a third line through P, this one having slope K_3. Its equation is

$$y = y_n + K_3(x - x_n).$$

The value of y for this third line at $x = x_n + h$ is $y_n + hK_3$. We define $K_4 = F(x_n + h, \; y_n + hK_3)$ as the value of y' at the fourth point.

Thus the numbers K_1, K_2, K_3, and K_4 represent the values of y' at four points, one with $x = x_n$, two with $x = x_n + \frac{1}{2}h$, and one with $x = x_n + h$. We now determine the weighted mean of these four numbers

$$K = \tfrac{1}{6}(K_1 + 2K_2 + 2K_3 + K_4),$$

and consider a line through P with slope K. Its equation is

$$y = y_n + K(x - x_n).$$

The value of y for this fourth line is

$$y_{n+1} = y_n + hK, \tag{7}$$

where

$$K = \tfrac{1}{6}(K_1 + 2K_2 + 2K_3 + K_4), \tag{8}$$

$$K_1 = F_n, \tag{9}$$

$$K_2 = F(x_n + \tfrac{1}{2}h, \; y_n + \tfrac{1}{2}hK_1), \tag{10}$$

$$K_3 = F(x_n + \tfrac{1}{2}h, \; y_n + \tfrac{1}{2}hK_2), \tag{11}$$

$$K_4 = F(x_n + h, \; y_n + hK_3). \tag{12}$$

The formulas (7) to (12) are due to Runge (1856–1927) and Kutta (1867–1944). The particular weighting factors assigned to the K_1, K_2, K_3, and K_4 in equation (8) are chosen so that the value of y_{n+1} computed by the Runge-Kutta method and the value computed by a five-term Taylor formula,

$$y_{n+1} = y_n + hy_n' + \frac{h^2 y_n''}{2!} + \frac{h^3 y_n'''}{3!} + \frac{h^4 y_n^{iv}}{4!}$$

differ by an amount that is proportional to h^5. The proof of this fact will not be given here but can be found in various texts on numerical analysis. We notice in passing, however, that if $F(x, y)$ does not explicitly involve the variable y, then the Runge-Kutta formulas reduce to the familiar Simpson's rule of elementary calculus. (See Ex. 4 below.)

EXAMPLE: Solve the example of Section 117 by the Runge-Kutta method.

We present in Table 7 the results of the computation for $x = 0.1$ and $x = 0.2$ and leave the remaining computations for the exercises.

TABLE 7

x	0	0.1	0.2
y	1.00	1.11	1.25
K_1	1.00	1.22	
$x + \frac{1}{2}h$	0.05	0.15	
$y + \frac{1}{2}hK_1$	1.05	1.17	
K_2	1.10	1.35	
$y + \frac{1}{2}hK_2$	1.06	1.18	
K_3	1.12	1.37	
$x + h$	0.10	0.20	
$y + hK_3$	1.11	1.25	
K_4	1.22	1.52	
K	1.11	1.36	

Exercises

1. Continue the computation of the example above to obtain approximate values of y for $x = 0.3, 0.4$, and 0.5.
2. Apply the Runge-Kutta method to Ex. 1, page 351, and compare the results with the correct values.
3. Use the Runge-Kutta method to compute approximate values for y at $x = 0.1$ and 0.2 for Ex. 2, page 351.
4. Show that if the function $F(x, y)$ in equation (1) of this section does not explicitly involve the variable y, then the Runge-Kutta formulas (7) to (12) reduce to a special case of Simpson's rule.

122. A continuing method

The methods used in the previous sections of this chapter may be called "starting" methods for finding approximations of solutions of the problem

$$y' = F(x, y); \qquad x = x_0, \quad y = y_0. \tag{1}$$

By this we mean that no additional information is known other than that given in the problem (1) itself. Once an approximate value of y_1 has been obtained for $x_1 = x_0 + h$, we have then used y_1 to compute y_2, and so on. We shall now describe a "continuing" method due to Milne (1890–   ).*

Suppose we know the values of y_n, y_{n-1}, y_{n-2}, and y_{n-3}. Then we can compute the values of F_n, F_{n-1}, F_{n-2}, F_{n-3} from equation (1). Next we approximate $y'(x)$ by a cubic polynomial which passes through the four points (x_n, F_n), (x_{n-1}, F_{n-1}), (x_{n-2}, F_{n-2}), and (x_{n-3}, F_{n-3}). It can be proved that this can be done and that the polynomial thus obtained is unique. Using this polynomial in place of $y'(x)$ in the integral

$$y_{n+1} - y_{n-3} = \int_{x_{n-3}}^{x_{n+1}} y'(x)\, dx, \tag{2}$$

performing the integration and simplifying gives an approximation for y_{n+1}. The result is

$$y_{n+1}^{(1)} = y_{n-3} + \frac{4h}{3}(2F_n - F_{n-1} + 2F_{n-2}). \tag{3}$$

The details of this derivation are discussed in Exercise 4 below.

The problem of estimating the error in our approximations and of designing programs for reducing or correcting for errors is of course crucial to any method we may use. In the method of Milne, (3) is called a predictor formula and the value $y_{n+1}^{(1)}$ obtained from it is then used to find a corrected value for y_{n+1}.

A derivation of the correction formula is suggested in Ex. 5 below. The result is

$$y_{n+1}^{(2)} = y_{n-1} + \frac{h}{3}(F_{n-1} + 4F_n + F_{n+1}), \tag{4}$$

where the value of F_{n+1} is calculated by using the $y_{n+1}^{(1)}$ obtained from the predictor formula.

To illustrate the procedure outlined previously we use Milne's method to find the value of y at $x = 0.4$ for the problem

$$y' = y^2 - x^2; \qquad x = 0, \quad y = 1.$$

---

* See for instance W. E. Milne, *Numerical Solutions of Differential Equations* (New York: John Wiley and Sons, 1953), Chapters 3 and 4.

For starting points we take the values of y_1, y_2, and y_3 which were computed using the Runge-Kutta method. These numbers are presented in Table 8.

TABLE 8

n	x_n	y_n	F_n
0	0.0	1.00	1.00
1	0.1	1.11	1.22
2	0.2	1.25	1.52
3	0.3	1.42	1.92

Now using the predictor formula (3), we obtain

$$y_4^{(1)} = y_0 + \frac{4h}{3}(2F_3 - F_2 - 2F_1)$$

$$= 1.00 + \frac{4(0.1)}{3}[2(1.92) - 1.52 + 2(1.22)]$$

$$= 1.63.$$

Using this value to compute F_4 and applying the corrector formula (4), we have

$$y_4^{(2)} = y_2 + \frac{h}{3}(F_2 + 4F_3 + F_4)$$

$$= 1.25 + \frac{0.1}{3}[1.52 + 4(1.92) + 2.50]$$

$$= 1.64.$$

Exercises

1. Continue the example of this section to estimate values of y at 0.5 and 0.6.
2. Using the values of y obtained by the Runge-Kutta method for 0.1, 0.2, and 0.3 in Ex. 2 in Section 121, compute approximations of $y(0.4)$ and $y(0.5)$ by Milne's method.
3. Estimate the values of y at $x = 0.4$ and 0.5 for the problem of Ex. 3 in Section 121.
4. Let

$$\nabla F_n = F_n - F_{n-1},$$

$$\nabla^2 F_n = \nabla(\nabla F_n) = \nabla(F_n - F_{n-1}) = F_n - 2F_{n-1} + F_{n-2},$$

$$\nabla^3 F_n = \nabla(\nabla^2 F_n).$$

(a) Verify that the graph of

$$y = F_n + \frac{\nabla F_n}{1!\,h}(x - x_n) + \frac{\nabla^2 F_n}{2!\,h^2}(x - x_n)(x - x_{n-1})$$

$$+ \frac{\nabla^3 F_n}{3!\,h^3}(x - x_n)(x - x_{n-1})(x - x_{n-2})$$

passes through the points (x_{n-3}, F_{n-3}), (x_{n-2}, F_{n-2}), (x_{n-1}, F_{n-1}), and (x_n, F_n).

(b) Using the above polynomial as a replacement for the integrand in equation (2) above, derive Milne's formula (3).

5. Suppose the value $y_{n+1}^{(1)}$ of equation (3) above is used to estimate F_{n+1}. By substitution into the differential equation and the use of Simpson's rule, show that a recalculation of y_{n+1} gives the result of formula (4) above.

CHAPTER **21**

Partial Differential Equations

123. Remarks on partial differential equations

A partial differential equation is an equation that contains one or more partial derivatives. Such equations occur frequently in applications of mathematics. They also enter pure mathematics. The subject of partial differential equations offers sufficient ramifications and difficulties to be of interest for its own sake.

In this book we shall devote the space allotted to partial differential equations almost entirely to a kind of boundary value problem which enters modern applied mathematics at every turn.

Partial differential equations can have solutions involving arbitrary functions and solutions involving an unlimited number of arbitrary constants. In rough language the general solution of a partial differential equation of order n may be defined as a solution involving n arbitrary functions.

The general solution of a partial differential equation is almost never (the wave equation is one of the few exceptions) of any practical use in solving boundary value problems associated with that equation.

124. Some partial differential equations of applied mathematics

Certain partial differential equations enter applied mathematics so frequently and in so many connections that their study is remarkably remunerative. A sufficiently thorough study of these equations would lead the student eventually into every phase of classical mathematics and, in particular, would lead almost at once to contact with special functions that are widely used in modern quantum theory and elsewhere in theoretical physics and engineering.

The derivation of the differential equations to be listed here is beyond the scope of this book. These derivations can be found (not all in each book) in the books listed for reference at the end of this section.

Some of the ways in which these equations are useful will appear in the detailed applications in Chapters 24 and 26.

Let x, y, z be rectangular coordinates in ordinary space. Then the equation

$$\frac{\partial^2 V}{\partial x^2} + \frac{\partial^2 V}{\partial y^2} + \frac{\partial^2 V}{\partial z^2} = 0 \tag{1}$$

is called Laplace's equation. It enters problems in steady-state temperature, electrostatic potential, fluid flow of the steady-state variety, etc.

If a problem involving equation (1) is such that a physical object in the problem is a circular cylinder, then it is possible that cylindrical coordinates will facilitate solution of the problem. We shall encounter such a problem later. It is possible to change equation (1) into an equation in which the independent variables are cylindrical coordinates r, θ, z, related to the x, y, z of equation (1) by the equations

$$x = r \cos \theta, \quad y = r \sin \theta, \quad z = z.$$

The resulting equation, Laplace's equation in cylindrical coordinates, is

$$\frac{\partial^2 V}{\partial r^2} + \frac{1}{r} \frac{\partial V}{\partial r} + \frac{1}{r^2} \frac{\partial^2 V}{\partial \theta^2} + \frac{\partial^2 V}{\partial z^2} = 0.$$

Note that the use of z in both coordinate systems above is safe in making the change of variables only because z is not involved in the equations with other variables. That is, in a change of independent variables such as

$$x = x_1 + y_1 + z_1, \quad y = x_1 - y_1, \quad z = z_1,$$

or its equivalent

$$x_1 = \tfrac{1}{2}(x + y - z), \quad y_1 = \tfrac{1}{2}(x - y - z), \quad z_1 = z,$$

incorrect conclusions would often result from any attempt to drop the subscript on the z_1, even though $z = z_1$. For instance, from the change of variables under discussion, it follows that

$$\frac{\partial V}{\partial z} = -\tfrac{1}{2}\frac{\partial V}{\partial x_1} - \tfrac{1}{2}\frac{\partial V}{\partial y_1} + \frac{\partial V}{\partial z_1}.$$

Hence

$$\frac{\partial V}{\partial z} \neq \frac{\partial V}{\partial z_1}$$

even though $z = z_1$.

Let us return to Laplace's equation. In spherical coordinates ρ, θ, ϕ, related to x, y, z by the equations

$$x = \rho \sin \theta \cos \phi, \quad y = \rho \sin \theta \sin \phi, \quad z = \rho \cos \theta,$$

Laplace's equation is

$$\frac{\partial^2 V}{\partial \rho^2} + \frac{2}{\rho}\frac{\partial V}{\partial \rho} + \frac{1}{\rho^2}\frac{\partial^2 V}{\partial \theta^2} + \frac{\cot \theta}{\rho^2}\frac{\partial V}{\partial \theta} + \frac{\csc^2 \theta}{\rho^2}\frac{\partial^2 V}{\partial \phi^2} = 0. \tag{3}$$

With an additional independent variable t representing time, and with a constant denoted by a, we can write the wave equation in rectangular coordinates,

$$\frac{\partial^2 V}{\partial t^2} = a^2 \left(\frac{\partial^2 V}{\partial x^2} + \frac{\partial^2 V}{\partial y^2} + \frac{\partial^2 V}{\partial z^2} \right). \tag{4}$$

Equation (4) occurs in problems involving wave motions. We shall meet it later in the problem of the vibrating string.

Whenever the physical problem suggests a different choice for a coordinate system, usually by the shape of the objects involved, the pertinent partial differential equation can be transformed into one with the desired new independent variables.

Suppose that for some solid under consideration, u represents the temperature at a point with rectangular coordinates x, y, z and at time t. The origin of coordinates and the initial time $t = 0$ may be assigned at our convenience. If there are no heat sources present, then the temperature u must satisfy the heat equation

$$\frac{\partial u}{\partial t} = h^2 \left(\frac{\partial^2 u}{\partial x^2} + \frac{\partial^2 u}{\partial y^2} + \frac{\partial^2 u}{\partial z^2} \right), \tag{5}$$

in which h^2 is a physical constant called thermal diffusivity. Equation (5) is derived under the assumption that the density, specific heat, and thermal conductivity are constant for the solid being studied. More comment on the question of the validity of equation (5) will be made in Section 141.

Equation (5) is the equation that pertains in many types of diffusion, not just when heat is being diffused. It is often called the equation of diffusion.

In the subject of elasticity, certain problems in plane stress can be solved with the aid of Airy's stress function ϕ, which must satisfy the partial differential equation

$$\frac{\partial^4 \phi}{\partial x^4} + 2 \frac{\partial^4 \phi}{\partial x^2 \, \partial y^2} + \frac{\partial^4 \phi}{\partial y^4} = 0. \tag{6}$$

Numerous other partial differential equations occur in applications, though not with the dominating insistency of equations (1), (4), and (5).

In this book two methods for solving boundary value problems in partial differential equations will be examined. The Laplace transform, which was studied in Chapters 10 and 11 and applied in Chapters 12 through 14, is a useful tool for certain kinds of boundary value problems. The transform technique will be further developed in Chapter 25 and then used in Chapter 26.

A second method, the classical one of separation of variables, will be discussed in the remainder of this chapter. We shall find that two other topics, orthogonal sets and Fourier series, need to be treated before we can proceed, in Chapter 24, to use separation of variables efficiently to solve problems involving partial differential equations.

References

CHURCHILL, R. V. *Fourier Series and Boundary Value Problems*, 2nd edition. New York: McGraw-Hill Book Co., 1963.

CHURCHILL, R. V. *Operational Mathematics*, 2nd edition. New York: McGraw-Hill Book Co., 1958.

HOPF, L. *Differential Equations of Physics*. New York: Dover Publications, 1948.

JEFFREYS, H. and JEFFREYS, B. S. *Methods of Mathematical Physics*. Cambridge: Cambridge Univ. Press, 1950.

125. Method of separation of variables

Before attacking an actual boundary value problem in partial differential equations, it is wise to become somewhat proficient in getting solutions of the differential equations. When we have acquired some facility in obtaining solutions, then we can tackle the tougher problem of fitting them together to satisfy stipulated boundary conditions.

The device to be exhibited here is particularly useful in connection with linear equations, although it does not always apply to such equations.

Consider the equation

$$\frac{\partial u}{\partial t} = h^2 \frac{\partial^2 u}{\partial x^2} \tag{1}$$

with h constant. A solution of equation (1) will in general be a function of the two independent variables t and x and of the parameter h.

Let us seek a solution that is a product of a function of t alone by a function of x alone. We put

$$u = f(t)v(x)$$

in equation (1) and arrive at

$$f'(t)v(x) = h^2 f(t)v''(x), \tag{2}$$

where primes denote derivatives with respect to the indicated argument.

Dividing each member of (2) by the product $f(t)v(x)$, we get

$$\frac{f'(t)}{f(t)} = \frac{h^2 v''(x)}{v(x)}. \tag{3}$$

Now equation (3) is said to have its variables (the independent variables) separated; that is, the left member of equation (3) is a function of t alone and the right member of equation (3) is a function of x alone.

Since x and t are independent variables, the only way in which a function of x alone can equal a function of t alone is for each function to be constant. Thus from (3) it follows at once that

$$\frac{f'(t)}{f(t)} = k, \tag{4}$$

$$\frac{h^2 v''(x)}{v(x)} = k, \tag{5}$$

in which k is arbitrary.

Another way of obtaining equations (4) and (5) is this. Differentiate each member of equation (3) with respect to t (either independent variable could be used) and thus get

$$\frac{d}{dt}\frac{f'(t)}{f(t)} = 0,$$

since the right member of equation (3) is independent of t. First we obtain equation (4) by integration and then equation (5) follows from (4) and (3).

Equation (4) may be rewritten

$$\frac{df}{dt} = kf,$$

from which its general solution

$$f = c_1 e^{kt}$$

follows immediately.

Before going further into the solution of our problem, we attempt to choose a convenient form for the arbitrary constant introduced in equations (4) and (5). Equation (5) suggests that k be taken as a multiple of h^2.

Let us then return to equations (4) and (5) and put $k = h^2 \beta^2$, so we have

$$\frac{f'(t)}{f(t)} = h^2 \beta^2 \tag{6}$$

and

$$\frac{h^2 v''(x)}{v(x)} = h^2 \beta^2. \tag{7}$$

Using real β and the choice $k = h^2 \beta^2$, we are implying that the constant k is positive. Later we shall obtain solutions corresponding to the choice of a negative constant.

From equations (6) and (7) we find at once that

$$f(t) = c_1 \exp (h^2 \beta^2 t) \tag{8}$$

and

$$v(x) = c_2 \cosh \beta x + c_3 \sinh \beta x. \tag{9}$$

Since $u = f(t)v(x)$, we are led to the result that the partial differential equation

$$\frac{\partial u}{\partial t} = h^2 \frac{\partial^2 u}{\partial x^2} \tag{1}$$

has solutions

$$u = \exp (h^2 \beta^2 t)[a \cosh \beta x + b \sinh \beta x], \tag{10}$$

in which β, a, and b are arbitrary constants. The a and b of equation (10) are respectively given by $a = c_1 c_2$ and $b = c_1 c_3$ in terms of the constants of equations (8) and (9).

If we return to equations (4) and (5) with the choice $k = -h^2 \alpha^2$, so k is taken to be a negative constant, then we find that the partial differential equation (1) has the solutions

$$u = \exp (-h^2 \alpha^2 t)[A \cos \alpha x + B \sin \alpha x], \tag{11}$$

in which α, A, and B are arbitrary constants.

Finally, let the constant k be zero. It is straightforward to determine that the corresponding solutions of the differential equation (1) are

$$u = C_1 + C_2 x, \tag{12}$$

in which C_1 and C_2 are constants.

Direct verification that equations (10), (11), and (12) are actually solutions of equation (1) is simple.

Since the partial differential equation (1) is linear, we may construct solutions by forming linear combinations of solutions. Thus from (10), (11), and (12) with varying choices of α, β, A, B, a, b, C_1, C_2, we can construct as many solutions of (1) as we wish.

The distinction between equations (10) and (11) is dependent upon the parameters and variables remaining real. Our aim is to develop tools for solving physical problems; hence we do intend to keep things real.

Exercises

Except where other instructions are given, use the method of separation of variables to obtain solutions in real form for each differential equation.

1. $\dfrac{\partial^2 u}{\partial t^2} = a^2 \dfrac{\partial^2 u}{\partial x^2}.$ ANS. $u = [A_1 \cos a\beta t + A_2 \sin a\beta t][B_1 \cos \beta x + B_2 \sin \beta x],$
$u = (A_3 + A_4 t)(B_3 + B_4 x),$ and
$u = [A_5 \cosh a\beta t + A_6 \sinh a\beta t][B_5 \cosh \beta x + B_6 \sinh \beta x],$
in which β and the A's and B's are arbitrary constants.

2. $\dfrac{\partial^2 v}{\partial x^2} + \dfrac{\partial^2 v}{\partial y^2} = 0.$ ANS. $v = [A_1 e^{\beta x} + A_2 e^{-\beta x}][B_1 \cos \beta y + B_2 \sin \beta y],$ and
$v = (A_3 + A_4 x)(B_3 + B_4 y),$
in which β and the A's and B's are arbitrary constants; the roles played by x and y in the former solution can be interchanged.

3. $\dfrac{\partial^2 u}{\partial t^2} + 2b \dfrac{\partial u}{\partial t} = a^2 \dfrac{\partial^2 u}{\partial x^2}.$
Show that this equation has the solutions:

$$u = g(t)[B_1 \cos kx + B_2 \sin kx],$$

where $g(t)$ can assume any one of the forms:

$$e^{-bt}[A_1 e^{\gamma t} + A_2 e^{-\gamma t}], \quad \gamma^2 = b^2 - a^2 k^2, \quad \text{if } b^2 - a^2 k^2 > 0,$$

or

$$e^{-bt}[A_3 \cos \delta t + A_4 \sin \delta t], \quad \delta^2 = a^2 k^2 - b^2, \quad \text{if } a^2 k^2 - b^2 > 0,$$

or

$$e^{-bt}[A_5 + A_6 t], \quad \text{if } a^2 k^2 - b^2 = 0,$$

and the solutions

$$u = (A_7 + A_8 e^{-2bt})(B_3 + B_4 x).$$

Find also solutions containing e^{kx} and e^{-kx}.

4. $\dfrac{\partial w}{\partial y} = y\dfrac{\partial w}{\partial x}$.   ANS. $w = A\exp[k(2x + y^2)]$, k and A arbitrary.

5. $x\dfrac{\partial w}{\partial x} = w + y\dfrac{\partial w}{\partial y}$.   ANS. $w = Ax^k y^{k-1}$, k and A arbitrary.

6. Subject the partial differential equation of Ex. 5 to the change of dependent variable $w = v/y$ and show that the resultant equation for v is

$$x\frac{\partial v}{\partial x} = y\frac{\partial v}{\partial y}.$$

7. Show that the method of separation of variables does not succeed, without modifications, for the equation

$$\frac{\partial^2 u}{\partial x^2} + 4\frac{\partial^2 u}{\partial x\,\partial t} + 5\frac{\partial^2 u}{\partial t^2} = 0.$$

8. For the equation of Ex. 7, seek a solution of the form

$$u = e^{kt}f(x)$$

and thus obtain the solutions

$$u = \exp[k(t - 2x)][A_1\cos kx + A_2\sin kx],$$

where k, A_1, A_2 are arbitrary. Show also that the equation of Ex. 7 has the solutions $u = Ax + B$ and $u = Ct + D$, with A, B, C, D arbitrary.

9. For the equation

$$\frac{\partial^2 u}{\partial x^2} + 4x\frac{\partial u}{\partial x} + \frac{\partial^2 u}{\partial y^2} = 0,$$

put $u = f(x)g(y)$ and thus obtain solutions

$$u = [A_1 e^{2ky} + A_2 e^{-2ky}][B_1 f_1(x) + B_2 f_2(x)],$$

in which $f_1(x)$ and $f_2(x)$ are any two linearly independent solutions of the equation

$$f'' + 4xf' + 4k^2 f = 0.$$

Obtain also the solutions that correspond to $k = 0$ in the above. For $k \neq 0$, the functions f_1 and f_2 should be obtained by the method of Chapter 17. They may be found in the form

$$f_1(x) = 1 + \sum_{m=1}^{\infty}\frac{(-4)^m (k^2)(k^2 + 2)(k^2 + 4)\cdots(k^2 + 2m - 2)x^{2m}}{(2m)!},$$

$$f_2(x) = x + \sum_{m=1}^{\infty}\frac{(-4)^m (k^2 + 1)(k^2 + 3)(k^2 + 5)\cdots(k^2 + 2m - 1)x^{2m+1}}{(2m + 1)!}.$$

Find similar solutions involving $\cos 2ky$ and $\sin 2ky$.

10. Use the change of variable $u = e^{\beta t}g(x)$ to find solutions of the equation

$$\frac{\partial^2 u}{\partial x^2} + 2\frac{\partial^2 u}{\partial x\,\partial t} + \frac{\partial^2 u}{\partial t^2} = 0.$$

ANS. $u = \exp[\beta(t - x)][A_1 + A_2 x]$.

11. Show by direct computation that if $f_1(y)$ and $f_2(y)$ are any functions with continuous second derivatives, $f_1''(y)$ and $f_2''(y)$, then

$$u = f_1(x - at) + f_2(x + at)$$

satisfies the simple wave equation (Ex. 1),

$$\frac{\partial^2 u}{\partial t^2} = a^2\frac{\partial^2 u}{\partial x^2}.$$

12. Show that $v = f(xy)$ is a solution of the equation of Ex. 6.
13. Show that $w = f(2x + y^2)$ is a solution of the equation of Ex. 4.
14. Show that $u = f_1(t - x) + xf_2(t - x)$ is a solution of the equation of Ex. 10.

126. A problem on the conduction of heat in a slab

Among the equations of applied mathematics already stated is the heat equation in rectangular coordinates,

$$\frac{\partial u}{\partial t} = h^2\left(\frac{\partial^2 u}{\partial x^2} + \frac{\partial^2 u}{\partial y^2} + \frac{\partial^2 u}{\partial z^2}\right), \tag{1}$$

in which

$$x, y, z = \text{rectangular space coordinates,}$$
$$t = \text{time coordinate,}$$
$$h^2 = \text{thermal diffusivity,}$$
$$u = \text{temperature.}$$

The constant h^2 and the variables x, y, z, t, u may be in any consistent set of units. For instance, we may measure x, y, z in feet, t in hours, u in degrees Fahrenheit, and h^2 in ft.^{2} per hour. The thermal diffusivity (assumed constant in our work) can be defined by

$$h^2 = \frac{K}{\sigma\delta},$$

in terms of quantities of elementary physics,

$$K = \text{thermal conductivity,}$$
$$\sigma = \text{specific heat,}$$
$$\delta = \text{density,}$$

all pertaining to the material composing the solid whose temperature we seek.

For our first boundary value problem in partial differential equations it seems wise to set up as simple a problem as possible. We now construct a temperature problem which is set in such a way that the temperature is independent of two space variables, say y and z. For such a problem, u will be a function of only two independent variables (x and t), which is the smallest number of independent variables possible in a partial differential equation.

Consider a huge flat slab of concrete, or some other material reasonably near homogeneity in texture. Let the thickness of the slab be c units of length. Choose the origin of coordinates on a face of the slab as indicated in Figure 47 and assume that the slab extends very far in the y and z directions.

Let the initial ($t = 0$) temperature of the slab be $f(x)$, a function of x alone, and let the surfaces $x = 0$, $x = c$ be kept at zero temperature for all $t > 0$. If the slab is considered infinite in the y and z directions, or more specifically if we treat only cross sections nearby (far from the distant surface of the

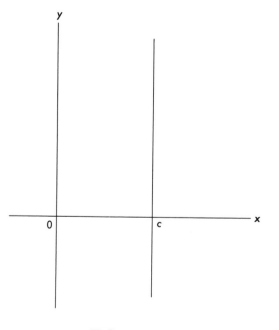

FIGURE 47

slab), then the temperature u at any time t and position x is determined by the boundary value problem:

$$\frac{\partial u}{\partial t} = h^2 \frac{\partial^2 u}{\partial x^2}, \quad \text{for } 0 < t, \quad 0 < x < c; \tag{2}$$

$$\text{As } t \to 0^+, \quad u \to f(x), \quad \text{for } 0 < x < c; \tag{3}$$

$$\text{As } x \to 0^+, \quad u \to 0, \qquad \text{for } 0 < t; \tag{4}$$

$$\text{As } x \to c^-, \quad u \to 0, \qquad \text{for } 0 < t. \tag{5}$$

In the boundary value problem (2) through (5), the zero on the temperature scale has been chosen as the temperature at which the surfaces of the slab are held. Then the $f(x)$ is really the difference between the actual initial temperature and the subsequent constant boundary temperature.

Such a set of symbols as $t \to 0^+$ means that t approaches zero through values greater than zero. Similarly, $x \to c^-$ means that x approaches c through values less than c, "c minus something" at each stage during the approach. We may say, for instance, that x approaches c from the left.

It is particularly to be noted that we do not require such a condition as that the function $u(x, t)$ be $f(x)$ when $t = 0$. We require only that as $t \to 0^+$, then $u \to f(x)$ for each x in the range $0 < x < c$.

The question of precisely how many boundary conditions, and of what nature, are to be associated with a given partial differential equation to assure the existence and uniqueness of a solution is a question of considerable difficulty. In this book we shall use the most popular practical guide, physical intuition. Existence is no problem: we seek a solution, and if we find one, we know it exists; if we don't find one, it is hardly balm for our wounds to be told that it exists. To the serious problem of uniqueness we close our eyes entirely.

Let us now attempt to solve the boundary value problem, to find a function $u(x, t)$ that will satisfy the partial differential equation

$$\frac{\partial u}{\partial t} = h^2 \frac{\partial^2 u}{\partial x^2}, \quad \text{for } 0 < x < c, \quad 0 < t; \tag{2}$$

and that will also satisfy the conditions:

$$\text{As } t \to 0^+, \quad u \to f(x), \quad \text{for } 0 < x < c; \tag{3}$$

$$\text{As } x \to 0^+, \quad u \to 0, \qquad \text{for } 0 < t; \tag{4}$$

$$\text{As } x \to c^-, \quad u \to 0, \qquad \text{for } 0 < t. \tag{5}$$

We already know how to get some solutions of the differential equation (2).

Indeed, on pages 362–364 the method of separation of variables was used to arrive at the solutions

$$u = \exp(h^2\beta^2 t)[a \cosh \beta x + b \sinh \beta x], \tag{6}$$

with a, b, β arbitrary constants, and the solutions

$$u = \exp(-h^2\alpha^2 t)[A \cos \alpha x + B \sin \alpha x] \tag{7}$$

with A, B, α arbitrary constants.

It is now necessary to attempt to adjust the solutions (6) or (7) to satisfy the boundary conditions (3), (4), and (5). Trial shows quickly that it is simpler to satisfy conditions (4) and (5) first and then to tackle (3).

Let us try to satisfy (4) and (5) with solutions in the form of equation (6) above. Now condition (4) requires that when we let $x \to 0^+$, then $u \to 0$ for all positive t. Letting $x \to 0^+$ in equation (6) we conclude that

$$0 = \exp(h^2\beta^2 t)[a + 0], \text{ for } 0 < t.$$

Thus we are forced to conclude that $a = 0$, so the solution (6) becomes

$$u = b \exp(h^2\beta^2 t) \sinh \beta x. \tag{8}$$

By condition (5) we must require that as $x \to c^-$, then again $u \to 0$ for all positive t; that is, from equation (8) and condition (5) we get

$$b \exp(h^2\beta^2 t) \sinh \beta c = 0, \text{ for } 0 < t.$$

The exponential $\exp(h^2\beta^2 t)$ cannot vanish. For real values of β and c the function $\sinh \beta c$ is zero only when $\beta c = 0$. Hence it follows that $\beta = 0$ or $b = 0$, so $u \equiv 0$ and we have no chance of satisfying the remaining condition, (3). Let us therefore abandon equation (6) and concentrate upon the solutions

$$u = \exp(-h^2\alpha^2 t)[A \cos \alpha x + B \sin \alpha x]. \tag{7}$$

Let us impose conditions (4) and (5) upon the u of equation (7). First we let $x \to 0^+$ and conclude that

$$0 = \exp(-h^2\alpha^2 t)[A + 0], \text{ for } 0 < t,$$

so we must choose $A = 0$. Then (7) reduces to

$$u = B \exp(-h^2\alpha^2 t) \sin \alpha x. \tag{9}$$

Next we impose condition (5), that $u \to 0$ when $x \to c^-$, so

$$0 = B \exp(-h^2\alpha^2 t) \sin \alpha c, \text{ for } 0 < t.$$

We must not choose $B = 0$, if we are to have any success in satisfying the additional condition (3). The function $\exp(-h^2\alpha^2 t)$ does not vanish. Therefore, for the u of (9) to satisfy condition (5), it is necessary that

$$\sin \alpha c = 0. \tag{10}$$

The sine function is zero when, and only when, its argument is an integral multiple of π; that is, $\sin z$ is zero when $z = 0, \pm\pi, \pm 2\pi, \ldots, \pm n\pi, \ldots$. Therefore from (10) it follows that

$$\alpha c = n\pi, \; n \text{ integral.} \tag{11}$$

Since c is given, equation (11) serves to determine the arbitrary parameter α—rather, to restrict the values of α to those given by (11).

With $\alpha = n\pi/c$, the solutions (9) above become

$$u = B \exp\left[-\left(\frac{n\pi h}{c}\right)^2 t\right] \sin \frac{n\pi x}{c}$$

with n integral and B arbitrary. Since we need not use the same arbitrary constant B for different values of n, it is wiser to write solutions

$$u_n = B_n \exp\left[-\left(\frac{n\pi h}{c}\right)^2 t\right] \sin \frac{n\pi x}{c}, \; n \text{ integral.} \tag{12}$$

We lose nothing by restricting the n in equation (12) to the positive integers $1, 2, 3, \ldots$, for $n = 0$ leads to the trivial solution $u \equiv 0$ and the negative integral values for n lead to essentially the same solutions as do the positive integral values.

Let us see where we stand at present. Each of the functions u_n defined by equation (12) is a solution of the differential equation

$$\frac{\partial u}{\partial t} = h^2 \frac{\partial^2 u}{\partial x^2}, \quad \text{for } 0 < x < c, \;\; 0 < t, \tag{2}$$

and each of those functions satisfies the two conditions

$$\text{As } x \to 0^+, \quad u \to 0, \quad \text{for } 0 < t, \tag{4}$$

and

$$\text{As } x \to c^-, \quad u \to 0, \quad \text{for } 0 < t. \tag{5}$$

It remains to find from the solutions u_n a solution $u(x, t)$ that will also satisfy the boundary (or initial) condition

$$\text{As } t \to 0^+, \quad u \to f(x), \quad \text{for } 0 < x < c. \tag{3}$$

Since the partial differential equation involved is linear and homogeneous in u and its derivatives, a sum of solutions is also a solution. From the known solutions $u_1, u_2, u_3 \ldots, u_n, \ldots$, we may thus construct others. With sufficiently strong convergence conditions it is true that even the infinite series

$$u = \sum_{n=1}^{\infty} u_n$$

or

$$u(x, t) = \sum_{n=1}^{\infty} B_n \exp\left[-\left(\frac{n\pi h}{c}\right)^2 t\right] \sin \frac{n\pi x}{c} \tag{13}$$

is also a solution of the differential equation (2).

The $u(x, t)$ of equation (13) satisfies equation (2) and the boundary conditions (4) and (5). If $u(x, t)$ is to satisfy condition (3), then for each x in the interval $0 < x < c$ the right member of equation (13) should approach $f(x)$ as $t \to 0^+$. We assume that we may interchange the order of limit (as $t \to 0^+$) and summation and conclude that condition (3) formally requires that

$$f(x) = \sum_{n=1}^{\infty} B_n \sin \frac{n\pi x}{c}, \text{ for } 0 < x < c. \tag{14}$$

Thus we can solve the problem under consideration if we can choose the constants B_n so that the infinite series on the right in (14) has $f(x)$ for its sum for each x in the interval $0 < x < c$. That there exist such coefficients B_n is far from evident. For a large class of functions $f(x)$, an expansion of the type of equation (14) does exist, as will be seen in Chapter 23. Once the B_n are known, they are to be inserted on the right in equation (13), which is then the final solution of the boundary value problem consisting of equation (2) and conditions (3), (4), and (5).

To be able to complete the solution of boundary value problems of the kind under consideration here, we need to acquire a knowledge of methods of expansion of functions into trigonometric series. Chapter 23 is devoted to the development of that type of expansion, providing us with tools for solving numerous boundary value problems in Chapter 24.

CHAPTER **22**

Orthogonal Sets

127. Orthogonality

A set of functions $\{f_0(x), f_1(x), f_2(x), \ldots, f_n(x), \ldots\}$, is said to be *an orthogonal set with respect to the weight function $w(x)$ over the interval $a \leqq x \leqq b$ if*

$$\int_a^b w(x)f_n(x)f_m(x)\,dx = 0 \text{ for } m \neq n,$$

$$\neq 0 \text{ for } m = n.$$

Orthogonality is a property widely encountered in certain branches of mathematics. Much use is made of the representation of functions in series of the form

$$\sum_{n=0}^{\infty} c_n\, f_n(x)$$

in which the c_n are numerical coefficients and $\{f_n(x)\}$ is an orthogonal set.

A tremendous literature exists regarding orthogonal sets of functions. A student who wishes to pursue the subject beyond the material in this chapter can get a thorough introduction to it in courses and books on orthogonal polynomials, Fourier series, Fourier analysis, etc. A short list of references is given at the end of Chapter 23.

One simple version of a theorem in the subject of orthogonal functions may be stated as follows:

Given a set of functions

$$\{\phi_0(x), \phi_1(x), \phi_2(x), \ldots, \phi_n(x), \ldots\},$$

linearly independent (Section 25) and continuous in the interval

$$a \leq x \leq b,$$

and given a weight function $w(x)$ positive and continuous in that same interval, then a set of functions

$$\{f_0(x), f_1(x), f_2(x), \ldots, f_n(x), \ldots\}$$

exists with the properties that:

(a) Each $f_n(x)$ is a linear combination of ϕ's;
(b) The $f_n(x)$ are linearly independent on the interval $a \leq x \leq b$;
(c) $\{f_n(x)\}$ is an orthogonal set with respect to the weight function $w(x)$ over the interval $a \leq x \leq b$.

We already know that the functions $1, x, x^2, \ldots, x^n, \ldots$, are linearly independent and are continuous over any finite interval. Linear combinations of powers of x are polynomials. Hence, given an interval and a proper weight function, there exists in particular a set of polynomials orthogonal with respect to that weight function over that interval. With added conditions on the weight function the restriction to a finite interval can be removed.

128. Simple sets of polynomials

A set of polynomials $\{f_n(x)\}$, $n = 0, 1, 2, 3, \ldots$, is called a simple set if $f_n(x)$ is of degree precisely n. The set then contains one polynomial of each degree, $0, 1, 2, \ldots, n, \ldots$.

An important property of simple sets is that if $g_m(x)$ is any polynomial of degree m and $\{f_n(x)\}$ is a simple set of polynomials, then there exist constants c_k such that

$$g_m(x) = \sum_{k=0}^{m} c_k f_k(x). \tag{1}$$

PROOF.   Let the highest degree term in $g_m(x)$ be $a_m x^m$ and the highest degree term in $f_m(x)$ be $b_m x^m$. Define $c_m = a_m/b_m$, noting that $b_m \neq 0$. Then the polynomial

$$g_m(x) - c_m f_m(x)$$

is of degree at most $(m-1)$. On this polynomial use the same procedure as was used on $g_m(x)$. It follows that c_{m-1} exists so that

$$g_m(x) - c_m f_m(x) - c_{m-1} f_{m-1}(x)$$

is of degree at most $(m-2)$. Iteration of the process yields equation (1) in $(m+1)$ steps. Note that any c_k except c_m may be zero.

129. Orthogonal polynomials

We next obtain for polynomials a condition equivalent to our definition (Section 127) of orthogonality.

THEOREM 21:   *If $\{f_n(x)\}$ is a simple set of polynomials, a necessary and sufficient condition that $\{f_n(x)\}$ be orthogonal with respect to $w(x)$ over the interval $a \leqq x \leqq b$ is that*

$$\int_a^b w(x)x^k f_n(x)\,dx = 0, \quad k = 0, 1, 2, \ldots, (n-1), \tag{1}$$

$$\neq 0, \quad k = n.$$

PROOF.   Suppose that (1) is satisfied. Since $\{x^k\}$ is a simple set, we can write

$$f_m(x) = \sum_{k=0}^{m} a_k x^k. \tag{2}$$

If $m < n$, it follows that

$$\int_a^b w(x)f_m(x)f_n(x)\,dx = \sum_{k=0}^{m} a_k \int_a^b w(x)x^k f_n(x)\,dx = 0$$

by (1), since each k involved is less than n. If $m > n$, interchange the roles of m and n, and repeat the argument. If $m = n$ in (2), then $a_n \neq 0$, and we have

$$\int_a^b w(x)f_n{}^2(x)\,dx = \sum_{k=0}^{n} a_k \int_a^b w(x)x^k f_n(x)\,dx$$

$$= a_n \int_a^b w(x)x^n f_n(x)\,dx \neq 0.$$

Thus we see that the condition (1) is sufficient for orthogonality of the set $\{f_n(x)\}$.

Next suppose the $f_n(x)$ satisfy the condition for orthogonality as laid down in Section 127. Since $\{f_n(x)\}$ is a simple set, we can write

$$x^k = \sum_{m=0}^{k} b_m f_m(x). \tag{3}$$

If $k < n$, it follows that

$$\int_a^b w(x) x^k f_n(x)\, dx = \sum_{m=0}^{k} b_m \int_a^b w(x) f_m(x) f_n(x)\, dx = 0,$$

since no m can equal n. If $k = n$ in (3), then $b_n \neq 0$, and we have

$$\int_a^b w(x) x^n f_n(x)\, dx = \sum_{m=0}^{n} b_m \int_a^b w(x) f_m(x) f_n(x)\, dx$$

$$= b_n \int_a^b w(x) f_n^2(x)\, dx \neq 0.$$

This completes the proof of Theorem 21.

130. Zeros of orthogonal polynomials

We shall show that real orthogonal polynomials have all their zeros real, distinct, and in the interval of orthogonality.

THEOREM 22: *If $\{f_n(x)\}$ is a simple set of real polynomials orthogonal with respect to $w(x)$ over the interval $a \leqq x \leqq b$, and if $w(x) > 0$ over $a < x < b$, then the zeros of $f_n(x)$ are distinct and all lie in the open interval $a < x < b$.*

PROOF. For $n \geqq 1$, the polynomial $f_n(x)$ does change sign in the interval $a < x < b$ because, by Theorem 21 (with $k = 0$),

$$\int_a^b w(x) f_n(x)\, dx = 0$$

and $w(x)$ cannot change sign in $a < x < b$.

Let $f_n(x)$ change sign in $a < x < b$ at precisely the distinct points $x = \alpha_1$, $\alpha_2, \ldots, \alpha_s$. The α's are precisely the zeros of odd multiplicity of $f_n(x)$ in the interval. Since $f_n(x)$ is of degree n, it has n zeros, multiplicity counted. Thus we know that $s \leqq n$.

Form the function

$$\psi(x) = (x - \alpha_1)(x - \alpha_2) \cdots (x - \alpha_s). \tag{1}$$

Then, in $a < x < b$, $\psi(x)$ changes sign at $x = \alpha_1, \alpha_2, \ldots, \alpha_s$ and nowhere else.

If $s < n$, $\psi(x)$ is of degree $< n$, so

$$\int_a^b w(x) f_n(x) \psi(x)\, dx = 0 \tag{2}$$

by the application of Theorem 21 to each term in the expanded form of $\psi(x)$. But the integrand in (2) does not change sign anywhere in the interval of integration, since $w(x) > 0$ and the functions $f_n(x)$ and $\psi(x)$ change sign at precisely the same points. Therefore the integral in (2) cannot vanish and the assumption $s < n$ has led us to a contradiction.

Thus we have $s = n$. That is, among the n zeros of $f_n(x)$ there are precisely n of odd multiplicity in the open interval $a < x < b$. Therefore each zero is of multiplicity one; the zeros are distinct. The proof of Theorem 22 is complete.

131. Orthogonality of Legendre polynomials

The Legendre polynomials

$$P_n(x) = F\left(-n, n + 1; 1; \frac{1 - x}{2}\right) \tag{1}$$

of Section 114 were obtained by solving the differential equation

$$(1 - x^2)y'' - 2xy' + n(n + 1)y = 0. \tag{2}$$

The $P_n(x)$ form a simple set of polynomials for which we now obtain an orthogonality property.

From (2) we have

$$(1 - x^2)P_n''(x) - 2xP_n'(x) + n(n + 1)P_n(x) = 0,$$

$$D[(1 - x^2)P_n'(x)] + n(n + 1)P_n(x) = 0; D = \frac{d}{dx}. \tag{3}$$

For index m we have

$$D[(1 - x^2)P_m'(x)] + m(m + 1)P_m(x) = 0. \tag{4}$$

We are interested in the product $P_m(x)P_n(x)$. Hence we multiply (3) throughout by $P_m(x)$, (4) throughout by $P_n(x)$, and subtract to obtain

$$P_m(x)D[(1 - x^2)P_n'(x)] - P_n(x)D[(1 - x^2)P_m'(x)]$$

$$+ [n(n + 1) - m(m + 1)]P_m(x)P_n(x) = 0.$$

The equation above may be rewritten as

$$(n^2 - m^2 + n - m)P_m(x)P_n(x)$$
$$= P_n(x)D[(1 - x^2)P'_m(x)] - P_m(x)D[(1 - x^2)P'_n(x)]. \quad (5)$$

Now, by the formula for differentiating a product, we get

$$D[(1 - x^2)P_n(x)P'_m(x)] = P_n(x)D[(1 - x^2)P'_m(x)] + (1 - x^2)P'_n(x)P'_m(x)$$

and

$$D[(1 - x^2)P'_n(x)P_m(x)] = P_m(x)D[(1 - x^2)P'_n(x)] + (1 - x^2)P'_n(x)P'_m(x).$$

Hence

$$D[(1 - x^2)\{P_n(x)P'_m(x) - P'_n(x)P_m(x)\}]$$
$$= P_n(x)D[(1 - x^2)P'_m(x)] - P_m(x)D[(1 - x^2)P'_n(x)].$$

Furthermore, $n^2 - m^2 + n - m = (n - m)(n + m + 1)$. Therefore we can write (5) as

$$(n - m)(n + m + 1)P_m(x)P_n(x)$$
$$= D[(1 - x^2)\{P_n(x)P'_m(x) - P'_n(x)P_m(x)\}]. \quad (6)$$

We have now expressed the product of any two Legendre polynomials as a derivative. Derivatives are easy to integrate. Equation (6) yields

$$(n - m)(n + m + 1) \int_a^b P_m(x)P_n(x) \, dx$$
$$= \left[(1 - x^2)\{P_n(x)P'_m(x) - P'_n(x)P_m(x)\}\right]_a^b \quad (7)$$

We may choose any a and b that we wish. Since $(1 - x^2)$ is zero at $x = -1$ and $x = 1$, we conclude that

$$(n - m)(n + m + 1) \int_{-1}^1 P_m(x)P_n(x) \, dx = 0. \quad (8)$$

Since n and m are to be non-negative integers, $n + m + 1 \neq 0$. Hence if $m \neq n$, $n - m \neq 0$ and (8) yields

$$\int_{-1}^1 P_m(x)P_n(x) \, dx = 0. \quad (9)$$

The Legendre polynomials are real, so $\int_{-1}^1 P_n{}^2(x) \, dx \neq 0$.

We have shown that the Legendre polynomials $P_n(x)$ form an orthogonal set with respect to the weight function $w(x) = 1$ over the interval $-1 < x < 1$.

Since $\{P_n(x)\}$ is a simple set of real polynomials, the theorems of Section 129 and 130 apply to it.

Further study of $P_n(x)$ would occupy more space than seems appropriate in an elementary differential equations text. We now list a few of the simplest from among the hundreds of known properties of these interesting polynomials:

$$(1 - 2xt + t^2)^{-1/2} = \sum_{n=0}^{\infty} P_n(x)t^n, \tag{10}$$

$$\int_{-1}^{1} P_n^2(x)\,dx = \frac{2}{2n + 1}, \tag{11}$$

$$P_n(x) = \frac{1}{2^n n!} D^n(x^2 - 1)^n; \; D = \frac{d}{dx}, \tag{12}$$

$$xP_n'(x) = nP_n(x) + P_{n-1}'(x), \tag{13}$$

$$(x^2 - 1)P_n'(x) = nxP_n(x) - nP_{n-1}(x), \tag{14}$$

$$nP_n(x) = (2n - 1)xP_{n-1}(x) - (n - 1)P_{n-2}(x). \tag{15}$$

132. Other orthogonal sets

In Chapter 19 we solved several differential equations of hypergeometric type. In Section 110 we encountered the Laguerre polynomial

$$L_n(x) = \sum_{k=0}^{n} \frac{(-n)_k x^k}{(k!)^2} = \sum_{k=0}^{n} \frac{(-1)^k n! x^k}{(k!)^2(n - k)!} \tag{1}$$

as a solution of the differential equation

$$xL_n''(x) + (1 - x)L_n'(x) + nL_n(x) = 0. \tag{2}$$

Equation (2) can be put in the form

$$D[xe^{-x}L_n'(x)] + ne^{-x}L_n(x) = 0, \tag{3}$$

from which the orthogonality of the set of Laguerre polynomials follows. (See Ex. 1 below.)

The Hermite polynomial of Section 113,

$$H_n(x) = \sum_{k=0}^{[n/2]} \frac{(-1)^k n!(2x)^{n-2k}}{k!(n - 2k)!}, \tag{4}$$

satisfies the differential equation

$$H_n''(x) - 2xH_n'(x) + 2nH_n(x) = 0. \tag{5}$$

Equation (5) can be put in the form

$$D[\exp(-x^2)H'_n(x)] + 2n \exp(-x^2)H_n(x) = 0, \tag{6}$$

from which the orthogonality of the set of Hermite polynomials follows. (See Ex. 3 below.)

The Bessel function $J_n(x)$ of Section 112 can be shown to have orthogonality properties also, but they are beyond the scope of this book. See, for example, R. V. Churchill, *Fourier Series and Boundary Value Problems*, 2nd ed. (New York: McGraw-Hill Book Co., 1963).

Exercises

1. Use equation (3) above and the method of Section 131 to show that the set of Laguerre polynomials is orthogonal with respect to the weight function e^{-x} over the interval $0 \leqq x < \infty$.
2. Show, with the aid of Ex. 1, that the zeros of the Laguerre polynomial $L_n(x)$ are distinct and positive.
3. Use equation (6) above and the method of Section 131 to show that the set of Hermite polynomials is orthogonal with respect to the weight function e^{-x^2} over the interval $-\infty < x < \infty$.
4. Show, with the aid of Ex. 3, that the zeros of the Hermite polynomial $H_n(x)$ are real and distinct.

CHAPTER **23**

Fourier Series

133. Orthogonality of a set of sines and cosines

The functions $\sin \alpha x$ and $\cos \alpha x$ occur in the formal solution of certain boundary value problems in partial differential equations, as was indicated in Chapter 21. We shall now obtain an orthogonality property for a set of such functions with α specified. An interval must be involved; let the origin be chosen at the center of the interval so the latter appears in the symmetric form: $-c \leqq x \leqq c$.

We shall show that the set of functions,

$$\begin{Bmatrix} \sin (n\pi x/c), & n = 1, 2, 3, \ldots \\ \cos (n\pi x/c), & n = 0, 1, 2, \ldots \end{Bmatrix}, \tag{A}$$

or

$$\begin{Bmatrix} \sin (\pi x/c), \sin (2\pi x/c), \sin (3\pi x/c), \ldots, \sin (n\pi x/c), \ldots \\ 1, \cos (\pi x/c), \cos (2\pi x/c), \cos (3\pi x/c), \ldots, \cos (n\pi x/c), \ldots \end{Bmatrix}, \tag{A}$$

is orthogonal with respect to the weight function $w(x) = 1$ over the interval

380

$-c \le x \le c$. That is, we shall prove that the integral from $x = -c$ to $x = +c$ of the product of any two different members of the set (A) is zero.

First consider the integral of the product of any of the sine functions in (A) and any of the cosine functions in (A). The result

$$I_1 = \int_{-c}^{c} \sin \frac{n\pi x}{c} \cos \frac{k\pi x}{c} \, dx = 0$$

follows at once from the fact that the integrand is an odd function of x; in this instance the result does not depend upon the fact that k and n are integers.

Next consider the integral of the product of two different sine functions from the set (A),

$$I_2 = \int_{-c}^{c} \sin \frac{n\pi x}{c} \sin \frac{k\pi x}{c} \, dx, \quad k \ne n.$$

Let us introduce a new variable of integration for simplicity in writing; put

$$\frac{\pi x}{c} = \beta,$$

from which

$$dx = \frac{c}{\pi} \, d\beta.$$

Then I_2 can be written

$$I_2 = \frac{c}{\pi} \int_{-\pi}^{\pi} \sin n\beta \sin k\beta \, d\beta.$$

Now from trigonometry we get the formula

$$\sin n\beta \sin k\beta = \tfrac{1}{2}[\cos (n - k)\beta - \cos (n + k)\beta]$$

which is useful in performing the desired integration. Thus it follows that the integral becomes

$$I_2 = \frac{c}{2\pi} \int_{-\pi}^{\pi} [\cos (n - k)\beta - \cos (n + k)\beta] \, d\beta$$

$$= \frac{c}{2\pi} \left[\frac{\sin (n - k)\beta}{n - k} - \frac{\sin (n + k)\beta}{n + k} \right]_{-\pi}^{\pi},$$

since neither $(n - k)$ nor $(n + k)$ can be zero. Because n and k are positive integers, $\sin (n - k)\beta$ and $\sin (n + k)\beta$ each vanish at $\beta = \pi$ and $\beta = -\pi$; then

$$I_2 = 0$$

for $n, k = 1, 2, 3, \ldots$, and $k \ne n$.

Finally, consider the integral of the product of two different cosine functions from the set (A),

$$I_3 = \int_{-c}^{c} \cos \frac{n\pi x}{c} \cos \frac{k\pi x}{c} \, dx,$$

where n, $k = 0$, 1, 2, 3, ...; $k \neq n$. The method used on I_2 works equally well here to yield

$$I_3 = \frac{c}{2\pi} \left[\frac{\sin (n - k)\beta}{n - k} + \frac{\sin (n + k)\beta}{n + k} \right]_{-\pi}^{\pi} = 0.$$

It is easy to see that the integral of the square of any function from the set (A) will not vanish—its integrand is positive except at an occasional point. The values of those integrals are readily obtained. The integral

$$I_4 = \int_{-c}^{c} \sin^2 \frac{n\pi x}{c} \, dx$$

has an even integrand. Hence it can be written as

$$I_4 = 2 \int_{0}^{c} \sin^2 \frac{n\pi x}{c} \, dx.$$

Elementary methods of integration yield

$$I_4 = \int_{0}^{c} \left(1 - \cos \frac{2n\pi x}{c} \right) dx$$

$$= \left[x - \frac{c}{2n\pi} \sin \frac{2n\pi x}{c} \right]_{0}^{c} = c.$$

Therefore

$$\int_{-c}^{c} \sin^2 \frac{n\pi x}{c} \, dx = c \text{ for } n = 1, 2, 3, \ldots.$$

In the same way it follows that, for $n > 0$, n integral,

$$I_5 = \int_{-c}^{c} \cos^2 \frac{n\pi x}{c} \, dx$$

$$= \left[x + \frac{c}{2n\pi} \sin \frac{2n\pi x}{c} \right]_{0}^{c} = c.$$

For $n = 0$ the integral I_5 becomes

$$I_6 = \int_{-c}^{c} 1 \cdot dx = 2c.$$

Thus

$$\int_{-c}^{c} \cos^2 \frac{n\pi x}{c} \, dx = c \text{ for } n = 1, 2, 3, \ldots,$$

$$= 2c \text{ for } n = 0.$$

We have shown that the set

$$\begin{cases} \sin{(n\pi x/c)}, & n = 1, 2, 3, \ldots \\ \cos{(m\pi x/c)}, & m = 0, 1, 2, \ldots \end{cases}, \tag{A}$$

is orthogonal with respect to the weight function $w(x) = 1$ over the interval $-c \leq x \leq c$. We have also evaluated the integrals of the squares of the functions of the set (A).

134. Fourier series: an expansion theorem

With the assumption that there exists a series expansion of the type

$$f(x) = \tfrac{1}{2}a_0 + \sum_{n=1}^{\infty} \left(a_n \cos \frac{n\pi x}{c} + b_n \sin \frac{n\pi x}{c} \right), \tag{1}*$$

valid in the interval $-c \leq x \leq c$, it is a simple matter to determine the coefficients, a_n and b_n. Indeed, disregarding the question of validity of interchange of order of summation and integration, we proceed as follows.

Multiply each term of equation (1) by $\sin{(k\pi x/c)} \, dx$, where k is a positive integer, and then integrate each term from $-c$ to $+c$, thus arriving at

$$\int_{-c}^{c} f(x) \sin \frac{k\pi x}{c} \, dx = \tfrac{1}{2}a_0 \int_{-c}^{c} \sin \frac{k\pi x}{c} \, dx$$

$$+ \sum_{n=1}^{\infty} \left[a_n \int_{-c}^{c} \cos \frac{n\pi x}{c} \sin \frac{k\pi x}{c} \, dx \right.$$

$$\left. + b_n \int_{-c}^{c} \sin \frac{n\pi x}{c} \sin \frac{k\pi x}{c} \, dx \right]. \tag{2}$$

As seen earlier,

$$\int_{-c}^{c} \cos \frac{n\pi x}{c} \sin \frac{k\pi x}{c} \, dx = 0 \text{ for all } k \text{ and } n, \tag{3}$$

and

$$\int_{-c}^{c} \sin \frac{n\pi x}{c} \sin \frac{k\pi x}{c} \, dx = 0 \text{ for } k \neq n; k, n = 1, 2, 3, \ldots. \tag{4}$$

---

* A reason for the apparently peculiar notation, $\tfrac{1}{2}a_0$, for the constant term will be seen quite soon, page 385.

Therefore each term on the right-hand side of equation (2) is zero except for the term $n = k$. Thus equation (2) reduces to

$$\int_{-c}^{c} f(x) \sin \frac{k\pi x}{c} \, dx = b_k \int_{-c}^{c} \sin^2 \frac{k\pi x}{c} \, dx. \tag{5}$$

Since

$$\int_{-c}^{c} \sin^2 \frac{k\pi x}{c} \, dx = c,$$

we have

$$b_k = \frac{1}{c} \int_{-c}^{c} f(x) \sin \frac{k\pi x}{c} \, dx, \, k = 1, 2, 3, \ldots,$$

from which the coefficients b_n in equation (1) follow by mere replacement of k with n; that is,

$$b_n = \frac{1}{c} \int_{-c}^{c} f(x) \sin \frac{n\pi x}{c} \, dx, \, n = 1, 2, 3, \ldots. \tag{6}$$

Let us obtain the a_n in a like manner. Using the multiplier $\cos (k\pi x/c) \, dx$ throughout equation (1) and then integrating term by term from $x = -c$ to $x = +c$, we get

$$\int_{-c}^{c} f(x) \cos \frac{k\pi x}{c} \, dx = \tfrac{1}{2} a_0 \int_{-c}^{c} \cos \frac{k\pi x}{c} \, dx$$
$$+ \sum_{n=1}^{\infty} \left[a_n \int_{-c}^{c} \cos \frac{n\pi x}{c} \cos \frac{k\pi x}{c} \, dx \right.$$
$$\left. + b_n \int_{-c}^{c} \sin \frac{n\pi x}{c} \cos \frac{k\pi x}{c} \, dx \right]. \tag{7}$$

The coefficient of b_n in (7) is zero for all n and k. If $k \neq 0$, we know that

$$\int_{-c}^{c} \cos \frac{n\pi x}{c} \cos \frac{k\pi x}{c} \, dx = 0 \text{ for } n \neq k,$$
$$= c \text{ for } n = k,$$

and also the coefficient of $\tfrac{1}{2} a_0$ is zero. Thus, for $k \neq 0$, equation (7) reduces to

$$\int_{-c}^{c} f(x) \cos \frac{k\pi x}{c} \, dx = a_k \int_{-c}^{c} \cos^2 \frac{k\pi x}{c} \, dx,$$

from which a_k, and therefore a_n, can be found in the way b_k was determined. Thus we get

$$a_n = \frac{1}{c} \int_{-c}^{c} f(x) \cos \frac{n\pi x}{c} \, dx, \quad n = 1, 2, 3, \ldots. \tag{8}$$

Next let us determine a_0. Suppose $k = 0$ in equation (7) so we have the equation

$$\int_{-c}^{c} f(x) \, dx = \tfrac{1}{2} a_0 \int_{-c}^{c} dx + \sum_{n=1}^{\infty} \left[a_n \int_{-c}^{c} \cos \frac{n\pi x}{c} \, dx + b_n \int_{-c}^{c} \sin \frac{n\pi x}{c} \, dx \right].$$

The terms involving $n \geq 1$ are each zero. Hence

$$\int_{-c}^{c} f(x) \, dx = \tfrac{1}{2} a_0 (2c),$$

from which we obtain

$$a_0 = \frac{1}{c} \int_{-c}^{c} f(x) \, dx. \tag{9}$$

Equation (9) fits in with equation (8) as the special case $n = 0$. Had the factor $\tfrac{1}{2}$ not been inserted as in equation (1), a separate formula would have been needed. As it is, we may write the formal expansion as follows:

$$f(x) = \tfrac{1}{2} a_0 + \sum_{n=1}^{\infty} \left(a_n \cos \frac{n\pi x}{c} + b_n \sin \frac{n\pi x}{c} \right) \tag{10}$$

with

$$a_n = \frac{1}{c} \int_{-c}^{c} f(x) \cos \frac{n\pi x}{c} \, dx, \quad n = 0, 1, 2, \ldots, \tag{11}$$

$$b_n = \frac{1}{c} \int_{-c}^{c} f(x) \sin \frac{n\pi x}{c} \, dx, \quad n = 1, 2, 3, \ldots. \tag{12}$$

Before proceeding to specific examples and applications it behooves us to state conditions under which the equality in (10) makes sense.

When a_n and b_n are given by (11) and (12) above, then the right-hand member of equation (10) is called the *Fourier series, over the interval* $-c \leq x \leq c$, *for the function* $f(x)$. A statement of conditions sufficient to insure that the Fourier series in (10) represents the function $f(x)$ in a reasonably meaningful manner follows.

Let $f(x)$ be continuous and differentiable at every point in the interval $-c \leq x \leq c$ except for at most a finite number of points and at those points

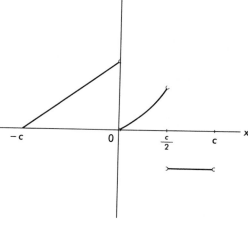

FIGURE 48

let $f(x)$ and $f'(x)$ have right- and left-hand limits. Such a function is exhibited in Figure 48.

THEOREM 23:   *Under the stipulations of the preceding paragraph, the Fourier series for $f(x)$, namely the series on the right in equation (10) with coefficients given by equations (11) and (12), converges to the value $f(x)$ at each point of continuity of $f(x)$; at each point of discontinuity of $f(x)$ the Fourier series converges to the arithmetic mean of the values approached by $f(x)$ from the right and the left.*

Since the Fourier series for $f(x)$ may not converge to the value $f(x)$ everywhere (for instance, at discontinuities of the function), it is customary to replace the equals sign in equation (10) by the sybmol $\sim$, which may be read "has for its Fourier series." We write

$$f(x) \sim \tfrac{1}{2}a_0 + \sum_{n=1}^{\infty} \left(a_n \cos \frac{n\pi x}{c} + b_n \sin \frac{n\pi x}{c} \right), \qquad (13)$$

with a_n and b_n given by equations (11) and (12).

An interesting fact and one often useful as a check in numerical problems is that $\tfrac{1}{2}a_0$ is the average value of $f(x)$ over the interval $-c < x < c$.

The sine and cosine functions are periodic with period 2π, so the terms in the Fourier series (13) for $f(x)$ are periodic with period $2c$. Therefore the series represents (converges to) a function that is as described above for the interval $-c < x < c$ and repeats that structure over and over outside that

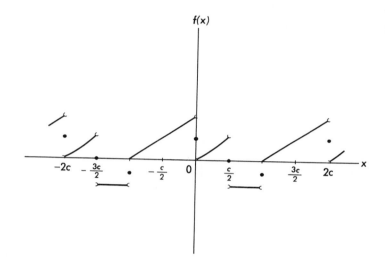

FIGURE 49

interval. For the function exhibited in Figure 48, the corresponding Fourier series would converge to the periodic function shown in Figure 49. Note the convergence to the average value at discontinuities, the periodicity, and the way in which the two together determine the value to which the series converges at $x = c$ and $x = -c$.

These statements will be amply illustrated in the numerical examples and exercises of the next section.

135. Numerical examples of Fourier series

We shall now construct the Fourier series for specific functions.

EXAMPLE (a): Construct the Fourier series, over the interval

$$-2 \leqq x \leqq 2$$

for the function defined by

$$f(x) = 2, \quad -2 < x \le 0, \tag{1}$$
$$= x, \quad 0 < x < 2,$$

and sketch the function to which the series converges.

First we sketch $f(x)$ itself, the result being exhibited in Figure 50. Note that $f(x)$ is undefined except for x between $x = -2$ and $x = +2$.

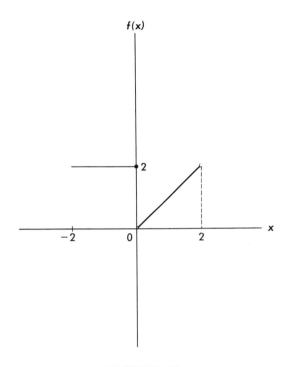

FIGURE 50

For the function described in (1),

$$f(x) \sim \tfrac{1}{2}a_0 + \sum_{n=1}^{\infty} \left(a_n \cos \frac{n\pi x}{2} + b_n \sin \frac{n\pi x}{2} \right),$$

in which

$$a_n = \tfrac{1}{2} \int_{-2}^{2} f(x) \cos \frac{n\pi x}{2} \, dx; \quad n = 0, 1, 2, \ldots, \tag{2}$$

and

$$b_n = \tfrac{1}{2} \int_{-2}^{2} f(x) \sin \frac{n\pi x}{2}\, dx; \; n = 1, 2, 3, \ldots. \tag{3}$$

Since in the description of $f(x)$, different formulas were used in the two intervals $-2 < x < 0$ and $0 < x < 2$, it is convenient to separate the integrals in (2) and (3) into corresponding parts. Thus inserting the $f(x)$ of (1) into the integral (2) leads us to the form

$$a_n = \tfrac{1}{2} \int_{-2}^{0} 2 \cos \frac{n\pi x}{2}\, dx + \tfrac{1}{2} \int_{0}^{2} x \cos \frac{n\pi x}{2}\, dx. \tag{4}$$

For these integrals, the method of integration will differ according to whether $n = 0$ or $n \neq 0$.

If $n \neq 0$, then

$$a_n = \frac{2}{n\pi} \left[\sin \frac{n\pi x}{2} \right]_{-2}^{0} + \tfrac{1}{2}\left[\frac{2}{n\pi} x \sin \frac{n\pi x}{2} + \left(\frac{2}{n\pi}\right)^2 \cos \frac{n\pi x}{2} \right]_{0}^{2},$$

or

$$a_n = \frac{2}{n\pi} [0 - 0] + \tfrac{1}{2}\left[0 + \left(\frac{2}{n\pi}\right)^2 \cos n\pi - 0 - \left(\frac{2}{n\pi}\right)^2 \right].$$

Hence for $n \neq 0$, the a_n are given by the formula

$$a_n = \frac{-2(1 - \cos n\pi)}{n^2\pi^2}, \quad n = 1, 2, 3, \ldots. \tag{5}$$

For $n = 0$ the above integrations are not valid (division by n), but we return to (4), put $n = 0$, and get

$$a_0 = \tfrac{1}{2} \int_{-2}^{0} 2\, dx + \tfrac{1}{2} \int_{0}^{2} x\, dx,$$

from which

$$a_0 = \left[x \right]_{-2}^{0} + \tfrac{1}{4}\left[x^2 \right]_{0}^{2} = 2 + 1 = 3.$$

The b_n may be obtained in a like manner. From (3) and (1) it follows that

$$b_n = \tfrac{1}{2} \int_{-2}^{0} 2 \sin \frac{n\pi x}{2}\, dx + \tfrac{1}{2} \int_{0}^{2} x \sin \frac{n\pi x}{2}\, dx.$$

Thus

$$b_n = \frac{2}{n\pi} \left[-\cos \frac{n\pi x}{2} \right]_{-2}^{0} + \tfrac{1}{2}\left[-\left(\frac{2}{n\pi}\right) x \cos \frac{n\pi x}{2} + \left(\frac{2}{n\pi}\right)^2 \sin \frac{n\pi x}{2} \right]_{0}^{2},$$

from which, since $\cos(-n\pi) = \cos n\pi$,

$$b_n = \frac{2}{n\pi}[-1 + \cos n\pi] + \tfrac{1}{2}\left[-\frac{2}{n\pi} \cdot 2\cos n\pi + 0 + 0 - 0\right],$$

or

$$b_n = -\frac{2}{n\pi}, \quad n = 1, 2, 3, \ldots. \tag{6}$$

For integral n, $\cos n\pi = (-1)^n$, as is seen by examining both sides for even and odd n. Therefore the formula (5) above can also be written

$$a_n = \frac{-2[1 - (-1)^n]}{n^2\pi^2}, \quad n = 1, 2, 3, \ldots. \tag{7}$$

We can now write the Fourier series, over the interval $-2 < x < 2$ for the $f(x)$ of this example,

$$f(x) \sim \tfrac{3}{2} - 2\sum_{n=1}^{\infty}\left[\frac{1 - (-1)^n}{n^2\pi^2}\cos\frac{n\pi x}{2} + \frac{1}{n\pi}\sin\frac{n\pi x}{2}\right]. \tag{8}$$

Several pertinent remarks can be made about (8). The right-hand member of (8) converges to the function shown in the sketch in Figure 51. It converges to $f(x)$ at each point where $f(x)$ is defined except at the discontinuity at $x = 0$. Though $f(0) = 2$, the series converges to unity at $x = 0$.

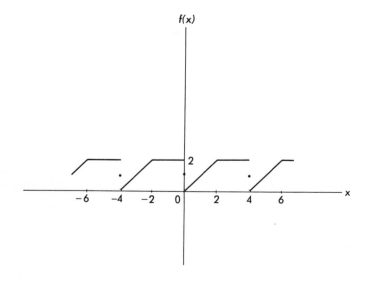

FIGURE 51

We may therefore write

$$f(x) = \tfrac{3}{2} - 2 \sum_{n=1}^{\infty} \left[\frac{1-(-1)^n}{n^2\pi^2} \cos\frac{n\pi x}{2} + \frac{1}{n\pi} \sin\frac{n\pi x}{2} \right] \tag{9}$$

for $-2 < x < 0$ and for $0 < x < 2$.

It is sometimes desirable to define a new function $\phi(x)$ as follows:

$$\begin{aligned}
\phi(x) &= f(x), & -2 &< x < 0, \\
&= 1, & x &= 0, \\
&= f(x), & 0 &< x < 2,
\end{aligned}$$

and

$$\phi(x + 4) = \phi(x).$$

This $\phi(x)$ is the function exhibited in Figure 51. If $\phi(x)$ is put in the place of $f(x)$ in (8) above, then the symbol $\sim$ may be replaced by the symbol $=$ for all x.

Because $[1 - (-1)^n]$ is zero for even n, the Fourier series on the right in (8) may be written in the somewhat more compact form

$$f(x) \sim \tfrac{3}{2} - \frac{4}{\pi^2} \sum_{k=0}^{\infty} \frac{\cos\left[(2k+1)\pi x/2\right]}{(2k+1)^2} - \frac{2}{\pi} \sum_{n=1}^{\infty} \frac{\sin(n\pi x/2)}{n}. \tag{10}$$

This is one instance in which an infinite rearrangement in the order of terms, passing from (8) to (10), is easily justified. Consider (10) again after studying the sections on Fourier sine series and Fourier cosine series.

Let us next use the expansion in (8) or (10) to sum two numerical series. For instance, if we put $x = 0$ in (10), then the series has the sum unity as indicated above. Hence

$$1 = \tfrac{3}{2} - \frac{4}{\pi^2} \sum_{k=0}^{\infty} \frac{1}{(2k+1)^2} - \frac{2}{\pi} \sum_{n=1}^{\infty} \frac{0}{n},$$

or

$$\sum_{k=0}^{\infty} \frac{1}{(2k+1)^2} = \frac{\pi^2}{8}. \tag{11}$$

For $x = 1$, the series in (10) has the sum unity again. Using $x = 1$ in (10) we are led to

$$1 = \tfrac{3}{2} - \frac{4}{\pi^2} \sum_{k=0}^{\infty} \frac{\cos\left[(2k+1)\pi/2\right]}{(2k+1)^2} - \frac{2}{\pi} \sum_{n=1}^{\infty} \frac{\sin(n\pi/2)}{n}.$$

Now $\cos\left[(2k+1)\pi/2\right] = 0$ and $\sin(n\pi/2)$ may be obtained as follows. For even n, $n = 2k$, we get

$$\sin\frac{2k\pi}{2} = \sin k\pi = 0.$$

For odd n, $n = 2k + 1$,

$$\sin \frac{(2k+1)\pi}{2} = \sin \left(k\pi + \tfrac{1}{2}\pi\right) = \cos k\pi = (-1)^k.$$

Thus we arrive at the equation

$$1 = \tfrac{3}{2} - \frac{2}{\pi} \sum_{k=0}^{\infty} \frac{(-1)^k}{2k+1},$$

or

$$\sum_{k=0}^{\infty} \frac{(-1)^k}{2k+1} = \frac{\pi}{4}, \tag{12}$$

which can be verified also by the fact that the left-hand member represents Arctan 1.

EXAMPLE (b): Obtain the Fourier series over the interval $-\pi$ to π for the function x^2. We know that

$$x^2 \sim \tfrac{1}{2}a_0 + \sum_{n=1}^{\infty} [a_n \cos nx + b_n \sin nx] \tag{13}$$

for $-\pi < x < \pi$, where

$$a_n = \frac{1}{\pi} \int_{-\pi}^{\pi} x^2 \cos nx \, dx; \quad n = 0, 1, 2, \ldots, \tag{14}$$

$$b_n = \frac{1}{\pi} \int_{-\pi}^{\pi} x^2 \sin nx \, dx; \quad n = 1, 2, 3, \ldots. \tag{15}$$

Now x^2 is an even function of x and $\sin nx$ is an odd function of x, so the product $x^2 \sin nx$ is an odd function of x. Therefore $b_n = 0$ for every n. Since $x^2 \cos nx$ is an even function of x,

$$a_n = \frac{2}{\pi} \int_{0}^{\pi} x^2 \cos nx \, dx; \quad n = 0, 1, 2, \ldots. \tag{16}$$

For $n \neq 0$,

$$a_n = \frac{2}{\pi} \left[\frac{x^2 \sin nx}{n} + \frac{2x \cos nx}{n^2} - \frac{2 \sin nx}{n^3} \right]_{0}^{\pi},$$

from which

$$a_n = \frac{2}{\pi} \left[\frac{2\pi \cos n\pi}{n^2} \right] = \frac{4(-1)^n}{n^2}, \quad n = 1, 2, 3, \ldots.$$

A separate integration is needed for a_0. We get

$$a_0 = \frac{2}{\pi} \int_{0}^{\pi} x^2 \, dx = \frac{2}{\pi} \cdot \frac{\pi^3}{3} = \frac{2\pi^2}{3}.$$

Therefore, in the interval $-\pi < x < \pi$,

$$x^2 \sim \frac{\pi^2}{3} + 4 \sum_{n=1}^{\infty} \frac{(-1)^n \cos nx}{n^2}.$$

Indeed, because of continuity of the function involved, we may write

$$x^2 = \frac{\pi^2}{3} + 4 \sum_{n=1}^{\infty} \frac{(-1)^n \cos nx}{n^2}, \quad \text{for } -\pi \leqq x \leqq \pi. \tag{17}$$

Beyond the indicated interval, the series on the right in equation (17) represents the periodic extension of the original function. The sum of the series is sketched in Figure 52.

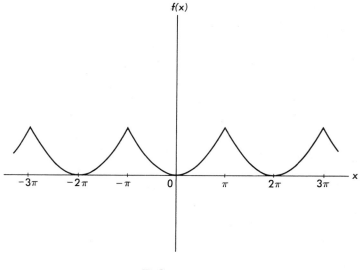

FIGURE 52

Exercises

In Exs. 1–22, obtain the Fourier series, over the indicated interval, for the given function. Always sketch the function that is the sum of the series obtained.

1. Interval, $-c < x < c$; function, $f(x) = 0, \qquad -c < x < 0,$
$$= c - x, \qquad 0 < x < c.$$

ANS. $f(x) \sim \dfrac{c}{4} + \dfrac{c}{\pi^2} \displaystyle\sum_{n=1}^{\infty} \dfrac{1}{n^2} \left[\{1 - (-1)^n\} \cos \dfrac{n\pi x}{c} + n\pi \sin \dfrac{n\pi x}{c} \right].$

2. Interval, $-c < x < c$; function, $f(x) = x$.

ANS. $f(x) \sim \dfrac{2c}{\pi} \displaystyle\sum_{n=1}^{\infty} \dfrac{(-1)^{n+1} \sin (n\pi x/c)}{n}$.

3. Interval, $-c < x < c$; function, $f(x) = x^2$. Check your answer with that in Example (b) in the text.

ANS. $f(x) \sim \dfrac{c^2}{3} + \dfrac{4c^2}{\pi^2} \displaystyle\sum_{n=1}^{\infty} \dfrac{(-1)^n \cos (n\pi x/c)}{n^2}$.

4. Interval, $-c < x < c$; function, $f(x) = 0,$ $-c < x < 0,$
                 $= (c - x)^2,$ $0 < x < c.$

ANS. $f(x) \sim \dfrac{c^2}{6} + \dfrac{c^2}{\pi^3} \displaystyle\sum_{n=1}^{\infty} \dfrac{1}{n^3} \left[2n\pi \cos \dfrac{n\pi x}{c} + \{n^2\pi^2 - 2 + 2(-1)^n\} \sin \dfrac{n\pi x}{c} \right]$.

5. Interval, $-c < x < c$; function, $f(x) = 0,$ $-c < x < 0,$
                 $= 1,$ $0 < x < c.$

ANS. $f(x) \sim \tfrac{1}{2} + \displaystyle\sum_{n=1}^{\infty} \dfrac{1 - (-1)^n}{n\pi} \sin \dfrac{n\pi x}{c}$,

or

$f(x) \sim \tfrac{1}{2} + \dfrac{2}{\pi} \displaystyle\sum_{k=0}^{\infty} \dfrac{\sin [(2k + 1)\pi x/c]}{2k + 1}$.

6. Interval, $-c < x < c$; function, $f(x) = x^3$.

ANS. $f(x) \sim \dfrac{2c^3}{\pi^3} \displaystyle\sum_{n=1}^{\infty} (-1)^{n+1} \dfrac{(n^2\pi^2 - 6) \sin (n\pi x/c)}{n^3}$.

7. Interval, $-\pi < x < \pi$; function, $f(x) = 3\pi + 2x,$ $-\pi < x < 0,$
                   $= \pi + 2x,$ $0 < x < \pi.$

ANS. $f(x) \sim 2\pi - 2 \displaystyle\sum_{k=1}^{\infty} \dfrac{\sin 2kx}{k}$.

8. Interval, $-c < x < c$; function, $f(x) = x(c + x),$ $-c < x < 0,$
                      $= (c - x)^2,$ $0 < x < c.$

ANS. $f(x) \sim \dfrac{c^2}{12} + \dfrac{c^2}{\pi^2} \displaystyle\sum_{n=1}^{\infty} \dfrac{1}{n^2} \left[\{3 + (-1)^n\} \cos \dfrac{n\pi x}{c} + n\pi \sin \dfrac{n\pi x}{c} \right]$.

9. Interval, $-2 < x < 2$; function, $f(x) = x + 1,$ $-2 < x < 0,$
                   $= 1,$ $0 \leqq x < 2.$

ANS. $f(x) \sim \tfrac{1}{2} + \dfrac{2}{\pi^2} \displaystyle\sum_{n=1}^{\infty} \dfrac{1}{n^2} [\{1 - (-1)^n\} \cos \tfrac{1}{2}n\pi x + n\pi(-1)^{n+1} \sin \tfrac{1}{2}n\pi x].$

10. Interval, $-1 < x < 1$; function, $f(x) = 0,$ $-1 < x < 0,$
                   $= 1,$ $0 < x < \tfrac{1}{2},$
                   $= 0,$ $\tfrac{1}{2} < x < 1.$

ANS. $f(x) \sim \tfrac{1}{4} + \dfrac{1}{\pi} \displaystyle\sum_{n=1}^{\infty} \dfrac{1}{n} \left[\sin \dfrac{n\pi}{2} \cos n\pi x + \left(1 - \cos \dfrac{n\pi}{2} \right) \sin n\pi x \right]$.

11. Interval, $-\pi < x < \pi$; function, $f(x) = 0,$ $-\pi < x < 0,$
                   $= x^2,$ $0 < x < \pi.$

ANS. $f(x) \sim \dfrac{\pi^2}{6} + 2 \displaystyle\sum_{n=1}^{\infty} \dfrac{(-1)^n \cos nx}{n^2}$

$+ \dfrac{1}{\pi} \displaystyle\sum_{n=1}^{\infty} \dfrac{1}{n^3} [(-1)^{n+1}n^2\pi^2 - 2 + 2(-1)^n] \sin nx.$

12. Interval, $-\pi < x < \pi$; function, $f(x) = \cos 2x$.   ANS. $f(x) \sim \cos 2x$.

13. Interval, $-\pi < x < \pi$; function, $f(x) = \cos (x/2)$.

$$\text{ANS.} \quad f(x) \sim \frac{2}{\pi} + \frac{4}{\pi} \sum_{n=1}^{\infty} \frac{(-1)^{n+1} \cos nx}{(2n-1)(2n+1)}.$$

14. Interval, $-\pi < x < \pi$; function, $f(x) = \sin^2 x$.

$$\text{ANS.} \quad \sin^2 x \sim \tfrac{1}{2} - \tfrac{1}{2} \cos 2x.$$

15. Interval, $-c < x < c$; function, $f(x) = e^x$.

$$\text{ANS.} \quad f(x) \sim \frac{\sinh c}{c} + \sum_{n=1}^{\infty} \frac{2(-1)^n \sinh c[c \cos (n\pi x/c) - n\pi \sin (n\pi x/c)]}{c^2 + n^2\pi^2}.$$

16. Interval, $-c < x < c$; function, $f(x) = 0$, $-c < x < 0$,

$$= e^{-x}, \quad 0 < x < c.$$

$$\text{ANS.} \quad f(x) \sim \frac{1 - e^{-c}}{2c} + \sum_{n=1}^{\infty} \frac{1 - (-1)^n e^{-c}}{c^2 + n^2\pi^2} \left(c \cos \frac{n\pi x}{c} + n\pi \sin \frac{n\pi x}{c} \right).$$

17. Interval, $-c < x < c$; function, $f(x) = 0$, $-c < x < \tfrac{1}{2}c$,

$$= 1, \quad \tfrac{1}{2}c < x < c.$$

$$\text{ANS.} \quad f(x) \sim \tfrac{1}{4} - \frac{1}{\pi} \sum_{n=1}^{\infty} \frac{1}{n} \left[\sin \tfrac{1}{2}n\pi \cos \frac{n\pi x}{c} + (\cos n\pi - \cos \tfrac{1}{2}n\pi) \sin \frac{n\pi x}{c} \right].$$

18. Interval, $-c < x < c$; function, $f(x) = 0$, $-c < x < 0$,

$$= x, \quad 0 < x < c.$$

$$\text{ANS.} \quad f(x) \sim \tfrac{1}{4}c - \frac{c}{\pi^2} \sum_{n=1}^{\infty} \frac{1}{n^2} \left[\{1 - (-1)^n\} \cos \frac{n\pi x}{c} + n\pi(-1)^n \sin \frac{n\pi x}{c} \right].$$

19. Interval, $-4 < x < 4$; function, $f(x) = 1$, $-4 < x < 2$,

$$= 0, \quad 2 < x < 4.$$

20. Interval, $-c < x < c$; function, $f(x) = 0$, $-c < x < 0$,

$$= x(c - x), \quad 0 < x < c.$$

21. Interval, $-c < x < c$; function, $f(x) = c + x$, $-c < x < 0$,

$$= 0, \quad 0 < x < c.$$

22. Interval, $-c < x < c$; function, $f(x) = x^4$.

$$\text{ANS.} \quad f(x) \sim \frac{c^4}{5} + 8c^4 \sum_{n=1}^{\infty} (-1)^n \frac{n^2\pi^2 - 6}{n^4\pi^4} \cos \frac{n\pi x}{c}.$$

23. Use the answer to Ex. 3 to show that $\displaystyle\sum_{n=1}^{\infty} \frac{(-1)^{n+1}}{n^2} = \frac{\pi^2}{12}$.

24. Use the answer to Ex. 8 to show that $\displaystyle\sum_{n=1}^{\infty} \frac{1}{n^2} = \frac{\pi^2}{6}$.

25. Use the answer to Ex. 22 to show that $\displaystyle\sum_{n=1}^{\infty} \frac{1}{n^4} = \frac{\pi^4}{90}$.

26. Use $x = 0$ in the answer to Ex. 15 to sum the series $\displaystyle\sum_{n=1}^{\infty} \frac{(-1)^n}{c^2 + n^2\pi^2}$.

$$\text{ANS.} \quad \frac{c - \sinh c}{2c^2 \sinh c}.$$

27. Let $c \to 0$ in the result of Ex. 26 and check with Ex. 23.

136. Fourier sine series

On page 371 we found it desirable to have an expansion of a function $f(x)$ in a series involving only sine functions, the expansion to represent the original $f(x)$ in an interval $0 < x < c$. With the notation we have been using, the Fourier series

$$\tfrac{1}{2}a_0 + \sum_{n=1}^{\infty} \left(a_n \cos \frac{n\pi x}{c} + b_n \sin \frac{n\pi x}{c} \right)$$

will reduce to a series with each term containing a sine function if somehow the a_n; $n = 0, 1, 2, \ldots$, can be made to be zero. Examining the formula for a_n, page 385, reveals that the a_n will vanish if the function being expanded is an odd function over the interval $-c < x < c$.

Therefore, to get a sine series for $f(x)$ we introduce a new function $g(x)$ defined to equal $f(x)$ in the interval $0 < x < c$ and to be the odd extension of that function in the remaining interval, $-c < x < 0$. That is, we define $g(x)$ by

$$g(x) = f(x), \qquad\qquad 0 < x < c,$$
$$= -f(-x), \quad -c < x < 0.$$

Then $g(x)$ is an odd function over the interval $-c < x < c$. Hence from

$$g(x) \sim \tfrac{1}{2}a_0 + \sum_{n=1}^{\infty} \left(a_n \cos \frac{n\pi x}{c} + b_n \sin \frac{n\pi x}{c} \right)$$

it follows that

$$a_n = \frac{1}{c} \int_{-c}^{c} g(x) \cos \frac{n\pi x}{c}\, dx = 0, \quad n = 0, 1, 2, \ldots,$$

and that

$$b_n = \frac{1}{c} \int_{-c}^{c} g(x) \sin \frac{n\pi x}{c}\, dx = \frac{2}{c} \int_{0}^{c} f(x) \sin \frac{n\pi x}{c}\, dx.$$

The resultant series represents $f(x)$ in the interval $0 < x < c$, since $g(x)$ and $f(x)$ are identical over that portion of the whole interval.

Thus we have

$$f(x) \sim \sum_{n=1}^{\infty} b_n \sin \frac{n\pi x}{c}, \quad 0 < x < c, \tag{1}$$

in which

$$b_n = \frac{2}{c} \int_0^c f(x) \sin \frac{n\pi x}{c} \, dx, \quad n = 1, 2, 3, \ldots. \tag{2}$$

The representation (1) is called the *Fourier sine series* for $f(x)$ over the interval $0 < x < c$.

It should be realized that the device of introducing the function $g(x)$ was a tool for arriving at (1) and (2); there is no need to repeat it in specific problems. Those we handle by direct use of (1) and (2) above.

EXAMPLE: Expand $f(x) = x^2$ in a Fourier sine series over the interval $0 < x < 1$.

At once we may write, for $0 < x < 1$,

$$x^2 \sim \sum_{n=1}^{\infty} b_n \sin n\pi x, \tag{3}$$

in which

$$b_n = 2 \int_0^1 x^2 \sin n\pi x \, dx$$

$$= 2\left[-\frac{x^2 \cos n\pi x}{n\pi} + \frac{2x \sin n\pi x}{(n\pi)^2} + \frac{2 \cos n\pi x}{(n\pi)^3} \right]_0^1$$

$$= 2\left[-\frac{\cos n\pi}{n\pi} + \frac{2 \cos n\pi}{n^3\pi^3} - \frac{2}{n^3\pi^3} \right]. \tag{4}$$

Hence the Fourier sine series, over $0 < x < 1$, for x^2 is

$$x^2 \sim 2 \sum_{n=1}^{\infty} \left[\frac{(-1)^{n+1}}{n\pi} - \frac{2\{1 - (-1)^n\}}{n^3\pi^3} \right] \sin n\pi x. \tag{5}$$

The series on the right in (5) converges to the function exhibited in Figure 53, that function being called the odd periodic extension, with period 2, of the function

$$f(x) = x^2, \quad 0 < x < 1.$$

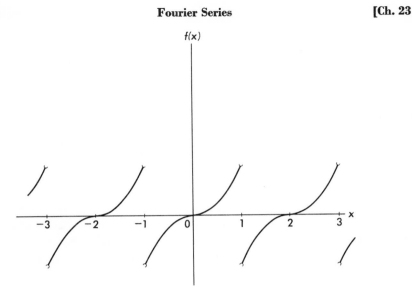

FIGURE 53

Exercises

In each exercise, obtain the Fourier sine series over the stipulated interval for the function given. Sketch the function that is the sum of the series obtained.

1. Interval, $0 < x < c$; function, $f(x) = 1$.

$$\text{ANS.} \quad f(x) \sim \frac{4}{\pi} \sum_{k=0}^{\infty} \frac{\sin\left[(2k+1)\pi x/c\right]}{2k+1}.$$

2. Interval, $0 < x < c$; function, $f(x) = x$. Compare your result with that in Ex. 2, page 394.

3. Interval, $0 < x < c$; function, $f(x) = x^2$. Check your answer with that for the example in the text above.

$$\text{ANS.} \quad f(x) \sim 2c^2 \sum_{n=1}^{\infty} \left[\frac{(-1)^{n+1}}{n\pi} - \frac{2\{1 - (-1)^n\}}{n^3\pi^3} \right] \sin\frac{n\pi x}{c}.$$

4. Interval, $0 < x < c$; function, $f(x) = c - x$. $\quad$ ANS. $\quad f(x) \sim \frac{2c}{\pi} \sum_{n=1}^{\infty} \frac{1}{n} \sin\frac{n\pi x}{c}.$

5. Interval, $0 < x < 2c$; function, $f(x) = c - x$. $\qquad$ ANS. $\quad$ Same as in Ex. 4.

6. Interval, $0 < x < 4c$; function, $f(x) = c - x$. Compare with Exs. 4 and 5.

$$\text{ANS.} \quad f(x) \sim \frac{2c}{\pi} \sum_{n=1}^{\infty} \frac{1 + 3(-1)^n}{n} \sin\frac{n\pi x}{4c}.$$

7. Interval, $0 < x < c$; function, $f(x) = x(c - x)$.

$$\text{ANS.} \quad f(x) \sim \frac{8c^2}{\pi^3} \sum_{k=0}^{\infty} \frac{\sin\left[(2k+1)\pi x/c\right]}{(2k+1)^3}.$$

8. Interval, $0 < x < 2$; function, $f(x) = x,$ $\quad 0 < x < 1,$
$$= 2 - x, \quad 1 < x < 2.$$

ANS. $f(x) \sim \dfrac{8}{\pi^2} \displaystyle\sum_{k=0}^{\infty} \dfrac{(-1)^k}{(2k+1)^2} \sin [(2k+1)\pi x/2].$

9. Interval, $0 < t < t_1$; function, $f(t) = 1,$ $\quad 0 < t < t_0,$
$$= 0, \quad t_0 < t < t_1.$$

ANS. $f(t) \sim \dfrac{2}{\pi} \displaystyle\sum_{n=1}^{\infty} \dfrac{1}{n} \left(1 - \cos \dfrac{n\pi t_0}{t_1} \right) \sin \dfrac{n\pi t}{t_1}.$

10. Interval, $0 < x < 1$; function, $f(x) = 0,$ $\quad 0 < x < \frac{1}{2},$
$$= 1, \quad \frac{1}{2} < x < 1.$$

ANS. $f(x) \sim \dfrac{2}{\pi} \displaystyle\sum_{n=1}^{\infty} \dfrac{1}{n} \left(\cos \dfrac{n\pi}{2} - \cos n\pi \right) \sin n\pi x.$

11. Interval, $0 < x < 1$; function, $f(x) = 0,$ $\quad 0 < x < \frac{1}{2},$
$$= x - \tfrac{1}{2}, \quad \tfrac{1}{2} < x < 1.$$

ANS. $f(x) \sim \displaystyle\sum_{n=1}^{\infty} \left[\dfrac{(-1)^{n+1}}{n\pi} - \dfrac{2 \sin (n\pi/2)}{n^2 \pi^2} \right] \sin n\pi x.$

12. Interval, $0 < x < \pi$; function, $f(x) = \sin 3x.$ $\qquad$ ANS. $f(x) \sim \sin 3x.$

13. Interval, $0 < x < \pi$; function, $f(x) = \cos 2x.$ Note the special treatment necessary for the evaluation of b_2.

ANS. $f(x) \sim \dfrac{4}{\pi} \displaystyle\sum_{k=0}^{\infty} \dfrac{(2k+1) \sin [(2k+1)x]}{(2k-1)(2k+3)}.$

14. Interval, $0 < x < \pi$; function, $f(x) = \cos x.$ $\quad$ ANS. $f(x) \sim \dfrac{8}{\pi} \displaystyle\sum_{k=1}^{\infty} \dfrac{k \sin 2kx}{4k^2 - 1}.$

15. Interval, $0 < x < c$; function, $f(x) = e^{-x}.$

ANS. $f(x) \sim \displaystyle\sum_{n=1}^{\infty} \dfrac{2n\pi [1 - (-1)^n e^{-c}] \sin (n\pi x/c)}{c^2 + n^2 \pi^2}.$

16. Interval, $0 < x < c$; function, $f(x) = \sinh kx.$

ANS. $f(x) \sim \sinh kc \displaystyle\sum_{n=1}^{\infty} \dfrac{(-1)^{n+1} 2n\pi}{(kc)^2 + (n\pi)^2} \sin \dfrac{n\pi x}{c}.$

17. Interval, $0 < x < c$; function, $f(x) = \cosh kx.$

ANS. $f(x) \sim \displaystyle\sum_{n=1}^{\infty} \dfrac{2n\pi [1 + (-1)^{n+1} \cosh kc]}{(kc)^2 + (n\pi)^2} \sin \dfrac{n\pi x}{c}.$

18. Interval, $0 < x < c$; function, $f(x) = x^3.$
19. Interval, $0 < x < c$; function, $f(x) = x^4.$ $\qquad$ ANS. See Ex. 6, p. 394.

ANS. $f(x) \sim \dfrac{2c^4}{\pi} \displaystyle\sum_{n=1}^{\infty} \left[(-1)^{n+1} \left(\dfrac{1}{n} - \dfrac{12}{\pi^2 n^3} + \dfrac{24}{\pi^4 n^5} \right) + \dfrac{24}{\pi^4 n^5} \right] \sin \dfrac{n\pi x}{c}.$

20. Interval, $0 < x < c$; function, $f(x) = x,$ $\quad 0 < x < \frac{1}{2}c,$
$$= 0, \quad \tfrac{1}{2}c < x < c.$$

ANS. $f(x) \sim \dfrac{c}{\pi^2} \displaystyle\sum_{n=1}^{\infty} \left(\dfrac{2}{n^2} \sin \dfrac{n\pi}{2} - \dfrac{\pi}{n} \cos \dfrac{n\pi}{2} \right) \sin \dfrac{n\pi x}{c}.$

21. Interval, $0 < x < 1$; function, $f(x) = (x - 1)^2.$

ANS. $f(x) \sim \dfrac{2}{\pi^3} \displaystyle\sum_{n=1}^{\infty} \dfrac{1}{n^3} [n^2 \pi^2 - 2 + 2(-1)^n] \sin n\pi x.$

137. Fourier cosine series

In a manner entirely similar to that used to obtain the Fourier sine series, it is possible to obtain for a function defined over the interval $0 < x < c$ a series of cosine terms including a constant term. Indeed, given $f(x)$ defined over the interval $0 < x < c$ and satisfying there the conditions stipulated in Section 134, we may define an auxiliary function $h(x)$ by

$$h(x) = f(x), \qquad 0 < x < c,$$
$$= f(-x), \quad -c < x < 0.$$

Then $h(x)$ is an even function of x and, of course, it is equal to $f(x)$ over the interval where $f(x)$ was defined. Since $h(x)$ is even, it follows that in its ordinary Fourier expansion over the interval $-c < x < c$, the b_n are all zero,

$$b_n = \frac{1}{c} \int_{-c}^{c} h(x) \sin \frac{n\pi x}{c} \, dx = 0,$$

because of the oddness of the integrand. Furthermore, since $h(x)$ is even, $h(x) \cos (n\pi x/c)$ is also even and

$$a_n = \frac{2}{c} \int_0^c h(x) \cos \frac{n\pi x}{c} \, dx = \frac{2}{c} \int_0^c f(x) \cos \frac{n\pi x}{c} \, dx.$$

Since $h(x)$ and $f(x)$ are identical over the interval $0 < x < c$, we may write what is customarily called the *Fourier cosine series* for $f(x)$ over that interval, namely,

$$f(x) \sim \tfrac{1}{2}a_0 + \sum_{n=1}^{\infty} a_n \cos \frac{n\pi x}{c}, \quad 0 < x < c, \tag{1}$$

in which

$$a_n = \frac{2}{c} \int_0^c f(x) \cos \frac{n\pi x}{c} \, dx. \tag{2}$$

EXAMPLE: Find the Fourier cosine series over the interval $0 < x < c$ for the function $f(x) = x$.
   At once we have

$$f(x) \sim \tfrac{1}{2}a_0 + \sum_{n=1}^{\infty} a_n \cos \frac{n\pi x}{c},$$

in which

$$a_n = \frac{2}{c} \int_0^c x \cos \frac{n\pi x}{c} \, dx.$$

For $n \neq 0$, the a_n may be evaluated as follows:

$$a_n = \frac{2}{c} \left[\frac{c}{n\pi} x \sin \frac{n\pi x}{c} + \left(\frac{c}{n\pi}\right)^2 \cos \frac{n\pi x}{c} \right]_0^c$$

$$= \frac{2}{c} \left[\left(\frac{c}{n\pi}\right)^2 \cos n\pi - \left(\frac{c}{n\pi}\right)^2 \right]$$

$$= -\frac{2c}{n^2 \pi^2} (1 - \cos n\pi), \quad n \neq 0.$$

The remaining coefficient a_0 is readily obtained;

$$a_0 = \frac{2}{c} \int_0^c x \, dx = \frac{2}{c} \cdot \frac{c^2}{2} = c.$$

Thus the Fourier cosine series over the interval $0 < x < c$ for the function $f(x) = x$ is

$$f(x) \sim \tfrac{1}{2}c - \frac{2c}{\pi^2} \sum_{n=1}^{\infty} \frac{1 - (-1)^n}{n^2} \cos \frac{n\pi x}{c},$$

which may also be written in the form

$$f(x) \sim \tfrac{1}{2}c - \frac{4c}{\pi^2} \sum_{k=0}^{\infty} \frac{\cos\left[(2k+1)\pi x/c\right]}{(2k+1)^2}. \tag{3}$$

In Figure 54 there is exhibited the sum of the series on the right in (3), often called the even periodic extension of the function x. The sum of the series is, of course, periodic with period $2c$.

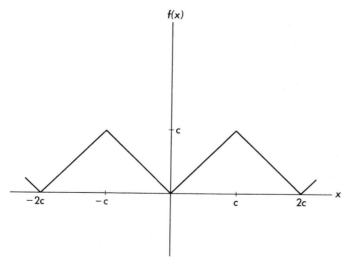

FIGURE 54

Exercises

In each exercise, obtain the Fourier cosine series for the given function over the stipulated interval and sketch the function to which the series converges.

1. Interval, $0 < x < 2$; function, $f(x) = x,$ $0 < x < 1,$
$$= 2 - x,   1 < x < 2.$$

ANS. $f(x) \sim \frac{1}{2} + \frac{4}{\pi^2} \sum\limits_{n=1}^{\infty} \frac{1}{n^2} \left[2 \cos \frac{n\pi}{2} - 1 - (-1)^n \right] \cos \frac{n\pi x}{2}.$

2. Interval, $0 < t < t_1$; function, $f(t) = 1,$ $0 < t < t_0,$
$$= 0,   t_0 < t < t_1.$$

ANS. $f(t) \sim \frac{t_0}{t_1} + \frac{2}{\pi} \sum\limits_{n=1}^{\infty} \frac{1}{n} \sin \frac{n\pi t_0}{t_1} \cos \frac{n\pi t}{t_1}.$

3. Interval, $0 < x < 1$; function, $f(x) = (x - 1)^2.$

ANS. $f(x) \sim \frac{1}{3} + \frac{4}{\pi^2} \sum\limits_{n=1}^{\infty} \frac{\cos n\pi x}{n^2}.$

4. Interval, $0 < x < c$; function, $f(x) = x(c - x).$

ANS. $f(x) \sim \frac{c^2}{6} - \frac{c^2}{\pi^2} \sum\limits_{k=1}^{\infty} \frac{\cos (2k\pi x/c)}{k^2}.$

5. Interval, $0 < x < c$; function, $f(x) = c - x.$

ANS. $f(x) \sim \frac{1}{2}c + \frac{4c}{\pi^2} \sum\limits_{k=0}^{\infty} \frac{\cos [(2k + 1)\pi x/c]}{(2k + 1)^2}.$

6. Interval, $0 < x < 1$; function, $f(x) = 0,$ $0 < x < \frac{1}{2},$
$$= 1,   \tfrac{1}{2} < x < 1.$$

ANS. $f(x) \sim \frac{1}{2} - \frac{2}{\pi} \sum\limits_{k=0}^{\infty} \frac{(-1)^k \cos [(2k + 1)\pi x]}{2k + 1}.$

7. Interval, $0 < x < 1$; function, $f(x) = 0,$ $0 < x < \frac{1}{2},$
$$= x - \tfrac{1}{2},   \tfrac{1}{2} < x < 1.$$

ANS. $f(x) \sim \frac{1}{8} + \frac{2}{\pi^2} \sum\limits_{n=1}^{\infty} \frac{1}{n^2} \left(\cos n\pi - \cos \frac{n\pi}{2} \right) \cos n\pi x.$

8. Interval, $0 < x < 1$; function, $f(x) = \frac{1}{2} - x,$ $0 < x < \frac{1}{2},$
$$= 0,   \tfrac{1}{2} < x < 1.$$

ANS. $f(x) \sim \frac{1}{8} + \frac{2}{\pi^2} \sum\limits_{n=1}^{\infty} \frac{1}{n^2} \left(1 - \cos \frac{n\pi}{2} \right) \cos n\pi x.$

9. Interval, $0 < x < \pi$; function, $f(x) = \cos 2x.$ ANS. $f(x) \sim \cos 2x.$

10. Interval, $0 < x < \pi$; function, $f(x) = \sin 2x.$

ANS. $f(x) \sim -\frac{8}{\pi} \sum\limits_{k=0}^{\infty} \frac{\cos [(2k + 1)x]}{(2k - 1)(2k + 3)}.$

11. Interval, $0 < x < c$; function, $f(x) = x,$ $0 < x < \frac{1}{2}c,$
$$= 0,   \tfrac{1}{2}c < x < c.$$

ANS. $f(x) \sim \frac{c}{8} + \frac{c}{\pi^2} \sum\limits_{n=1}^{\infty} \frac{1}{n^2} [n\pi \sin \tfrac{1}{2}n\pi - 2(1 - \cos \tfrac{1}{2}n\pi)] \cos \frac{n\pi x}{c}.$

12. Interval, $0 < x < c$; function, $f(x) = e^{-x}$. Notice how the a_0 term fits in with the others this time, making separate integration unnecessary.

$$\text{ANS.} \quad f(x) \sim \frac{1 - e^{-c}}{c} + 2c \sum_{n=1}^{\infty} \frac{1 - (-1)^n e^{-c}}{c^2 + n^2 \pi^2} \cos \frac{n\pi x}{c}.$$

13. Interval, $0 < x < c$; function, $f(x) = \cosh kx$.

$$\text{ANS.} \quad f(x) \sim \frac{\sinh kc}{kc} + \sinh kc \sum_{n=1}^{\infty} \frac{2kc(-1)^n}{(kc)^2 + (n\pi)^2} \cos \frac{n\pi x}{c}.$$

14. Interval, $0 < x < c$; function, $f(x) = \sinh kx$.

$$\text{ANS.} \quad f(x) \sim \frac{\cosh kc - 1}{kc} + \sum_{n=1}^{\infty} \frac{2kc[(-1)^n \cosh kc - 1]}{(kc)^2 + (n\pi)^2} \cos \frac{n\pi x}{c}.$$

15. Interval, $0 < x < c$; function, $f(x) = x^3$.

$$\text{ANS.} \quad f(x) \sim \frac{c^3}{4} + \frac{6c^3}{\pi^2} \sum_{n=1}^{\infty} \left[\frac{(-1)^n}{n^2} + \frac{2}{\pi^2} \cdot \frac{1 - (-1)^n}{n^4} \right] \cos \frac{n\pi x}{c}.$$

16. Interval, $0 < x < c$; function, $f(x) = x^4$.   ANS.   See Ex. 22, p 395.

138. Numerical Fourier analysis

In the preceding sections and in the applications in the next chapter, the functions for which Fourier series are required are expressed by means of formulas, as for example

$$f(x) = x, \qquad 0 < x < 1,$$
$$= 2 - x, \quad 1 < x < 2.$$

Then the Fourier coefficients, a_n, b_n, are obtained by formal integrations.

In practice it often happens that a function will in the first place be described only by a graph or by a table of numerical values. Then the Fourier coefficients should be determined by performing the appropriate integrations by some numerical, mechanical, or graphical method. For instance, in the heat-conduction problem studied in Section 126, page 366, the initial temperature distribution $f(x)$ might well consist of a table of initial temperature readings for points at various distances from one surface of the slab. At the end of Section 126, on page 371, it is seen that the solution

$$u(x, t) = \sum_{n=1}^{\infty} B_n \exp\left[-\left(\frac{n\pi h}{c}\right)^2 t\right] \sin \frac{n\pi x}{c} \tag{13}$$

of the temperature problem involves the coefficients B_n, which are to be chosen so that

$$f(x) = \sum_{n=1}^{\infty} B_n \sin \frac{n\pi x}{c}, \quad \text{for } 0 < x < c. \tag{14}$$

We can see now that (14) is to be the Fourier sine series expansion of $f(x)$. Hence the B_n are given by

$$B_n = \frac{2}{c} \int_0^c f(x) \sin \frac{n\pi x}{c} \, dx$$

from which B_n is to be found numerically and then inserted in (13).

It is natural that in this book there is a marked tendency to consider each topic encountered only in the light of its bearing on differential equations, or even on a particular phase of the subject of differential equations. In all fairness it must be mentioned that Fourier series are involved in many other ways in mathematics and in other sciences. For contact with the subject of curve-fitting and the method of least squares, see Churchill's *Fourier Series and Boundary Value Problems*, cited at the end of Section 124.

139. Improvement in rapidity of convergence

In practical problems, trigonometric series occur sometimes without the sum function being known in any other form. Computations with such series can be irksome unless the series converge with reasonable rapidity.

Suppose that it is desired to compute, at several points in the interval $0 < x < \pi$, the sum of the series

$$\sum_{n=1}^{\infty} \frac{(-1)^n n \cos nx}{n^3 + 7}. \tag{1}$$

The series in (1) converges absolutely since its general term is less in absolute value than $1/n^2$ and $\sum_{n=1}^{\infty} 1/n^2$ converges. Let the sum of the series in (1) be denoted by $\phi(x)$.

For large n the coefficients in the series (1) are well approximated by $(-1)^n/n^2$. But we know the sum of the corresponding series with those coefficients; on pages 392–393 we showed that

$$x^2 = \frac{\pi^2}{3} + 4 \sum_{n=1}^{\infty} \frac{(-1)^n \cos nx}{n^2}, \quad \text{for } -\pi \leqq x \leqq \pi. \tag{2}$$

Therefore,

$$\frac{1}{4} \left(x^2 - \frac{\pi^2}{3} \right) = \sum_{n=1}^{\infty} \frac{(-1)^n \cos nx}{n^2}, \quad -\pi \leqq x \leqq \pi. \tag{3}$$

Since the coefficients in the series in (3) and those in the series for $\phi(x)$,

$$\phi(x) = \sum_{n=1}^{\infty} \frac{(-1)^n n \cos nx}{n^3 + 7}, \quad 0 < x < \pi, \tag{4}$$

are nearly equal for large n, it follows that the difference of those coefficients should be small. So we subtract the members of equation (3) from the corresponding ones of equation (4) and get

$$\phi(x) - \frac{1}{4}\left(x^2 - \frac{\pi^2}{3}\right) = \sum_{n=1}^{\infty}(-1)^n\left[\frac{n}{n^3+7} - \frac{1}{n^2}\right]\cos nx$$

$$= \sum_{n=1}^{\infty}\frac{7(-1)^{n+1}\cos nx}{n^2(n^3+7)}.$$

Thus we obtain for $\phi(x)$ the formula

$$\phi(x) = \frac{1}{4}\left(x^2 - \frac{\pi^2}{3}\right) + 7\sum_{n=1}^{\infty}\frac{(-1)^{n+1}\cos nx}{n^2(n^3+7)}, \quad 0 < x < \pi, \qquad (5)$$

with which computation of $\phi(x)$ is simplified, since the coefficients of $\cos nx$ in (5) get small more rapidly than those in (4) as n increases.

The device illustrated above is worth keeping in mind when computing with infinite series—whether trigonometric or not. The method is largely dependent upon the presence of a collection of series for which the sum is known.

References on Fourier series

CHURCHILL, R. V. *Fourier Series and Boundary Value Problems*, 2nd edition. New York: McGraw-Hill Book Co., 1963.

JACKSON, DUNHAM. *Fourier Series and Orthogonal Polynomials*. Carus Mathematical Monograph No. 6. Menasha, Wis.: Mathematical Association of America, 1941.

LANGER, R. E. *Fourier Series, The Genesis and Evolution of a Theory*. The first Slaught memorial paper, published as a supplement to the *Amer. Math. Monthly*, **54**, 1947.

CHAPTER 24

Boundary Value Problems

140. The one-dimensional heat equation

The equation that governs the conduction of heat,

$$\frac{\partial u}{\partial t} = h^2 \left(\frac{\partial^2 u}{\partial x^2} + \frac{\partial^2 u}{\partial y^2} + \frac{\partial^2 u}{\partial z^2} \right),$$ (1)

was introduced on page 360. The symbols in it, and a set of consistent units often employed in engineering practice, are described below:

$$x, y, z = \text{rectangular space coordinates (ft.),}$$
$$t = \text{time (hours),}$$
$$u = \text{temperature (°F),}$$
$$h^2 = \text{thermal diffusivity (ft.}^2/\text{hr.).}$$

Another frequently used set of units for the above quantities replaces feet by centimeters, hours by seconds, and degrees Fahrenheit by degrees centigrade.

It has already been indicated in Section 126 that under proper physical conditions it is reasonable to study a certain special case of equation (1), the one-dimensional heat equation

$$\frac{\partial u}{\partial t} = h^2 \frac{\partial^2 u}{\partial x^2}.$$

In Section 126 we obtained from the boundary value problem

$$\frac{\partial u}{\partial t} = h^2 \frac{\partial^2 u}{\partial x^2}, \quad \text{for } 0 < t, \quad 0 < x < c; \tag{2}$$

$$\text{As } t \to 0^+, \quad u \to f(x), \quad \text{for } 0 < x < c; \tag{3}$$

$$\text{As } x \to 0^+, \quad u \to 0, \qquad \text{for } 0 < t; \tag{4}$$

$$\text{As } x \to c^-, \quad u \to 0, \qquad \text{for } 0 < t, \tag{5}$$

the relation

$$u(x, t) = \sum_{n=1}^{\infty} B_n \exp\left[-\left(\frac{n\pi h}{c}\right)^2 t\right] \sin \frac{n\pi x}{c}, \tag{6}$$

where the B_n were to be determined so that

$$f(x) = \sum_{n=1}^{\infty} B_n \sin \frac{n\pi x}{c}, \quad \text{for } 0 < x < c. \tag{7}$$

Then in Chapter 23 we found that equation (7) suggests that the series on the right be the Fourier sine series for $f(x)$ over the interval $0 < x < c$, and therefore that

$$B_n = \frac{2}{c} \int_0^c f(x) \sin \frac{n\pi x}{c} \, dx. \tag{8}$$

It is not difficult, but requires material beyond this course, to verify that (6) with coefficients B_n given by (8) is actually a solution; that is, that (6) possesses, for properly chosen $f(x)$, the required convergence properties in addition to its formal satisfaction of the differential equation (2) and the boundary conditions (3), (4), and (5).

The amount of heat that flows across an element of surface in a specified time is proportional to the rate of change of temperature in the direction normal (perpendicular) to that surface. Thus the flux of heat in the x direction (across a surface normal to the x direction) is taken to be

$$-K \frac{\partial x}{\partial u},$$

the constant of proportionality being K, the thermal conductivity of the material involved. The significance of the negative sign can be seen by considering an example in which the temperature increases with increasing x.

Then $\partial u/\partial x$ is positive, but heat flows toward negative x, from the warmer portion to the colder portion; hence the flux is taken to be negative.

For us the expression for flux of heat will be used most often in forming boundary conditions involving insulation. If there is total insulation at a surface normal to the x direction, then there is no flux of heat across that surface, so

$$\frac{\partial u}{\partial x} = 0$$

at that surface.

EXAMPLE: Find the temperature in a flat slab of unit width such that:

(a) Its initial temperature varies uniformly from zero at one face to u_0 at the other;

(b) The temperature of the face initially at zero remains at zero for $t > 0$; and

(c) The face initially at temperature u_0 is insulated for $t > 0$.

If x is measured from the face at zero temperature, the problem may be written

$$\frac{\partial u}{\partial t} = h^2 \frac{\partial^2 u}{\partial x^2}, \quad \text{for } 0 < x < 1, \quad 0 < t; \tag{9}$$

$$\text{As } t \to 0^+, \quad u \to u_0 x, \quad \text{for } 0 < x < 1; \tag{10}$$

$$\text{As } x \to 0^+, \quad u \to 0, \quad \text{for } 0 < t; \tag{11}$$

$$\text{As } x \to 1^-, \quad \frac{\partial u}{\partial x} \to 0, \quad \text{for } 0 < t. \tag{12}$$

First we seek functions that satisfy the differential equation (9), using the technique of separating the independent variables. As before we get

$$u = \exp(-h^2\alpha^2 t)[A \cos \alpha x + B \sin \alpha x] \tag{13}$$

with α, A, and B arbitrary. Condition (11) demands that

$$0 = A \exp(-h^2\alpha^2 t), \quad \text{for } 0 < t,$$

so we must take $A = 0$. We now have

$$u = B \exp(-h^2\alpha^2 t) \sin \alpha x, \tag{14}$$

which satisfies (9) and (11). From (14) it follows that

$$\frac{\partial u}{\partial x} = \alpha B \exp(-h^2\alpha^2 t) \cos \alpha x,$$

so condition (12) requires that

$$0 = \alpha B \exp(-h^2\alpha^2 t) \cos \alpha, \quad \text{for } 0 < t.$$

We must not choose $\alpha = 0$ or $B = 0$ because then (14) would yield $u = 0$, which cannot satisfy the remaining condition (10). The factor $\exp(-h^2\alpha^2 t)$ cannot vanish for any t, much less for all positive t. Thus we conclude that

$$\cos \alpha = 0. \tag{15}$$

From (15) it follows that

$$\alpha = (2k + 1)\pi/2; \quad k = 0, 1, 2, \ldots.$$

We now have the functions

$$u = B_k \exp\left[-\tfrac{1}{4}h^2(2k + 1)^2\pi^2 t\right] \sin\left[(2k + 1)\pi x/2\right]; \quad k = 0, 1, 2, \ldots,$$

each of which satisfies (9), (11), and (12). To attack the condition (10), we form the series

$$u(x, t) = \sum_{k=0}^{\infty} B_k \exp\left[-\tfrac{1}{4}h^2(2k + 1)^2\pi^2 t\right] \sin\left[(2k + 1)\pi x/2\right] \tag{16}$$

and require, because of (10), that

$$u_0 x = \sum_{k=0}^{\infty} B_k \sin\left[(2k + 1)\pi x/2\right], \quad \text{for } 0 < x < 1. \tag{17}$$

Comparison of the right member of (17) with the general Fourier sine series expansion for the interval $0 < x < c$ shows that the series in (17) is an expansion over the interval

$$0 < x < 2$$

and that its even-numbered terms are missing. That is, we seek a Fourier sine series expansion

$$f(x) \sim \sum_{n=1}^{\infty} b_n \sin \frac{n\pi x}{2}, \quad \text{for } 0 < x < 2 \tag{18}$$

where

$$f(x) = u_0 x, \quad \text{for } 0 < x < 1,$$

and $f(x)$ is so chosen for $1 < x < 2$ that in (18) the terms with even n will drop out.

Physically, it is not difficult to see that we wish to extend the slab its own width beyond $x = 1$ in some way to prevent the heat from flowing across the insulated face $x = 1$. Once that fact is realized it soon follows that we need all temperature conditions to be symmetric with respect to that insulated face $x = 1$.

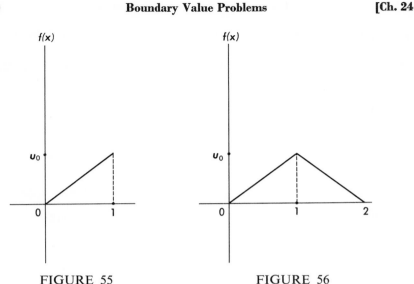

FIGURE 55   FIGURE 56

The initial temperature $f(x)$ of our original slab is shown in Figure 55. Let us prescribe $f(x)$ over $1 < x < 2$ to be the reflection through $x = 1$ of the initial temperature, so in $0 < x < 2$ the initial temperature of the extended slab is as shown in Figure 56.

The boundary value problem (9) through (12) can now be replaced by a new one with slab width 2, initial temperature as exhibited in Figure 56, and with faces $x = 0$ and $x = 2$ held at zero temperature for $t > 0$. The solution to the old problem is the same as that to the new problem except that it is to be used only for $0 < x < 1$.

An alternative procedure is to revert to equation (18) with

$$f(x) = u_0 x, \qquad \text{for } 0 < x < 1,$$
$$= u_0(2 - x), \quad \text{for } 1 < x < 2,$$

and thus to obtain b_n from which the B_k of (16) and (17) follows.

One more method deserves mention. After justification, such as in Ex. 10 below, it is permissible to obtain the B_k directly from equation (17) without open recourse to any devices such as the ones above.

The student can show in one or more of these ways that the problem (9) through (12) has for a solution

$$u(x, t) = \frac{8u_0}{\pi^2} \sum_{k=0}^{\infty} \frac{(-1)^k}{(2k + 1)^2} \exp\left[-\tfrac{1}{4}h^2(2k + 1)^2\pi^2 t\right] \sin \frac{(2k + 1)\pi x}{2}. \quad (19)$$

Exercises

1. Use the method, not the formulas, of this section to solve the problem of a slab initially at a constant temperature u_0 throughout and having its faces $x = 0$ and $x = c$ held at zero temperature for $t > 0$.

ANS. $u = \dfrac{4u_0}{\pi} \displaystyle\sum_{k=0}^{\infty} \dfrac{1}{2k+1} \exp\left[\dfrac{-h^2\pi^2(2k+1)^2 t}{c^2}\right] \sin \dfrac{(2k+1)\pi x}{c}$.

2. Obtain the average temperature across the slab of Ex. 1 for $t > 0$.

ANS. $u_m(t) = \dfrac{8u_0}{\pi^2} \displaystyle\sum_{k=0}^{\infty} \dfrac{1}{(2k+1)^2} \exp\left[-\dfrac{h^2\pi^2(2k+1)^2 t}{c^2}\right]$.

3. For the one-dimensional heat equation, (2) above, find a solution u such that u is independent of t, $u = A$ for $x = 0$, and $u = 0$ for $x = c$; A is constant.

ANS. $u = A(c - x)/c$.

4. With the aid of the result of Ex. 3, solve the problem of a slab of width c, with initial temperature zero throughout, and with faces $x = 0$ and $x = c$ held at temperatures A and zero respectively for $t > 0$.

ANS. $u = A(c - x)/c - \dfrac{2A}{\pi} \displaystyle\sum_{n=1}^{\infty} \dfrac{1}{n} \exp\left[-\left(\dfrac{hn\pi}{c}\right)^2 t\right] \sin \dfrac{n\pi x}{c}$.

5. Combine the result of Ex. 4 with the material of this section to solve the problem of the slab such that

$$\begin{aligned} \text{As } t \to 0^+, \quad & u \to f(x), \quad \text{for } 0 < x < c; \\ \text{As } x \to 0^+, \quad & u \to A, \qquad \text{for } 0 < t; \\ \text{As } x \to c^-, \quad & u \to 0, \qquad \text{for } 0 < t. \end{aligned}$$

6. For a particular concrete, the thermal diffusivity h^2 is about 0.04 (ft.^{2}/hr.), so we may reasonably choose $h^2\pi^2 = 0.4$. A slab 20 feet thick is initially at temperature 130°F and has its surfaces held at 60°F for $t > 0$. Show that the temperature in degrees Fahrenheit at the center of the slab is given by the formula

$$u = 60 + \dfrac{280}{\pi} \sum_{k=0}^{\infty} \dfrac{(-1)^k}{2k+1} \exp\left[-\dfrac{(2k+1)^2 t}{1000}\right].$$

7. Two slabs of the concrete of Ex. 6 (with $h^2\pi^2 = 0.4$ ft.^{2}/hr.), one slab 15 feet thick and the other 5 feet thick, are placed side by side. The thicker slab is initially at temperature 120°F, the thinner one at 30°F. The outside faces are to be held at 30°F for $t > 0$. Find the temperature throughout the slab for $t > 0$. Measure x from the outer face of the thicker slab.

ANS. $u = 30 + \dfrac{180}{\pi} \displaystyle\sum_{n=1}^{\infty} \dfrac{1 - \cos(3n\pi/4)}{n} \exp\left(-\dfrac{n^2 t}{1000}\right) \sin \dfrac{n\pi x}{20}$.

8. Two slabs of the same material, one 2 feet thick and the other 1 foot thick, are to be placed side by side. The thicker slab is initially at temperature A, the thinner one initially at zero. The outside faces are to be held at zero temperature for $t > 0$. Find the temperature at the center of the 2-foot slab.

ANS. $\dfrac{4A}{\pi} \displaystyle\sum_{n=1}^{\infty} \dfrac{1}{n} \sin^3 \dfrac{n\pi}{3} \exp\left[-\left(\dfrac{hn\pi}{3}\right)^2 t\right]$.

9. Knowing that the temperature function that is the answer to Ex. 8 has the value A at $t = 0$, show that

$$\sum_{k=0}^{\infty} \frac{(-1)^k(2k+1)}{(3k+1)(3k+2)} = \frac{2\pi}{9\sqrt{3}}.$$

10. By extending $f(x)$ in a proper way (see the example of this section), prove that with an $f(x)$ defined in $0 < x < c$ and satisfying the conditions of the convergence theorem stated in Section 134, the right member in the expansion

$$f(x) \sim \sum_{k=0}^{\infty} B_k \sin \frac{(2k+1)\pi x}{2c}, \text{ for } 0 < x < c,$$

in which

$$B_k = \frac{2}{c} \int_0^c f(x) \sin \frac{(2k+1)\pi x}{2c} \, dx,$$

represents the extended function in the sense of Section 134.

11. Interpret as a heat conduction problem and solve equation (2) of this section with the conditions that

$$\text{As } x \to 0^+, \quad \partial u/\partial x \to 0, \quad \text{for } 0 < t;$$
$$\text{As } x \to c^-, \quad u \to 0, \quad \text{for } 0 < t;$$
$$\text{As } t \to 0^+, \quad u \to f(x), \quad \text{for } 0 < x < c.$$

FIGURE 57

12. Two metal rods of the same material, each of length L, have their sides insulated so that heat can flow only longitudinally. One rod is at temperature A, the other at temperature zero. At time $t = 0$ the rods are placed end to end as in Figure 57. The exposed end of the first rod is then insulated; the exposed end of the second rod is thereafter held at temperature B. Determine the temperature at the juncture of the rods for $t > 0$.

141. Experimental verification of the validity of the heat equation

It is reassuring to have our mathematical formulas supported in comparison with observed phenomena and pleasant to see those same formulas being of practical* value. Both experiences are encountered in the study of the conduction of heat in concrete dams.

When concrete is poured a chemical reaction causes heat to be generated in the material. Exposure to air temperatures cools the concrete, the inner portions cooling more slowly than those near the surface. The temperature differences create stresses and cause expansions and contractions. Because of these facts it is customary when building a large dam to leave contraction joints, openings to facilitate the safe expansion and contraction of the concrete. After the concrete has lost most of its heat of setting, the dam is grouted (the contraction joints filled) and the dam is ready for use so far as the temperature problem is concerned.

The question of when the dam will be ready for grouting is a serious one for the designer. If it is known that the waiting period would be extremely long without special procedures, the concrete may be cooled as it is poured. This was done with Boulder Dam (Hoover Dam), which was designed by the United States Bureau of Reclamation. For Boulder Dam the waiting period would have been one-and-a-half centuries; it is a large dam.

The temperature problem needs extensive idealization to bring it down to the level for which decently computable solutions are known. Figure 58 shows a typical dam cross section; on it is indicated the thickness c at a random elevation. The designing engineers sometimes proceed to determine

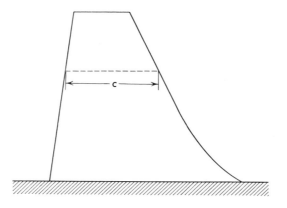

FIGURE 58

---

* There is a story, perhaps a legend, that H. J. S. Smith, a mathematician of no mean standing, once proposed the toast: "To pure mathematics, may it never be of use to anyone!" Many mathematicians regard as pure any part of mathematics that seems to us worthy of study primarily because of its inherent beauty, regardless of applicability to mundane affairs.

FIGURE 59

the temperatures to be expected at various elevations by replacing the temperature problem for Figure 58 by that for the flat slab in Figure 59. The width c may be varied to approximate the thickness at various elevations.

The designer knows what the initial temperature of the concrete will be (laboratory tests) and he knows what air temperatures to expect (United States Weather Bureau). The solution of the heat problem for Figure 59, with known initial temperature and variable surface temperatures, may be handled by superposition of solutions (see the next section), using, for instance, the successive mean monthly anticipated air temperatures. The designer can then predict concrete temperatures across the dam at various elevations and from them conclude when it would be safe to grout the dam.

Replacing Figure 59 by a wedge-shaped cross section to get closer to the appearance of Figure 58 seems to make a negligible difference in the end result, the predicted time for grouting.

During the construction of some large dams, thermocouples are installed to permit future readings of temperature at various points in the dam. Years later computations are made by the method described above and the computed temperature curves are compared to the observed ones. The results are pleasant to behold. Frequently, the observed temperature history and the predicted temperature agree within two or three degrees Fahrenheit for years at a time, through the gradual dissipation of the heat of setting and the nearly periodic fluctuations due to seasonal changes in air temperatures.

142. Surface temperature varying with time

As indicated in the preceding section, a practical problem may force us to consider variable surface temperatures. A commonly encountered example is that of a slab initially at constant temperature A_0 and with surfaces maintained thereafter at the variable air temperature $A(t)$. We are thus led to consider the simple heat equation

$$\frac{\partial u}{\partial t} = h^2 \frac{\partial^2 u}{\partial x^2}, \quad \text{for } 0 < t, \quad 0 < x < c, \tag{1}$$

with conditions

$$\text{As } t \to 0^+, \quad u \to A_0, \quad \text{for } 0 < x < c; \tag{2}$$

$$\text{As } x \to 0^+, \quad u \to A(t), \quad \text{for } 0 < t; \tag{3}$$

$$\text{As } x \to c^-, \quad u \to A(t), \quad \text{for } 0 < t. \tag{4}$$

Here $A(t)$ represents surface (air) temperature as a function of time. We are concerned only with $A(t)$ of the form exhibited in Figure 60. It may help to think of $A(t)$ as giving mean monthly predicted air temperature, A_1 over the first month

$$0 < t < t_1,$$

A_2 over the second month

$$t_1 < t < t_2,$$

etc.

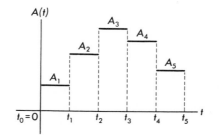

FIGURE 60

The function $A(t)$ may be expressed, using $t_0 = 0$, by

$$A(t) = A_n, \quad \text{for } t_{n-1} < t < t_n; \quad n = 1, 2, 3, \ldots. \tag{5}$$

For our purpose there is no need for the time intervals to be equal, but it is necessary that $A(t)$ be constant within each time interval. This problem is also amenable to treatment by Laplace transform methods, but will be solved by only one method in this book.

Since equation (1) is linear and homogeneous in u, any linear combination of solutions of (1) is also a solution. Since t enters (1) only in $\partial u/\partial t$, any solution remains a solution under a translation of the time origin; that is, if $u(x, t)$ satisfies equation (1), then $u(x, t - t_n)$ satisfies (1) for any constant t_n.

The fundamental solution on which we base our treatment of the problem (1) through (4) is

$$F(x, t) = 1 - \frac{4}{\pi} \sum_{k=0}^{\infty} \frac{1}{2k+1} \exp\left[-\frac{(2k+1)^2 h^2 \pi^2 t}{c^2}\right] \sin\frac{(2k+1)\pi x}{c}, \tag{6}$$

for $0 < t$, $0 < x < c$. Directly, or by comparison with Ex. 1, page 398, the function $F(x, t)$ of (6) can be seen to be a solution of the heat equation (1) and to have the properties:

$$\text{As } t \to 0^+, \quad F(x, t) \to 0, \quad \text{for } 0 < x < c; \tag{7}$$

$$\text{As } x \to 0^+, \quad F(x, t) \to 1, \quad \text{for } 0 < t; \tag{8}$$

$$\text{As } x \to c^-, \quad F(x, t) \to 1, \quad \text{for } 0 < t. \tag{9}$$

Since $F(x, t)$ in (6) was undefined for $t \leq 0$, let us take the liberty of defining it as identically zero whenever its second argument t is nonpositive.

$$F(x, t) \equiv 0, \quad \text{for } t \leq 0. \tag{10}$$

Then the desired solution of the problem (1) through (4) can be written at once as

$$u(x, t) = A_0 + \sum_{n=1}^{\infty} (A_n - A_{n-1})F(x, t - t_{n-1}), \quad \text{for } 0 < t, \quad 0 < x < c. \tag{11}$$

Note that the series on the right in (11) terminates for any specific t, since sooner or later (as n increases) the argument $(t - t_{n-1})$ becomes and remains negative.

The u of (11) is a linear combination of solutions of (1); it satisfies (2) because of (7). As $x \to 0^+$ or $x \to c^-$, in any range $t_{k-1} < t \leq t_k$,

$$u \to A_0 + \sum_{n=1}^{k} (A_n - A_{n-1}) = A_k,$$

because of (8) and (9) and the fact that $F(x, t - t_{n-1}) \equiv 0$ for $t \leq t_{n-1}$.

In actual practice, computations with the solution (11) are greatly simplified because the $F(x, t)$ of (6) is essentially the same for all diffusivities and all slab widths. In equation (6), put $h^2\pi^2 t/c^2 = \tau$ and $\pi x/c = \zeta$. The manner in which the new arguments τ and ζ are chosen will be discussed in Section 153.

We may now write

$$F(x, t) = 1 - \frac{4}{\pi} \sum_{k=0}^{\infty} \frac{\exp\left[-(2k+1)^2\tau\right] \sin(2k+1)\zeta}{2k+1} = \phi(\zeta, \tau),$$

for $0 < \tau, 0 < \zeta < \pi$. The function ϕ can be tabulated at intervals of ζ and τ. For a particular slab problem, values of h^2, c, t, and x are used to compute the pertinent ζ and τ and the values of ϕ are read from the table.

143. Heat conduction in a sphere

Consider a solid sphere initially at a known temperature that depends only upon distance from the center of the sphere. Let the surface of the sphere be held at zero temperature for $t > 0$. We shall determine the temperature in the sphere for positive t under the assumption that the heat equation

$$\frac{\partial u}{\partial t} = h^2 \left(\frac{\partial^2 u}{\partial x^2} + \frac{\partial^2 u}{\partial y^2} + \frac{\partial^2 u}{\partial z^2} \right) \tag{1}$$

is valid.

Since the object under study is a sphere, we choose the origin at the center of the sphere and introduce spherical coordinates, related to x, y, z, by

$$x = \rho \sin \theta \cos \phi, \quad y = \rho \sin \theta \sin \phi, \quad z = \rho \cos \theta.$$

Then the heat equation (1) becomes

$$\frac{\partial u}{\partial t} = h^2 \left(\frac{\partial^2 u}{\partial \rho^2} + \frac{2}{\rho} \frac{\partial u}{\partial \rho} + \frac{1}{\rho^2} \frac{\partial^2 u}{\partial \theta^2} + \frac{\cot \theta}{\rho^2} \frac{\partial u}{\partial \theta} + \frac{\csc^2 \theta}{\rho^2} \frac{\partial^2 u}{\partial \phi^2} \right). \tag{2}$$

For the problem we wish to solve, the temperature is independent of the coordinates θ and ϕ, so equation (2) reduces to

$$\frac{\partial u}{\partial t} = h^2 \left(\frac{\partial^2 u}{\partial \rho^2} + \frac{2}{\rho} \frac{\partial u}{\partial \rho} \right). \tag{3}$$

Let R be the radius of the sphere and $f(\rho)$ be the initial temperature. Then the problem confronting us is

$$\frac{\partial u}{\partial t} = h^2 \left(\frac{\partial^2 u}{\partial \rho^2} + \frac{2}{\rho} \frac{\partial u}{\partial \rho} \right), \quad \text{for } 0 < t, \quad 0 < \rho < R; \tag{4}$$

$$\text{As } \rho \to R^-, \quad u \to 0, \quad \text{for } 0 < t; \tag{5}$$

$$\text{As } t \to 0^+, \quad u \to f(\rho), \quad \text{for } 0 \leq \rho < R. \tag{6}$$

The student can easily show that the change of dependent variable,

$$u = \frac{v}{\rho},\tag{7}$$

transforms the problem (4) through (6) into the problem

$$\frac{\partial v}{\partial t} = h^2 \frac{\partial^2 v}{\partial \rho^2}, \quad \text{for } 0 < t, \quad 0 < \rho < R;\tag{8}$$

$$\text{As } \rho \to R^-, \quad v \to 0, \qquad \text{for } 0 < t;\tag{9}$$

$$\text{As } \rho \to 0^+, \quad \frac{v}{\rho} \to \text{a limit}, \quad \text{for } 0 < t;\tag{10}$$

$$\text{As } t \to 0^+, \quad v \to \rho f(\rho), \quad \text{for } 0 < \rho < R.\tag{11}$$

The added condition (10) is a reflection of the fact that the temperature u is to exist at $\rho = 0$ in spite of relation (7). The new problem (8) through (11) is much like those treated at the beginning of this chapter. Its solution is left as an exercise.

The corresponding problem of finding the temperatures in a solid cylinder is less elementary and involves series of Bessel functions. It may be found worked out in many books.*

Exercises

1. Solve the problem (4) through (6) by the method outlined above.

ANS. $u = \dfrac{1}{\rho} \displaystyle\sum_{n=1}^{\infty} b_n \exp\left[-\left(\dfrac{hn\pi}{R}\right)^2 t\right] \sin\dfrac{n\pi\rho}{R}$, in which

$$b_n = \frac{2}{R} \int_0^R \rho f(\rho) \sin\frac{n\pi\rho}{R}\, d\rho.$$

2. A sphere of radius R is initially at a constant temperature u_0 throughout, then has its surface held at temperature u_1 for $t > 0$. Find the temperature throughout the sphere for $t > 0$ and in particular the temperature u_c at the center of the sphere.

ANS. $u = u_1 + \dfrac{2R(u_0 - u_1)}{\rho\pi} \displaystyle\sum_{n=1}^{\infty} \dfrac{(-1)^{n+1}}{n} \exp\left[-\left(\dfrac{hn\pi}{R}\right)^2 t\right] \sin\dfrac{n\pi\rho}{R};$

$u_c = u_1 + 2(u_0 - u_1) \displaystyle\sum_{n=1}^{\infty} (-1)^{n+1} \exp\left[-\left(\dfrac{hn\pi}{R}\right)^2 t\right],$ for $t > 0.$

---

* See, for example, E. D. Rainville, *Intermediate Differential Equations*, 2nd ed. (New York: The Macmillan Co., 1964), p. 279; or R. V. Churchill, *Fourier Series and Boundary Value Problems*, 2nd ed. (New York: McGraw-Hill Book Co., 1963).

144. The simple wave equation

If an elastic string held fixed at two points is taut, and then is displaced from its equilibrium position and released, the subsequent displacements from the position of equilibrium may be determined by solving a boundary value problem. Figure 61 shows a representative displacement of the string, which is to be held fixed at $x = 0$ and $x = c$. The displacement y for $0 < x < c$

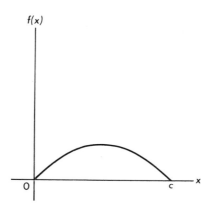

FIGURE 61

and $0 < t$ is to be found from the known initial displacement $f(x)$, the initial velocity $\phi(x)$, and the fact that y must satisfy the one-dimensional wave equation

$$\frac{\partial^2 y}{\partial t^2} = a^2 \frac{\partial^2 y}{\partial x^2}, \tag{1}$$

in which the parameter a is a constant which depends upon the physical properties of the string.

The boundary value problem to be solved is

$$\frac{\partial^2 y}{\partial t^2} = a^2 \frac{\partial^2 y}{\partial x^2}, \quad \text{for } 0 < x < c, \quad 0 < t; \tag{2}$$

$$\text{As } x \to 0^+, \quad y \to 0, \quad \text{for } 0 < t; \tag{3}$$

$$\text{As } x \to c^-, \quad y \to 0, \quad \text{for } 0 < t; \tag{4}$$

$$\text{As } t \to 0^+, \quad y \to f(x), \quad \text{for } 0 < x < c; \tag{5}$$

$$\text{As } t \to 0^+, \quad \frac{\partial y}{\partial t} \to \phi(x), \quad \text{for } 0 < x < c. \tag{6}$$

It is inherent in the string problem that $f(x)$ be continuous and that $f(0) = f(c) = 0$. Either $f(x)$ or $\phi(x)$ may be zero throughout the interval. Indeed, the boundary value problem (2) through (6) can always be replaced by two problems, one with $f(x)$ replaced by zero, the other with $\phi(x)$ replaced by zero. The sum of the solutions of those two problems is the solution of the problem with both an initial velocity and an initial displacement.

The solution of problems such as (2) through (6) with various $f(x)$ and $\phi(x)$ can be accomplished by the method of separation of variables and use of Fourier series as was done with the heat conduction problems earlier. That work is left for exercises for the student, since it involves no new technique. Note the usefulness of the solutions determined in Ex. 1, page 364.

Exercises

In Exs. 1–5, find the displacement for $t > 0$ of the vibrating string problem of this section under the condition that the initial velocity is to be zero and that the initial displacement is given by the $f(x)$ described.

1. $f(x) = x$, for $0 \leq x \leq c/2$,
  $= c - x$, for $c/2 \leq x \leq c$.

  ANS. $y = \dfrac{4c}{\pi^2} \displaystyle\sum_{k=0}^{\infty} \dfrac{(-1)^k \cos [(2k+1)a\pi t/c] \sin [(2k+1)\pi x/c]}{(2k+1)^2}.$

2. $f(x) = x(c-x)/c.$ ANS. $y = \dfrac{8c}{\pi^3} \displaystyle\sum_{k=0}^{\infty} \dfrac{\cos [(2k+1)a\pi t/c] \sin [(2k+1)\pi x/c]}{(2k+1)^3}.$

3. $f(x) = x$, for $0 \leq x \leq c/4$,
  $= c/4$, for $c/4 \leq x \leq 3c/4$,
  $= c - x$, for $3c/4 \leq x \leq c$.   See Figure 62.

  ANS. $y = \dfrac{2c}{\pi^2} \displaystyle\sum_{n=1}^{\infty} \dfrac{1}{n^2} \left(\sin \dfrac{n\pi}{4} + \sin \dfrac{3n\pi}{4} \right) \cos \dfrac{na\pi t}{c} \sin \dfrac{n\pi x}{c}.$

4. $f(x) = x$, for $0 \leq x \leq \frac{1}{4}c$,
  $= \frac{1}{4}c - x$, for $\frac{1}{4}c \leq x \leq 3c/4$,
  $= x - c$, for $3c/4 \leq x \leq c$. See Figure 63.

  ANS. $y = \dfrac{2c}{\pi^2} \displaystyle\sum_{k=0}^{\infty} \dfrac{(-1)^k \cos [(4k+2)\pi a t/c] \sin [(4k+2)\pi x/c]}{(2k+1)^2}.$

5. $f(x) = x$, for $0 \leq x \leq \frac{1}{4}c$,
  $= \frac{1}{4}c - x$, for $\frac{1}{4}c \leq x \leq \frac{1}{2}c$,
  $= 0$, for $\frac{1}{2}c \leq x \leq c$.

  ANS. $y = \dfrac{2c}{\pi^2} \displaystyle\sum_{n=1}^{\infty} \dfrac{1}{n^2} (2 \sin \tfrac{1}{4}n\pi - \sin \tfrac{1}{2}n\pi) \cos \dfrac{n\pi a t}{c} \sin \dfrac{n\pi x}{c}.$

6. Find the displacement of the string of this section if the initial displacement is zero and the initial velocity is given by $\phi(x) = ax(c - x)/(4c^2)$.

  ANS. $y = \dfrac{2c}{\pi^4} \displaystyle\sum_{k=0}^{\infty} \dfrac{\sin [(2k+1)a\pi t/c] \sin [(2k+1)\pi x/c]}{(2k+1)^4}.$

FIGURE 62

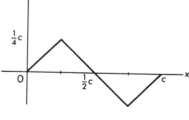

FIGURE 63

7. Find the displacement of the string of this section if the initial displacement is zero and the initial velocity is given by

$$\phi(x) = 0, \text{ for } 0 \leq x \leq c/3,$$
$$= v_0, \text{ for } c/3 \leq x \leq 2c/3,$$
$$= 0, \text{ for } 2c/3 \leq x \leq c.$$

ANS. $y = \dfrac{2v_0 c}{\pi^2 a} \displaystyle\sum_{n=1}^{\infty} \dfrac{[\cos{(n\pi/3)} - \cos{(2n\pi/3)}] \sin{(n\pi a t/c)} \sin{(n\pi x/c)}}{n^2}.$

8. Solve the problem (2) through (6) of this section with $\phi(x) = 0$.

9. Solve the problem (2) through (6) of this section with $f(x) = 0$.

ANS. $y = \displaystyle\sum_{n=1}^{\infty} B_n \sin{\dfrac{n\pi a t}{c}} \sin{\dfrac{n\pi x}{c}}$, in which $B_n = \dfrac{2}{n\pi a} \displaystyle\int_0^c \phi(x) \sin{\dfrac{n\pi x}{c}} \, dx$.

145. Laplace's equation in two dimensions

We conclude this chapter with a discussion of Laplace's equation, in particular of the two-dimensional case

$$\frac{\partial^2 u}{\partial x^2} + \frac{\partial^2 u}{\partial y^2} = 0. \tag{1}$$

The dependent variable u may represent any one of various quantities, steady-state temperature, electrostatic potential, etc., although in this section we shall use the language of steady-state temperature problems for simplicity in working and visualization.

The Fourier series method as it is being utilized in this chapter is particularly well adapted to solving steady-state temperature problems for a flat rectangular plate. Let the two faces of the plate be insulated; let no heat flow in the direction normal to them. Then the problem is two-dimensional. Each edge of the plate may be either insulated or held at a known temperature.

Consider a flat rectangular plate with edges of length a and b. Let three edges be kept at zero temperature and the remaining one, one of those of length a, be kept at a specified temperature, a function of distance along that edge. Let us choose a coordinate system and accompanying notation as shown in Figure 64.

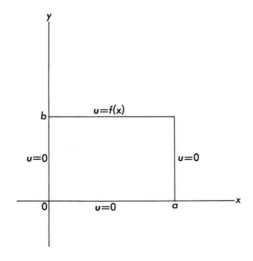

FIGURE 64

The steady-state temperature problem associated with Figure 64 may be written

$$\frac{\partial^2 u}{\partial x^2} + \frac{\partial^2 u}{\partial y^2} = 0, \quad \text{for} \quad 0 < x < a, \quad 0 < y < b; \tag{2}$$

$$\text{As } x \to 0^+, \quad u \to 0, \qquad \text{for } 0 < y < b; \tag{3}$$

$$\text{As } x \to a^-, \quad u \to 0, \qquad \text{for } 0 < y < b; \tag{4}$$

$$\text{As } y \to 0^+, \quad u \to 0, \qquad \text{for } 0 < x < a; \tag{5}$$

$$\text{As } y \to b^-, \quad u \to f(x), \quad \text{for } 0 < x < a. \tag{6}$$

The solution of the problem (2) through (6) is found by the same method as was used on boundary value problems for the one-dimensional heat equation. Results appear in the exercises below.

When a rectangular plate has nonzero temperatures at more than one edge, the problem can be separated into two or more problems of the type of (2) through (6). Insulation of an edge can be treated by doubling the size of the plate with the insulated edge becoming the new center line and then creating temperature conditions symmetric about that center line so no heat can flow across it. See the methods used in Section 140 at the start of this chapter.

Next let us consider a flat circular plate of radius R subjected to assigned fixed temperatures at its edge and left until it reaches the steady-state condition. Using cylindrical coordinates r, θ, z and conditions that permit no heat flow normal to the faces of the plate, we arrive at a two-dimensional problem,

$$\frac{\partial^2 u}{\partial r^2} + \frac{1}{r}\frac{\partial u}{\partial r} + \frac{1}{r^2}\frac{\partial^2 u}{\partial \theta^2} = 0, \quad \text{for } 0 < r < R, \quad 0 < \theta < 2\pi; \tag{7}$$

$$\text{As } r \to R^-, \quad u \to f(\theta), \quad \text{for } 0 \leq \theta < 2\pi; \tag{8}$$

$$\underset{r \to 0^+}{\text{Lim}} u \text{ exists}, \quad \text{for } 0 \leq \theta < 2\pi; \tag{9}$$

$$\underset{\theta \to 0^+}{\text{Lim}} u = \underset{\theta \to 2\pi^-}{\text{Lim}} u, \quad \text{for } 0 \leq r < R. \tag{10}$$

If we are willing to define the edge temperature $f(\theta)$ for all θ and make it have the period 2π, then the condition (10) can be replaced by the requirement that u be a periodic function of θ with period 2π.

The corresponding problems of a wedge, or of a portion of a wedge with concentric circular edges, do not involve any requirement of periodicity in their physical nature.

Separation of variables in equation (7) leads to a need for solving an ordinary equation of Euler-Cauchy type,

$$r^2\psi''(r) + r\psi'(r) - \alpha^2\psi(r) = 0, \tag{11}$$

where α is constant. See Exs. 19–34, page 302.

Exercises

Each of Exs. 1–7 below refers to the steady-state temperature problem for the rectangular plate of Figure 64, but with edge conditions as described in the individual exercise.

1. Edges $x = 0$, $x = a$, $y = 0$ held at zero temperature; the edge $y = b$ held at temperature $f(x)$.

ANS. $u = \sum\limits_{n=1}^{\infty} c_n \sinh \dfrac{n\pi y}{a} \sin \dfrac{n\pi x}{a}$, in which $c_n \sinh \dfrac{n\pi b}{a} = \dfrac{2}{a} \int_0^a f(x) \sin \dfrac{n\pi x}{a}\, dx$.

2. Edges $x = 0$, $x = a$, $y = 0$ held at zero; the edge $y = b$ held at temperature unity. Solve the problem directly or by using the result of Ex. 1.

ANS. $u = \dfrac{4}{\pi} \sum\limits_{k=0}^{\infty} \dfrac{\sinh\,[(2k+1)\pi y/a] \sin\,[(2k+1)\pi x/a]}{(2k+1)\sinh\,[(2k+1)\pi b/a]}$.

3. Ex. 2 with the change that the edge $y = b$ is to be held at unity for $0 < x < a/2$ and at zero for $a/2 < x < a$.

ANS. $u = \dfrac{2}{\pi} \sum\limits_{n=1}^{\infty} \dfrac{[1 - \cos\,(n\pi/2)]\sinh\,(n\pi y/a) \sin\,(n\pi x/a)}{n \sinh\,(n\pi b/a)}$.

4. Edges $x = 0$ and $x = a$ held at zero; edge $y = 0$ insulated; edge $y = b$ held at temperature $f(x)$.

5. Edge $x = 0$ insulated; edges $x = a$ and $y = 0$ held at zero; edge $y = b$ held at temperature unity.

ANS. $u = \dfrac{4}{\pi} \sum\limits_{k=0}^{\infty} \dfrac{(-1)^k \sinh\,[(2k+1)\pi y/(2a)] \cos\,[(2k+1)\pi x/(2a)]}{(2k+1)\sinh\,[(2k+1)\pi b/(2a)]}$.

6. Edges $x = 0$ and $y = 0$ held at zero; edge $x = a$ insulated; edge $y = b$ held at temperature unity.

ANS. $u = \dfrac{4}{\pi} \sum\limits_{k=0}^{\infty} \dfrac{\sinh\,[(2k+1)\pi y/(2a)] \sin\,[(2k+1)\pi x/(2a)]}{(2k+1)\sinh\,[(2k+1)\pi b/(2a)]}$.

7. Edges $x = 0$ and $y = 0$ insulated; edge $x = a$ held at zero; edge $y = b$ held at temperature unity.

ANS. $u = \dfrac{4}{\pi} \sum\limits_{k=0}^{\infty} \dfrac{(-1)^k \cosh\,[(2k+1)\pi y/(2a)] \cos\,[(2k+1)\pi x/(2a)]}{(2k+1)\cosh\,[(2k+1)\pi b/(2a)]}$.

8. Show that the temperature at the center of the plate of Ex. 2 above is

$$\frac{2}{\pi} \sum_{k=0}^{\infty} \frac{(-1)^k \operatorname{sech}\,[(2k+1)\pi b/(2a)]}{2k+1}.$$

9. For a square plate, show by superposition of solutions, without obtaining any solution explicitly, that when one face is held at temperature unity and the others are held at zero, then the temperature at the center is $\tfrac{1}{4}$. Then, by comparing your result with Ex. 8, using $b = a$, conclude that

$$\sum_{k=0}^{\infty} \frac{(-1)^k \operatorname{sech} [(2k+1)\pi/2]}{2k+1} = \frac{\pi}{8}.$$

10. A circular plate has radius R. The edge $r = R$ of the plate is held at temperature unity for $0 < \theta < \pi$, at zero temperature for $\pi < \theta < 2\pi$. Find the temperature throughout the plate.

ANS. $u = \tfrac{1}{2} + \dfrac{2}{\pi} \displaystyle\sum_{k=0}^{\infty} \left(\dfrac{r}{R}\right)^{2k+1} \dfrac{\sin (2k+1)\theta}{2k+1}.$

11. A plate with concentric circular boundaries $r = a$ and $r = b$, $0 < a < b$, has its inner boundary held at temperature A, its outer one at temperature B. Find the temperature throughout.

ANS. $u = \dfrac{B \ln (r/a) - A \ln (r/b)}{\ln (b/a)}.$

12. The plate of Ex. 11 has its inner edge $r = a$ insulated, its outer edge held at temperature unity for $0 < \theta < \pi$ and held at temperature zero for $\pi < \theta < 2\pi$. Find the temperature throughout.

ANS. $u = \tfrac{1}{2} + \dfrac{2}{\pi} \displaystyle\sum_{k=0}^{\infty} \dfrac{(r/b)^{2k+1} + (a/r)^{2k+1}(a/b)^{2k+1}}{1 + (a/b)^{4k+2}} \cdot \dfrac{\sin (2k+1)\theta}{2k+1}.$

13. A flat wedge is defined in polar coordinates by the region $0 < r < R$, $0 < \theta < \beta$. Find the temperature throughout if the edges $\theta = 0$ and $\theta = \beta$ are held at temperature zero and the curved edge $r = R$ is held at temperature unity.

ANS. $u = \dfrac{4}{\pi} \displaystyle\sum_{k=0}^{\infty} \left(\dfrac{r}{R}\right)^{(2k+1)\pi/\beta} \dfrac{\sin[(2k+1)\pi\theta/\beta]}{2k+1}.$

14. For the flat wedges of Ex. 13, find the temperature if the edge $\theta = 0$ is held at zero, the edge $\theta = \beta$ is held at temperature unity, and the curved edge $r = R$ is held at temperature $f(\theta)$ for $0 < \theta < \beta$.

ANS. $u = \theta/\beta + \displaystyle\sum_{n=1}^{\infty} A_n \left(\dfrac{r}{R}\right)^{n\pi/\beta} \sin \dfrac{n\pi\theta}{\beta}$, in which

$$A_n = \frac{2}{\beta} \int_0^{\beta} [f(\theta) - \theta/\beta] \sin \frac{n\pi\theta}{\beta} \, d\theta.$$

CHAPTER 25

Additional Properties of the
Laplace Transform

146. Power series and inverse transforms

To use the Laplace transform on boundary value problems involving partial differential equations, we need certain transforms and inverse transforms that we did not obtain in Chapters 10 and 11.

Before proceeding to illustrative examples, we list certain elementary power series expansions for easy reference.

$$\frac{1}{1-x} = \sum_{n=0}^{\infty} x^n, \qquad |x| < 1; \qquad (1)$$

$$e^x = \sum_{n=0}^{\infty} \frac{x^n}{n!}, \qquad \text{all } x; \qquad (2)$$

$$\cos x = \sum_{n=0}^{\infty} \frac{(-1)^n x^{2n}}{(2n)!}, \qquad \text{all } x; \qquad (3)$$

$$\sin x = \sum_{n=0}^{\infty} \frac{(-1)^n x^{2n+1}}{(2n+1)!}, \qquad \text{all } x; \qquad (4)$$

$$\cosh x = \sum_{n=0}^{\infty} \frac{x^{2n}}{(2n)!}, \qquad \text{all } x; \tag{5}$$

$$\sinh x = \sum_{n=0}^{\infty} \frac{x^{2n+1}}{(2n+1)!}, \qquad \text{all } x; \tag{6}$$

$$\text{Arctan } x = \sum_{n=0}^{\infty} \frac{(-1)^n x^{2n+1}}{2n+1}, \qquad |x| < 1; \tag{7}$$

$$\frac{1}{(1-x)^m} = 1 + \sum_{n=1}^{\infty} \frac{m(m+1)\cdots(m+n-1)x^n}{n!}, \qquad |x| < 1; \tag{8}$$

$$\ln(1+x) = \sum_{n=0}^{\infty} \frac{(-1)^n x^{n+1}}{n+1} \qquad |x| < 1; \tag{9}$$

$$\ln\frac{1+x}{1-x} = 2\sum_{n=0}^{\infty} \frac{x^{2n+1}}{2n+1}, \qquad |x| < 1. \tag{10}$$

In seeking the Laplace transform, or the inverse transform, of a given function, we may find it inconvenient, difficult, or even beyond us to obtain the desired result by direct use of the theorems of Chapters 10 and 11 in a finite number of steps. Then we frequently turn to infinite series. If we can expand our function into a series such that we know how to obtain the desired transform or inverse transform of each term, we can thus solve our original problem.

EXAMPLE (a):   Given that $L^{-1}\{f(s)\} = F(t)$, evaluate

$$L^{-1}\left\{\frac{f(s)}{\sinh(cs)}\right\}.$$

We know that $\sinh z = \frac{1}{2}(e^z - e^{-z})$. Then

$$\frac{f(s)}{\sinh(cs)} = \frac{2f(s)}{e^{cs} - e^{-cs}}. \tag{11}$$

For $h > 0$, $s > 0$, we know how to evaluate $L^{-1}\{e^{-hs}f(s)\}$ by Theorem 19, page 180. Indeed,

$$L^{-1}\{e^{-hs}f(s)\} = F(t-h)\alpha(t-h), \qquad h > 0, \quad s > 0. \tag{12}$$

We therefore rewrite (11) as

$$\frac{f(s)}{\sinh(cs)} = \frac{2f(s)e^{-cs}}{1 - e^{-2cs}} \tag{13}$$

because we can use the power series (1) to expand $(1 - e^{-2cs})^{-1}$ in a series of exponentials with negative arguments. From (1) we get

$$\frac{1}{1 - e^{-2cs}} = \sum_{n=0}^{\infty} \exp\left(-2ncs\right),$$

so, by (13),

$$\frac{f(s)}{\sinh(cs)} = 2 \sum_{n=0}^{\infty} f(s) \exp\left(-2ncs - cs\right). \tag{14}$$

We now use (12) to obtain, for $c > 0$, $s > 0$,

$$L^{-1} \frac{f(s)}{\sinh(cs)} = 2 \sum_{n=0}^{\infty} F(t - 2nc - c)\alpha(t - 2nc - c). \tag{15}$$

It is important to realize that the series on the right in (15) is a finite series. No matter how large the value of t nor how small the (positive) c, the argument of the α function will become negative for sufficiently large n and for all succeeding n-values. Thus each term of the series will be zero for all n such that $(2n + 1)c > t$.

The procedure used in this example is of value to us in applications involving boundary value problems in partial differential equations, to be discussed in Chapter 26.

EXAMPLE (b):   Evaluate $L\left\{\dfrac{1 - e^{-t}}{t}\right\}$.

By (2) we obtain

$$e^{-t} = \sum_{n=0}^{\infty} \frac{(-1)^n t^n}{n!} = 1 + \sum_{n=1}^{\infty} \frac{(-1)^n t^n}{n!}.$$

Therefore we may write

$$\frac{1 - e^{-t}}{t} = \sum_{n=1}^{\infty} \frac{(-1)^{n+1} t^{n-1}}{n!}.$$

A shift in index from n to $(n + 1)$ yields

$$\frac{1 - e^{-t}}{t} = \sum_{n=0}^{\infty} \frac{(-1)^n t^n}{(n + 1)!}.$$

We know that $L\left\{\dfrac{t^n}{n!}\right\} = \dfrac{1}{s^{n+1}}$. Hence

$$L\left\{\frac{1 - e^{-t}}{t}\right\} = \sum_{n=0}^{\infty} \frac{(-1)^n}{(n + 1)s^{n+1}},$$

so comparison with (9) above yields

$$L\left\{\frac{1-e^{-t}}{t}\right\} = \ln\left(1 + \frac{1}{s}\right), \qquad s > 0. \tag{16}$$

The restriction $s > 0$ may be obtained by examining the integral definition of the left member of (16). Note also the connection with Ex. 19, page 173.

EXAMPLE (c):   Evaluate $L^{-1}\left\{\ln\frac{s+1}{s-1}\right\}$.

From (10) we have

$$\ln\frac{s+1}{s-1} = \ln\frac{1 + \frac{1}{s}}{1 - \frac{1}{s}} = 2\sum_{n=0}^{\infty}\frac{1}{(2n+1)s^{2n+1}}.$$

Now $L^{-1}\left\{\frac{1}{s^{2n+1}}\right\} = \frac{t^{2n}}{(2n)!}$. Hence

$$L^{-1}\left\{\ln\frac{s+1}{s-1}\right\} = 2\sum_{n=0}^{\infty}\frac{t^{2n}}{(2n+1)!},$$

which, with the aid of (6), yields

$$L^{-1}\left\{\ln\frac{s+1}{s-1}\right\} = \frac{2}{t}\sinh t. \tag{17}$$

Exercises

1. Evaluate $L\left\{\frac{\sin kt}{t}\right\}$.   ANS. $\text{Arctan}\frac{k}{s}, s > 0.$

2. Evaluate $L\left\{\frac{1 - \cos kt}{t}\right\}$.   ANS. $\frac{1}{2}\ln\left(1 + \frac{k^2}{s^2}\right), \quad s > k > 0.$

3. Evaluate $L\left\{\frac{\sinh(kt)}{t}\right\}$.   ANS. $\frac{1}{2}\ln\frac{s+k}{s-k}, \quad s > k > 0.$

4. Evaluate $L\left\{\frac{1 - \cosh(kt)}{t}\right\}$.   ANS. $\frac{1}{2}\ln\left(1 - \frac{k^2}{s^2}\right), \quad s > k > 0.$

5. Evaluate $F(t) = L^{-1}\left\{\frac{1}{s^3(1 - e^{-2s})}\right\}$ and compute $F(5)$.

ANS. $F(t) = \frac{1}{2}\sum_{n=0}^{\infty}(t - 2n)^2\alpha(t - 2n); F(5) = 17.5.$

6. Evaluate $F(t) = L^{-1}\left\{\frac{1}{s^3\cosh(2s)}\right\}$ and compute $F(12)$.

ANS. $F(t) = \sum_{n=0}^{\infty}(-1)^n(t - 4n - 2)^2\alpha(t - 4n - 2); F(12) = 68.$

7. Let $\phi(t) = L^{-1}\left\{\dfrac{3}{s^4 \sinh (3s)}\right\}$. Compute $\phi(10)$.   ANS.   344.

8. Let $c > 0$, $s > 0$, and let $L^{-1}\{f(s)\} = F(t)$. Prove that

$$L^{-1}\left\{\frac{f(s)}{\cosh (cs)}\right\} = 2 \sum_{n=0}^{\infty} (-1)^n F(t - 2nc - c)\alpha(t - 2nc - c).$$

9. Let $c > 0$, $s > 0$, and let $L^{-1}\{f(s)\} = F(t)$. Prove that

$$L^{-1}\{f(s) \tanh (cs)\} = F(t) + 2 \sum_{n=1}^{\infty} (-1)^n F(t - 2nc)\alpha(t - 2nc).$$

10. Let $0 < x < 1$, where x does not depend on s.
Find the inverse transform $y(x, t)$ of

$$\frac{4e^{xs}}{s^3(e^s + e^{-s})}$$

and then compute $y(\tfrac{1}{2}, 5)$, assuming continuity of y.   ANS. $y(\tfrac{1}{2}, 5) = 28.5$.

11. In Ex. 4, page 238, replace the alternating current element $E \sin \omega t$ by $EQ(t, c)$ in which Q is the square-wave function of Figure 17, page 171.

ANS. $I(t) = \dfrac{E}{R} \exp\left(-\dfrac{t}{RC}\right) + \dfrac{2E}{R} \sum_{n=1}^{\infty} (-1)^n \exp\left(-\dfrac{t - nc}{RC}\right)\alpha(t - nc).$

12. In Ex. 4, page 238, replace $E \sin \omega t$ by $EF(t)$ in which $F(t)$ is the halfwave rectification of $\sin \omega t$ as described in Ex. 17, page 173.
ANS. $I(t) =$

$$\frac{E}{\omega C Z^2} \sum_{n=0}^{\infty} \left[(-1)^n(\cos \omega t + \omega RC \sin \omega t) - \exp\left(-\frac{\omega t - n\pi}{\omega RC}\right)\right]\alpha\left(t - \frac{n\pi}{\omega}\right).$$

147. The error function

The error function, abbreviated "erf," which was mentioned briefly in Section 23, page 79, is defined by

$$\text{erf } x = \frac{2}{\sqrt{\pi}} \int_0^x \exp (-\beta^2) \, d\beta. \tag{1}$$

This function arises in many ways. It is sometimes studied in elementary courses. We also encounter erf x in evaluating inverse transforms of certain simple functions of s.

We know that $L^{-1}\{s^{-1/2}\} = (\pi t)^{-1/2}$ and therefore that

$$L^{-1}\left\{\frac{1}{\sqrt{s + 1}}\right\} = \frac{e^{-t}}{\sqrt{\pi t}}.$$

Then the convolution theorem yields

$$L^{-1}\left\{\frac{1}{s\sqrt{s + 1}}\right\} = \int_0^t 1 \cdot \frac{e^{-\beta}}{\sqrt{\pi\beta}} \, d\beta. \tag{2}$$

On the right in (2) put $\sqrt{\beta} = \gamma$. Then $\beta^{-1/2} d\beta = 2d\gamma$ and we obtain

$$L^{-1}\left\{\frac{1}{s\sqrt{s+1}}\right\} = \frac{2}{\sqrt{\pi}} \int_0^{\sqrt{t}} \exp\left(-\gamma^2\right) d\gamma.$$

That is,

$$L^{-1}\left\{\frac{1}{s\sqrt{s+1}}\right\} = \operatorname{erf}\left(\sqrt{t}\right). \tag{3}$$

A few basic properties of erf x are useful in our work and will now be obtained. Directly from the definition (1) it follows that the derivative of erf x is given by

$$\frac{d}{dx} \operatorname{erf} x = \frac{2}{\sqrt{\pi}} \exp\left(-x^2\right). \tag{4}$$

From (1) and the power series for $\exp\left(-\beta^2\right)$ we get

$$\operatorname{erf} x = \frac{2}{\sqrt{\pi}} \sum_{n=0}^{\infty} \frac{(-1)^n x^{2n+1}}{(2n+1)n!}. \tag{5}$$

In elementary calculus we found that

$$\int_0^{\infty} \exp\left(-\beta^2\right) d\beta = \frac{\sqrt{\pi}}{2}. \tag{6}$$

From (6) we get

$$\operatorname*{Lim}_{x \to \infty} \operatorname{erf} x = 1. \tag{7}$$

The values of erf x are easily computed for small x from (5) above and for larger x from the asymptotic expansion*

$$\operatorname{erf} x \sim 1 - \frac{\exp\left(-x^2\right)}{\sqrt{\pi}} \sum_{n=0}^{\infty} \frac{(-1)^n [1 \cdot 3 \cdot 5 \cdots (2n-1)]}{2^n x^{2n+1}}. \tag{8}$$

It is convenient in our work to use what is called the complementary error function, denoted by erfc x and defined by

$$\operatorname{erfc} x = 1 - \operatorname{erf} x, \tag{9}$$

which means also that

$$\operatorname{erfc} x = \frac{2}{\sqrt{\pi}} \int_x^{\infty} \exp\left(-\beta^2\right) d\beta. \tag{10}$$

---

* See, for example, E. D. Rainville, *Special Functions* (New York: The Macmillan Co., 1960), pp. 36–38. The function erf x is tabulated under the name "The Probability Integral," in B. O. Peirce and R. M. Foster, *A Short Table of Integrals*, 4th ed. (New York: Ginn and Co., 1956), pp. 128–132.

The properties of erf x are readily converted to properties of erfc x. It is important that for any fixed m,

$$\lim_{x \to \infty} x^m \operatorname{erfc} x = 0, \tag{11}$$

which the student can demonstrate by considering the indeterminate form

$$\frac{\operatorname{erfc} x}{x^{-m}}$$

and using the derivative of erfc x as obtained from (4) above. See the exercises at the end of this section for other properties of erf x and erfc x.

A transform which is important in certain applications (Sections 152–155) is

$$L\left\{\operatorname{erfc}\left(\frac{k}{\sqrt{t}}\right)\right\}$$

in which k is to be independent of t and $k > 0$.

By the definition of erfc x we have

$$\operatorname{erfc}\left(\frac{k}{\sqrt{t}}\right) = \frac{2}{\sqrt{\pi}} \int_{k/\sqrt{t}}^{\infty} \exp\left(-\beta^2\right) d\beta. \tag{12}$$

In (12) put $\beta = k/\sqrt{v}$ so that the limits of integration become $v = t$ to $v = 0$. Since $d\beta = -\frac{1}{2} k v^{-3/2} dv$, we obtain (using the minus sign to reverse the order of integration)

$$\operatorname{erfc}\left(\frac{k}{\sqrt{t}}\right) = \frac{k}{\sqrt{\pi}} \int_0^t v^{-3/2} \exp\left(-\frac{k^2}{v}\right) dv. \tag{13}$$

The integral on the right in (13) is a convolution integral. Hence

$$L\left\{\operatorname{erfc}\left(\frac{k}{\sqrt{t}}\right)\right\} = \frac{k}{\sqrt{\pi}} L\{1\} \cdot L\left\{t^{-3/2} \exp\left(-\frac{k^2}{t}\right)\right\},$$

or

$$L\left\{\operatorname{erfc}\left(\frac{k}{\sqrt{t}}\right)\right\} = \frac{k}{s\sqrt{\pi}} L\left\{t^{-3/2} \exp\left(-\frac{k^2}{t}\right)\right\}. \tag{14}$$

Now let

$$A(s) = L\left\{t^{-3/2} \exp\left(-\frac{k^2}{t}\right)\right\}. \tag{15}$$

Note that the functions $t^m \exp\left(-\frac{k^2}{t}\right)$ are of class A, page 161, for each m.

From (15) it follows, by Theorem 13, page 167, that

$$\frac{dA}{ds} = L\left\{-t^{-1/2} \exp\left(-\frac{k^2}{t}\right)\right\} \tag{16}$$

and

$$\frac{d^2A}{ds^2} = L\left\{t^{1/2} \exp\left(-\frac{k^2}{t}\right)\right\}. \tag{17}$$

But also, by Theorem 9, page 164,

$$L\left\{\frac{d}{dt} t^{1/2} \exp\left(-\frac{k^2}{t}\right)\right\} = sL\left\{t^{1/2} \exp\left(-\frac{k^2}{t}\right)\right\} - \underset{t\to 0^+}{\text{Lim}}\left[t^{1/2} \exp\left(-\frac{k^2}{t}\right)\right],$$

or

$$L\left\{\tfrac{1}{2}t^{-1/2} \exp\left(-\frac{k^2}{t}\right) + k^2 t^{-3/2} \exp\left(-\frac{k^2}{t}\right)\right\} = sL\left\{t^{1/2} \exp\left(-\frac{k^2}{t}\right)\right\} - 0. \tag{18}$$

Because of (15), (16), and (17), equation (18) may be written

$$-\frac{1}{2}\frac{dA}{ds} + k^2 A = s\frac{d^2A}{ds^2}.$$

Therefore the desired function $A(s)$ is a solution of the differential equation

$$s\frac{d^2A}{ds^2} + \frac{1}{2}\frac{dA}{ds} - k^2 A = 0. \tag{19}$$

We need two boundary conditions to go with equation (19). We know that as $s \to \infty$, $A \to 0$. Now consider what happens as $s \to 0^+$.

By (15),

$$\underset{s\to 0^+}{\text{Lim}} A(s) = \underset{s\to 0^+}{\text{Lim}} \int_0^\infty e^{-st} t^{-3/2} \exp\left(-\frac{k^2}{t}\right) dt$$

$$= \int_0^\infty t^{-3/2} \exp\left(-\frac{k^2}{t}\right) dt.$$

Equation (13) yields (with y replacing t)

$$\int_0^y v^{-3/2} \exp\left(-\frac{k^2}{v}\right) dv = \frac{\sqrt{\pi}}{k} \operatorname{erfc}\left(\frac{k}{\sqrt{y}}\right). \tag{20}$$

Therefore

$$\underset{s\to 0^+}{\text{Lim}} A(s) = \frac{\sqrt{\pi}}{k} \underset{y\to\infty}{\text{Lim}} \operatorname{erfc}\left(\frac{k}{\sqrt{y}}\right) = \frac{\sqrt{\pi}}{k} \operatorname{erfc} 0 = \frac{\sqrt{\pi}}{k}.$$

To get the general solution of the differential equation (19), we change independent variable* from s to $z = \sqrt{s}$. Now by the chain rule of elementary calculus,

$$\frac{dA}{ds} = \frac{dz}{ds}\frac{dA}{dz} = \frac{1}{2\sqrt{s}}\frac{dA}{dz} = \frac{1}{2z}\frac{dA}{dz},$$

and

$$\frac{d^2A}{ds^2} = \frac{1}{4s}\frac{d^2A}{dz^2} - \frac{1}{4s\sqrt{s}}\frac{dA}{dz}.$$

Thus

$$s\frac{d^2A}{ds^2} = \frac{1}{4}\frac{d^2A}{dz^2} - \frac{1}{4z}\frac{dA}{dz}$$

and equation (19) becomes

$$\frac{d^2A}{dz^2} - 4k^2A = 0. \tag{21}$$

The general solution of (21) is

$$A = b_1 \exp(-2kz) + b_2 \exp(2kz),$$

so the general solution of (19) is

$$A = b_1 \exp(-2k\sqrt{s}) + b_2 \exp(2k\sqrt{s}). \tag{22}$$

We must determine the constants b_1 and b_2 from the conditions that $A \to 0$ as $s \to \infty$ and $A \to \sqrt{\pi}/k$ as $s \to 0^+$. As $s \to \infty$, A will not approach a limit unless $b_2 = 0$. Then, letting $s \to 0^+$, we get

$$\frac{\sqrt{\pi}}{k} = b_1.$$

Therefore

$$A(s) = L\left\{t^{-3/2} \exp\left(-\frac{k^2}{t}\right)\right\} = \frac{\sqrt{\pi}}{k}\exp(-2k\sqrt{s}).$$

We return to (14) to write the desired transform

$$L\left\{\text{erfc}\left(\frac{k}{\sqrt{t}}\right)\right\} = \frac{1}{s}\exp(-2k\sqrt{s}), \qquad k > 0, \quad s > 0. \tag{23}$$

---

* Such a change of variable is dictated by the test on page 16 of E. D. Rainville, *Intermediate Differential Equations*, 2nd ed. (New York: The Macmillan Co., 1964).

We shall use (23) in the form

$$L^{-1}\left\{\frac{1}{s}\exp\left(-2k\sqrt{s}\right)\right\} = \operatorname{erfc}\left(\frac{k}{\sqrt{t}}\right), \qquad k > 0, \quad s > 0. \tag{24}$$

In Chapter 26 it will be important to combine the use of equation (24) and the series methods of Section 146.

Consider the problem of obtaining

$$L^{-1}\left\{\frac{\sinh\left(x\sqrt{s}\right)}{s\sinh\sqrt{s}}\right\}, \qquad 0 < x < 1, \quad s > 0. \tag{25}$$

If x were greater than unity, the inverse in (25) would not exist because of the behavior of $\sinh\left(x\sqrt{s}\right)/\sinh\sqrt{s}$ as $s \to \infty$.

Because we know (24), it is wise to turn to exponentials. We write

$$\frac{\sinh\left(x\sqrt{s}\right)}{\sinh\sqrt{s}} = \frac{\exp\left(x\sqrt{s}\right) - \exp\left(-x\sqrt{s}\right)}{\exp\left(\sqrt{s}\right) - \exp\left(-\sqrt{s}\right)}. \tag{26}$$

As in Section 146 we seek a series involving exponentials of negative argument. We therefore multiply numerator and denominator on the right in (26) by $\exp\left(-\sqrt{s}\right)$ and find that

$$\frac{\sinh\left(x\sqrt{s}\right)}{\sinh\sqrt{s}} = \frac{\exp\left[-(1-x)\sqrt{s}\right] - \exp\left[-(1+x)\sqrt{s}\right]}{1 - \exp\left(-2\sqrt{s}\right)}. \tag{27}$$

Now

$$\frac{1}{1 - \exp\left(-2\sqrt{s}\right)} = \sum_{n=0}^{\infty}\exp\left(-2n\sqrt{s}\right). \tag{28}$$

Therefore,

$$\frac{\sinh\left(x\sqrt{s}\right)}{s\sinh\sqrt{s}} = \sum_{n=0}^{\infty}\frac{1}{s}\{\exp\left[-(1-x+2n)\sqrt{s}\right] - \exp\left[-(1+x+2n)\sqrt{s}\right]\}.$$

For $0 < x < 1$ the exponentials have negative arguments and we may use (24) to conclude that

$$L^{-1}\left\{\frac{\sinh\left(x\sqrt{s}\right)}{s\sinh\sqrt{s}}\right\} = \sum_{n=0}^{\infty}\left[\operatorname{erfc}\left(\frac{1-x+2n}{2\sqrt{t}}\right) - \operatorname{erfc}\left(\frac{1+x+2n}{2\sqrt{t}}\right)\right]. \tag{29}$$

Exercises

1. Show that for all real x, $|\operatorname{erf} x| < 1$.

2. Show that $\operatorname{erf} x$ is an odd function of x.

3. Show that $\displaystyle\lim_{x\to 0} \frac{\operatorname{erf} x}{x} = \frac{2}{\sqrt{\pi}}$.

4. Use integration by parts to show that

$$\int_0^x \operatorname{erf} y \, dy = x \operatorname{erf} x - \frac{1}{\sqrt{\pi}}[1 - \exp(-x^2)].$$

5. Obtain equation (11), page 432.

6. Start with the power series for erf x, equation (5), page 431, and show that

$$L\{t^{-1/2} \operatorname{erf}(\sqrt{t})\} = \frac{2}{\sqrt{\pi s}} \operatorname{Arctan} \frac{1}{\sqrt{s}}, \quad s > 0.$$

7. Use the fact that

$$\frac{1}{1 + \sqrt{1+s}} = \frac{1 - \sqrt{1+s}}{1-(1+s)} = -\frac{1}{s} + \frac{\sqrt{1+s}}{s} = -\frac{1}{s} + \frac{1+s}{s\sqrt{1+s}}$$

and equation (3), page 431, to show that

$$L^{-1}\left\{\frac{1}{1 + \sqrt{1+s}}\right\} = -1 + \operatorname{erf}(\sqrt{t}) + \frac{e^{-t}}{\sqrt{\pi t}} = \frac{e^{-t}}{\sqrt{\pi t}} - \operatorname{erfc}(\sqrt{t}).$$

8. Use equation (3), page 431, to conclude that

$$L^{-1}\left\{\frac{1}{(s-1)\sqrt{s}}\right\} = e^t \operatorname{erf}(\sqrt{t})$$

and therefore that

$$L^{-1}\left\{\frac{1}{\sqrt{s}(\sqrt{s}+1)}\right\} = e^t \operatorname{erfc}(\sqrt{t}).$$

9. Evaluate $L^{-1}\left\{\dfrac{1}{\sqrt{s}+1}\right\}$.   ANS. $\dfrac{1}{\sqrt{\pi t}} - e^t \operatorname{erfc}(\sqrt{t})$.

10. Evaluate $L^{-1}\left\{\dfrac{1}{\sqrt{s}-1}\right\}$.   ANS. $\dfrac{1}{\sqrt{\pi t}} + e^t + e^t \operatorname{erf}(\sqrt{t})$.

11. Define the function $\phi(t)$ by

$$\phi(t) = L^{-1}\left\{\operatorname{erf} \frac{1}{s}\right\}.$$

Prove that

$$L\{\phi(\sqrt{t})\} = \frac{2}{\sqrt{\pi s}} \sin \frac{1}{\sqrt{s}}.$$

12. Show that for $x > 0$,

$$L^{-1}\left\{\frac{\operatorname{sech} x\sqrt{s}}{s}\right\} = 2\sum_{n=0}^{\infty}(-1)^n \operatorname{erfc}\left[\frac{(2n+1)x}{2\sqrt{t}}\right].$$

13. Show that for $x > 0$,

$$L^{-1}\left\{\frac{\operatorname{csch} x\sqrt{s}}{s}\right\} = 2 \sum_{n=0}^{\infty} \operatorname{erfc}\left[\frac{(2n+1)x}{2\sqrt{t}}\right].$$

14. Derive the result

$$A(s) = L\left\{t^{-3/2} \exp\left(-\frac{k^2}{t}\right)\right\} = \frac{\sqrt{\pi}}{k} \exp(-2k\sqrt{s}), \qquad k > 0, \quad s > 0$$

directly from the definition of a transform. In the integral

$$A(s) = \int_0^{\infty} \exp(-st - k^2 t^{-1}) t^{-3/2} \, dt$$

put $\beta = \sqrt{t}$ to get

$$A(s) = 2 \int_0^{\infty} \beta^{-2} \exp(-s\beta^2 - k^2\beta^{-2}) \, d\beta$$

or

$$A(s) = 2 \exp(-2k\sqrt{s}) \int_0^{\infty} \beta^{-2} \exp[-(\beta\sqrt{s} - k\beta^{-1})^2] \, d\beta.$$

Show that

$$\frac{dA}{ds} = -2 \int_0^{\infty} \exp(-s\beta^2 - k^2\beta^{-2}) \, d\beta$$

$$= -2 \exp(-2k\sqrt{s}) \int_0^{\infty} \exp[-(\beta\sqrt{s} - k\beta^{-1})^2] \, d\beta.$$

Thus arrive at the differential equation

$$\sqrt{s}\,\frac{dA}{ds} - kA = -2\sqrt{\pi} \exp(-2k\sqrt{s})$$

and from it obtain the desired function $A(s)$.

148. Bessel functions

The Bessel function

$$J_n(z) = \sum_{k=0}^{\infty} \frac{(-1)^k (\tfrac{1}{2}z)^{2k+n}}{k!\,\Gamma(k+n+1)}, \tag{1}$$

of the first kind and of index n, appeared in Sections 111 and 112. We meet $J_n(z)$ in a simple application of the series technique of Section 146. If we can expand a given function of s in negative powers of s, surely we can get the inverse transform term by term. A simple example is the following:

$$\frac{1}{s} \exp\left(-\frac{x}{s}\right) = \sum_{k=0}^{\infty} \frac{(-1)^k x^k}{k! \, s^{k+1}},$$

which leads immediately to

$$L^{-1}\left\{\frac{1}{s} \exp\left(-\frac{x}{s}\right)\right\} = \sum_{k=0}^{\infty} \frac{(-1)^k x^k t^k}{k! \, k!}. \tag{2}$$

When $n = 0$ in (1) we get, since $\Gamma(k + 1) = k!$,

$$J_0(z) = \sum_{k=0}^{\infty} \frac{(-1)^k (\frac{1}{2}z)^{2k}}{k! \, k!}. \tag{3}$$

By comparing (2) with (3) we get

$$L^{-1}\left\{\frac{1}{s} \exp\left(-\frac{x}{s}\right)\right\} = J_0(2\sqrt{xt}); \qquad x > 0, \quad s > 0. \tag{4}$$

From

$$\frac{1}{s^{n+1}} \exp\left(-\frac{x}{s}\right) = \sum_{k=0}^{\infty} \frac{(-1)^k x^k}{k! \, s^{k+n+1}}$$

we get

$$L^{-1}\left\{\frac{1}{s^{n+1}} \exp\left(-\frac{x}{s}\right)\right\} = \sum_{k=0}^{\infty} \frac{(-1)^k x^k t^{k+n}}{k! \, \Gamma(k + n + 1)}$$

$$= x^{-\frac{1}{2}n} t^{\frac{1}{2}n} \sum_{k=0}^{\infty} \frac{(-1)^k (\sqrt{xt})^{2k+n}}{k! \, \Gamma(k + n + 1)}.$$

Therefore, at least for $n \geq 0$,

$$L^{-1}\left\{\frac{1}{s^{n+1}} \exp\left(-\frac{x}{s}\right)\right\} = \left(\frac{t}{x}\right)^{\frac{1}{2}n} J_n(2\sqrt{xt}), \qquad s > 0, \quad x > 0. \tag{5}$$

With more knowledge of the Gamma function, we could use series methods to obtain the transform of $J_n(xt)$ for general n. Here we restrict ourselves to $n = 0$ for simplicity.

From (1) we obtain

$$J_0(xt) = \sum_{k=0}^{\infty} \frac{(-1)^k (\frac{1}{2}x)^{2k} t^{2k}}{k! \, k!}.$$

Then

$$L\{J_0(xt)\} = \sum_{k=0}^{\infty} \frac{(-1)^k (\frac{1}{2}x)^{2k} (2k)!}{k! \, k! \, s^{2k+1}}.$$

But $(2k)! = 2^k k! [1 \cdot 3 \cdot 5 \cdots (2k - 1)]$. Hence

$$L\{J_0(xt)\} = \frac{1}{s}\left[1 + \sum_{k=1}^{\infty} \frac{(-1)^k[1 \cdot 3 \cdot 5 \cdots (2k - 1)]x^{2k}}{2^k \cdot k! s^{2k}}\right],$$

or

$$L\{J_0(xt)\} = \frac{1}{s}\left(1 + \frac{x^2}{s^2}\right)^{-1/2}.$$

Therefore

$$L\{J_0(xt)\} = \frac{1}{\sqrt{s^2 + x^2}}. \tag{6}$$

From (1) it is easy to conclude that

$$\frac{d}{dz} J_0(z) = -J_1(z).$$

Then

$$\frac{d}{dt} J_0(xt) = -xJ_1(xt)$$

and we obtain

$$L\{-xJ_1(xt)\} = L\left\{\frac{d}{dt} J_0(xt)\right\}$$

$$= sL\{J_0(xt)\} - J_0(0).$$

But $J_0(0) = 1$, so

$$L\{-xJ_1(xt)\} = \frac{s}{\sqrt{s^2 + x^2}} - 1,$$

or

$$L\{J_1(xt)\} = \frac{\sqrt{s^2 + x^2} - s}{x\sqrt{s^2 + x^2}}. \tag{7}$$

Exercise

1. The modified Bessel function of the first kind and of index n is

$$I_n(z) = \sum_{k=0}^{\infty} \frac{(\tfrac{1}{2}z)^{2k+n}}{k!\Gamma(k + n + 1)}.$$

Show that

$$L^{-1}\left\{\frac{1}{s^{n+1}} \exp\left(\frac{x}{s}\right)\right\} = \left(\frac{t}{x}\right)^{\tfrac{1}{2}n} I_n(2\sqrt{xt}).$$

149. Differential equations with variable coefficients

Any reader who has become overly optimistic about the efficacy of the Laplace transform as a tool in treating linear differential equations should keep in mind that we have restricted our work so far to equations with constant coefficients.

Suppose that we are confronted with an initial value problem involving the equation

$$F''(t) + t^2 F(t) = 0. \tag{1}$$

Let $L\{F(t)\} = f(s)$ and put $F(0) = A$, $F'(0) = B$. Then application of the operator L transforms equation (1) into

$$s^2 f(s) - sA - B + \frac{d^2}{ds^2} f(s) = 0,$$

or

$$f''(s) + s^2 f(s) = As + B. \tag{2}$$

The problem of getting the complementary function for equation (2) is the same as it is for equation (1); no progress has been made. The left member of (1) remained essentially unchanged under the Laplace transformation.

The behavior of (1) under L is not unique. Indeed, the differential equations with polynomial coefficients that remain invariant under the Laplace transformation have been classified.*

Since $L\{t^n F(t)\} = (-1)^n (d^n/ds^n) f(s)$, it follows that the operator L can be used to transform a differential equation with polynomial coefficients into a differential equation with polynomial coefficients and that the order of the new equation will equal the maximum degree of the polynomial coefficients in the original equation. The Laplace transform is simply not the proper tool for attacking differential equations with variable coefficients. For such a purpose, the classical method of solution by power series is a good tool to use.

* E. D. Rainville, "Linear Differential Invariance Under an Operator Related to the Laplace Transformation," *Amer. Journal of Math.*, **62** (1940), 391–405.

CHAPTER **26**

Partial Differential Equations;
Transform Methods

150. Boundary value problems

For some boundary value problems involving partial differential equations, the Laplace transform provides an effective method of attack; for other problems the transform method contributes additional information even when the older techniques, such as separation of variables and Fourier series, may be easier to use. There remain problems for which the Laplace transform method contributes nothing but complications.

In this chapter we present a few applications and a detailed study of the solution of some simple problems. Our goal is to give the student sufficient background to enable him to use the Laplace transform on problems he encounters in practice and to give him some criteria to use in deciding whether the transform method is an appropriate tool for a given problem.

We first solve some artificial problems which have been constructed to exhibit the technique and underlying ideas without introducing the complexities common to many physical applications. The student who fully understands and can execute the solutions of such simple problems will find no difficulty, other than an increase in amount of labor, in solving corresponding problems arising in physical situations.

EXAMPLE: Solve the problem consisting of the equation

$$\frac{\partial^2 y}{\partial x^2} = 16 \frac{\partial^2 y}{\partial t^2}, \qquad \text{for } t > 0, \quad x > 0; \tag{1}$$

with the conditions

$$t \to 0^+, \quad y \to 0, \qquad \text{for } x > 0; \tag{2}$$

$$t \to 0^+, \quad \frac{\partial y}{\partial t} \to -1, \qquad \text{for } x > 0; \tag{3}$$

$$x \to 0^+, \quad y \to t^2, \qquad \text{for } t > 0; \tag{4}$$

$$\text{Lim}_{x \to \infty} y(x, t) \text{ exists, for fixed } t > 0. \tag{5}$$

The characteristics of the problem that suggest that it is worthwhile to try the Laplace transform technique are:

(a) The differential equation is linear (necessary),
(b) The equation has constant coefficients (highly desirable),
(c) At least one independent variable has the range 0 to ∞ (highly desirable),
(d) There are appropriate initial ($t = 0$) conditions involving the independent variable in (c) above (desirable).

In this problem the independent variable x also has the range 0 to ∞, but there is only one condition at $x = 0$; two conditions are needed in transforming a second derivative. We shall therefore attack this problem with Laplace transforms with respect to the variable t.

Let

$$L\{y(x, t)\} = w(x, s), \tag{6}$$

in which x is treated as a constant (parameter) as far as the Laplace transformation is concerned. Since we shall verify our solution, there is no risk in assuming that the operations of differentiations with respect to x and Laplace transforms with respect to t are commutative.

Because (1) has constant coefficients, derivatives with respect to the transform variable s will not appear. The partial differential equation (1) will be transformed into an ordinary differential equation with independent variable x and with s involved as a parameter. In view of (6), application of the operator L transforms (1), (2), and (3) into

$$\frac{d^2 w}{dx^2} = 16(s^2 w + 1), \qquad x > 0. \tag{7}$$

The conditions (4) and (5) become

$$x \to 0^+, \quad w \to \frac{2}{s^3}, \tag{8}$$

$$\operatorname*{Lim}_{x \to \infty} w(x, s) \text{ exists.} \tag{9}$$

We now solve the new problem, (7), (8), and (9), for $w(x, s)$ and then obtain $y(x, t)$ as the inverse transform of w. Let us rewrite (7) in the form

$$\frac{d^2 w}{dx^2} - 16s^2 w = 16 \tag{10}$$

and keep in mind that x is the independent variable and s is a parameter. When we get the general solution of (10) the arbitrary constants in it may well be functions of s; they must not involve x.

The general solution of (10) should be found by inspection. It is

$$w = -\frac{1}{s^2} + c_1(s) \exp(-4sx) + c_2(s) \exp(4sx), \qquad x > 0, \quad s > 0. \tag{11}$$

Because of (9), the w of (11) is to approach a limit as $x \to \infty$. The first two terms on the right in (11) approach limits as $x \to \infty$, but the term with the positive exponent, $\exp(4sx)$, will not do so unless

$$c_2(s) \equiv 0. \tag{12}$$

That is, (9) forces (12) upon us. The w of (11) then becomes

$$w = -\frac{1}{s^2} + c_1(s) \exp(-4sx), \qquad x > 0, \quad s > 0. \tag{13}$$

Application of condition (8) to the w of (13) yields

$$\frac{2}{s^3} = c_1(s) - \frac{1}{s^2}; \qquad c_1(s) = \frac{2}{s^3} + \frac{1}{s^2}.$$

Thus we find that

$$w(x, s) = -\frac{1}{s^2} + \left(\frac{2}{s^3} + \frac{1}{s^2}\right) \exp(-4sx), \qquad x > 0, \quad s > 0. \tag{14}$$

We already know that if

$$L^{-1}\{f(s)\} = F(t),$$

$$L^{-1}\{e^{-cs} f(s)\} = F(t - c)\alpha(t - c). \tag{15}$$

Therefore the application of the operator L^{-1} throughout (14) gives us

$$y(x, t) = -t + [(t - 4x)^2 + (t - 4x)]\alpha(t - 4x), \qquad x > 0, \quad t > 0. \tag{16}$$

It is our contention that the y of (16) satisfies the boundary value problem (1) through (5). Let us now verify the solution in detail.

From (16) it follows that

$$\frac{\partial y}{\partial t} = -1 + [2(t - 4x) + 1]\alpha(t - 4x), \qquad x > 0, \quad t > 0, \quad t \neq 4x. \quad (17)$$

Note the discontinuity in the derivative for $t = 4x$. This is forcing us into the admission that we obtain a solution of the problem only on each side of the line $t = 4x$ in the first quadrant of the xt-plane. Our y will not satisfy the differential equation along that line because the second derivative cannot exist there. This is a reflection of the fact that (1) is a "hyperbolic differential equation." Whether the "solution" does or does not satisfy the differential equation along what are called the characteristic lines of the equation depends upon the specific boundary conditions. We shall treat each problem individually with no attempt to examine the general situation.

From (17) we obtain

$$\frac{\partial^2 y}{\partial t^2} = 2\alpha(t - 4x), \qquad x > 0, \quad t > 0, \quad t \neq 4x. \quad (18)$$

Equation (16) also yields

$$\frac{\partial y}{\partial x} = [-8(t - 4x) - 4]\alpha(t - 4x), \qquad x > 0, \quad t > 0, \quad t \neq 4x, \quad (19)$$

and

$$\frac{\partial^2 y}{\partial x^2} = 32\alpha(t - 4x), \qquad x > 0, \quad t > 0, \quad t \neq 4x. \quad (20)$$

Equations (18) and (20) combine to show that the y of (16) is a solution of the differential equation (1) in the xt region desired except along the line $t = 4x$ where the second derivatives do not exist.

Next we verify that our y satisfies the boundary conditions. To see whether y satisfies condition (2), we must hold x fixed, but positive, and then let t approach zero through positive values. As

$$t \to 0^+, \quad y \to 0 + [(-4x)^2 + (-4x)]\alpha(-4x) = 0, \qquad \text{for } x > 0.$$

Thus (2) is satisfied. Note that $\alpha(-4x)$ would not have been zero for negative x.

From (17), with x fixed and positive, it follows that as

$$t \to 0^+, \quad \frac{\partial y}{\partial t} \to -1 + [2(-4x) + 1]\alpha(-4x) = -1, \qquad \text{for } x > 0.$$

Thus (3) is satisfied. Once more the fact that x is positive plays an important role in the verification.

Consider condition (4). In it we must hold t fixed and positive. Then, by (16), as

$$x \to 0^+, \quad y \to -t + (t^2 + t)\alpha(t) = -t + t^2 + t = t^2, \qquad \text{for } t > 0.$$

Then (4) is satisfied.

Finally, the y of (16) satisfies condition (5), since

$$\underset{x \to \infty}{\text{Lim}} \; y(x, t) = -t + 0 = -t, \qquad \text{for } t > 0,$$

because for sufficiently large x and fixed t, $(t - 4x)$ is negative and therefore $\alpha(t - 4x) = 0$. This completes the verification of the solution (16).

Exercises

In each exercise, solve the problem and verify your solution completely.

1. $\dfrac{\partial y}{\partial x} + 4\dfrac{\partial y}{\partial t} = -8t,$ for $t > 0$, $x > 0$;

$t \to 0^+, \quad y \to 0,$ for $x > 0$;

$x \to 0^+, \quad y \to 2t^2,$ for $t > 0$.

ANS. $y(x, t) = -t^2 + 3(t - 4x)^2\alpha(t - 4x).$

2. $\dfrac{\partial y}{\partial x} + 2\dfrac{\partial y}{\partial t} = 4t,$ for $t > 0$, $x > 0$;

$t \to 0^+, \quad y \to 0,$ for $x > 0$;

$x \to 0^+, \quad y \to 2t^3,$ for $t > 0$.

ANS. $y(x, t) = t^2 + [2(t - 2x)^3 - (t - 2x)^2]\alpha(t - 2x).$

3. Solve Ex. 1 with the condition as $t \to 0^+$ replaced by $t \to 0^+, y \to x$.

ANS. $y(x, t) = x - \tfrac{1}{4}t - t^2 + [3(t - 4x)^2 + \tfrac{1}{4}(t - 4x)]\alpha(t - 4x).$

4. Solve Ex. 2 with the condition as $t \to 0^+$ replaced by $t \to 0^+, y \to 2x$.

ANS. $y(x, t) = 2x - t + t^2 + [2(t - 2x)^3 - (t - 2x)^2 + (t - 2x)]\alpha(t - 2x).$

5. $\dfrac{\partial^2 y}{\partial x^2} = 16\dfrac{\partial^2 y}{\partial t^2},$ for $t > 0$, $x > 0$;

$t \to 0^+, \quad y \to 0,$ for $x > 0$;

$t \to 0^+, \quad \dfrac{\partial y}{\partial t} \to -2,$ for $x > 0$;

$x \to 0^+, \quad y \to t,$ for $t > 0$;

$\underset{x \to \infty}{\text{Lim}} \; y(x, t)$ exists for $t > 0$.   ANS. $y = 3(t - 4x)\alpha(t - 4x) - 2t.$

6. $\dfrac{\partial^2 y}{\partial t^2} = 4\dfrac{\partial^2 y}{\partial x^2},$ for $t > 0$, $x > 0$;

$t \to 0^+, \quad y \to 0,$ for $x > 0$;

$t \to 0^+, \quad \dfrac{\partial y}{\partial t} \to 2,$ for $x > 0$;

$x \to 0^+, \quad y \to \sin t,$ for $t > 0$;

$\underset{x \to \infty}{\text{Lim}} \; y(x, t)$ exists for $t > 0$.

ANS. $y = 2t + [\sin(t - \tfrac{1}{2}x) - 2(t - \tfrac{1}{2}x)]\alpha(t - \tfrac{1}{2}x).$

151. The wave equation

The transverse displacement y of an elastic string must satisfy the one-dimensional wave equation

$$\frac{\partial^2 y}{\partial t^2} = a^2 \frac{\partial^2 y}{\partial x^2}$$

of Section 144, in which the positive constant a has the dimensions of a velocity, cm. per sec., etc.

Suppose a long elastic string is initially taut and at rest so that we may take, at $t = 0$,

$$y = 0 \quad \text{and} \quad \frac{\partial y}{\partial t} = 0, \qquad \text{for } x \geqq 0.$$

We assume the string long enough that the assumption that it extends from $x = 0$ to ∞ introduces no appreciable error over the time interval in which we are interested.

Suppose also that that end of the string far distant from the y-axis is held fixed, $y \to 0$, as $x \to \infty$, but that at the y-axis end the string is moved up and down according to some prescribed law, $y \to F(t)$ as $x \to 0^+$, with $F(t)$ known. Figure 65 shows the position of the string at some $t > 0$.

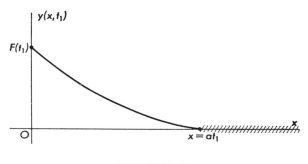

FIGURE 65

The problem of determining the transverse displacement y in terms of x and t is that of solving the boundary value problem:

$$\frac{\partial^2 y}{\partial t^2} = a^2 \frac{\partial^2 y}{\partial x^2}, \qquad \text{for } t > 0, \quad x > 0; \tag{1}$$

$$t \to 0^{+}, \quad y \to 0, \qquad \text{for } x \geqq 0; \tag{2}$$

$$t \to 0^{+}, \quad \frac{\partial y}{\partial t} \to 0, \qquad \text{for } x > 0; \tag{3}$$

$$x \to 0^{+}, \quad y \to F(t), \qquad \text{for } t \geqq 0; \tag{4}$$

$$\operatorname*{Lim}_{x \to \infty} y(x, t) = 0, \qquad \text{for all } t \geqq 0. \tag{5}$$

The prescribed function $F(t)$ must vanish at $t = 0$ to retain continuity of the string.

This problem satisfies the criteria, page 442, that suggest the use of the Laplace transform. Let

$$L\{y(x, t)\} = u(x, s), \qquad L\{F(t)\} = f(s). \tag{6}$$

Note that $F(t)$ must be continuous because of its physical meaning here. The operator L converts the problem (1) through (5) into the new problem

$$s^2 u = a^2 \frac{d^2 u}{dx^2}, \qquad \text{for } x > 0; \tag{7}$$

$$x \to 0^{+}, \quad u \to f(s); \tag{8}$$

$$\operatorname*{Lim}_{x \to \infty} u(x, s) = 0. \tag{9}$$

From (7) we write at once the general solution

$$u(x, s) = c_1(s) \exp\left(-\frac{sx}{a}\right) + c_2(s) \exp\left(\frac{sx}{a}\right). \tag{10}$$

With $s > 0$, $x > 0$, the condition (9) requires

$$c_2(s) \equiv 0. \tag{11}$$

Thus (10) becomes

$$u(x, s) = c_1(s) \exp\left(-\frac{sx}{a}\right), \tag{12}$$

and (8) requires that

$$f(s) = c_1(s).$$

We therefore have

$$u(x, s) = f(s) \exp\left(-\frac{sx}{a}\right), \qquad x > 0, \quad s > 0. \tag{13}$$

Equation (13) yields the desired solution

$$y(x, t) = F\left(t - \frac{x}{a}\right)\alpha\left(t - \frac{x}{a}\right), \qquad x > 0, \quad t > 0, \tag{14}$$

in which we assume that $F(t)$ is defined in some manner for negative argument so that Theorem 19, page 180, can be used.

Verification of the solution (14) is a simple matter. Note that

$$\frac{\partial y}{\partial t} = F'\left(t - \frac{x}{a}\right)\alpha\left(t - \frac{x}{a}\right), \qquad \frac{\partial y}{\partial x} = -\frac{1}{a}F'\left(t - \frac{x}{a}\right)\alpha\left(t - \frac{x}{a}\right)$$

and

$$\frac{\partial^2 y}{\partial t^2} = F''\left(t - \frac{x}{a}\right)\alpha\left(t - \frac{x}{a}\right), \qquad \frac{\partial^2 y}{\partial x^2} = \frac{1}{a^2}F''\left(t - \frac{x}{a}\right)\alpha\left(t - \frac{x}{a}\right).$$

We are forced to assume existence of two derivatives of the prescribed function $F(t)$. It is particularly convenient to choose $F(t)$ so that $F'(0)$ and $F''(0)$ vanish along with $F(0)$, so that the continuity of y and its derivatives is not interrupted along the line $x = at$. Completion of the verification of the solution is left to the student.

In Section 144 we studied the transverse displacement of a string of finite length held fixed at both ends. Fourier series methods seem superior to Laplace transform techniques for such problems. Try, for instance, transform methods on Ex. 1, p. 420.

Exercise

1. Interpret and solve the problem:

$$\frac{\partial^2 y}{\partial t^2} = \frac{\partial^2 y}{\partial x^2}, \qquad \text{for } t > 0, \quad 0 < x < 1;$$

$$t \to 0^+, \quad y \to x - x^2, \qquad \text{for } 0 < x < 1;$$

$$t \to 0^+, \quad \frac{\partial y}{\partial t} \to 0, \qquad \text{for } 0 < x < 1;$$

$$x \to 0^+, \quad y \to 0, \qquad \text{for } t > 0;$$

$$x \to 1^-, \quad y \to 0, \qquad \text{for } t > 0.$$

Verify your solution directly.

ANS. $y = x - x^2 - t^2 + \sum\limits_{n=0}^{\infty} (-1)^n[(t - n - x)^2\alpha(t - n - x)$

$$+ (t - n - 1 + x)^2\alpha(t - n - 1 - x)].$$

152. Diffusion in a semi-infinite solid

Consider the solid defined by $x \geqq 0$, occupying one half of three dimensional space. If the initial temperature within the solid and the conditions at the surface $x = 0$ are independent of the coordinates y and z, the temperature u will be independent of y and z for all $t > 0$. We may visualize, for example, a huge flat slab of concrete with an initial temperature distribution dependent upon only the distance from the plane surface of the slab. If the temperature at that surface is thereafter ($t > 0$) maintained at some specified function of t, or if the surface is insulated, the problem of finding the temperature for all positive x and t is one involving the simple heat equation (2) of Section 140.

EXAMPLE: Consider a semi-infinite slab $x \geqq 0$, initially at a fixed temperature $u = A$ and thereafter subjected to a surface temperature ($x \to 0^+$) which is $u = B$ for $0 < t < t_0$ and then $u = 0$ for $t \geqq t_0$. Find the temperature within the solid for $x > 0$, $t > 0$.

The boundary value problem to be solved is:

$$\frac{\partial u}{\partial t} = h^2 \frac{\partial^2 u}{\partial x^2}, \qquad \text{for } x > 0, \quad t > 0; \tag{1}$$

$$t \to 0^+, \quad u \to A, \qquad \text{for } x > 0; \tag{2}$$

$$x \to 0^+, \quad u \to B, \qquad \text{for } 0 < t < t_0, \tag{3}$$

$$u \to 0, \qquad \text{for } t > t_0 \, ; $$

$$\underset{x \to \infty}{\text{Lim}} \, u(x, t) \text{ exists, for each fixed } t > 0. \tag{4}$$

In this problem A, B, and h^2 are constants. We use the α function to reword the boundary condition (3) in the form

$$x \to 0^+, \quad u \to B[1 - \alpha(t - t_0)], \qquad \text{for } t > 0. \tag{5}$$

Note also that the physical problem dictates that the value of the limit in (4) is to be A. This furnishes us with an additional check on our work.

The problem satisfies the criteria, page 442, that suggest the use of the Laplace transform. Let

$$L\{u(x, t)\} = w(x, s), \qquad x > 0, \quad s > 0. \tag{6}$$

The equation (1) with condition (2) is transformed into

$$sw - A = h^2 \frac{d^2 w}{dx^2}, \qquad x > 0,$$

or

$$\frac{d^2w}{dx^2} - \frac{s}{h^2} w = -\frac{A}{h^2}, \qquad x > 0. \tag{7}$$

Conditions (4) and (5) become

$$\text{Lim } w(x, s) \text{ exists, for fixed } s > 0, \tag{8}$$
$$\underset{x \to \infty}{}$$

and

$$x \to 0^+, \quad w \to \frac{B}{s} [1 - \exp(-t_0 s)]. \tag{9}$$

The differential equation (7) has the general solution

$$w = c_1 \exp\left(-\frac{x\sqrt{s}}{h}\right) + c_2 \exp\left(\frac{x\sqrt{s}}{h}\right) + \frac{A}{s}, \qquad x > 0, \quad s > 0, \tag{10}$$

in which c_1 and c_2 may be functions of s, but not of x. As $x \to \infty$, the w of (10) will approach a limit if and only if $c_2 = 0$. Hence condition (8) yields the result

$$c_2 = 0 \tag{11}$$

and the w of (10) becomes

$$w = c_1 \exp\left(-\frac{x\sqrt{s}}{h}\right) + \frac{A}{s}. \tag{12}$$

Using (9) we obtain, by letting $x \to 0^+$,

$$\frac{B}{s} [1 - \exp(-t_0 s)] = c_1 + \frac{A}{s}. \tag{13}$$

Therefore the solution of the problem (7) through (9) is

$$w(x, s) = \frac{A}{s} \left[1 - \exp\left(-\frac{x\sqrt{s}}{h}\right)\right] + \frac{B}{s} \exp\left(-\frac{x\sqrt{s}}{h}\right)[1 - \exp(-t_0 s)]. \tag{14}$$

We know that

$$L^{-1}\left\{\frac{1}{s} \exp\left(-\frac{x\sqrt{s}}{h}\right)\right\} = \text{erfc}\left(\frac{x}{2h\sqrt{t}}\right), \qquad x > 0. \tag{15}$$

Hence we may write

$$L^{-1}\left\{\frac{1}{s} \exp\left(-\frac{x\sqrt{s}}{h}\right) \exp(-t_0 s)\right\} = \text{erfc}\left(\frac{x}{2h|t - t_0|^{1/2}}\right)\alpha(t - t_0), \tag{16}$$

where absolute value signs have been inserted to permit t to be used in the range 0 to t_0 in which range the α function will force the right member of (16) to be zero.

We are now in a position to write the inverse transform of the w of equation (14). For $x > 0$ and $t > 0$,

$$u(x, t) = A\left[1 - \operatorname{erfc}\left(\frac{x}{2h\sqrt{t}}\right)\right]$$

$$+ B\left[\operatorname{erfc}\left(\frac{x}{2h\sqrt{t}}\right) - \operatorname{erfc}\left(\frac{x}{2h\,|t - t_0|^{1/2}}\right)\alpha(t - t_0)\right], \quad (17)$$

or

$$u(x, t) = A\operatorname{erf}\left(\frac{x}{2h\sqrt{t}}\right) + B\left[\operatorname{erfc}\left(\frac{x}{2h\sqrt{t}}\right) - \operatorname{erfc}\left(\frac{x}{2h\,|t - t_0|^{1/2}}\right)\alpha(t - t_0)\right].$$

$$(18)$$

The u of (17), or of (18), is the desired solution.

It is a matter of direct substitution to show that each term of (18) is a solution of the one-dimensional heat equation. That the conditions (2), (3), and (4) are also satisfied follows rapidly from the properties

$$\operatorname{Lim}_{z \to 0} \operatorname{erf} z = 0, \qquad \operatorname{Lim}_{z \to \infty} \operatorname{erf} z = 1$$

and the corresponding properties of the erfc function. Indeed, for the u of (18),

As $x \to 0^+$, $u \to A \cdot 0 + B[1 - \alpha(t - t_0)] = B[1 - \alpha(t - t_0)]$,   for $t > 0$;

As $t \to 0^+$, $u \to A \cdot 1 + B(0 - 0) = A$,   for $x > 0$;

As $x \to \infty$, $u \to A \cdot 1 + B \cdot 0 = A$,   for $0 < t < t_0$;

As $x \to \infty$, $u \to A \cdot 1 + B(0 - 0) = A$,   for $t > t_0$.

153. Canonical variables

As we attack problems of increasing complexity, it becomes important that we simplify our work by the introduction of what are called *canonical variables*. These variables are dimensionless combinations of the physical variables and parameters of the original problem. We now illustrate a method for selecting such variables.

In Section 154 we shall solve a diffusion problem which can be expressed in the following way:

$$\frac{\partial u}{\partial t} = h^2 \frac{\partial^2 u}{\partial x^2}, \qquad \text{for } t > 0, \quad 0 < x < c; \tag{1}$$

$$t \to 0^+, \quad u \to A, \quad \text{for } 0 < x < c; \tag{2}$$

$$x \to 0^+, \quad u \to 0, \quad \text{for } t > 0; \tag{3}$$

$$x \to c^-, \quad u \to 0, \quad \text{for } t > 0. \tag{4}$$

A consistent set of units for the measure of the various constants (parameters) and variables in this problem is:

$$u = \text{temperature (°F)},$$
$$t = \text{time (hr.)},$$
$$x = \text{space coordinate (ft.)}$$
$$h^2 = \text{thermal diffusivity (ft.}^2 \text{ per hr.)},$$
$$c = \text{length (ft.)},$$
$$A = \text{initial temperature (°F)}.$$

We seek dimensionless new variables ζ, τ, ψ, proportional to the physical variables x, t, u. For the moment let

$$x = \beta \zeta, \quad t = \gamma \tau, \quad u = \delta \psi, \tag{5}$$

in which β, γ, δ are positive constants to be so determined that the new variables will each be of dimension zero. The changes of variable (5) transform (1) through (4) into

$$\frac{\delta}{\gamma} \frac{\partial \psi}{\partial \tau} = \frac{h^2 \delta}{\beta^2} \frac{\partial^2 \psi}{\partial \zeta^2}, \quad \text{for } \tau > 0, \quad 0 < \beta \zeta < c; \tag{6}$$

$$\tau \to 0^+, \quad \delta \psi \to A, \quad \text{for } 0 < \beta \zeta < c; \tag{7}$$

$$\zeta \to 0^+, \quad \psi \to 0, \quad \text{for } \tau > 0; \tag{8}$$

$$\beta \zeta \to c^-, \quad \psi \to 0, \quad \text{for } \tau > 0. \tag{9}$$

Because of (7), we choose $\delta = A$ and $\beta = c$. Because of (6), we choose

$$\frac{1}{\gamma} = \frac{h^2}{\beta^2},$$

from which

$$\gamma = \frac{c^2}{h^2}.$$

We thus find that the introduction of the new variables

$$\zeta = \frac{x}{c}, \quad \tau = \frac{h^2 t}{c^2}, \quad \psi = \frac{u}{A}, \tag{10}$$

transforms the problem (1) through (4) into the canonical form

$$\frac{\partial \psi}{\partial \tau} = \frac{\partial^2 \psi}{\partial \zeta^2}, \qquad \text{for } \tau > 0, \quad 0 < \zeta < 1; \tag{11}$$

$$\tau \to 0^+, \quad \psi \to 1, \qquad \text{for } 0 < \zeta < 1; \tag{12}$$

$$\zeta \to 0^+, \quad \psi \to 0, \qquad \text{for } \tau > 0; \tag{13}$$

$$\zeta \to 1^-, \quad \psi \to 0, \qquad \text{for } \tau > 0. \tag{14}$$

Note that the canonical variables in (10) are of dimension zero; ζ has dimension ft. over ft., etc.

The solution of (11) through (14) is independent of the parameters h^2, c, and A of the original problem, a fact of great importance in applications. The solution of the original problem (1) through (4) is a function of two variables and three parameters,

$$u = f(x, t, c, h, A). \tag{15}$$

The solution of (11) through (14), for which see Section 154, is a function of two variables

$$\psi = F(\zeta, \tau), \tag{16}$$

so (15) actually takes the form

$$u = AF\left(\frac{x}{c}, \frac{h^2 t}{c^2}\right). \tag{17}$$

The function F, of two variables, can be tabulated and it thus yields the solution of the original problem no matter what the values of c, A and h^2.

There are problems, such as in the study of temperatures in a concrete dam, in which it is important to know the mean value with respect to x of the temperature u of (15) over the range $0 < x < c$. That mean value may be computed by using (16) and the result is a function of the one variable τ. Thus a single curve can be drawn in the $\psi\tau$-plane to give the pertinent mean temperature for all problems (1) through (4).

154. Diffusion in a slab of finite width

We shall now solve by transform methods the slab problem of Section 126 for the special case $f(x) = A$. Let the thickness of the slab be c units of length. Let the coordinate x denote distance from one face of the slab and assume that the slab extends very far in the y and z directions. Assume that the initial temperature of the slab is a constant A and that the surfaces $x = 0$, $x = c$ are maintained at zero temperature for all $t > 0$. If the slab is considered infinite in the y and z directions, or more specifically, if we treat only cross-sections nearby (far from the distant surfaces of the slab), then the temperature u at any time t and position x is determined by the boundary value problem:

$$\frac{\partial u}{\partial t} = h^2 \frac{\partial^2 u}{\partial x^2}, \qquad \text{for } t > 0, \quad 0 < x < c; \tag{1}$$

$$t \to 0^+, \quad u \to A, \qquad \text{for } 0 < x < c; \tag{2}$$

$$x \to 0^+, \quad u \to 0, \qquad \text{for } t > 0; \tag{3}$$

$$x \to c^-, \quad u \to 0, \qquad \text{for } t > 0. \tag{4}$$

We shall solve the corresponding problem in canonical variables. That is, in (1) through (4) we put

$$\zeta = \frac{x}{c}, \qquad \tau = \frac{h^2 t}{c^2}, \qquad \psi = \frac{u}{A}. \tag{5}$$

In the new variables ζ, τ, ψ, the problem to be solved is

$$\frac{\partial \psi}{\partial \tau} = \frac{\partial^2 \psi}{\partial \zeta^2}, \qquad \text{for } \tau > 0, \quad 0 < \zeta < 1; \tag{6}$$

$$\tau \to 0^+, \quad \psi \to 1, \qquad \text{for } 0 < \zeta < 1; \tag{7}$$

$$\zeta \to 0^+, \quad \psi \to 0, \qquad \text{for } \tau > 0; \tag{8}$$

$$\zeta \to 1^-, \quad \psi \to 0, \qquad \text{for } \tau > 0. \tag{9}$$

Let

$$L\{\psi(\zeta, \tau)\} = w(\zeta, s) = \int_0^\infty e^{-s\tau} \psi(\zeta, \tau)\, d\tau. \tag{10}$$

Application of the Laplace operator transforms the problem (6) through (9) into

$$sw - 1 = \frac{d^2 w}{d\zeta^2}, \qquad \text{for } 0 < \zeta < 1; \tag{11}$$

$$\zeta \to 0^+, \quad w \to 0; \tag{12}$$

$$\zeta \to 1^-, \quad w \to 0. \tag{13}$$

The general solution of (11) may be written

$$w = c_1 \sinh\left(\zeta\sqrt{s}\right) + c_2 \cosh\left(\zeta\sqrt{s}\right) + \frac{1}{s}. \tag{14}$$

From (12) it follows that

$$0 = c_2 + \frac{1}{s} \tag{15}$$

and (13) yields

$$0 = c_1 \sinh \sqrt{s} + c_2 \cosh \sqrt{s} + \frac{1}{s}. \tag{16}$$

By solving (15) and (16) we obtain

$$c_2 = -\frac{1}{s}, \qquad c_1 = \frac{\cosh \sqrt{s} - 1}{s \sinh \sqrt{s}}, \tag{17}$$

from which we see that

$$w = \frac{1}{s} + \frac{(\cosh \sqrt{s} - 1) \sinh (\zeta \sqrt{s}) - \sinh \sqrt{s} \cosh (\zeta \sqrt{s})}{s \sinh \sqrt{s}}. \tag{18}$$

Since

$$\sinh B_1 \cosh B_2 - \cosh B_1 \sinh B_2 = \sinh (B_1 - B_2),$$

the w of (18) may be written in the form

$$w(\zeta, s) = \frac{1}{s} \left[1 - \frac{\sinh (\zeta \sqrt{s})}{\sinh \sqrt{s}} - \frac{\sinh \{(1 - \zeta)\sqrt{s}\}}{\sinh \sqrt{s}} \right]. \tag{19}$$

The desired solution $\psi(\zeta, \tau)$ is the inverse of the $w(\zeta, s)$ of (19), with ζ on the range $0 < \zeta < 1$.

We already know from equation (29), page 435, that for $0 < x < 1$,

$$L^{-1} \left\{ \frac{\sinh (x\sqrt{s})}{s \sinh \sqrt{s}} \right\} = \sum_{n=0}^{\infty} \left[\operatorname{erfc} \left(\frac{1 - x + 2n}{2\sqrt{t}} \right) - \operatorname{erfc} \left(\frac{1 + x + 2n}{2\sqrt{t}} \right) \right]. \tag{20}$$

Applying (20) twice, once with ζ and once with $(1 - \zeta)$ replacing x, we obtain from (19) the desired solution

$$\psi(\zeta, \tau) = 1 - \sum_{n=0}^{\infty} \left[\operatorname{erfc} \left(\frac{1 - \zeta + 2n}{2\sqrt{\tau}} \right) - \operatorname{erfc} \left(\frac{1 + \zeta + 2n}{2\sqrt{\tau}} \right) \right]$$
$$- \sum_{n=0}^{\infty} \left[\operatorname{erfc} \left(\frac{\zeta + 2n}{2\sqrt{\tau}} \right) - \operatorname{erfc} \left(\frac{2 - \zeta + 2n}{2\sqrt{\tau}} \right) \right]. \tag{21}$$

The complementary error functions in (21) may be replaced by error functions, since

$$\operatorname{erfc} z = 1 - \operatorname{erf} z. \tag{22}$$

With the aid of the properties

$$\text{erfc } 0 = 1, \qquad \underset{z \to \infty}{\text{Lim erfc } z = 0}, \tag{23}$$

the solution (21) is easily verified, assuming that the summation sign and the pertinent limits may be interchanged. With the theorems of advanced calculus the assumption can be shown to be valid.

From (21) we get, as $\zeta \to 0^+$,

$$\psi \to 1 - \sum_{n=0}^{\infty} \left[\text{erfc } \left(\frac{2n+1}{2\sqrt{\tau}} \right) - \text{erfc } \left(\frac{2n+1}{2\sqrt{\tau}} \right) \right]$$

$$- \sum_{n=0}^{\infty} \left[\text{erfc } \left(\frac{n}{\sqrt{\tau}} \right) - \text{erfc } \left(\frac{n+1}{\sqrt{\tau}} \right) \right].$$

In the first series each term is zero. The second series telescopes; in it we replace the series by the limit of the partial sums to get

$$\psi \to 1 - \underset{n \to \infty}{\text{Lim}} \sum_{k=0}^{n} \left[\text{erfc } \left(\frac{k}{\sqrt{\tau}} \right) - \text{erfc } \left(\frac{k+1}{\sqrt{\tau}} \right) \right],$$

or

$$\psi \to 1 - \underset{n \to \infty}{\text{Lim}} \left[\text{erfc } 0 - \text{erfc } \left(\frac{n+1}{\sqrt{\tau}} \right) \right].$$

For fixed $\tau > 0$, $(n+1)/\sqrt{\tau} \to \infty$ as $n \to \infty$. Hence, by (23),

$$\psi \to 1 - 1 + 0 = 0, \qquad \text{as } \zeta \to 0^+. \tag{24}$$

The solution (21) is unchanged when ζ is replaced by $(1 - \zeta)$, because the two series merely change places. Therefore, because of (24),

$$\psi \to 0, \qquad \text{as } \zeta \to 1^-. \tag{25}$$

For any ζ in the range $0 < \zeta < 1$, the argument of each erfc in (21) is positive and approaches infinity as $\tau \to 0^+$. Hence each erfc $\to 0$ and each term of the two series $\to 0$. Thus, because the order of limit and summation can be interchanged,

$$\psi \to 1, \quad \text{as } \tau \to 0^+, \qquad \text{for } 0 < \zeta < 1. \tag{26}$$

Perhaps the most valuable single fact about the solution (21) is the fact that the series converge very rapidly for small τ because the arguments of the various erfc functions are then very large. By the methods of separation of variables and Fourier series, the problem (6) through (9) at the start of this section can be shown to have the solution

$$\psi(\zeta, \tau) = \frac{4}{\pi} \sum_{k=0}^{\infty} \frac{\exp\left[-\pi^2(2k+1)^2\tau\right] \sin\left[(2k+1)\pi\zeta\right]}{2k+1}. \tag{27}$$

The solutions given by (21) and (27) are identical, though the uniqueness of such solutions is not proved here.

The series in (27) converges rapidly for large τ and slowly for small τ. The series in (21) converge rapidly for small τ and slowly for large τ. The two forms of solution complement each other neatly.

The solution of the original problem (1) through (4) may be obtained from (21) or (27) by making the substitutions in (5).

Exercise

1. Interpret and solve the following problem.

$$\frac{\partial u}{\partial t} = \frac{\partial^2 u}{\partial x^2}, \quad \text{for } t > 0, \ 0 < x < 1;$$

$$t \to 0^+, \quad u \to 1, \quad \text{for } 0 < x < 1;$$

$$x \to 0^+, \quad u \to 0, \quad \text{for } t > 0;$$

$$x \to 1^-, \quad \frac{\partial u}{\partial x} \to 0, \quad \text{for } t > 0.$$

ANS. $u = 1 - \sum_{n=0}^{\infty} (-1)^n \left[\operatorname{erfc}\left(\frac{2n+x}{2\sqrt{t}}\right) + \operatorname{erfc}\left(\frac{2n+2-x}{2\sqrt{t}}\right) \right].$

155. Diffusion in a quarter-infinite solid

As a final application let us study the temperatures near a square corner of a huge slab initially at a constant temperature and having its surfaces thereafter held at a constant temperature different from the initial interior temperature. We assume that all temperatures are independent of one rectangular space coordinate. By introducing canonical variables, we may express the mathematical problem as follows:

$$\frac{\partial u}{\partial t} = \frac{\partial^2 u}{\partial x^2} + \frac{\partial^2 u}{\partial y^2}, \quad \text{for } t > 0, \ x > 0, \ y > 0; \tag{1}$$

$$t \to 0^+, \quad u \to 1, \quad \text{for } x > 0, \ y > 0; \tag{2}$$

$$x \to 0^+, \quad u \to 0, \quad \text{for } t > 0, \ y > 0; \tag{3}$$

$$y \to 0^+, \quad u \to 0, \quad \text{for } t > 0, \ x > 0. \tag{4}$$

$$\text{Lim}_{x \to \infty} u(x, y, t) \text{ exists, for fixed positive } t \text{ and } y; \tag{5}$$

$$\text{Lim}_{y \to \infty} u(x, y, t) \text{ exists, for fixed positive } t \text{ and } x. \tag{6}$$

The solution of the problem (1) through (6) will be accomplished by combining separation of variables with the Laplace transform technique. First we separate the function u of the three variables x, y, t into the product of a function of x and t alone by a function of y and t alone. This separation is possible only because of the peculiar simplicity of the boundary value problem. Let

$$u(x, y, t) = v(x, t)w(y, t). \tag{7}$$

From (7) it follows that

$$\frac{\partial u}{\partial t} = v \frac{\partial w}{\partial t} + w \frac{\partial v}{\partial t},$$

$$\frac{\partial^2 u}{\partial x^2} = w \frac{\partial^2 v}{\partial x^2},$$

$$\frac{\partial^2 u}{\partial y^2} = v \frac{\partial^2 w}{\partial y^2}.$$

Hence equation (1) yields

$$v \frac{\partial w}{\partial t} + w \frac{\partial v}{\partial t} = w \frac{\partial^2 v}{\partial x^2} + v \frac{\partial^2 w}{\partial y^2}, \tag{8}$$

which will be satisfied if both

$$\frac{\partial v}{\partial t} = \frac{\partial^2 v}{\partial x^2}, \qquad \text{for } t > 0, \quad x > 0, \tag{9}$$

and

$$\frac{\partial w}{\partial t} = \frac{\partial^2 w}{\partial y^2}, \qquad \text{for } t > 0, \quad y > 0, \tag{10}$$

are satisfied.

If we impose the conditions

$$t \to 0^+, \quad v \to 1, \qquad \text{for } x > 0, \tag{11}$$

$$t \to 0^+, \quad w \to 1, \qquad \text{for } y > 0, \tag{12}$$

condition (2) will be satisfied.

From condition (3) we get

$$x \to 0^+, \quad v \to 0, \qquad \text{for } t > 0, \tag{13}$$

and from (4),

$$y \to 0^+, \quad w \to 0, \quad \text{for } t > 0. \tag{14}$$

Conditions (5) and (6) will be satisfied if

$$\text{Lim}_{x \to \infty} v(x, t) \text{ exists, for fixed positive } t, \tag{15}$$

and

$$\text{Lim}_{y \to \infty} w(y, t) \text{ exists, for fixed positive } t. \tag{16}$$

We must now find v from

$$\frac{\partial v}{\partial t} = \frac{\partial^2 v}{\partial x^2}, \quad \text{for } t > 0, \quad x > 0; \tag{9}$$

$$t \to 0^+, \quad v \to 1, \quad \text{for } x > 0; \tag{11}$$

$$x \to 0^+, \quad v \to 0, \quad \text{for } t > 0; \tag{13}$$

$$\text{Lim}_{x \to \infty} v(x, t) \text{ exists, for fixed positive } t. \tag{15}$$

The function w must satisfy (10), (12), (14), and (16); it is therefore the same function as v except that y replaces x.

To obtain v we use the Laplace transform. Let

$$L\{v(x, t)\} = g(x, s) = \int_0^\infty e^{-st} v(x, t) \, dt. \tag{17}$$

Then (9) and (11) yield

$$sg - 1 = \frac{d^2 g}{dx^2}, \tag{18}$$

for which the general solution is easily written by inspection because of our experience in handling equations with constant coefficients. We thus get

$$g = \frac{1}{s} + c_1(s) \exp(-x\sqrt{s}) + c_2(s) \exp(x\sqrt{s}). \tag{19}$$

The function g must, because of (13) and (15), satisfy the conditions

$$x \to 0^+, \quad g \to 0, \tag{20}$$

$$\text{Lim}_{x \to \infty} g(x, s) \text{ exists.} \tag{21}$$

Because of (21), $c_2(s) = 0$. Because of (20),

$$0 = \frac{1}{s} + c_1(s).$$

Therefore

$$g(x, s) = \frac{1}{s} - \frac{1}{s} \exp(-x\sqrt{s}). \tag{22}$$

The function $v(x, t)$ is an inverse transform of $g(x, s)$:

$$v(x, t) = 1 - \text{erfc}\left(\frac{x}{2\sqrt{t}}\right). \tag{23}$$

But $1 - \text{erfc } z = \text{erf } z$. Hence

$$v(x, t) = \text{erf}\left(\frac{x}{2\sqrt{t}}\right). \tag{24}$$

Therefore the solution of our original problem (1) through (6) is

$$u = \text{erf}\left(\frac{x}{2\sqrt{t}}\right) \text{erf}\left(\frac{y}{2\sqrt{t}}\right). \tag{25}$$

The student should verify that the u of (25) satisfies all the conditions of the boundary value problem (1) through (6) introduced at the beginning of this section.

Exercises

1. Show that for the u of (25), $0 < u < 1$, for all $x, y, t > 0$.
2. Let the point with coordinates (x, y, t) be in the first octant of the rectangular x, y, t space. Let that point approach the origin along a curve

$$x^2 = 4a^2 t,$$
$$y^2 = 4a^2 t,$$

in which a is positive but otherwise arbitrary. Show that as $x, y, t \to 0^+$ in the manner described above, u may be made to approach any desired number between zero and unity.

Index